P9-CKX-576

CAVALCADE OF THE NORTH

CAVALCADE OF THE NORTH

An Entertaining Collection of Distinguished Writing by Canadian Authors with an Introduction by

THOMAS B. COSTAIN

Selected by

GEORGE E. NELSON

DOUBLEDAY & COMPANY, INC.
Garden City, New York

Printed in the United States of America

CONTENTS

INTRODUCTION

I have been convinced that few readers pay much attention to the introductions prepared for volumes of this character. They prefer to browse at their leisure without the aid of literary finger posts and to arrive in due course at their own conclusions. There are two reasons why an introduction is needed, however, for *Cavalcade of the North*. The first is the unusual scope of the volume, which includes not only a large selection of Canadian short stories but two novels complete and a selection from a third, and most particularly because it offers some unusual and provocative articles which call for explanation. The second reason is the lurking presence of an inferiority complex which obtrudes itself into all discussion of the state of literature in Canada. Is it true, as so many commentators have declared, that Canada has not yet developed a literature of her own? That the country has produced few fine writers because the financial rewards are too small and the reader response too limited? That Canadian writers aim at outside markets (believing that American and English editors have no interest in this country) and so do not deal with Canadian problems and national backgrounds? It is not my intention to enter into any discussion of these familiar points in an effort to prove their fallacy (although I believe strongly that such views are fallacious), save to say I am convinced that partial answers at least will be found by the discerning eye in the contents of this volume.

It must have been clear to the editor, when he approached the task of selecting the two novels to be printed in full, that no detrimental conditions had been operating to make this difficult. The last quarter century has seen the appearance of books which may fairly be described as Canadian classics, many of them minor classics, it is true, but all with enough sustained interest and charm to command wide attention and sufficient vitality to stand up against the passage of time. Consider the authors included in such a list: Hugh MacLennan, Mazo de la Roche, Louis Hemon, Morley Callaghan, Thomas H. Raddall, Gabrielle Roy, Lionel Shapiro, Roger Lemelin, Gwethalyn Grahame, W. G. Hardy, Robertson Davies, W. O. Mitchell, to mention some only: no reason, here, to speak with scorn of the present and gloom of the future. The editor's selection of novels by the first two named was an admirable one in all respects but he would not have been seriously at fault had he decided instead on books by any of the others.

Two Solitudes by Hugh MacLennan might have been taken instead of *Barometer Rising* but I think Mr. Nelson was wise in his final choice. *Barometer Rising* is the earlier of the two, and it is a prime function of anthologies to recall old favorites to mind. It deals, moreover, with one of the most dramatic incidents of the world wars, the explosion at Halifax, a calamity which will never be forgotten. It is a story which can never be forgotten, which will be as fresh to future generations as it was to those who were alive when that cataclysmic echo was heard in the land.

I gave up the editorship of *Maclean's Magazine* nearly forty years ago and at that time the task of securing novels about Canada by Canadian authors of suitable stature was not an easy one. What jubilation there would have been in the editorial offices if *Jalna* had been written then and had been available! I can recall how excited I was when I read, at my home in Philadelphia, the first of this remarkable series of novels and realized that a new sun had climbed into Canadian skies. Every editor knows how difficult it is for a novelist to continue with a succession of books about the same characters without becoming threadbare in theme and repetitious in treatment. Mazo de la Roche has, I think, broken records by doing nearly a score about the Whiteoaks family, each new one seeming as fresh as those which went before and winning a continuously rising chorus of acclaim. It is eminently fitting that the first of the *Jalna* novels should be selected for this volume.

In this age of visual entertainment it is not as certain as it should be that authors will continue to exist on the earnings of patient pens, that publishers can continue to print what they write, and that periodicals can be expected to go on swimming against an ebb tide. On this account it is inspiring to see the need for the printed word expressed so forcibly in the brief article "Read!" from Canada's most colorful and successful financial wizard. We may well listen to Max Aiken, better known as Lord Beaverbrook, because he has demonstrated a fantastic capacity to make the public of England read by the success of his London *Express*.

A fantastic man, Lord Beaverbrook. Making a fortune for himself easily and quickly in a country where fortunes are seldom made either easily or quickly, he took his talents to one of the toughest of all market places, London. Unlike most of the young Napoleons of finance who rush to break a lance against more experienced champions, he came off spectacularly well in the international tilting grounds of Westminster. To further dumfound the watchers, he accomplished two widely divergent miracles. He published metropolitan newspapers with sensational success and he went into the House of Commons, where for years he was one of the most unpredictable and most closely watched members. During these days he was in the habit of returning to Canada once a year and so I had a chance to observe other evidences of his versatility. I suggested to him, rather timorously, that he write an article for us. He obliged with an exceptionally fine paper, without benefit, as I had reasons to know, of editorial aid or "ghost." It was so good that Colonel Maclean, who was not an easy publisher to please, spoke glowingly of it. That same autumn a dinner was given at the Arts and Letters Club in Toronto to say farewell to Peter O'Donovan (do you recall him, P. O'D. of "Saturday Night" and his mane of prematurely white hair?) who was taking a post in the Beaverbrook newspaper empire. Beaverbrook himself gave an extemporaneous speech which was charming, witty, and always very much to the point. It was a delight to all of us, particularly when he began to speak of himself in the third person and tossed off such lines as "this strange and gnome-like intruder." During dinner a rumor began to circulate that another member of the party was preparing to flit, that I, in fact, had received an offer from the Curtis Publishing Company. It was Beaverbrook's belief that if a Canadian left home, he must go to London, and during dinner I felt his accusing eye resting on me. But it was true; and several weeks later, with my bundle on my shoulder, I was off for Philadelphia.

Stephen Leacock was perhaps the most steady contributor we had at *Maclean's* in my day and I was one of his most ardent admirers. To select the best paper from the great volume he left behind him would be an impossible task for me, I liked so many of them so well. Editor Nelson has been discerning, I think, in fixing upon *The Speculations of Jefferson Thorpe*; it is one of the best pieces in the always remembered, always loved, *Sunshine Sketches*.

One of the last times I saw Stephen Leacock was at his summer home on Old Brewery Bay near Orillia. He met me at the gate, with an open letter in his hand. "Good morning," he said. "Now here is a fellow who believes in living his own thesis." He was shaking the sheet in exasperation. "This is from a college man and he's working on an anthology of stories about the absent-minded professor. Wants me to write an introduction. I'd gladly do it. For nothing, mind you. But the envelope's postmarked Chicago and there's no address inside. And I would defy all the handwriting experts who ever appeared at all the murder trials in history to make out his absurd signature!"

If all the wonderful bits that Stephen Leacock tossed off for nothing during his busy lifetime could be found! All the wry and whimsical pieces for college publications, the rhymed catches he wrote on place cards for the dinners given by friends, the skits for amateur performances, the witticisms which convulsed his clubs, the rare passages in the lectures and speeches he made, all extemporaneous and all lost in bald and hurried newspaper reports. If all these could be gathered together, what an anthology it would be! What an example of the kindliness and sweetness which must be a part of humor!

There are many things that people who live elsewhere do not know about Canada. They do not know, for instance, that the telephone was invented in Brantford, Ontario, my home town, and not in Boston. Most particularly they do not know that there are two sides to the story of the expulsion of the Acadians from their homes in Nova Scotia and that the one popularized by Longfellow in his *Evangeline* is a most biased version indeed. As this is a point of great historical importance, it is most fortunate that Mr. Nelson decided to use the chapter "This Stubborn Breed" from *Century of Conflict* by Joseph Lister Rutledge. It will be an eye-opener to the myriads of readers who were raised on *Evangeline* and who know nothing of the tangled motives, the strange mixture of rights and wrongs on both sides, the mutual hatreds, the Indian raids, the butcheries and the burnings which led finally to the need for separation of the races.

Once in the midst of a debate in the British House of Commons, Gladstone was confronted with a government report which knocked the argument he was employing into a cocked hat. "My eyes have grown dim in the service of my country!" he cried, tossing the volume across the floor. "And I can't read the unimportant footnote that the worthy member has found!" Every veteran editor reaches the stage after a lifetime of reading, morning, noon, and night—books, manuscripts, galley proofs, source material, memos, footnotes—when his eyes rebel and he has to give up. This is my only excuse for not having read Bruce Hutchison's biography of MacKenzie King, *The Incredible Canadian*, when it first came out. It was, I knew, a book of first importance and I felt that I should perhaps toss everything else aside in its favor. But it happened that my eyes chose that moment to rebel most seriously and it was not until I read the chapter "The Awakening," which is offered in this volume, that I cast discretion to the winds and turned with eager interest to the beginning. I emerged with a new understanding of King and the part he played. I commend this chapter most strongly as a striking portrait of a political leader at the crossroads of an important decision.

It is when we come to the short stories included in this weighty volume that we get the answers to the questions raised at the beginning. Here we have a score of stories which not only deal exclusively with Canadian life and problems but which are drawn from all corners of the land. I must confess that a few of the names were new to me when I read the stories printed here, but I have been assured that all of them are familiar to the readers of books and magazines in Canada. Of this I am certain, they will become increasingly familiar as the years roll on, for it is not hard to predict a bright future for all of them. Most of the short stories are of recent vintage, very few having been culled from the past. Sir Gilbert Parker, Marjorie Pickthall, and Thomas Chandler Haliburton are the exceptions. I was delighted in particular with the sensitive and fine story by Marjorie Pickthall. She is remembered for her poetry rather than her prose and I am certain that "The Worker in Sandalwood" will be as pleasant a "discovery" to all readers as it was to me.

Mr. Nelson was wise to put the emphasis on the new school of short-story writers. So many of the things we admired long ago, sad to relate, prove to be dated when we pick them up again. There is freshness and vigor in the stories he has assembled and we need no better reason for viewing the future with a confident eye.

THOMAS B. COSTAIN

CAVALCADE OF THE NORTH

BAROMETER RISING

Hugh MacLennan

SUNDAY

Four o'Clock He had been walking around Halifax all day, as though by moving through familiar streets he could test whether he belonged here and had at last reached home. In the west the winter sky was brilliant and clouds massing under the sun were taking on color, but smoke hung low in the streets, the cold air holding it down. He glanced through the dirty window of a cheap restaurant, saw the interior was empty and went in through the double doors. There was a counter, and a man in a soiled apron behind it, a few tables and chairs, and a smell of mustard. He sat on one of the warped stools at the counter and ordered bovril and a ham sandwich.

"You English?" the man behind the counter said.

"No. I used to live around here."

"Funny, I thought you were an English fella. You been over there, though?"

"I just got back."

He glanced restlessly over his shoulder before he let his muscles relax, but there was no need for caution in a restaurant like this. No one he had ever known in Halifax would be seen in the place.

"You been away long?" the restaurant man said. He poured steaming water over the glutinous bovril essence after he had ladled it into a thick mug.

"Quite a while."

The man set the drink on the counter and began cutting slices from a loaf of brown bread.

"Guess you been in the war, too," he said. "I was in it myself for a while but I didn't get very far. I got to Quebec. My wife thinks that's funny. She says, when you got in the army you started moving backwards before you even began." He pulled a thin slice of boiled ham loose from a pile on a plate and slapped it on the bread.

"What was your outfit?" he said.

The customer stared at the counter without answering and the restaurant man shifted his feet uneasily.

"I was only asking. Hell, it's no skin off my ass."

"Never mind. I was with a lot of outfits, and I didn't sail from here in the first place."

"Mustard?" When he received no answer the man passed the sandwich over the counter. "A lot goes on in town these days. You'd be surprised."

The sandwich was eaten in a fierce silence, then he swallowed the bovril in one passage of the cup to his mouth. He drew a deep breath and asked for more, and while the restaurant man was supplying it he asked casually, "Are you still in with the army around here?"

"No. They let me out on account of varicose veins. That's why I only got to Quebec."

A tram rumbled around the corner in the gathering shadows of the street and its flanges screamed on the uneven rails. The young man jerked nervously at the sudden noise and cleared his throat. All his muscles had tightened involuntarily, giving him a rigid appearance like an animal bunched for a spring. He remained taut and this physical tenseness invested his words with a dramatic value he did not intend.

"There's a chap I knew overseas," he said. "I was wondering if you'd ever heard of him. Alec MacKenzie . . . Big Alec, we called him."

"I knew a man called Alec MacKenzie once, but he was a little fella."

"Do you know Colonel Wain?"

The man shoved the second cup of bovril closer to his customer. "How would a guy like me be knowing colonels?"

"I didn't mean was he a friend of yours. I meant, did you ever hear of him?"

"There's one Colonel Wain here in Halifax." He glanced at the younger man's thin and shabby overcoat. "But you wouldn't be meaning him, either. He's pretty rich, they say."

"So?" He picked up the mug and drained it slowly, then stood straight and looked at himself in the mirror behind the counter. The war had made as big a change in him as it seemed to have made in Halifax. His shoulders were wide, he was just under six feet tall, but his appearance was of rundown ill health, and he knew he looked much older than when he had left three years ago. Although he was barely twenty-eight, deep lines ran in parentheses around his mouth, and there was a nervous tic in his left cheek and a permanent tension in the expression of his eyes. His nails were broken and dirty, he carried himself without confidence, and it seemed an effort for him to be still for more than a moment at a time. In England he would have been labeled a gentleman who had lost caste.

He buttoned his coat and laid some coins on the counter. He turned to leave and then turned back. "This Colonel Wain . . . is he in town now?" he said.

"I saw his picture in the *Chronicle* last week sometime," the restaurant man said. "I guess he must be."

When he left the cafe he turned toward George Street and slowly began the climb toward Citadel Hill. When he reached the last intersection he continued across the pavement, then upward along a wavering footpath through the unkempt grasses which rustled over the slope of the hill. He pulled himself up slowly, with a jerky nervousness that indicated he was not yet accustomed to his limping left leg, which seemed more to follow his body than propel it forward. At the top of the hill he stopped on a narrow footpath that outlined the rim of the star-shaped moat which defended the half-hidden buildings of the central garrison. An armed soldier stood guard over an open drawbridge giving access to the military enclosure. Over it all rose a flagpole and signal masts.

He turned about and surveyed the town. A thin breeze was dragging in from the sea; it was a soundless breath on the cheek, but it made him feel entirely solitary. Though it was early December, the winter snow had not yet fallen and the thin soil had frozen onto the rocks, the trees were bare and the grass was like straw, and the land itself had given up most of its color.

The details of Halifax were dim in the fading light but the contours were clear and he had forgotten how good they were. The Great Glacier had once packed, scraped and riven this whole land; it had gouged out the harbor and left as a legacy three drumlins . . . the hill on which he stood and two islands in the harbor itself. Halifax covers the whole of an oval peninsula, and the Citadel is about in the center of it. He could look south to the open Atlantic and see where the park at the end of the town thrusts its nose directly into the outer harbor. At the park the water divides, spreading around the town on either side; to the west the inlet is called the Northwest Arm, to the east it is called the Stream, and it is here that the docks and ocean terminals are built. The Stream bends with the swell of Halifax peninsula and runs inland a distance of four miles from the park to a deep strait at the northern end of town called the Narrows. This strait opens directly into Bedford Basin, a lake-like expanse which bulges around the back of the town to the north.

He followed the footpath and looked for familiar landmarks, walking around the moat until he had boxed the compass. From here even a landsman could see why the harbor had for a century and a half been a link in the chain of British sea power. It is barricaded against Atlantic groundswells by McNab's Island at the mouth of the outer harbor, and by the smaller bowl of George's Island at the entrance to the Stream. It was defended now against enemy battle squadrons by forts set on rocky promontories running over the horizon into the sea. It was fenced off from prowling submarines by a steel net hung on pontoons from McNab's to the mainland. This harbor is the reason for the town's existence; it is all that matters in Halifax, for the place periodically sleeps between great wars. There had been a good many years since Napoleon, but now it was awake again.

The forests to the far west and north were nothing but shadows under the sky at this time of day. Above the horizon rim the remaining light was a turmoil of rose and saffron and pallid green, the colors of blood and flowers and the sheen of sunlight on summer grass. As his eyes shifted from the dull floor of the distant sea to this shredding blaze of glory crowning the continent, he felt an unexpected wave of exultation mount in his mind. Merely to have been born on the western side of the ocean gave a man something for which the traditions of the Old World could never compensate. This western land was his own country. He had forgotten how it was, but now he was back, and to be able to remain was worth risking everything.

After sunset the hilltop grew colder. The colors died quickly and as the landscape faded into darkness the street lights of the city came on. They made bluish pools at intervals along the narrow thoroughfares that fanned away from the roots of the hill, and all the way down to the waterfront the life of Halifax began to reveal itself in flashes. Barrington, Granville, and Hollis Streets, running north and south, were visible only at the intersections where the inclines plunging from the hill to the waterfront crossed them, and at these corners pedestrians could be seen moving back and forth, merged in irregular streams.

Children were playing a game with a whole block of a George Street slum for their playground. They darted in and out of his vision as they pursued each other in and out of doorways and back and forth across the street. Here and there in the withered grass along the slope of the Citadel the forms of men and girls lay huddled, scarcely moving; they clung together on the frozen ground in spite of the cold, sailors with only a night on shore and local girls with no better place to be.

Halifax seemed to have acquired a meaning since he had left it in 1914. Quietly, almost imperceptibly, everything had become harnessed to the war. Long ribbons of light crossed on the surface of the water from the new oil refinery on the far shore of the Stream, and they all found their focus in himself. Occasionally they were broken, as undiscernible craft moved through the harbor, and he suddenly realized that this familiar inlet had become one of the most vital stretches of water in the world. It still gleamed faintly in the dusk as its surface retained a residual glow of daylight. Ferryboats glided like beetles across it, fanning ruffled water in their wake. A freighter drifted inland with a motion so slight he had to watch a full minute before it was perceptible. Its only identification was riding lights; no one but the port authorities knew its home port or its destination. While he watched, its anchor ran out with a muted clatter to the bottom and its bow swung to the north.

Then the Stream became static. The smoke of Halifax lay like clouds about a mountain; the spire of St. Mary's Cathedral cut George's Island in two; the only moving object was the beam of the lighthouse on McNab's, circling like a turning eye out to sea, along the coast and into the harbor again.

He descended the hill slowly, easing his left leg carefully along the dirt path. Down on the street the contours of Halifax were lost in the immediate reality of grim red brick and smoky stone. In the easy days before the war he had winced at the architecture, but it no longer bothered him. Halifax was obviously more than its buildings. Its functional aspect was magnificent, its solid docks piled with freight to the edge of deep water, Bedford Basin thronged with ships from all over the world, the grimy old naval and military buildings crowded once more with alert young men. However much he loathed the cause of this change, he found the throbbing life of the city at once a stimulation and a relief.

For twelve hours he had been back, and so far he had been recognized by no one. He stopped in the shadow of a doorway and the muscles of his face tightened again as his mind returned to its endless calculations. Big Alec MacKenzie had returned from France—and so had Wain. The colonel had probably been back for more than a year. The problem was to find MacKenzie before he himself was discovered by Wain. If only he could get to Big Alec first. . . . He began to smile to himself.

When he reached Barrington Street and the shops he found himself in a moving crowd. Girls with English faces brushed by him in twos and threes, sailors from a British cruiser rolled as though the pavement were a ship's deck. Although most of them were walking the main street because they had no better place to go—soldiers, dock-workers in flat cloth caps, civilians—they did not appear aimless. Even their idleness seemed to have a purpose, as though it were also part of the war.

By the time he had walked to the South End where the crowds were thinner, he realized that underneath all this war-begotten activity Halifax remained much the same. It had always looked an old town. It had a genius for looking old and for acting as though nothing could possibly happen to surprise it. Battalions passed through from the West, cargoes multiplied, convoys left every week and new ships took over their anchorages; yet underneath all this the old habits survived and the inhabitants did not alter. All of them still went to church regularly; he had watched them this morning. And he was certain they still drank tea with all their meals. The field gun used in the past as a curfew for the garrison was fired from the Citadel every noon and at nine-thirty each night, and the townspeople took out their watches automatically twice a day to check the time. The Citadel itself flew the Union Jack in all weathers and was rightly considered a symbol and bastion of the British Empire.

Grinding on the cobblestones behind a pair of plunging Clydesdales came one of Halifax's most typical vehicles, a low-swung dray with a high driver's box, known as a sloven. This one was piled high with bags of feed and it almost knocked him down as the driver brought it around to level ground. He cursed as he jumped clear of the horses and the driver spat and flourished his whip, and the lash flicked in a quick, cracking arc over the sidewalk. The sloven moved north onto Barrington Street as the horses were pulled into a walk. Traffic slowed down behind it, a few horns sounded and the column stopped behind a stationary tram.

His leg pained after the sudden pull on his muscles and he walked more slowly until the soreness abated. Images flashed through his mind and out again . . . shell shock simultaneous with a smashed thigh and no time to be frightened by either; the flash of destruction out of the dark; who knew until it was experienced how intense the molten whiteness could be at the heart of an exploding chemical? . . . Naked when they picked him up, unconscious . . . and afterwards memory gone and no identity disk to help the base hospital.

The English doctor had done a fine job in mending his thigh and a better one in saving his reason. This, at least, had been no accident; more than twenty centuries of medical history had been behind that doctor. Even though his world was composed now of nothing but chance, it was unreasonable to believe that a series of accidents should ultimately matter. One chance must lead to another with no binding link but a peculiar tenacity which made him determined to preserve himself for a future which gave no promise of being superior to the past. It was his future, and that was all he could say of it. At the moment it was all he had.

A motor horn sounded and he leaped convulsively again. Every time a sudden noise struck his ears his jangled nerves set his limbs jumping and trembling in automatic convulsions which made him loathe his own body for being so helpless. He stopped and leaned against a lamp post until the trembling stopped. Like a fish on the end of a hook, he thought, squirming and fighting for no privilege except the opportunity to repeat the same performance later.

People moved past him in both directions, laughing, talking, indifferent. Were they too stupid to care what was happening to the world, or did they enjoy the prospect of a society in process of murdering itself? Did he care himself, for that matter? Weren't any emotions he had left reduced to the simple desire for an acknowledged right to exist here in the place he knew as home? He had long ago given up the attempt to discover a social or spiritual reason which might justify what had happened to himself and millions of others during the past three years. If he could no longer be useful in the hell of Europe, then he must find a way to stay in Canada where he had been born.

He took his bearings when the trembling in his limbs subsided and was astonished to see how far south he had walked. Had the years in London made him lose all perspective of distance? He walked slowly to the next corner and knew he had reached his objective. But now he was here he felt nervous and unreasonably disappointed. He surveyed the cross street to his right as though he were searching casually for his bearings, but he knew every inch of it and every doorway as far up the hill as he could see.

It seemed to have lost all its graciousness, and yet nothing was actually changed. Then he realized that he had been remembering it as it was in summer with the horse chestnuts and elms and limes towering their shade over the roofs, with the doorways secluded under vine-covered porches, with everything so quiet that it always seemed to be Sunday afternoon. Actually there was little difference; winter had always made it look bare, stripped as ruthlessly as the rest of Halifax. There was no town anywhere that changed in appearance so quickly when the foliage went.

He fumbled for a cigarette and lit it slowly, looking carefully in all directions as though he were deciding which way to shield himself from the wind. Then he began the steep ascent of the hill, his movements furtive and his hat pulled low over his left eye. He stopped at the crest and stood panting, hardly believing that after so much time he was really here, that the red house opposite had stayed just as he remembered it, that the trees still crowded its windows and the high wooden fence shut the garden away from the eyes of the passers-by.

At least the war had not dulled his trained appreciation of good architecture. Among the many nondescript Victorian houses of Halifax, this one stood out as a masterpiece. It was neither gracious nor beautiful, in a way it was almost forbidding, but it so typified the history and character of its town that it belonged exactly as it was: solid British colonial with a fanlight over the door, about six feet of lawn separating it from the sidewalk, four thick walls and no ells or additions, high ceilings and high windows, and shutters on the inside where they could be useful if not decorative. It had stood just as it was for over a hundred years; it looked permanent enough to last forever.

To cross the street and knock on the door, to take a chance on the right person opening it, would be so easy. Just a few movements and it would be done, and then whatever else he might feel, this loneliness which welled inside like a salt spring would disappear. Spasmodically he clasped one hand with the other and squeezed it hard, then turned back down the hill and followed it to Barrington Street.

There was nothing more he could do today. Sunday was the worst possible time to hunt for Alec MacKenzie or anyone else too poor to own a telephone. He walked north to the junction of Spring Garden Road and waited for a tram. Evening service was under way in St. Matthew's Church and the sound of a hymn penetrated its closed Gothic doors. "O God of Bethel, by whose hand thy people still are fed . . . Who, through this weary pilgrimage, Hast all our fathers led. . . ."

The girls went by in twos and threes, sailors rolled past, evening loafers lounged against the stone wall of the military cemetery opposite, a soldier picked up a girl in front of the iron gate of the Crimean monument. "God of our fathers, be the God of their succeeding race." With a muffled sigh the congregation sat down.

A tram ground around the corner and stopped, heading north. Fifteen minutes later when he left it he could hear a low, vibrant, moaning sound that permeated everything, beating in over the housetops from the sea. For a second he was puzzled; it sounded like an animal at some distance, moaning with pain. Then he realized that the air was salty and moist and the odor of fishmeal was in his nostrils. The wind had changed and now it was bringing in the fog. Pavements were growing damp and bells and groaning buoys at the harbor mouth were busy. When he reached his room in the cheap sailors' lodging he had rented that morning he lay down, and the sounds of the harbor seemed to be in the walls.

Five o'Clock From a window in her office at the Shipyards Penelope Wain stood watching the evening draw in over the water. It was invading the Stream like a visible and moving body. It spilled over from the land and lapped the massive sides of the graving dock and the hulls of vessels riding at anchor; it advanced westward from the hidden sea; and because fog was behind the darkness, the air was alive with the clanging of bells.

She stood quite still, alone in her unlighted office. The mauve depths of the sky were slashed starkly by the upthrust angles of the great cranes, by the row of hoppers lining the dock to the north, by the two masts and three funnels of the cruiser which lay at the naval dockyard lower down the Stream. From somewhere in the recesses of the enormous building at her back came the sound of a closing door. She turned slightly to listen, but if there were faint footsteps they receded, and she turned back to watch the harbor.

This assembly of enormous and potent apparatus was so familiar she hardly noticed it. Yet even while she rested her eyes on the soft colors of the twilight, she was conscious of objects that the advancing darkness had partially covered. There was the long skeleton of the ship under construction, lying with its keel buried in the night and its ribs caged in the net of a great gantry. Flat in the open spaces of the yard under her window sprawled three bronze propellers waiting to be connected to their shafts. And there was a row of parked trucks and a line of freight cars standing on a siding, all part of her work. She handled none of them and had no immediate authority over their disposal, yet ultimately the results of her daily work became parts of the whole of which these also were parts.

There was something delicate, something extremely fragile in the appearance of the girl alone against that angular background of motionless machinery and silent engines. She appeared slight because the lines of her waist were slim and her fingers and feet dainty. A second glance would discover definite curves at her hips and breasts, a latent fullness the more pleasing because it revealed itself as a surprise. She had quantities of reddish brown hair pulled back onto the nape of her neck, but no amount of tidying could hide the graceful manner in which it grew from her forehead and temples. Now, in repose, her face seemed absorbed and private, and because this was the only expression she was able to discover from a mirror, she fancied that she was a plain, average girl of twenty-nine.

But contact with another person transformed her. In conversation her face opened and disclosed a sympathetic and comprehensive mind. She seemed to become part of the experience and emotions of anyone who engaged her interest, and the town was filled with individuals who would like to have found excuses for talking with her. But of this she was entirely unaware. The most striking and piquant feature of her appearance at any time was a lock of white hair running from the left side of her forehead along the temple and over her ear. It set her apart from other women and arrested men's attention by its obscure appeal to their sensuality, though it seldom succeeded in making her thoroughly attractive to them. When they discovered her profession, when they learned that she was a ship designer with an office of her own at the Shipyards, they kept their distance in fear of the excessively unfamiliar.

She slipped back into the high swivel chair before her desk and turned on the goose-neck lamp at her elbow. It threw a yellow pool over the disarray of papers, pencils, T-squares and erasers on the desk and shut the rest of the room away in darkness. She began to gather the papers together, checking each one carefully before laying the lot in a lower drawer. A list of figures engaged her attention as she ticked them off slowly with a pencil, and then this paper was placed on top of a pile of blueprints in another drawer.

She dropped the pencil with a clatter and leaned back, stretching her arms. She was tired and knew she should stop, but this was a chronic state with her now that a further speed-up in war work was being pressed, and she welcomed the lassitude as an anodyne to thought. To be a woman and work at a profession pre-eminently masculine meant that she must be more than good. She had to be better than her male colleagues; she had to work longer hours and be doubly careful of all that she did, for a mistake would ruin her. It had taken a war to open such a job to her in the first place, but she was undeceived as to how superior she must be to continue to keep it.

A door opened and shut in the far distance again, but this time she knew the footsteps that advanced along the corridor were coming her way. She glanced at her watch. When old Simon Perry knocked and then came in clutching a grubby paper in his large fist, she smiled and he touched his cap.

"I was about to leave," she said. "I thought you'd decided you didn't need any help after all. Pull up that chair."

"No. I was coming," he replied. And with his cap still on his head and a white forelock projecting stiffly from under its peak, he leaned against the edge of her desk and thrust his paper at her. "I made a drawing. So you can see what I mean."

She had no need of the drawing to understand his difficulty, but from innate politeness she pretended to study it.

"It's no time to be working on the Sabbath Day," he muttered. "But with one like you there's no other way of seeing you. The rest of the days you're too busy. . . ." He paused until she looked up from the paper, and then he said, "That mechanic you sent me is a God damn liar."

"Don't be so cross," she said. "The mechanic made a mistake and you're the boss. Whatever you say is bound to be right, and all you have to do is make him obey."

He took out of his pocket a clay pipe filled with half-burned shag and lit it. The stench made her cough. "He don't think so," he said. "He don't know anything about a ship and so far as I can see he don't know much more about his own trade. He tells me his engine's going to have a certain weight—like you told me—and now I find it weighs nigh onto a hundredweight more. That means I got to set it eighteen inches farther forrad or the craft'll ride like a canoe. He gives me the argument. The shaft don't allow for them extra eighteen inches, he says."

Penelope listened to all this with a grave face even though she was perfectly familiar with Simon's problem. The mechanic had telephoned her about it the day before. But the old man had to be handled carefully. He must be over seventy now; he had been an old man twenty years ago when she first had known him, when he worked as her Uncle John's assistant in his yacht-building yard on the South Shore. Heaven knew how many years before that he had taken part in the construction of great three-masters, of brigs and barquentines which had passed from the seas before she was born. Now he owned a small place of his own where he built light harbor craft, and the cause of his present difficulty was a motor launch for the use of local naval authorities.

"What did you tell the mechanic finally?" she said.

"I told him to bugger off."

"Well—he'll have to get a longer shaft, that's all. Tell him I said so, if that's any help."

"You'll fix it up with them naval fellas, Miss Penny?"

"They probably won't even notice the difference."

"Maybe not, but they'll pretend they do. They don't trust nothing except what comes out of a factory." He spat into her wastebasket, making its metal sides clang. "That blueprint you did for me—you still got it around?"

"I've got a copy." She ran her fingers over the edges of a tightly packed file in an open drawer, then extracted the papers.

"Mind you, I never said they were any use to anybody. I'd kind of feel easier if I had a look, that's all."

Like most of the old craftsmen of the province, Simon Perry worked from models of his own contriving, miniatures exquisitely carved out of soft wood and complete to the last detail. But to get a contract from the government the submission of a blueprint was necessary, and Penny had offered to draw one from his model. He did not understand much about gasoline engines and required a mechanic to help with that part of the work, and it was his secret grievance that the engine was perhaps the most important part of his craft. He leaned now over the blueprints he could not understand and tried to look wise, his elbows holding the stiff paper flat and his horny hands on his jaws. The smoke from the shag puffed out, billowing through the pool of light.

Penny got up to escape it. She rested her elbows on the high window sill, unconsciously repeating the pattern of the old man's posture. Nothing but the contour of the land about the Stream was visible now; the darkness was nearly total.

Simon breathed noisily and stood upright. "You going to change this print now?" he said.

"I doubt if that's necessary. If so, I'll change it. Stop worrying, Simon. You've forgotten more about shipbuilding than the rest of us will ever know. Go ahead and finish the job."

She was thankful that in this case his judgment was right, for it would have been impossible to tell him anything. He joined her at the window and stared gloomily over her shoulder at the stark outlines of the cranes and the long, high lines of the building opposite.

"How the likes of you works in a place like this beats me. In the old days a shipyard used to be something, what with the clean smell of lumber and the tar and the smoke of the open fires. Now what's in it? It ain't natural for a woman to be smart at this sort of work."

When she made no answer he stood off and surveyed her with a calculating candor, even to cocking his head on one side and making movements with his hands as though he were actually feeling the curves of her hips and waist. "You got a figure ought to fill any man's eye, even though it's on the lean side."

She knew that if Simon were twenty years younger he would be attempting to take liberties with her now and decided not to answer. He moved away from the window and pulled his cap more firmly over his stiff hair.

"Well," he said, "I can't say you don't know your trade, even though it ain't natural you should." He hesitated. "I thought John Macrae's boy had his eye on you once, but I guess you lost him, for all that. I guess he couldn't stand it when you started out trying to beat him at his own job. A man don't like that, Miss Penny. Where is he now? I haven't seen Neil in a mighty long time."

Small tight lines appeared about the corners of her mouth and she had to close her lips to keep from telling him to mind his own business. The old man's memory was so hazy he had forgotten that her cousin Neil Macrae was dead.

"Old John Macrae now, he knew how to build a ship. Funny thing him marrying that sister of your father's. Seemed to get on all right with her, too. Seems only yesterday since you and Neil used to stand around and watch us work. That boy was good. It ought to be him here in this office, not you."

Penny made an abrupt movement and again checked the words that came to her lips. She began to roll up the blueprints and hunt rubber bands to hold them, and her breathing became more easy as the current of her mind settled back into its worn channel. Simon was still talking, but she felt immune to anything he might say now.

"What's your father doing around town these days, Miss Penny? I hear he's still running his shipping business in spite of the war and him being in the army. It must be a mighty nice business for him these days. I guess he's better at that than soldiering."

"Simon!" Once more she checked herself and forced a smile. It seemed pointless to object to this old man making a statement with which she agreed herself. "Father's still on active duty, but it's a special sort of job that leaves him free part of the time."

Simon had his hand on the doorknob and stood there with his feet firmly set apart as though he were bracing himself against the roll of a ship's deck. "Well, I guess I better thank you for helping. Maybe if this launch is all right they'll give me something else to do. But I don't like working for the government. There's too much red tape. If they'd just tell me what they want and let me give it to them, things'd be better." He opened the door and stepped across the threshold, then paused again. "Neil went to France, too, didn't he?"

"Yes," Penny said quietly.

"I guess that's why I ain't been seeing him. Last I remember, he was at that engineering school in the Boston States."

"Good night, Simon," she said. "And don't worry any more about that engine. Just send the mechanic over to me if he makes any more trouble for you."

"I can handle the bugger all right," he said, and the door closed behind him. The sound of his heavy boots echoed down the corridor, followed by the muffled slam of a second door; then the cavernous building was silent.

Penny continued sitting at her desk, tense and solitary in the empty room. It was as though a stone had been plunged into the pool of her mind until her memories were surging like troubled waters, and for a few moments her whole body ached with loneliness and a sense of loss. The anaesthetic of hard work could never compensate for the feeling of life and growth that had departed from her; and now, like a man in the desert obsessed by thoughts of green grass and running water, she remembered things as they had been before the war. She saw herself dancing at an Admiralty House ball. She recollected the odor of lime trees heavy in the streets on close summer nights when there were shooting stars, and how those evenings as she walked alone it had been possible to imagine an aeon of tranquillity broadening out like a sea under the sky, herself growing old gently, with children about her, the land where she had been born mellowing slowly into maturity.

And yet she knew that her earlier life had never been especially contented, nor were the things on which she had spent her time calculated to induce any such picture as the one which now filled her mind. She had gone to college and astonished her professors by her ability at mathematics and her precision in the science laboratories. After her graduation she had lived for two years with her family, and being bored by the monotony of it, had ordered the best books on marine engineering she could find and studied them. During the first year of the war she had visited an aunt and uncle in Montreal, but instead of finding a place for herself in the social life of the city, had spent almost all her time at a technical school studying ship designing.

Now, as she sat alone at her desk, looking through the pool of yellow light at the blank face of the window, she quivered at the thought of how helpless her existence had been in the current of forces she had been able neither to predict nor control. Yet, when she examined with detachment what had happened to herself and her relatives during the past three years, she was forced to admit that their experiences had not been unique. The war had taken control of them just as it had of everyone else.

The moment passed and Penny got to her feet, remembering that it was time to go home. Since the death of her mother ten years ago she had tried to be mistress of her father's house while she lived in Halifax, and on Sunday evenings she was expected to supervise the late supper invariably served to those of her relatives who chose to come in after church. She swept her desk clear of pencils and closed the drawers, and then reached for her hat and coat. When she had pulled the hat down over her forehead and stuffed her hands into the pockets of the coat, her face broke into a soft and surprising smile. With an impulsive movement she returned to her desk, picked up the telephone and asked for the number of a hotel.

"May I speak to Major Murray, if he's in?"

She waited minutes, and then Angus Murray's voice sounded at the end of the wire.

"Don't say you're busy, please," she said. "I want you to have supper with me tonight. You know . . . at home . . . the family and everything."

His voice rose in protest. "For heaven's sake! They'd faint at the sight of me."

"Maybe they'd think of it, but on the whole they'd consider it too undignified. Please, Angus . . . I just can't stand them tonight all by myself."

"Where are you now . . . home?"

"No. I'm still at the office. I was just about to leave."

"Then why don't you meet me at the hotel?"

"Can't. That would be asking too much of Sadie. And there's my young brother Roddie. He doesn't like the relatives any better than I do."

"Who's Sadie?"

"Oh, she's our indispensable Newfoundland maid. You've got to come tonight because I want to celebrate. Just you and me, surrounded by aunts and uncles."

There was a pause and she heard Murray clear his throat huskily. "I must say you make it sound attractive! Who's celebrating what?"

"My design. It's been accepted by the Admiralty."

"What design?" She could almost hear him trying to remember.

"I told you all about it long ago. I had a delayed cable from London this morning."

"Oh." His voice suddenly rose in amazement. "You mean—you mean Whitehall's accepted that design for a submarine chaser you were talking about? The one you finished last spring?"

"Don't sound so upset about it, Angus."

There was another pause, filled with silence this time.

"But, good Lord! That means—that must mean you're really good!"

She thought Murray was reconciled to the fact that she had ability; indeed, he seemed to admire her for it. Now she was suddenly sorry she had told him, for it had been her experience that few people know how to be pleased at the success of their friends.

"Never mind, Angus. It's not very important, not really. They'll probably only test it and reject it. I just became a little too pleased with myself, that's all. You'll come anyway, won't you? About nine o'clock?"

"No, Penny. I know my limitations, and my sense of humor isn't up to an evening with the Wains. Yours isn't either."

She twisted the wires of the telephone extension and a wry smile crossed her face. "Didn't anyone ever tell you, Angus, that I'm supposed to be a respectable girl? People see us together and they tell my family and my family knows you never so much as see me home. Pretty soon there'll be a lot of fine talk going around town."

"Why should you care?"

"The odd thing is, I don't. It's you I'm thinking of. You'd care."

"What do you mean by that?"

"Merely that you're conventional, my dear. Most men are, especially those who think they have a reputation for the opposite. Once you hear the gossip, you'll stop seeing me, and I wouldn't like that at all."

She could hear him grunt and again clear his throat, a frequent and individual trade-mark.

"Pretty shrewd, aren't you, Penny?"

"Have it your own way, Angus." She was laughing now as she teased him. "But the family's awfully partial to a uniform. If you'll take a stiff drink and chance it, I'll send them home early, and you can stay as long as you please."

"Well . . . I'll think about it. Don't mind if I'm late, though."

She replaced the receiver and stood up. Through the window she could see tracks of lights shimmering across the still water. An inbound cargo steamer slid silently past the end of the graving dock below, on its way to the Basin to await convoy. From this angle, the ferries crossing the Stream and passing each other were two ovals of light, accompanied by their own following reflections in the water. This harbor with its queer congeries of the very new and the very old, often depressed strangers, but to her it was so much a part of her life, so patiently and quietly beautiful, that she missed it wherever else she went. Her eye wandered back to the freighter sliding upstream: a commonplace ship, certainly foreign and probably of Mediterranean origin, manned by heaven knew what conglomeration of Levantines, with maybe a Scotsman in the engine room and a renegade Nova Scotian somewhere in the forecastle. The war had brought so many of these mongrel vessels to Halifax, they had become a part of the landscape.

Seven o'Clock When Penny reached home she found everything quiet except for faint bumps that seemed to come from the attic. That would be Roddie playing one of his eternal war games by himself. Since his withdrawal from boarding school a year ago he had become obsessed with the war. She pulled off her old felt hat and dropped it on the hall table, then moved it to see if it had shown up any dust. Sadie was asleep in the kitchen when she opened the door; the girl woke blinking as the light flashed in her eyes.

"Never mind," Penny said. "I just wanted to make sure there was plenty of food in the house. Has the colonel told you how many to expect tonight?"

Sadie got to her feet and rubbed her eyes with a corner of her apron. "Just Mr. Halfred and Mrs. Halfred and Mr. Fraser and Mrs. Fraser," she said. "And Master Roddie and the colonel 'isself."

"All right. And set one extra place. I've asked someone else to come in, too. I couldn't stand an unprotected evening with Uncle Alfred and Aunt Maria, even though Jim and Mary Fraser might help out a little. Not tonight, I couldn't."

"Ho, Miss Penny!" Sadie giggled, and added with a mixture of deference and intimacy, "Mr. Halfred, 'e do heat something terrible!"

"You can't hear his teeth clacking all the way out here, can you?"

"Ho, Miss Penny, wot a thing to say!"

"Well, have supper ready by eight-thirty. They won't be here then, of course. But if church isn't too crowded tonight Uncle Alfred ought to have the collection counted in time to get here around nine. What's the matter with Uncle Cecil? Lumbago again?"

" 'E 'as sore bones, Mrs. Cecil said. And she 'as, too, today."

"They probably only have colds, but if it pleases them to think it's grippe I suppose we ought to be thankful. Their absence tonight will help a lot."

"Miss Penny—don't you feel well, too?"

"I feel all right. Don't take me so seriously, Sadie."

On her way through the hall she glanced into the living room and saw that the map of Jamaica over the fireplace was hanging crooked again. She straightened it, then gave a cursory look to make sure the rest of the room was in order. The somber, heavy but comfortable furniture depressed her, but to change it was out of the question. Nothing in this house was ever changed, and her relatives derived a peculiar satisfaction from the thought that in this ancestral establishment even the dust behind the pictures was permanent. She pulled one of the wide, chintz-covered armchairs out of its accustomed position and turned it with its back to the room, so that it faced the French windows overlooking the shadowy cavern of the garden, and then she dropped into it.

Outside, the earth was frozen hard and the flower beds were stiff with frost. It was impossible to see the details of the garden with its stone wall separating it from the street, its great lime trees like buttresses beside the house walls, its benches and summerhouse in the distant corner. The garden was the only part of the property she really loved; to her, the rest of the house was an incubus.

For five generations the Wains had been leading citizens in Halifax, and the history of the family was to some extent the history of the town itself. In 1749 a Wain had been a sergeant in one of the regiments brought to Nova Scotia by Cornwallis to found a garrison city against Louisburg, the fortress in Cape Breton which secured the Gulf of St. Lawrence for the French and was a permanent threat to New England. This Wain later fought at Quebec, then returned to the garrison at Halifax, where he died.

His grandson became a privateer in the war of 1812, and with prize money acquired from the American ships he captured, founded the fortunes of the family, built a wharf and a warehouse, and established an exporting and importing business with the West Indies, exchanging dried apples and fish for rum, tobacco and molasses. From that time until now, the Wain fortune had remained stationary, in the sense that it increased only in proportion to the growth of the family's offshoots, which were fairly numerous.

Wains owned several establishments in Halifax, but the principal one belonged to Geoffrey Wain, the eldest son of the main branch. He was Penny's father and the head of the shipping business. This house which he had inherited stood on the crest of a hill in the South End, in a district no longer fashionable. The years had so mellowed the property that it had acquired a charm rare among the houses of Halifax. The side walls of the house were covered with Virginia creeper and in summer the front was entirely obscured by giant horse-chestnut trees which rose above the third story. The fragrance of the lime trees in the garden was sufficiently intense to permeate the entire neighborhood in the dampness of June evenings.

There was nothing pompous about this house, but it was the kind of place which had become too much for its owners. It patterned most of them and held them down, and no matter where any of them wanted to go, it usually managed to call them back. The Wain estates had passed regularly from father to son, each one's will containing the proviso that if the heir should marry a Roman Catholic the legacy was forfeit. The family was not rich by American standards, but by those of Nova Scotia it was opulent.

Penny got up restlessly and went out to the hall. She picked up her hat and coat where they had been dropped and started for the stairs. As she passed the full-length mirror hanging beside the marble-topped radiator her own reflection startled her. She *had* lost weight during the past six months! If she looked to others as fragile as she now appeared to herself, it was no wonder they never believed her capable of the sort of work she did. Automatically her hand went to her hair to try to hide some of the white lock, though she knew it was impossible to conceal it entirely.

Everything else about her seemed undramatically the same. Only this inward process of changing, this increased sense of her vulnerability! And if only her family knew it, the credit for her success did not belong to her at all. The entire idea of the design for the submarine chaser had been outlined by her cousin Neil before the war. All she had done had been to work out his principles in detail, to check figures of construction costs and the weights of various alloys, to estimate the ratio of horsepower to tonnage, and merge such pedestrian details with her own knowledge of construction and with Neil's general plan. She felt sure that any other engineer could have done as much. The essential design, the conception of the long, wide-shouldered hull with the step in the keel just abaft the forequarter, had been contrived in fifteen careless minutes, years before. The pity of it was that Neil had forgotten it just as carelessly.

She reached her bedroom and began to undress. It was impossible to realize that within another six months a product of Neil's brain and her patience would be heaving a seasick crew through the chop of the North Sea. The step in the keel would prevent its bow from protruding out of the water when the vessel was at speed, but in spite of this, enormous sheets of water would be hurled over the nameless, oil-skinned men who manned her. It would convey to the vicinity of invisible Germans a pair of torpedo tubes, a light, quick-firing cannon, and a considerable number of depth charges. It would maintain itself away from port for a duration of four days and condemn its crew to cold rations only slightly mitigated by navy rum. It would be the most uncomfortable craft in the Royal Navy.

And yet originally it had merely been a problem in physics, an attempt to solve the dilemma of how to construct a motor boat which would travel fast and yet keep its stem in the water. The use to which such a craft might be put had probably never entered Neil's head. As she stretched out on her bed she decided that so far as she was concerned it would continue to be what it was now in her own mind, an abstraction, a monstrous abortion of an attempt to avoid thinking too deeply about matters she could not control. And then she fell asleep.

Eight o'Clock Clocks began striking all over the house, and Penny opened her eyes and got up before the last of their reverberations had died away. She turned on the lights in her bedroom and sat before her dressing table to brush out her hair. She worked slowly, allowing the automatic motions of her arms to circulate the blood and wake her gradually. Many minutes later she selected a dress and put it on, arranging the belt carefully, and then snapped off the lights and left the room.

On the way downstairs she met her twelve-year-old brother Roddie, who had slicked down his hair with water and wanted her to adjust the stud and tie to his Eton collar. Although it was the second of December, Roddie was wearing short trousers with his knees bare, for it was a matter of pride among the boys in his school to see how long they could go into the winter before covering their knees with knickerbockers.

"Did you hear about the submarine today?" Roddie asked, grimacing as she pressed the back of the stud against his throat.

"Come upstairs to the light." She went up the steps and he followed. "What submarine are you talking about?"

"There was a German submarine off the harbor this morning. Didn't you hear?"

"How do you know there was?" These wartime rumors irritated her, as Roddie dimly suspected. "Don't tell me you saw it from the Citadel!"

"Ouch, Penny, that hurts! Willie Moffat told me. His uncle was on the duty boat and he saw it."

She squared away from him and studied the tie and collar carefully. His thumbs had made a smudge on one side of the collar, but it was too small to be noticeable. "If Willie Moffat's uncle was on the duty boat you know perfectly well he didn't see a submarine. The duty boat never leaves the harbor."

Roddie looked crestfallen, for he was proud of his knowledge of ship movements. Apart from his father, Penny was the hardest mortal he knew to convince of anything.

"Will there be anyone tonight but family?" he said.

"Major Murray will be here."

"Oh." His face assumed a serious expression and his forehead wrinkled. "Penny, *what* does Major Murray drink?"

"Hold still till I get this tie straight. I don't know what you're talking about."

"I heard Uncle Alfred say he drank something terrible."

She stood away and this time looked him in the eyes, but he answered the stare with a bland and innocent expression that was defeated by nothing but its own perfection.

"Roddie, you must be the champion liar of your class."

"But he did say that . . . honest, Penny."

"I'm quite sure he did. Honest, Roddie, and you didn't know what he meant, either."

"Well, does he?"

"You run along downstairs and try to keep your hands clean till supper. Your father may be late and you'll have to be the man of the house until he arrives. And don't stare when you greet Major Murray, either."

At a quarter to nine the doorbell rang, a prolonged jangling sound from the basement as half a dozen bells answered the puller by the front door. Before Penny could reach the hall, Alfred Wain and his wife Maria had let themselves in and were taking off their coats.

"'Lo, Penelope," Alfred muttered absently. "Where's your father?"

"He's not back yet. How are both of you?"

"Not very good," Alfred said.

Aunt Maria's voice blared out like a trumpet. "Nonsense, there's nothing the matter with you. Penelope, why weren't you in church? There was a terrible sermon." She squinted at herself in the long mirror and patted the sides of her pompadour with a pair of powerful hands. "I ran into Mrs.

Taylor this evening as we came out, that woman I was telling you about in the Red Cross. She's dreadful. People like that shouldn't be allowed to take part in the war."

Alfred was already on his way to the living room, muttering as he went. "Geoffrey works too much. He's almost as bad as you, though I must say there's some sense to his job." He stood in front of the fire and rocked on his heels, while his hands, cupped behind his back, hoisted the tails of his jacket so that the hot fire could toast his buttocks. He was a gangling man with mutton-chop whiskers and a squeaky voice; he rarely did any work and his chief interest was the Presbyterian church in which he was an elder. There, twice a week and once at Wednesday prayer meeting, he snored through sermons he later condemned, but he could estimate the collection value of any congregation to within half a dollar.

Aunt Maria stalked into the living room and sat down in Geoffrey Wain's armchair, which she adequately filled. "Why is your father still working, Penelope?"

"I'm afraid that's one of the things I can't tell you, Aunt Maria."

"Nonsense, you mean you don't choose to. You're all the same. And look at Roddie. I wouldn't be surprised to see him turn out the worst of the lot."

There was a moment in which the room held no sound but the noise of Aunt Maria's breathing, which permeated it. She was a powerful woman with curly gray hair, ruddy cheeks, deep chest and a bosom that projected like a battlement. Although she was always dowdily dressed, nothing less than a crinoline could have concealed the contours of her thighs, which looked potent enough to appease a Hercules.

The clocks ticked noisily; there was a distant moan from the harbor buoys. Then Aunt Maria's voice broke out again. "Cecil has the grippe but Jim and Mary will be here. Who else is coming?"

"I've asked Major Angus Murray," Penny said.

"Who?" Her aunt stared. "Well, of all the things!"

"Eh?" said Alfred. "Who was that?"

"That man," Aunt Maria explained. "That Major Murray everyone knows about." She turned to Penny: "Is this your father's idea of a joke on us?"

"No." Penny got up from the arm of the chair where she had been sitting and moved towards the door. She hoped she had heard footsteps outside. "It was my idea," she said. "I thought he might enjoy it."

But instead of encountering Angus Murray she opened the door to her Aunt Mary and Jim Fraser. These were the two she called her only nice relations. Mary was the youngest of her father's sisters and was unlike anyone else in the Wain family. She was extremely thin and wiry, with quick and vivacious movements; graying hair surmounted a tawny, sun-browned forehead and she had the easy, reckless laugh of a woman who has spent a lifetime in moderate defiance of her environment. She greeted Penny with affection and slipped an arm about her waist, and the two women stood in the hall smiling at their reflections in the mirror while Jim Fraser bent to take off his rubbers.

Mary's warm voice was speaking eagerly in its clear, English-sounding Halifax accent. "It's simply marvelous news, darling! Jim told me about it this morning. Let's look at you properly. Let's hug you. I'm so proud I could burst."

Fraser straightened and grinned. "Here, Penny, got one for me?" He kissed her loudly. "Well, and what did your father say when you told him?"

"Nothing much."

"My God, what a family I married into! Isn't that like Geoffrey?"

Penny stood aside from the living room door to let them pass. "How's Jean today?" she said.

"Wonderful! We fairly had to tie that little brat or she'd have followed us. The way she's growing is almost indecent. When are you coming out to see her again?"

Penny followed them into the living room. "I've been so busy lately. Each week-end I think the next few days will give us a let-up and they never seem to. But I'll get out this week somehow. I promise."

Alfred Wain greeted them with a melancholy squeak from the hearth. "I never could see why you and Jim want to live at Prince's Lodge. You might as well be at the back of beyond as out there. We've always lived in town."

Jim Fraser, his face a walnut-brown from years on the South African veldt, looking tough and rugged behind a handle-bar mustache, greeted his in-laws and dropped into the nearest comfortable chair. "No, Alfred, I'm damn sure you don't see why we prefer to live out there. There's so much you say you don't understand that sometimes I think you're lucky."

Aunt Maria, disregarding his remark, invaded the conversation. "Did Penny tell you who she's asked here tonight? Major Murray! That man who used to ruin his practice with drink wherever he went."

"Angus Murray?" Jim grinned and looked at Penny in surprise. "I didn't know you knew him. I haven't seen Angus in years. Wasn't he in Geoffrey's regiment?"

"What's that got to do with his coming here?" Aunt Maria said. "I'd like to hear what Geoffrey says when he sees him. I'd like to hear that very much."

Penny might have been listening to empty compliments for all the evidence she gave of minding these remarks. It seemed to her that her relatives had been talking about different sides of the same thing for the last twenty years. "Major Murray's right arm is in a sling," she said. "You should adore him, Aunt Maria. He nearly lost his arm in the service of his country." The bells jangled again and she rose to answer them. "Now for heaven's sake don't stare when he comes in. Roddie's already promised not to."

When she had left the room, Alfred Wain shifted his feet and his face slowly assumed an expression of uneasiness. Jim looked at him in open amusement, for he always enjoyed the spectacle of his brother-in-law endeavoring to think.

"That young woman's too sure of herself," Alfred said finally.

Mary broke out impatiently, "Don't be such an old fool! After what she's done all you can think of is to complain because she knows her own mind."

"Stuff!" said Alfred. "She should be ashamed of herself."

Then the room was silent until Penny returned with Angus Murray at her heels. Jim Fraser rose to welcome him and the women looked expectant, but the only part of Alfred which moved was his head. It craned sideways as though its mechanism had no connection with the rest of his body and the worried expression on his face deepened.

In spite of his uniform Murray looked disreputable. He entered shyly, like a long-legged, alien dog in a strange place, his head held slightly on one side. His thinning hair stuck out from the back of his scalp in a short tuft, his tunic had one button hanging by a thread and his trousers palpably had been slept in. His right hand was splinted and swathed in bandages, and a sling of black silk hung from his shoulder like a bandoleer.

He bowed to the room, and Aunt Maria broke the momentary silence. "Major, *do* tell us about your work."

It was a command, and Murray blinked. He tapped his twisted nose with the knuckles of his left hand and under the loose tunic his shoulders were seen to shift uneasily. Then his gaunt face broke into a grin and he glanced at his wounded arm.

"I don't work," he said.

Aunt Maria bulged forward from the armchair. "Of course you don't now. I mean France. I mean the war."

"Oh, that!" Murray's voice was slow and markedly soft, lilting with an overtone of native Gaelic. "That was just one unpleasant job after the other, and the conditions of work were very poor." Seeing Alfred Wain staring at him with the dumb look of an Aberdeen terrier, he added, "The average war wound presents few interesting problems, medically speaking. Unless you're a plastic surgeon, there's not much to be learned."

"But you must have operated on all sorts of people we know," Aunt Maria said. "After all, you were in my brother-in-law's battalion. Or weren't you?"

"Indeed I was, Mrs. Wain. But you know, I can't remember that any of the boys in the dressing station mentioned you. They were usually pretty tired when the stretcher bearers brought them in."

Penny looked at the clock and the rest looked at their shoes. Then the front door was heard opening and Colonel Wain's step was audible in the hall. Under the weight of his projected presence, their immediate tongue-tied condition was exempted from embarrassment.

When Geoffrey Wain entered the room his presence tightened the atmosphere. He was a tall, broad-shouldered man in his middle fifties. He held himself straight and looked as though he had worn a colonel's uniform all his life. He nodded towards his relatives, hesitated a second as he recognized Murray, then crossed the floor and greeted him with cordiality.

"You weren't in church tonight," Alfred said.

Geoffrey ignored the remark and shook Murray's left hand. "This is a pleasant surprise, Major. I hadn't been aware that you people knew one another. Now that my daughter's a professional woman she's always surprising us. Quite pleasantly, I may say."

Wain's smile showed a row of large, white teeth. The effect of it was brilliant rather than pleasant, and something in its quality took Murray aback. He mumbled incoherently and cleared his throat as he responded to his former chief.

"I heard about your arm," Wain continued easily. "I was told you'd lost it. It's good to know the report was exaggerated."

"It nearly wasn't," Murray said. "Some of my colleagues advised amputation. I had to battle hard to save it."

"You seem to have made a good diagnosis. As usual, if you don't mind a layman saying so. Might I ask when you were wounded?"

"Last June at Lens. Shrapnel splinter just below the elbow. My hand got peppered, too."

Sadie entered to say that supper was ready, and no one waited for Penny to lead the way to the dining room but her father, who continued to look into the fire and talk to Murray as though he had heard nothing. There was something in the man not even his most intimate associates had ever been able to calculate, a discrepancy between the sense of ruthless and indifferent power he radiated and the mediocre record of his achievement. Everything about Geoffrey Wain looked strong, yet his life had been soft and his habits easy. He was broad and burly where his brother Alfred was scrawny. The lines of his face were deeply cut and the flesh between them hard with muscle. His hands were abnormally large, with thick knuckles and a powder of dark hair between the joints. The hair on his head was cropped close, revealing the outline of an evenly molded skull, and the hair being of a uniform shade of silver, it contrasted oddly with his mustache, which was still black. Everything in his manner indicated an ambitious man confident of his own ability. Yet up to the present neither the ability nor the force with which he had been born had been put to much evident use.

For Murray, the hour spent at the supper table was a dreary experience. It was dominated almost entirely by Aunt Maria, and Penny's efforts to improve the conversation were stillborn. They finally returned to the living room and it was a relief to be able to smoke. Sadie brought in coffee, and Penny sat behind a small table to serve it. Colonel Wain passed around cigars and was complimented on their quality, and Murray had resigned himself to another futile hour of desultory talk when he suddenly realized that the atmosphere of the room had changed. They were discussing Penny's successful design, and Jim Fraser was arguing vehemently with his sister-in-law.

"Can't you people get it into your heads that Penny's not working at the Shipyards just for amusement? To hear you talk, a man would think her work was nothing better than knitting socks for the Red Cross. That craft of Penny's is a revolutionary design."

"Revolution?" Alfred flushed and stuttered. "Stuff!"

Fraser's voice rose. "That's the trouble with everyone around here. This is supposed to be a new country, and half the population——"

Alfred assumed the self-righteous expression of one about to be persecuted for his principles, and sighed heavily. "Yes, I suppose it's a crime nowadays not to believe that the newer a thing is, the better it is."

"Oh, for God's sake, it's not a matter of Penny's work being new. It's a matter of its being good."

"But who says it's good?" Alfred pulled at his whiskers.

Geoffrey Wain's voice, indifferently courteous, interrupted. "I'm under the impression that the British Admiralty believes it's good, Alfred. Do you find it necessary to be shocked at that?"

Mary got up impatiently and handed her empty cup to Penny to be refilled. She seemed to be trying to discover something to say and her mouth opened several times, but no audible sounds issued.

"If it will make anyone feel better," Penny said with the trace of a smile as she filled Mary's cup, "I don't deserve credit for the wretched thing. The whole idea for the design was Neil's."

It was as though she had said something indecent. Murray found himself sitting on the edge of his chair, bracing himself. He was aware that irritation had developed into an emotion deeper than anger behind the faces he watched. At the mention of this name, Aunt Maria had flushed and Alfred was drumming his fingers together. Fraser looked at his shoes, and Mary at the light flush on Penny's cheeks. The colonel's expression had not altered, though his emotions obviously required control.

Then Aunt Maria exploded. "Penelope—you don't know what you're saying! Even if you did, you have no right to mention his name in this house." The varicose veins in her face seemed to spread themselves. "Wasn't it enough that he disgraced the whole family without your——"

"Maria . . ." Geoffrey Wain got to his feet and looked straight at his sister-in-law . . . "For Major Murray's benefit, don't you think you might spare our feelings on the subject? He doesn't even know that you happen to be talking about my nephew, Neil Macrae. I believe the major knew him personally. As for Penny's statement—Neil ought to have been able to design a good ship. We could never interest him in doing anything else."

He pivoted about and addressed Murray; as he did so, his action and manner seemed to exclude everyone else in the room. "By the way, Murray, do you still have a palate for port?"

"I'm supposed to like it."

"Then come along to the library with me. I'm sure the others will excuse us. Jim, would you care to join us?"

Fraser shook his head tactfully, and the colonel led Murray to the library, closed the door behind them and took two glasses and a bottle of old tawny from the cupboard of a side table. He poured a little into a glass and sniffed it, then filled both glasses and held them quizzically to the light.

"There is at least one advantage in the shipping business," he said. "One can get good port and good cigars. I think you'll like this. It's very dry. It's almost an Amontillado, in my opinion."

"I wouldn't know the difference," Murray said.

He took the glass Wain offered and sat down, stretching his legs. Wain sat opposite, in a long leather-covered chair on the other side of the hearth. They sipped the wine in silence, and each held his glass once more to the light to savor its color.

"You must find it pretty dull back here?" Wain said.

"If I had a job it wouldn't be so bad."

Murray went on to explain that he was always pleased to return to Nova Scotia, even though he had never wished to live in the province permanently. Halifax was a city which offered more than met the eye, and there were wonderful places to walk in the near vicinity. He had derived a great deal of pleasure from studying various sections of the city which seemed to him to be homogeneous. One section about a mile long and two streets wide was mostly Irish. In the North End there were districts peopled largely by descendants of English garrison soldiers. He had discovered one street where every inhabitant was a Newfoundlander.

Wain smiled. "I'm afraid I take it all for granted. Really, Halifax is a pretty hopeless place. It has a harbor. It used to have a good university. You don't intend to stay here indefinitely, do you?"

"I've given up making plans for the duration." Murray gave one of his sudden, shy smiles. "You seem busy enough?"

"A clerk's job," Wain said. "Transportation officer, they call it."

"I should think that was fairly responsible."

"Some people tell me it is. I still do a fair amount of work at my own business. I shouldn't regret that, but it's not what an officer on active service ought to be doing."

"If the generals had any sense," Murray said, "the war would be over now. At least they could reduce casualties. All they need do is sit tight and wait for the Germans to have a revolution."

"So you think that would solve it, eh?" Wain smiled and drew on his cigar. "No, an outright military victory is essential and it's going to take a long time. Three years, perhaps. Besides, a German revolution isn't desirable. We don't want the rag, tag and bobtail at a peace conference." He studied the smoke circling from his cigar. "Tell me, Murray—what impressed you most in France?"

"The general cowardice of everybody."

"You knew my nephew, of course . . . the one they were just talking about?"

"I wasn't thinking of Macrae when I said that."

"I didn't presume you were. You mean, I suppose, that if the generals had any courage they'd call the whole thing off and admit the war is beyond them? Or that the men would show some spirit? Leave their trenches the way the Russians have done?"

"Something like that," Murray said, watching Wain closely. "I was merely thinking it, not suggesting it."

Wain looked reflective and laid down his cigar while he refilled Murray's empty glass. "There's something in that idea of yours," he said, "though if it ever happens I wouldn't call it an act of courage. The Russian revolution was the last act of a panic-stricken horde. I'm afraid I don't believe the ordinary man is capable of real courage. He's afraid all the time, particularly of his neighbor's opinion. That's the main thing that gets him into the army and keeps him there. When another sort of fear becomes stronger than that one, he panics. I fancy we both know it to be true."

"Frankly," Murray said, "I haven't enough experience of armies to be able to agree with you."

Wain surveyed Murray candidly. "You said you knew my nephew, Neil Macrae. Tell me, what was your opinion of that affair?"

Murray became acutely uncomfortable; he detected an urgency behind Wain's urbanity. What the cause of it was, he had no idea.

"If you don't mind," he said, "I'd rather not talk about Neil Macrae. I only knew him casually and he seemed a good fellow. The night he was killed I was busy in a dressing station. I merely heard the next day that he had been blown to pieces."

"You knew, of course, that he was under guard at the time?"

"I was told so."

Wain seemed disappointed at Murray's unresponsiveness, but he concealed his disappointment almost perfectly. "His arrest was not a particularly pleasant decision for me to have to make," he said. "Now that both of us are out of the battalion I'd like to take the opportunity of saying so to a brother officer. There is no doubt whatever that his flagrant disobedience of my orders in the middle of the attack the day before he was killed was responsible for the failure of the operation. It was perhaps as well that shell found him. A court-martial would have been extremely painful to us all, for it would have been my duty to appear as chief witness against him."

Murray drained off his second glass and rose to his feet. Wain did likewise and the two men looked at each other.

"Your daughter," Murray said slowly, "seems to have a high opinion of his work."

"Yes, it's a great pity about that boy. He had real ability but he was always too unstable to make it count. If it hadn't been for the war he might have outgrown his impetuosity, but . . . he grew up in this house, you know. He was virtually Penelope's brother."

When they reached the living room they could hear the high voice of Alfred Wain explaining an invention which was going to end the war by next March. It was a secret, he insisted, but he had heard about it confidentially from an itinerant British staff officer in Toronto.

"Maybe it's Penny's ship," Fraser said, and rose with a glance at the clock. "We'll have to be on our way, Mary. It's ten-thirty."

The whole company rose, and to Murray's surprise, the colonel said he must leave also. As they moved toward the door Penelope slipped her arm through Murray's and whispered, "Please stay a bit."

Murray hesitated and Geoffrey Wain, as though he had overheard Penny's remark, said, "Stay and have some more port, Murray. Unfortunately I must work. The *Olympic* always keeps me busy."

"The *Olympic?*" Murray's eyebrows rose. "She only arrived yesterday."

"So did about a dozen troop trains. Passchendaele is still going on, and the generals are hungry. I'll hope to see you again before long. Good night."

Murray waited in the armchair quitted by Aunt Maria until Penny had seen the others away. Now that the room was empty, he was forced to admit that it fascinated him. The Wain house represented an aspect of Nova Scotia he had formerly seen only from the outside, for he had been born in a farmhouse in Cape Breton. The people in his district were plain and rugged, and they compensated for their poverty by pride and the hope of emigration; and because few of their ancestors from the Highlands had owned property of any sort, few of them had any sense of it. Murray's eyes wandered from the map of Jamaica to the rest of the room. The tables were heavy mahogany and the curtains the color of ox blood; there were four models of sailing ships, all reproductions of famous Nova Scotiamen which had once been laded at the Wain wharf. It did not seem to Murray a gracious room, yet there was something proper and fitting about it, and it had dignity. There were no late-Victorian frills. At this moment in its silence he could hear the rhythmic pulsating of the fog signals coming in from the harbor which had given this old house its reason for life.

Finally the outer door closed, and Penny returned to the room and curled herself on the chesterfield opposite the fire. She looked at him and smiled. "Poor Angus—I'm afraid I've given you a pretty bad evening!"

"At least it's been different from my usual run." He took a deep breath. "No wonder this house has such high ceilings. A good many cubic feet of air are necessary in it."

"Want something to drink?"

"Yes, but not this minute."

He kept his eyes on hers until she looked away, and then they were silent, feeling the comfort of each other's presence and finding speech unnecessary. The room was alive. The periodic moaning of the fog signals continued to throb through it; there were low vibrations from a steamer's horn and the faint, almost inaudible whine of a locomotive whistle. Mysteriously, all these sounds were creeping in through the crannies of the old house, reminding Murray of eerie noises he had sometimes heard on silent nights on the western front, when the rumble of transport was audible from behind the enemy's lines.

Penny was staring into the fire, and her abstraction made it easier for him to observe her with the detachment he desired. To appraise women, to study their figures and estimate how the planes and curves of their bodies would balance when revealed, had always seemed to him a delightful manner of passing the time. It pleased him particularly to consider shy or diffident girls in this way, for he believed that any sensitive woman had enormous potentialities of pleasure within herself, and the prospects of awakening them never failed to stir his imagination.

"What's going on behind that funny smile?" Penny said suddenly.

"I was thinking about you."

"Oh, Angus—I'd expected a better reply than that."

"If you could see the shape of my thoughts you'd probably think the reply adequate enough. Penny, I suppose you're the most brilliant woman in Canada. That's very nice, but it inhibits me. It's not easy to tell a genius she's adorable."

"It must be awkward." She slipped her legs off the chesterfield. "I'll get you a drink. You could probably use something stronger than port."

When she returned she held a decanter in her left hand and a crystal tumbler in her right, but before she could set them down, a bell jangled again. "Here," she said. "Fix it yourself. Apparently I'm on door-bell duty tonight."

He heard a murmur of voices in the hall, and then the sound of feet running upstairs. He filled the glass and sat down. A cold draft of air crawled along the floor from the opened door and with it came the louder sound of the bells ringing in the harbor. The creeping noises of this old town never ceased; for as long as there were wars and she remained the terminus of the longest railway in the world, her back to the continent and her face to the Old Country, she would lie here in all weathers unchangeably the same, and her bells would ring in the darkness.

Leaning back in his chair, warmed by the fire and the whisky, Murray wondered why he felt moved by the thought. The long failure of his life, the inability to alter the nature with which he had been born, had made him a fatalist against all his wishes. And Halifax, more than most towns, seemed governed by a fate she neither made nor understood, for it was her birthright to serve the English in time of war and to sleep neglected when there was peace. It was a bondage Halifax had no thought of escaping because it was the only life she had ever known; but to Murray this seemed a pity, for the town figured more largely in the calamities of the British Empire than in its prosperities, and never seemed able to become truly North American.

Penny's feet sounded on the stairs again, the outer door closed and she returned to the room and her place on the chesterfield.

"Who was that, the police?"

"How did you guess?" Penny smiled. "A light was showing in Roddie's bedroom. He'd turned it on to read with the windows open, and shut it off when he heard me coming. What a youngster! He'll always be able to look after himself. He'll never starve when he grows up, but I wish I didn't worry so much about other sides of his make-up."

Murray rose and prowled about the room before settling finally on the chesterfield beside her. She made no movement when the fingers of his good hand slipped about the soft flesh of her inner arm and caressed the skin where the tracery of the veins was visible. The expression on his haggard face, usually strained and ironic, had softened and now his eyes appeared larger.

"Penny—are you as lonely as I am?"

There was an instant's flash of fear in her eyes as she turned to him. "I don't know." Her body seemed to tighten to defend itself.

Murray continued to look at her and to caress her inner arm; his manner was candid and there were no overtones of drama. "We're both mature people, Penny. Even if I *am* eighteen years too old for you." He hesitated. "Surely you know what I mean?"

She nodded, and her arm was still under his fingers.

"You probably know I was married before? An American girl. She was much younger than you when she died. The strange thing is, I remember her only as she used to be, and myself as I used to be when we were together. I'd be a shock to her now, if she could— I shouldn't be running on like this. I'm sorry."

"Please, Angus—it's all right."

"I married her when I was still in medical school and she died when I was just getting on my feet. I used to blame her death for all those years" —his face twisted as though shrinking from his own words—"those years of drinking and moving around in the States and letting everything slide. But I was wrong to blame anything but myself. It was only a bad habit, letting an old sorrow dominate my whole existence. I found that out in France. Death suddenly seemed unimportant and life seemed everything." He got abruptly to his feet. "Penny, I don't know whether you give a hoot in hell for me, but I do know it's no good either of us going on as we are."

"Do you think I'm doing so badly, then?"

Again there was the flash of fear in her eyes. He returned to the chesterfield.

"I don't know, Penny. Are you?"

"I have my own work, and I like it."

"I had my work, too, and liked it." He shook his head. "No, it doesn't sound convincing. With a body like yours, with that look I see in your face sometimes—no." He got up once again and stared at the map of Jamaica, leaning his elbow on the fireplace. "You could still have your work. With me on your hands you'd probably need it. Penny, I'm trying to tell you I want you to marry me."

A grandfather's clock sounded from the back hall, striking eleven. It was followed by the other clocks in the house, and during the length of their striking Murray remained motionless with his back to the room. When the last note died away he was aware that Penny was beside him and that her arm was slipping about his waist, and his eyes blinked through moisture so that all he could think of was the poignancy of that slim lock of white hair lacing the brown of her head.

"That's the nicest thing anyone has said to me in years," she whispered.

He drew himself away. "Never mind," he said, "I've always been noted for my nerve."

With a quick impulse she put her arms about his neck and kissed him, but his lips let her go almost at once. She returned to the chesterfield and stared beyond him into the fire.

"I didn't mean it the way you think," she said. "I'd rather not dismiss it like this, Angus."

He kicked a falling log back across the andirons. "Yes, Penny?"

"You don't really know me," she said. "If you did . . ."

"I've always estimated myself high as a judge of women. I admit I didn't know how good you were at your job, but that's got nothing to do with your being a woman."

He began to walk about and ended finally in front of the whisky decanter, poured himself a short drink and downed it.

"I'm afraid you don't even know so much about me as a woman, Angus." She smiled at him. "I don't mean that to sound nasty."

He looked at her over the rim of his glass, and his eyes suddenly changed expression as a new idea struck him. "You're not in love with someone else, are you?" He smiled then and cleared his throat.

Seeing that his sense of humor had returned, she held out a hand. "Come on back here and sit down. I'll tell you *my* story."

"As you like," he said.

"Would you rather I didn't? I've never tried talking about myself to anyone yet."

Murray sat down in silence, watching her. Then he bent and kissed her gently, tilting her head back with the fingers of his right hand. She answered his gaze and his kiss calmly, and to Murray her manner seemed the only answer he required. He settled back into the far end of the chesterfield and slowly lit a cigarette. "You were in love with your cousin, Neil Macrae . . ." His voice had a delicacy of tone which surprised her. "If you like, you can go on from there."

She waited, looking at her own hands lying in her lap, and the only sound was the fire crackling as another log broke in two. She breathed deeply, and there was a tiny flutter under the skin of her throat. "Yes," she said, "you *are* a good judge of women, Angus."

He made no comment.

"Did you know him well?" she asked.

"Not very. We were both in your father's battalion, of course. But the M.O. in any outfit is in an odd position. I certainly had little time or chance to get acquainted with the younger men."

"Father spoke to you about him tonight, of course?"

Murray looked startled. "Yes," he admitted.

"Was Neil really killed in action?"

He sensed an undertone of apprehension, a state of mind which was not far short of horror. "What the devil do you mean?" he said.

"Father hated him. I think he hated him from the time he was born."

"But—"

"Since father's return from France I've heard nothing but hints and whispers about Neil. The whole town's heard them, and you must know it. Father never mentions it outright, but it's hardly an accident that everyone thinks Neil would have been shot for cowardice if he had lived and that father's discharge from active service was Neil's fault."

"Your father wasn't discharged. He was transferred."

Penny smiled bitterly. "Never mind, we both know about that kind of transfer. You haven't answered my question." Her voice took on an urgency that seemed dreadful because it was so unusual in her. "Please tell me—was Neil really killed in action?"

"Penny!" Murray's voice rose and assumed authority. "In this war no one can afford an excessive imagination. If a man's killed, it's a recorded fact. If he's missing, that's recorded, too. Mistakes are possible, but they're not probable."

Her hand swept suddenly upward over her hair and she rose from the chesterfield. "It would be as easy to believe I were dead myself."

Murray took both her hands in his and waited until she met his eyes. Even through deep-sprung emotion she seemed able to keep intact her dignity and her power to grasp facts. "I mightn't be so silly," she said, "if someone would tell me what happened that day they say he was killed. Will you?"

Murray eyed the burning end of his cigarette.

"In the first place," he said deliberately, "I only know the story second-hand. Your cousin was put under guard for disobeying an order of your father's in the middle of an attack. He was killed a few hours later in the German counter-bombardment."

"The attack, of course, was a total failure?"

"I rarely saw one that wasn't, in 1915."

"But father was blamed for it? He was colonel and was sent home to a place where he could do no more harm?"

Murray shrugged, and tapped his twisted nose. "I don't know why you're so obsessed with that angle of the case, Penny."

She leaned on the mantel, her cheek resting on her hand, her eyes staring into the fire. "All right, please go on."

"Perhaps I ought to add that your father lost touch with his battalion for several hours that day." She turned quickly to face him, but he continued before she could interrupt. "That's a thing that might have happened to anybody. Don't make too much of it."

"What did Neil have to do with this attack?"

"Well, the colonel had to send up his orders by runner. I think your cousin was the first front-line officer the runner encountered. He may well have been senior officer on the spot, for all the company commanders had been killed in the initial attack and even the adjutant was wounded."

"And then—according to my father—Neil disobeyed that order?"

"Perhaps." Murray's forehead wrinkled and he puffed hard on his cigarette. "Maybe he misunderstood it. Or perhaps it was an impossible order to carry out."

"I don't believe that Neil was afraid. He might have felt fear but I don't believe he could ever have been incapacitated by fear. Either he or my father was wrong. And my father made him responsible."

"Now, Penny—" Murray was beginning to show signs of discomfort—"if I were you I wouldn't put it that way. There are no drumhead court-martials in the British army. All orders are given in writing, and if the boy had obeyed—well, all he'd have had to do in any case was to produce the written order. But no court was held, of course."

Misery clouded Penny's face and Murray stopped talking. Yet, when she finally spoke, her voice was so calm and controlled that the expression on her face seemed an accident, or a trick of the light which fell across it.

"Thank you, Angus. For two years my family has been insinuating that if Neil had faced a court-martial he'd have been shot. In that event, presumably, father's military career would have marched gloriously on, and he'd not be in Halifax now. They don't mean to persecute me, but that's what they'll never allow me to forget. If Neil had been convicted before he was killed, father would have been freed of all official responsibility for the failure."

"That's stinking rotten."

Murray stubbed out his cigarette and got to his feet. He felt tired and there were sudden twinges of pain in his bad arm. "Penny, if that's how you feel—get away from here!"

"And leave Roddie to them?"

Murray made a gesture of hopelessness with his shoulders and turned away. He realized that he was no longer young, and that at forty-seven there was no resiliency left in him. Penny continued to talk, and as he listened it seemed unnatural that a girl could carry about such a burden in her mind and still look no older than twenty-nine.

"Neil had such a rotten time in this family," she said. "His mother died when he was born—she was my Aunt Jamsie. And his father could never fit into this menagerie, so he stayed away from us as much as he could. I still remember Uncle John's place where he used to build yachts. When Neil and I were small we used to go there in the summers."

"John Macrae?" Murray looked thoughtful. "He was from Cape Breton, wasn't he? Came from one of the villages? How on earth did he ever meet your father's sister? That's one of the oddest matches I ever heard of."

"That's what my family thought. He met Aunt Jamsie when he was building that yawl father still owns. I suppose he seemed new and different to her. And with her background she probably seemed glamorous to him."

"Yes," said Murray, "I can understand that. What about Neil? I gather he became a designer, too?"

"Neil was quite out of the ordinary." Penny was trying to be dispassionate, but she was not able to keep the warmth from her voice. "I suppose it's an accident when a woman loves a man and still is able to estimate his work professionally. Neil had that extra something that all the diligence in the world can't make up for."

"But what did your father have against him? It doesn't make sense."

"Father's a peculiar person. You see, Aunt Jamsie was his favorite sister. He loathed John Macrae for marrying into his family and when Aunt Jamsie died—I don't know how to put it. He'd never say anything openly, but he resented Neil. You'd almost think he held Neil responsible for Aunt Jamsie's death."

"But surely John Macrae——"

"Uncle John died when Neil was ten."

"I see."

"Then there was nothing except for Neil to come to us. It's not that father neglected him. He sent him away to school in Montreal. He wanted him to study law. Father's funny that way. At least, he's generous with money."

"What about Neil himself? Did he dislike your father?"

"He could hardly help it. When he left school he left our house, too, and then he only came back on vacations sometimes. He tried several jobs and finally won a scholarship at M.I.T. Then the war broke out and he came back to enlist."

Murray did not attempt to say anything, and for several moments there was silence between them. The fire was smoldering low, and he got up to set more wood across the irons and work on the coals with a bellows. Then he resumed his place on the chesterfield and took his right arm out of its sling and spread the fingers gingerly out along his thigh, manipulating their joints slowly.

"If this war lasts as long as your father thinks it will," he said, "this old hand of mine may see service again."

With an impulsive movement that tossed her hair she leaned against him and her arms went about his neck. He felt the firm outline of her shoulders and her chest tensely strained as she pressed herself against him, and then he was aware that she was quivering and that her cheeks were wet.

"Poor Penny!" He took out a clean handkerchief and awkwardly wiped her cheeks. "There now—it's better, now you've talked it out."

Under the pressure of emotion the soft cadence of his native Gaelic had returned to his voice, and the extreme tenderness of this disappointed, embittered man touched her.

"You're very good to me," she whispered. "I don't know why." She stopped crying and wiped her eyes. Finally she got to her feet and smiled, looking shy and daintily awkward like a young colt. "I ought to know better than this."

Murray felt so tired he could hardly make his legs respond to his will to stand. "If you'll let me," he said, "I'm going to keep on coming around to see you. But now—if you don't mind, I think I'll call myself a taxi."

MONDAY

The stale, sour smell of the telephone booth bit into his nostrils when he closed himself inside. He thumbed through the telephone book and then called a number. A luxurious feeling of relief passed over him when the impersonal voice of someone who could not see him answered the call. "Military hospital," it said. "What division, please?"

"I don't exactly know," he replied. "I want to locate a man who returned from France a year ago and has probably been discharged. I thought he might have been treated by you. Corporal Alec MacKenzie."

"It may take a while to go through our records. Who's speaking, please?"

"That's not important. I'm a friend of his from over there."

"Hold the line."

There was a wait of several minutes and the receiver at the hospital end caught and transmitted the distorted sounds of people moving in long corridors, of shuffling feet, of nurses and orderlies making inquiries at the desk. He could almost smell carbolic acid.

Then the voice spoke again. "There are three Alec MacKenzies on the lists we have, two privates and a lieutenant. What was the battalion?"

He gave the numeral.

"None of these men were connected with that unit. Are you sure he was registered here?"

"I thought he might be."

"You'd better try the other hospitals. If you don't get anything from them, call the Y.M.C.A. If he's still in uniform all you need do is mail a letter to him, with his battalion number."

"Thanks."

He heard the receiver click, hung up his own and left the booth. He was trembling and his shirt was moist with sweat. His wounded leg ached, yet he felt an immediate desire to run, to move rapidly in any direction in order to feel the motion of his body and escape the throng of pedestrians from which Barrington Street would never be free. The sidewalk ought to be widened, if Haligonians could find nothing better to do than walk up and down this street.

The Parade, a pre-Victorian square fenced in by a stone wall with the City Hall at the end, was opposite the drug store from which he had phoned. He remembered there were benches in it and not too many loafers at this hour in the morning. When he had found an empty bench, he opened his copy of the *Morning Chronicle* and hid behind its pages while he read about how good the spirits of the boys were after Passchendaele.

"For God's sake—Macrae!"

There was no chance of getting away. A man his own age, wearing the uniform of a sub-lieutenant of the navy, was standing by the far end of the bench when he turned around, and as his brain raced with subterfuges he suddenly felt a thrill of elation and then he became calculating. The fellow did not belong to Halifax. Where had they met? A hockey team—that was it, they had been at school together. Years ago, in Montreal.

"Charley Baxter!" He shook hands as though Baxter were the one man he had come home to see. "What are you doing here?"

"Waiting around. I'm due to sail for England any time soon." Baxter shook his head and grinned. "What a chance meeting you here! I could hardly believe it was really you sitting there."

Neil sat down and fumbled to get out some cigarettes, hoping that if Baxter smoked one of his he would also light them both. His hands were trembling even after the smoke reached his lungs, and he dared not risk anyone seeing how they shook. With exaggerated deliberation he clasped them behind his head and leaned back on the bench. But his face felt unprotected against the other man's eyes. The strange thing was that during the past two years his voice had rarely gone out of control; at most for only a few seconds. It was always his hands that bothered him most.

"How's everything in Montreal?" Neil said.

"I don't know," Baxter replied. "Same, I guess. What have you been doing with yourself? I'd have thought you'd have had a permanent job in the Dockyard, the way you used to be keen about ships."

"No, I was in France. Demobbed now, of course. Got hit quite a while ago, back in '15. So you're going to England? Getting a berth in the Royal Navy?"

"Minesweepers, I guess. They have a few around here, but, hell—what's the use of sticking on this side? All you see of the war is bad weather and when you get ashore there's nothing but Halifax to look at."

"Don't know many people, then?"

"Hardly anyone. Old women around the canteens wanting to mother the boys—you know the sort of thing. If I'd known you were here I'd have cashed in on it. You must know all the girls in town."

Neil shook his head. "I haven't lived in Halifax for years. Sorry I can't help you. It's a tough town to find the right sort of girl. They're all one thing or they're all the other. Well, I don't have to worry about that. I'm leaving for Toronto. It's not much better so far as girls go, but it's got better jobs."

Baxter eyed the shabby clothes, the worn shoes and the sharply lined face and wondered. Once they had been in the same class. Once Neil had been one of the natural leaders in the school. He looked at him now and felt uneasy, as though his old friend were a symbol of something ominous.

"So you don't know many people around here?" Neil watched him coolly, his hands still clasped behind his head.

"I thought I'd already told you that."

Now that Neil was sure this meeting with Baxter could make no difference, he became almost reckless in his desire to escape. He got hastily to his feet and put his hands in the pockets of his worn overcoat. "It's damn cold, don't you think? I'd better get along." He held out his hand abruptly. "It was great seeing you, Charley."

Baxter's face showed palpable bewilderment, but he rose automatically and shook hands. "I hope everything goes all right for you in Toronto. Most of the boys are in the army now, but I tell you what–write the Head in Montreal and get a few addresses from him."

"That's a fine idea." He hesitated. "Well, so long, Charley."

He walked quickly with his head bent and his shoulders hunched, and it was not until he was on Barrington Street with the stone wall between himself and further recognition that he relaxed and realized that his shirt was dripping wet once more. His mind was blank and he could think of nothing except a desire to get some place where he would not have to talk again.

He turned the first corner and walked down the hill, and stopped only when he reached Water Street, where the pavement was cobbled and he could smell the docks and see the funnels and spars of the ships. He began to remember Montreal, seeing fragments of it so clearly he might still have been there. It was a Saturday, cold and dry on a winter morning with Mount Royal snow-covered and bulging against a glittering sky. The hockey team was off for the Bishop's game. Then the sheet of ice in the Coliseum, Charley Baxter on the right wing and himself on the left, skates ringing and the puck banging against the boards and the Head standing still as a stork, his long neck gangling over the players' bench. Afterward, lunch in the school hall, its walls lined with the heads of moose and buffalo, and Charley and he trying to get permission from the housemaster to go out that night and watch Canadiens play Ottawa. And then it was night and the trams were jammed along Ste. Catherine Street and the ice on the rink was frozen like gray-yellow oil under the lights and thousands of French-Canadians in the rush-end were shouting, and Vezina in the nets moved easily, loose and slow and then quick like a cat, blinking sleepily every time he kicked a puck away.

"Excuse me–" He snapped around. "'Ave you got a match, guvnor?"

"Sure." He handed the man several, hesitated, then asked, "You off a ship?"

"Not bloody likely I ain't." He puffed the fire of the match down into his pipe. "Know where a bloke can get a drink around 'ere?"

"There used to be plenty of places right on this street. I haven't been around lately, though."

"It's 'ard," the man began to move off, "to get a bloody thing in this blasted town."

This time there had been no prickly feeling at meeting another human being. The man was too obviously a stranger. A wind began to suck its way down the corridor of the street, baffling slightly but cold and northerly, and his coat was too thin for it. He wished it were spring. But the trouble was that Canada had no proper spring: that season was always skipped when winter leaped right into summer. One week there would be snow flurries and then, towards the end of May, it would be blazing summer with the leaves unfurling on the trees, and the blackflies chewing your ears off when you went fishing on the Queen's Birthday, and walks with girls in the long warm twilights, and whisperings after dark.

These thoughts and these emotions made no sense. Here in Nova Scotia, right here in sight of docks and shipyards, and seamen, he felt rooted and at home. Yet it had been in Montreal that all the good things had happened. There were no fine memories to hold him here, nothing of beauty that had ever been his own; in fact nothing at all but instinct.

A girl came out of a shipping office and crossed the street, walking ahead of him. Her neat, long legs and slim waist made him hungry. He quickened his pace and passed her, glancing sideways. The face was disappointing, for she had a nose like a bird and her lips were thin and mean. A waste, he thought, a waste of a lot of things.

Once he had known dozens of girls in Halifax, but now he had forgotten the names of most of them and their faces and figures were blurred in his memory. Montreal seemed easier to recall. This time it was June. A heat haze was clamped down over the St. Lawrence valley and the streets shimmered and the leaves were warm and heavy on the trees. He had just been told his transport was to leave the next day; only twenty hours left when he had counted on another week. He had gone out on the crowded tram to Notre Dame des Graces where she was living with Jim and Mary Fraser, and for the rest of that afternoon they had walked through the humid and sweltering air under the trees on the summit of Mount Royal, seeing the city spread beneath them like a map and the blurred bow of the river curving out from the Lachine Rapids to the thin web of Victoria Bridge. The air vibrated with the faint pulse of the distant traffic. Walking couples moved slowly. The clouds built up an enormous, purple wall over the American border to the south.

As the hours slipped by they had seemed to grow into an intense and aching privacy with one another and to become conscious of nothing else. Her dress was pale yellow, and in her haste to be off with him she had forgotten to wear a hat. Her face was flushed with the heat and their constant movement; it seemed as though they could never rest, for during these hours their whole life was being distilled before their eyes. This day was at the zenith of the season; it should have been the longest day of the year. Yet they seemed unable to hoard it for themselves, and because they could not decide what to do and were afraid to confess what they wanted to do, they wasted the daylight with aimless walking.

And then they were in a restaurant in St. Denis Street and the French-

Canadian voices were splashing all around them. White wine stood in a bucket sweated with frost.

Finally they were in the hot darkness of the streets and only the faintest of glows lingered from the sunset over the roofs. She had decided that they should not marry until he returned. So, after all this, they should not marry. And because his instinct agreed with her, he did not press the point.

In Phillips Square they found an old woman selling peonies and he bought a huge bunch of blooms heavy and drooping on the stem. And almost before he realized it, they had reached the hotel where he had engaged a room for the duration of his leave, and without a word she had gone in, too, and stayed with him.

Dawn entered the room at four in the morning, the peonies he had bought for her stirred in a vase, and he woke and realized that the wind had changed and that now it was cool. She was awake, too, and they were alone in the dawn together, incredibly desirous, and it had not seemed possible that this familiar girl's body could be such an adventure for a man. He could see her hair tumbled on the pillow as the dawn grew, her features becoming distinct, the shadows fading from her opened lips. He could feel the wonder of discovering her so much slimmer than he had imagined, and her limbs as delicately flexible as though they had been contrived purposely for this moment with himself. He could remember the solitary man who had walked up the street from the Windsor Station whistling so clearly they had been able to hear him for nearly five minutes. And still they had felt no need of sleep. . . .

Now he was surveying himself in the plate-glass window of a telegraph office in Hollis Street, in Halifax. The awkward posture induced by his bad leg accentuated the droop which had developed in his shoulders. For a second he dreaded that passers-by might be able to guess what a scrawny, weakened frame was hidden by the cheap suit he was wearing. He was tired. He had been tired for two years because his mind was never able to rest. In all this time he had not once wakened up in the morning and looked forward to the coming day.

Behind the plate-glass window was a polished oak counter with pads and pencils ready for people who wanted to say something to someone else who was far away. His mind cleared, only to encounter a sharp sense of loss. There was no one in the world to whom he could send a telegram, even if he should discover something to say. He might as well be dead as the way he was, since the chief loss in death was the ability to communicate.

He turned from the window. A couple of private soldiers approached and his right hand involuntarily left his pocket to wait for their salute. They passed without a glance at his civilian clothes. He turned into a restaurant at the corner, and after taking several minutes to nerve himself, entered another phone booth and called in succession all the remaining hospitals in Halifax. Half an hour passed before he discovered that Big Alec MacKenzie was unknown to any of the military authorities, the hospitals, or the Y.M.C.A.

Eagerness to discover this man had become a torment, yet for the moment there was nothing he could think of doing. The memory of MacKenzie was clear in his mind: a man about six feet four, but so burly he hardly seemed tall; about forty-five years old, skin freckled and sandy, hair reddish brown. Alec's movements were slow, his walk had the melancholy rhythm of a ruminant animal, and his wrists and hands were strong enough to bend a steel bar. Neil remembered that he also had a slow manner of talking and that he held the words in his mouth as though they were a cud and he feared to relinquish them, but when the voice finally issued it was hauntingly musical and crowded with Gaelic idioms. English was Alec MacKenzie's second language.

What would he have done had he been in Alec's place, a man with a family, discharged from the army with a small pension? He did not know, for he was not informed of the nature of Alec's wound. Before the war Alec had been a fisherman, and had also tilled a few acres of rugged ground on the Cape Breton shore. If he were still capable of such work, he would probably be back among his own people; if not, he might be living on his pension almost anywhere in Canada. It did not occur to Neil that the war might have changed Alec sufficiently to cause him voluntarily to leave his old trade and take up another.

There seemed nothing to do but wait until he could think of some safe way of finding his man. So he continued his aimless walking through the streets, and their very familiarity introduced into his present mood and situation a sensation of overpowering unreality. It was an effort to force himself to be careful and to walk always against the main stream of traffic so that if he recognized someone approaching he would be able to turn about and escape. It was the sudden encounter he feared, someone he knew stepping out of a shop or a doorway and meeting him face to face. The problem of eating bothered him particularly: if he were sitting in a restaurant when this happened he would be hopelessly trapped.

No one was likely to discover him in the cheap room he had hired in the North End, so he began walking in that direction. He proceeded north nearly half a mile; then he suddenly realized that native Haligonians rarely ate in the station restaurant and would not be expecting to encounter acquaintances if they did so. In the waiting rooms and restaurant of the station he would be able to sit and read the papers and eat his meals, even to talk with strangers, and allow himself the illusion that he still had a place in the world of the living.

His body felt increasingly tired, and this feeling of exhaustion exasperated him, for he recognized that its cause was entirely mental. His wound was healed. It required a sudden and violent noise to produce any aftermath of shell shock. His frame was thin and not too well nourished, but his muscles in themselves were sound enough. These alternating fits of nervous activity and dull apathy spread from his mind to his body, which answered his moods like a parrot. And now he felt physically exhausted and no longer wished to walk. He leaned against a lamp post on the corner just like any other of the loafers with which Halifax, like all seaports, is crowded. He looked straight ahead of him down the funnel of the street to a patch of harbor visible in the gap at its end. While he watched, a procession of five freighters, painted in dazzle colors and loaded to the plimsoll lines, passed seaward in line ahead. Evidently what he had read was true: the war had made Halifax the third port in the Empire.

TUESDAY

The morning was dry and crisp, the ground frozen hard, and white clouds rushed through a glittering sky out to sea. Dust blew through the streets and made people turn their faces aside as the wind eddied around corners, and the dingy buildings in the downtown area looked outrageously unkempt as the brilliant light sharpened their outlines and mercilessly disclosed their need of new paint. On the streets there was the sound of marching men and the music of bagpipes and military bands, and occasionally from the harbor there came a booming sound, deeper than thunder, from the horn of a great ship. Halifax was alive this morning and there was no person in the town who did not feel the change in the air. The *Olympic* was about to sail with another cargo of troops.

Eleven-thirty o'Clock Angus Murray, walking towards the waterfront with a captain of engineers whom he had met casually a few weeks before, found the activity depressing.

"Living in this town is like being quartered in a railway station," he said, as they waited on a corner for a battalion to pass. "Four months of it. You're lucky; you've only been here since October."

"I don't mind it so much." The engineer was from Ontario. "Must be a lot worse around here in peacetime, though. The war's done a lot for Halifax."

Not, Murray thought, any more than the war has done a lot for physics or chemistry. The war and the prospect of wars to come is what keeps the place fundamentally the same through the years. He preferred to remember Halifax as he had found it when he had first come here to college years ago and this had been the largest city he had ever seen. He liked to recall its English gardens in summer: the lazy and affable existence of its inhabitants who seemed to assume that nothing they could do in peacetime could possibly matter to anyone; the way Halifax had of seeming not so much a town as a part of the general landscape; its chameleon-like power of identifying itself with the weather. There were fine days with westerly winds and you could smell the odor of spruce trees in the downtown streets and the atmosphere of the place was like a tonic. But there were almost as many wet days when Halifax was worse than any town he could remember, when the fog isolated it from the ocean and the forests until there was nothing to see but streaming pavements, and the bells moaned in the distance and the stained old buildings seemed to expect the bad weather to go right on to the end of the world. The worst of it was that one knew Halifax did not really care about this. It seemed willing to lie out in the wet forever, to take what other people and powers prepared for it; and no matter what happened, Murray realized, it could never change its nature. It would do its duty by the English as long as there was an England left.

The battalion passed finally, and Murray and the engineer followed it with the crowd to the head of Pier Two, where the *Olympic* was berthed. The Shipyards lay just beyond, but Penny would not be finished with her work for at least another half-hour. He decided that he might as well stay here as anywhere else; troops embarking on the *Olympic* made a spectacle in spite of the familiarity of the sight.

Directly in front of him towered the sharp bow of the *Olympic* with soldiers' heads protruding over the coaming like a row of coconuts. The engineer pointed: "Nice target for a Vickers. Wouldn't that be something to get inside a beaten zone!"

Murray grunted. "Pretty mind you've got. I suppose that would be just another technical problem, so far as you were concerned? Or would it be even that?"

"You needn't get so serious about it."

"That's what I've heard ever since this war started. Don't get serious! Don't interfere with the experts' war. Don't say anything to spoil their fun."

The engineer grinned. "What's the matter? The whisky I gave you last night sour on the stomach? The trouble with you is, you can't take your liquor any more."

"Smith—did you by any chance ever live in a really big city?"

"I worked in Detroit once."

"I thought so."

"Only for a few years, though."

"They must have been mighty important years. I have a theory and you'd make a beautiful example of it."

"You've always got a theory," Smith said.

"I've a theory this war is the product of the big city, and that everything—" Murray became aware that a bicycle tire was brushing the back of his leg and that its owner wanted to be recognized. He turned around. "Hullo! Roddie, isn't it? What are you doing here?"

"Hullo, sir."

"Why aren't you in school?"

"Well——" Roddie suddenly pointed to another boy his own age, a shabby youngster in a roll-neck sweater with a tough, freckled face who also had a bicycle. "This is Willie Moffat. His father was in a German submarine."

"What's that got to do with your not being in school?" Murray grinned amiably. "Don't tell me you have a holiday?"

"Not exactly. But it's all right if we get back by two."

"I'll bet it isn't. Do you want me to tell your sister that we met and it's all right if you get back by two? I'm seeing her in half an hour."

"Oh, sir!" Roddie looked uneasy, but brightened almost immediately.

"Willie has a cousin on the *Olympic*. Do you think we can get on board?"

"Not a chance. I couldn't get on myself."

"Well, I guess we better be moving on. I guess we better get closer so we can see better." The boy shifted away. "Good day, sir. You won't tell Penny, will you?"

Murray grinned and looked back at Smith.

A dark green dory, heavy with many years' accumulation of oil and brine and dirt, glided out from a nearby wharf. A longshoreman was sitting on its gunwale, sculling over the stern with a long, flat oar, while another sat astride the central thwart as though it were a saddle. They were staring up at the *Olympic*.

"Germans got a bounty on her," one of them said, "like she was a wolf or something."

"They don't get her," his companion said.

"One of them fellas was telling me th' other day they don't take the same course twice going across. Last time he says they went pretty nigh onto Bermuda before they headed north again."

"That's what they say." A moment of silence, then the man added, "Them naval fellas!"

"When I hear about the Germans getting some of them tubs been coming in here lately it don't make much difference, I says. But I'd feel pretty bad if I heard they got this one. She's sort of part of the place, you might say. I'd miss seeing her around. She ought to be convoyed through. One of these days they're going to get her."

"She's too fast for them ordinary convoys. She takes care of herself."

"Yeah. I guess that Captain Hayes is all right."

Twelve o'Clock The shipyard was flooded with sunshine and the air reverberated with the savage striking of the riveting machines, punctuated occasionally by a ringing clang of heavy metals knocking together. The outlines of the ship they were building were gaunt and uncouth in this merciless light, and the workmen moving about her looked so small it was hard to realize they could be doing anything that mattered.

Penny looked out of her window at this familiar scene and felt alien to it. After her talk with Murray on Sunday night it had been impossible for her to settle back into the groove of her profession. This morning she had spent two hours in the loft, that gigantic room where the plan of the ship was marked out full size on the floor; her mind, filled with figures, had recorded information with the efficient precision of an adding machine, had played with their totals and given them out again in a different combination. The loft foreman had said it was all right. What was all right? Estimates, combinations of angles, balances of stresses and strains, abstractions which had no reality in themselves and never would have reality in anything else unless other experts approved of them. Then they would be translated into steel of a peculiar construction and the sum total would be an ungainly, high-bowed, high-sterned freight carrier which would only have a life significance when a crew her builders would never meet had filled it with the smell of bacon grease and dishwater, hung up their dungarees in cabins unkempt with their own living habits, and blown tobacco smoke into the thrice-breathed air between its decks.

She glanced at the clock and saw she was due to meet Murray in less than half an hour. Her morning's work was done, and she began to clear up her desk. One of the junior superintendents entered as she was closing the last drawer.

He smiled genially. "I thought you'd like to have a look at these," he said. As he handed her the papers his eyes ran over her shoulders and he smiled again. "Those mass-produced vessels they're building in the States. When I was in Wilmington in the fall that was all they were talking about." He continued to slide his glance down her arms, though there was nothing directly impertinent in it.

Penny took the papers and laid them on her desk. "Don't tell me we're going to start that sort of mass production here!" she said.

"No, we haven't come to that yet. But the Yanks are smart." His eyes left her waist and focused out the window. "Look at that ship out there. What's the point in being particular about its construction when it has a one-to-five chance of getting itself sunk the first voyage it makes?"

She thumbed through the papers methodically, ignoring the remark. After waiting a few minutes, he left her. She continued to examine the details of these strange new craft which the builders knew would never last more than a few years but which could be made and launched inside a few months. The idea of building ships this way appalled her. The worst aspect of it was that the principle was sensible. What was the use of quality in a world like this? In God's name, what was the use of a person like Neil Macrae with his dreams of excellence which he had never satisfied? If the war continued much longer they would be forced to build like that up here, and what was left of the old Nova Scotian tradition of shipcraft would disappear entirely. It was going fast enough as it was. Fifty years of governmental neglect, years in which the politicians had turned their backs on the rest of the world in their eagerness to make money out of the West, had reduced British North America from her rank as the fourth mercantile seapower of the world to insignificance.

She got to her feet and reached for her coat, impatient at herself for yielding to generalizations and equally helpless to steer her mind into duller channels. It was the end of ships if they mass-produced them. A good ship could never be duplicated exactly. Vessels in crates, and the devil with quality; men like John and Neil reduced to the assembly line! It was coming. Craftsmanship was already being apologized for, these days. The real skill of the future would be the manipulating of men, and ever-increasing dexterities would be developed to fit masses of men into the molds produced by the designers.

She opened the door and set out down the long corridor. After her talk with Murray the other night she was almost reluctant to meet him now. Some moments she regretted her confidence, other times she was glad she had trusted his understanding. At least she was aware of feeling alive again, for since Sunday night the restless gnawing in her mind had refused to be quieted.

The departure of the *Olympic* was one of the few events in Halifax sure to draw a crowd. Although its sailing hour was never publicized, it could never be entirely concealed, for it was invariably preceded by a march through the streets of thousands of soldiers, who were accompanied by considerable band music and swarms of children. The Citadel was already dotted with spectators, and hundreds were gathered in the narrow streets near the dock. Haligonians had seen the *Olympic* come and go so often during the past few years they had acquired a personal affection for her. Yet each time she returned, she was strange as well as familiar because her pattern of camouflage was repeatedly altered. This voyage she was painted black and gray and white, with vast sweeps of color going up and forward in a crazy rhythm from the plimsoll line to the first promenade deck, then veering around as though a wind up there were blowing the colors backwards. Sometimes her stern was blacked down to the wake and the picture of a tramp ship was painted amidships on her hull. But her cargo had remained the same on every voyage since the beginning of the war: three bars of khaki lining the rails, five thousand Canadians traveling in bond, going to Europe with nothing to declare.

Perhaps some scientist of the future, Murray thought, would be able to analyze the nature of the chain which bound Canada to England. Certainly no one could do so now, for the links were tenuous. Hardly anyone in Canada really understood the legal obligations of his own country to England. Hardly anyone cared. Yet the chain was stronger than the skeptics guessed, for twice within the last fifteen years it had pulled Canada into England's wars, and Canadians had offered their lives without question.

A pipe band, invisible in the dock shed, was playing *Lochaber No More*, and the music was making every nerve in Murray's body quiver. This was the lament the village pipers had played a hundred years ago when the clansmen who were the ancestors of half the people in Nova Scotia had left Scotland for the New World. Now Nova Scotian pipers were playing their men back to the Old World again. Was this another of England's baits, or did the pipers really feel their music? He did not know; as he thought about it, it hardly seemed to matter, because he felt the music himself, felt his fingers clenched and a salty constriction behind his eyes. Reason had nothing to do with his feelings; reason had nothing to do with anything that happened until it had become a fact which could be analyzed. By reason he disapproved of the war, of Canada's participation in it, of three-quarters of the governments which made the policies for the British Empire. He was irritated by most of the Englishmen he met, and liked Americans better. Yet, in spite of all this, nothing could alter his intuitive belief that the best in England was the finest the world had yet seen, and that a world without England would be intolerable.

They were playing the lament over again. By God, that at least had no place in a war like this! He remembered his father in old-fashioned black serge reading the Bible on the Sabbath in the farmhouse where he had been born, his mother speaking in Gaelic to his sister, and the whole family on their knees each morning before breakfast. Oh, give thanks unto the Lord, for he is good, for his mercy endureth forever!

He glanced sideways at Smith, still examining the *Olympic* with a professional eye. The unbelievable and blind stupidity of this man, coupled with his unquestioned ability and decency, seemed to Murray terrifying. His attitude towards the war was that of a well-brought-up and precocious child playing with a set of meccano. The only difference between Smith in war and Smith in peace was that now he had unlimited funds at his disposal.

For Roddie Wain, the departure of the great ship crystallized all the impressions he had formed of the past few years, what he had seen and read and what he imagined the purpose of the world to be. The purpose of the world was doing things, and doing them better than the other fellow. It was troops passing schools on route marches, and bugle calls from the Citadel each night and morning, and sudden surprises which turned an ordinary moment into a significant date, and Halifax filled constantly with the shuffle and movement of men wearing the same kind of clothes and doing the same kind of things.

Sometimes when the sound of night practice from the forts woke him he would lie in bed with visions: ships plunging in total darkness through storms in the North Sea with surges washing the decks and sailors clinging to stanchions as the green water leaped over them, while he clung to the coaming of the bridge and guided the ship towards an unseen enemy, uncomfortable but dauntless; shells bursting and Germans pouring across wasted land into the whip of the machine gun which he, a solitary survivor, directed against them. Sometimes the visions were impersonal. Sometimes it was nothing but a rhythm, a tread of millions of unseen, tired feet moving in time all over the curved surface of the globe. Sometimes he remembered a picture he had seen of Dover headland under the moonlight. The waves rolled in against it and the waves broke, the sea washed slowly away but the headland remained; and behind it were small villages with thatch for roofs and smoke mounting upward in the twilight and fields which were greener and trees more lush than in any other land on earth: England, whose preservation was the reason and the justification of all that happened here in Halifax.

He pushed his way through the crowd to a vantage point. Willie Moffat followed him, and there, resting on the handlebars of their bicycles, they watched the bayonets of the last company sweeping out arcs as the men entered the dock. Roddie wondered why the English used such a short length of steel. German bayonets were longer and those of the French twice as long, and yet they said the British soldier was the finest bayonet fighter in the world. He turned to his friend. "Why do we use such short bayonets?"

"Those don't count, except for something like this," Willie said. "They're just for practice. When they fight they use battle bayonets and grind them sharp. I know. My brother's in the Twenty-fifth." Willie turned and jogged a strange man's elbow. "Mister, when does she sail?"

"Pretty soon now, son."

"That man *I* was talking to is a major," Roddie said. "He was wounded, too. He's a friend of my sister."

"That's nothing. My cousin got gassed at Vimy Ridge and he was killed."

"I had a cousin that was killed, too."

"The first Canadian soldier that was killed lived on our street."

They tried to get closer to the entrance of the dock, but a policeman pushed them back; so they continued to stand where they had been, open-eyed and delighted and slightly afraid in the center of all this excitement, conscious of the noises of feet and the music of the pipes, of the smell of the water, the pressure of the crowd and the eddies of cold air blowing past them under the sun.

Exactly at twelve the horn of the *Olympic* coughed, then plumed itself and roared, making the air shudder. Longshoremen on the tugs shouted to sailors on the steamer's deck and there was a jangle of bells signaling the engine room. Then two floods of dirty water raced along the ship's flanks and burst hissing against the sea wall fronting her prow. The liner began to back slowly out. As the people watched her, someone started a cheer and a flurry shook the crowd like wind in the leaves of a tree. Then silence fell on them all and they watched dumbly as the ship drew away.

Another surge broke from the port screws and churned the sleek waters of the harbor. This maneuver swung the ship broadside on and she looked gigantic.

A man standing near Roddie became informative and said to his neighbor, "She'll likely anchor out there in the Stream and wait. That's what she often does. They say not even Captain Hayes knows his course till he clears port. They say he doesn't even know when he's to sail till the last minute."

But this time the captain must have had his orders, for the *Olympic*, under heavy steam, began to belch out smoke and give warning blasts on her horn. Another gurgle sounded from the stern and a mound of white and hissing water was spewed out. A wave appeared at the cutwater and built itself up, and then a great murmur rose from the watching crowd in a sigh, like an involuntary suspiration of mingled relief and anxiety.

Roddie turned and pushed his bicycle through to the fringe of the crowd. Having escaped Willie Moffat, he mounted and set out for the South End of town. By hard pedaling he managed to reach the park on the nose of Halifax peninsula before the *Olympic* had cleared the submarine nets. She was standing seaward a mile beyond him and traveling at full speed; in the wide spaces of the outer harbor even this ship looked dwarfed.

He dropped his bicycle and watched. Behind him lay the park and behind that, the city. Hidden by trees on his left, the waves made by the ship were crashing noisily on the shores of the inner harbor. In the space before him he could see the bow waves marching in long lines at right angles to himself across the reaches of the outer harbor towards the bluff of York Redoubt and Sandwich Battery. Somewhere on those hills were 9.2 cannon, guarding the town. He thought they were invincible.

For half an hour the boy stood looking seaward until the *Olympic* was hull down. Soon nothing remained of her but a scroll of smoke, singularly purified by the wind and the sun, drifting across the horizon. And then at last he remembered that he was late for school and he felt empty and alone. The waves, breaking lightly on the smooth stones of the shore, were like an unearthly laughter and their sound was constant and all-pervading, wiping out the reality of what he had just seen and filling his mind with an unreasonable sense of disenchantment. He picked up his bicycle to return to school, without being aware that in doing so he was moving back into the continent.

Three o'Clock The entrance to Wain's Wharf had been built during the war of 1812 and looked like the gateway to a colonial fort. A warehouse of cut granite ran for about fifty yards along a bend of Water Street and its blackened walls were broken at intervals by narrow, grilled windows. In the center of this wall a deep Roman arch led to the wharf itself and divided the warehouse into two separate sections. Directly above the keystone hung the faded legend—*Charles Wain & Sons, Shippers.* Over this, again, was a window behind which Geoffrey Wain sat at his work. The whole establishment was as solid as it had ever been, its stone and mortar were in excellent condition, yet it managed to give the impression that at some time in its past it had been besieged.

Wain's office above the arch was a long rectangle with long windows on either side and a floor of planked hardwood like the deck of a ship. One of the end walls was covered with dusty maps no one had examined for fifty years; at the other end was a partition of frosted glass, behind which three girls were busy at typewriters and filing cabinets so high a stepladder was used to reach the topmost drawers. At the window overlooking the wharf two desks faced each other, one belonging to Wain himself, the other to his secretary. Although he was on active service with full pay, his duties as transportation officer kept him busy only in spurts and he still had time to manage his own firm, which was busier than it had been in a century.

This afternoon Wain had come to his office two hours after the departure of the *Olympic* and there had found a pair of visitors he had not expected, one wearing the uniform of a staff colonel, the other an American major of engineers. The colonel had known Wain in France, and he shook hands with the hearty violence of a man who deems it a privilege for others to meet him, but is determined to be democratic about it.

"Is everyone around this port as busy as you are, Wain?" the colonel said. "I've been trying to get you for hours. This is Major Thomson—of the American Army."

Wain shook hands and motioned the visitors to chairs, then opened one of the lower drawers of his desk and produced a bottle of whisky and three glasses. The men made themselves comfortable.

"I thought you were still in France, Eliot," Wain said. "Just get back?"

"Via New York." Colonel Eliot grinned. "This war gets bigger all the time—and better. A different proposition from 1915, I can tell you. It's become a permanent career."

"I heard some time ago about your staff appointment," Wain said. "Like the work?"

"You bet. What a bit of luck to be in the States while the rest of them are stuck with Passchendaele! Wonder who they'll make the goat for it." He glanced sideways at the American and lowered his voice confidentially. "Between ourselves, some of them hadn't the slightest idea of the conditions for that battle. It serves them damn well right. There'll have to be some changes over the winter." Then, raising his voice once more and smiling contentedly, he changed the subject. "Major Thomson's up here on business and I told him you're the man he's come to see."

The American leaned forward and cleared his throat nervously as Wain, with his habitual air of distant courtesy, indicated that he was listening.

"We're going to establish a seaplane base up here," he said, and paused as though waiting for help. As Wain's expression did not alter, he continued unassisted. "You see, the problem at the moment seems to be one of supplies. The colonel here tells me you're the only active-service officer in Halifax with a business on the waterfront."

"That's more or less true." Wain's lips altered slightly into a position that might pass for a smile. "Do you want building supplies?"

"Well, not exactly. Food, mostly. We don't want to bring up an entire army-service unit for the small number of men involved."

Wain blinked and glanced towards Eliot, but the colonel was looking out the window. He looked back at Thomson. "That's hardly a problem, is it? I could undertake a certain kind of provisioning for you, of course. But the whole question would solve itself when your men arrived. Might I ask if that is all you have to settle on this trip?"

The American looked exceedingly uncomfortable and unsure of himself; it seemed as though he had only a vague idea of why he was here at all. "I thought you might give me some advice about the actual site for the base," he said.

"Oh." Wain held his glass against the light and cocked his eye at the milky movement of the whisky in the water. "But surely that's a matter for the government, not for me?"

"Thomson's visit is supposed to be more or less unofficial," Eliot remarked.

"That's it exactly," the American said quickly. "The colonel here tells me you know these parts well enough to show me the best prospect. Maybe if we find our place before it gets around we want it, the price'll be cheaper."

"I doubt it," Wain said. "And with the war on, who cares what anything costs?" He opened another drawer and took out an old telescope, which he carefully removed from its case. The two men watched him sight along the barrel with the interest of a pair of children being shown a new toy. "You can see the best location in the province from here," he said, and guided his visitors to the window. "Look across there."

He pointed down the harbor to the place where McNab's Island curves in towards the opposite shore. The American tapped the telescope and set it against his eye, looked for a few moments and passed it on to Eliot. "Is that a refinery over there?" he muttered.

"A subsidiary of Standard Oil. Just seaward are several acres of fields. I think you could rent them for next to nothing if the government were agreeable."

Eliot was playing with the telescope, sweeping it back and forth across the waterfront. "This is a nice glass," he said. "I can see a hole in a sailor's drawers hanging in the rigging of that Dutch ship out there. Right in the crotch, too. Bloody uncomfortable for him, eh?"

"What's that cove back of the island called?" Thomson asked.

"The Eastern Passage."

"It seems pretty far away from things."

Wain's eyebrows rose slightly as he took the telescope from Eliot and snapped it shut. "We could hardly build an air base in the center of town, could we, Major? You see, that bight of water back of the island is about the only stretch of the harbor we're not actually using. It's open to the sea and there are no surface obstructions, but it's too shallow for navigation. A Confederate cruiser escaped through it during your Civil War, but I believe she had the assistance of several dozen rowboats to haul her over the bar."

"I see." The American's face looked brighter. "I heard about that place somewhere."

Wain glanced at Eliot with the trace of a smile. "I don't own that land, you know."

"Well—" Eliot grinned. "You might, mightn't you?"

"I'm sorry. . . . No." Wain looked coldly at his brother officer as he said to Thomson, "If you want to inspect the place I can arrange to have a naval launch take you across. We could have it surveyed for you, I suppose. Really, the whole thing is outside my province. The Harbor Commission might help you, but I can't."

"Thomson only wants a look around," Eliot said distantly. "You know how it is."

"Yes, I know how it is."

Ten minutes later, when the American had left in a naval car for the dockyard, Wain poured out two more whiskies and laughed silently. "I'm not interested in money," he said.

Eliot drained the whisky with a single gulp. "I don't blame you, seeing you've got enough. I met Thomson on the train and thought you might be, that's all. You got a raw deal in France, as I remember. I thought—"

"Who's responsible for Thomson," Wain interrupted. "Our government or his? If the Americans really want this base, all they have to do is ask for it."

"God knows. Things get more and more devious the longer the war goes on and the more fingers get into the pie." He grinned sympathetically. "You sound pretty fed up. Things slow around here?"

Wain made a slight sucking sound with his lips and teeth and looked out the window. He had rarely felt more in a mood for giving orders than he did at this moment. During the last three years he had seen more misfits in important posts than even his low opinion of human ability had considered possible. Eliot had formerly sold insurance. Thomson looked like an estate agent. The war was a game with them and they were incapable of understanding the first thing about its possibilities. To him it was the greatest power bonanza in the history of mankind; he saw it continuing indefinitely. And here he was in Halifax, a transportation officer doing the work of a glorified clerk with permanent authority over a batman and a pair of army stenographers!

Eliot reached for more whisky and said, "What are you wasting your time here for?"

Wain's face was a dark and muscular mask as his eyes watched the other man's.

"You shouldn't be stuck in a spot like this," Eliot went on. "Why don't you raise hell until you get a staff job?"

"How long do you think the war's going to last?" The voice was nonchalant. "Or do you know any better than the rest of us?"

"About two years more. It all depends on the lengths they're prepared to go. Maybe three."

"I should guess three at the least."

Wain rose and went to the window. The prospect below might have been satisfying if he had not taken it completely for granted for so long. Two freighters were lying at his wharf, one on either side of the long central shed, and he could hear their donkey engines clank and their winches bang and occasionally the guttural cry of a stevedore directing the movement of the cranes. A frosty evening was drawing in with all the brilliant colors of a Canadian winter. The sky was a translucent globe of pale blue and the shadows cast by the docks looked stark on the water of the harbor. A vessel flying the tricolor was gliding out to sea a few fathoms from the end of his own wharf, and as he studied her lines and the way she was trimmed he guessed her cargo was munitions. He estimated her tonnage and tried to gauge the volume of her freight, and from this point his mind busied itself with a series of figures as he added up totals of munition shipments over a period of months. Without turning, he said sharply, "My God, but the generals are wasting shells!"

"Eh?"

"Up to a hundred thousand tons of munitions must go out of Halifax every month, in one form or another. I said they're wasting shells."

He sat down heavily and toyed with the telescope, while Eliot poured himself another whisky and sprawled in a straight-back chair with his knees apart, breathing heavily and studying his own fingernails as though he had just discovered them. One of the typists became a darkened blur behind the frosted glass and opened the door. There she hesitated, a small and diffident figure in the long expanse of the outer office, and when Wain gave her no notice she went back to her work, carefully closing the door behind her.

"Look"–Eliot suddenly forgot his fingernails–"you and I were together at brigade that night before the wonky attack that broke you. Or am I wrong?"

"You aren't."

"The attack was your idea, if I remember rightly. You practically planned it."

"It was."

Eliot drained the last of his whisky and eased his belt. He glanced at the bottle to make sure it was dry and cleared his throat in resignation. "That attack was one of those things. If it had been successful you'd have had a brigade before the year was out." The toneless voice hesitated, then resumed its droning as though talking to itself. "And by now you'd have had a division at the very least. You're a man with ideas."

"Well?" If Wain was tense there was nothing in his voice to suggest it.

"I've been thinking. The trouble was, your men retreated before they got killed. If they'd been killed a quarter of a mile farther ahead it would have been all right."

Wain shrugged his shoulders.

"But they weren't farther ahead because one of your subordinates got cold feet–that was it, wasn't it?" Eliot looked straight at Wain. "Why didn't you court-martial him?"

Wain said nothing and Eliot resumed the study of his fingernails. "Then it was true, the man was a relation of yours?" he said, without looking up.

"The officer in question was killed the night after the attack."

Once more Eliot was unable to detect any overt emotion in Wain's voice. "So that was it," he said. "Well, no one can court-martial a corpse. You know, I'd almost forgotten that angle of the case. Two years is a long time in a war like this, and everyone else has forgotten about that mess by this time." He rose abruptly. "I've got to be going. How would you like a staff job–in France?"

"Are you making an offer?"

"I haven't exactly the power to make an offer, but there are plenty of strings that can be pulled. The smell of that old affair wasn't too good while it lasted but it's died out now. I think I can promise you a brass hat, if you want it?"

"I want it," Wain said.

"Good! I forgot to say I'm on my way to Ottawa now."

After Eliot had gone, Wain stood for many minutes staring out the window at the glow of sunset reeking over the sheds and spilling onto the flat water of the harbor. He wondered why Eliot had bothered to look him up and decided that the man was so impressed by the position the war had given him that the ability to appear as a benefactor flattered his vanity. It was a humiliating thought. The trouble with himself was that he was proud and resented having to ask or receive favors. Eliot was a fool to have thought he might have been interested in making some petty graft out of a seaplane base. It was an insult both to himself and to the American, who probably was honest and who certainly didn't know Eliot well. But one thing was certain: if a man like Eliot could maintain himself as a staff colonel, a man like himself could do a lot better. The trouble was in getting started again.

He went back to his desk and began to study the papers that lay in a neat pile before him, and for nearly half an hour there was no sound but the ticking of a clock and the muffled clatter of the typewriters behind the glass. Then the phone rang; it sounded twice before he picked it up, and when he heard the voice of his sister-in-law he took the receiver from his ear and eyed it distastefully. When it had ceased to vibrate, he said, "Maria, is there really anything important you have to say to me?"

The receiver crackled. "It's about Penelope."

"Oh?"

"I simply must talk to you about her. I've been trying to get you all day."

"A certain large vessel, which shall be nameless over the telephone, left port today and I was busy. Well, what about Penelope?"

"You've got to do something about her. People are talking."

"What people?"

One of his typists opened the door again but drew back as she saw the dilation of his nostrils. It was his only palpably animalistic reaction. Its appearance was rare, but she knew it well enough to be afraid of it. She closed the door discreetly and he looked back at the telephone. "Just what people are saying what, Maria?"

"There's no use your trying to bully me, Geoffrey Wain. You practically insulted us by allowing that Murray man in your house last Sunday, which was bad enough. But now I hear your daughter is keeping company with him and that's too much. You know it is."

Wain tapped the receiver against the desk, a gesture which brought a clamorous outbreak from the other end of the wire. Then he said, "What do you know about Major Murray?"

"Why, everybody knows about him."

"Do they, now? It's been my experience that few people know anything about anything. Suppose, in fifty words, you try to say what *you* know about him. I'll hold the line and you can have a minute to think about it."

He set the receiver down, and leaning back in his chair, tapped a hand bell. One of his girls appeared with a sheaf of papers in her hand and without speaking he took them from her. She remained standing awkwardly in front of him and he studied her casually for a moment before glancing at his watch. "It's nearly five," he said. "If you and the other girls are finished you can go for the day. I'll stay and check these invoices."

"Thank you, Colonel Wain."

"Did Miss Phillips say when she'd return?"

"I think she said something about being back at four-thirty, sir."

"All right." He adjusted his pince-nez and began skimming the edges of the papers with his fingers. "On your way out, step over to the shed and ask Mr. MacKenzie to report to me at once."

The girl went back to her section of the office and he could see the shadows of the other typists rise from their desks as she spoke to them. Meanwhile cracklings had been sounding intermittently from the idle receiver on his desk. He picked it up and said sharply, "Maria, you're a persistent woman. Now, tell me who has been talking to you and—if you know—what they said."

He held the receiver away from his ear while she told him what she thought of his rudeness, and only replaced it when she grew quieter.

"They've been seen taking long walks with each other," she said. "They've been together more than once."

"And what difference does that make?"

"What difference! Either Penelope is misbehaving or else she ought to be warned. Does a man like that Murray trouble his head over a young girl just for—just for—— You know very well what I'm talking about."

Wain bit his lip delicately, and his voice became unpleasantly polite. "I think that's quite enough. But let me warn you. If I find you've been saying anything about Penelope to a soul in this town I'll make you sorry for the tongue in your head. A woman your age ought to have more sense. Good-bye."

He hung up the receiver and turned back to the invoices, but a cold anger grew in him. His large hands opened and closed spasmodically and he sat very still as his eyes ran over the papers without taking in the least sense of their contents. He could not understand why he was so angry. The situation was not serious and his sister-in-law was a fool. But being reprimanded about such a matter somehow diminished his stature in his own eyes and made him appear petty to himself. Mingled with this emotion was an intense and sudden dislike of Murray, of whom he already had no good opinion. Probably what Maria said was true, and if it was, then he would put a stop to Murray's flirtations at once. The decision was not caused by any fear for Penny's virtue but by a habit of aloofness and a commanding sense of insult when other people stretched out a hand towards something belonging to him.

He reached toward a humidor and drew out a cigar, lit it and leaned back in his chair until the anger subsided. Before a quarter of the cigar was in ashes the door of his office opened and his wharf foreman, Big Alec MacKenzie, stood there with his cap in his hand.

"You would be wanting to see me?" Alec said.

The Gaelic accent was thick enough to cut, and the face looked an anachronism from primitive times. It was like a cross between a Presbyterian minister and a Scotch terrier.

"Are those ships nearly finished loading?" Wain asked sharply.

Alec reflected. "Well now, that English one has been doing fine. But those Eyetalians—my glory, they've been here since——"

"Will they be out of here in time?"

Big Alec's jaw bulged as he shifted a wad of gum from the path of his tongue. He shuffled his feet and reflected again. "I would think so," he said finally. "The English one is ready now."

"I suppose everything went all right today?"

"Indeed, yes."

"Then before you go, look in the storeroom and take out two cases of whisky you'll find there. Give them to the captains with my compliments."

Alec bent stiffly to tighten a shoe lace, displaying an enormous width of shoulders and backside as he did so. Presently he straightened up and looked at Wain with an expression of deep concern.

"Well, MacKenzie—what's the matter?"

"I was thinking about them Eyetalians. It's an awful pity to waste the whisky."

"Then don't think about it. Just give it to them."

"The likes of them would not be drinking whisky."

"What difference does that make?" Wain snapped out the words in irritation. "They must have their gratuity. Try to think, MacKenzie. Will those ships be on their way before dark for the Basin or will they be spending the night here?"

"Well, the English fellas——"

"I know about them. I mean the Italians."

"In about half an hour now, if everything goes all right, I would say the Eyetalians would be ready."

Wain looked away to hide his growing exasperation. "You might have said that in the first place. Anyway, go home as soon as they've cleared the wharf. You've had a long day."

Big Alec still seemed to be waiting for something else.

"Never mind," Wain said, "whether the Italians drink whisky or not. Give a case of it to the skipper. If he wants to sell it when he reaches Genoa he can buy spaghetti with the proceeds."

"It's an awful waste," Alec said, as he went out.

Now Wain was alone in the office, sitting in the gloom beyond the glow of his desk lamp. His mood had changed, and the satisfaction left him by Eliot's last words had almost evaporated. His contempt for loneliness, which he imagined to be the most commonplace ailment in the world, was so great that he refused to acknowledge its presence in himself. He tilted his chair farther back into the darkness of the room, and with slow and almost studious movements carried the cigar to his lips and away again, trying to savor the tobacco. The smoke eddied across the light and disappeared each time until he renewed it. Gradually his body relaxed.

He glanced at the calendar and wondered if years from now he would remember this date in his career. He was pervaded by a quiet and unquestioned confidence that the present had pulled adrift from the past and that his future held unlimited possibilities. Here in Nova Scotia his family had gone as far as the limitations of the province permitted. He had been born at the top of things with no wider horizon to aim for; it had required nothing less than a war to better his prospects and give him a zest for advancement. His first attempt to escape his milieu had been a failure; the next time there would be no mistakes.

Yet, as he reflected on this he was conscious of disappointment, of resentment because he had for so long been under a sense of failure. He laid down the shortened cigar and put his hands on his hips and pressed his powerful fingers against the wall of muscles guarding his abdomen. Their resilient ridges resisted the pressure firmly. He was still in good condition; indeed, he had never been physically better in his life. Like many men his age, he was thankful that the war had found him neither too old to profit by it nor too young to hope for a guiding position. If the war lasted another three years anything might happen in his career. It was not reasonable to suppose that general officers who had been under full responsibility from the beginning could endure the strain indefinitely without replacement. Generals wore out as well as lieutenants.

One of the freighters blew its horn and Wain rose to watch it back away from the wharf. Big Alec had sent the last crane-load aboard the Italian ship and now was walking up the slide with a case of whisky clamped under his arm. Wain puffed a lungful of smoke against the windowpane. MacKenzie was the only man in the world capable of upsetting his apple-cart, of canceling out all the patient work he had done in Halifax since his return from France. But the big man had no notion of this. When he had accepted the job and brought his wife and family to Halifax he had never guessed that it had been Wain's motive to make him a dependent. Even if Alec had been incompetent, Wain would never have risked his being unemployed. As it was, Big Alec had become the best wharf foreman he ever had.

The door leading to the outside hall opened behind him, and as he heard the tapping of high heels he turned around and moved back to his desk. "You've been quite a while, haven't you?" he said casually. "What did Harrigan finally say?"

After dropping her hat and coat on a chair, the girl leaned against the edge of the desk. "Mr. Harrigan said to tell you that the railroad accepts your suggestion *in toto*. He says he'll be writing to you shortly. What does *in toto* mean?"

He surveyed her figure as it emerged behind the veil of smoke he had blown in her direction, his eyes passing coolly along the curve of her thighs to the contour of her upper arms, exceptionally plump in so slight a girl. The muscles under his cheek bones hardened as his lips parted into the beginning of a smile. "You aren't trying to tell me you were away three hours just for that?"

"You told me to get his answer, didn't you?"

"I did, my dear Evelyn. And I also told you I'd be waiting for it."

She shrugged her shoulders and began to search for something in her handbag. Her expression contained a paradoxical mixture of deference, indifference and condescension, but her manner towards him was obviously intimate. He ceased smiling and with an abrupt movement picked her up and swung her into the air as though she were a child, then rested her on his knees with her face tilted upward under his own.

"Ow!" she said, frowning angrily. "You know I don't like things sudden."

His hand tightened against her thigh, then moved slowly with a hard and even pressure, feeling the flesh warm under its palm and curving gently upward towards the hips.

"Right *here?*" she said.

"Did I say anything?"

"Ouch—that hurts! Do you have to be so——"

She stopped talking and closed her eyes, for she knew that a protest would not affect him and that he liked to enjoy her without talking about it. Under the pressure of his stroking hands her face grew set and concentrated, and though her expression seemed to indicate pain, it was evident that the pain was at least as welcome to one part of her mind as it was repulsive to another. Hers was the satisfaction of knowing that with so small a body she could tame this man of wealth and position and physical strength, but she was humiliated because he was always the one to choose the occasion. Whenever he made love to her he seemed to be studying the effect he produced, and she knew that the basis of his desire lay in the fact that her perfectly formed body was as diminutive as a miniature, that it was easy to hurt, and that he could goad it into the convulsions of a pleasure she could rarely control. If he would only talk more, it would be fun; but as he never did, she usually managed to make him pay for it.

"My, but you've got a gleam in your eye!" She looked up at him without expression. "You like it, don't you?"

He said nothing, and making a gesture of annoyance she wriggled free. "I wish you wouldn't love me up so sudden," she said. "It's not decent."

He winced at her vulgarity, then pushed her away so sharply she nearly fell to the floor. She recovered herself and stood upright with her legs apart, smoothing her dress. "I'm hungry," she said.

"It's not six yet. Didn't you have any lunch?"

"I'm hungry just the same."

"Well—there's not much we can do about it here."

She left him and turned on the lamp over her own desk. "Guess what? I got a letter from my mother today."

"Was it interesting?"

"She wants to come to Halifax. Will that be all right?"

"No," said Wain.

"I don't see why not. She says it's on account of my father."

"Your what?"

"Oh, he's been gassed or something. Anyway, he's coming home and mamma wants to be here when he gets off the ship."

"Evelyn"—his voice sounded nasty—"you're a damned little liar. You told me a year ago your father was dead."

She shrugged her shoulders and resumed her perch on his desk, swinging her legs.

"What did your father do?" he said. "Before the war, I mean?"

"He was a fisherman," she said sullenly. "And he needn't think he can get me back to the village just because he's home from the war."

Wain's nostrils dilated as he placed the papers before him in a filing basket. Her remark revealed a situation he well understood. Firms like his own had done much to cause it, and he took it for granted that she was taunting him with the fact. Few fishermen in Nova Scotia made any money because they could not easily market their catches, and prices paid by wholesalers like himself were infinitesimal. It was steadily becoming more difficult to persuade members of the younger generation in the fishing towns to stay there. In her native village, a girl like Evelyn would have had some standing in the community; in Halifax nothing but his patronage had elevated her beyond the status of a domestic servant.

"So your dear father was a fisherman before he became a soldier?" He watched her steadily. "And you've become too good for him?"

"He never makes any money. None of them ever do."

"I suppose you know men like your father are about the finest seamen in the world?"

"Where does that get them?"

He laughed harshly, and she disliked the sound of it. "The queer part of it is, my dearest Evelyn, that you're really quite a competent secretary. Yes, you've learned a lot."

"What are you looking at me that way for? Let me tell you something——"

He puffed a cloud of smoke at her. "Well, why don't you go on? I'm waiting."

"I guess I didn't mean anything," she said sullenly. But her eyes were crafty. It didn't get you anywhere saying what you really thought. "What about my mother?" she said.

"She can do what she likes, but I don't want her in your flat. Tell her to go to a hotel. I'll pay for it."

"But mamma wouldn't let me do that. She thinks I'm poor. She wouldn't come at all if she had to stay in a hotel."

"So you really care what your mother thinks about you?"

"No use bothering folks, that's my motto. Besides—well, I say she's got it coming to her, working like she does."

"Yes." Wain's voice was urbane. "Mrs. Phillips deserves better luck. You can tell her to come at the end of the week. I happen to know that there won't be any soldiers returning before Saturday at the earliest."

He got up and put on his coat, somewhat surprised at the unusual confusion of emotions which the girl's remarks had roused in him. For Nova Scotia he had no real respect; he merely felt it was a little less inferior than the rest of North America. Yet there were certain qualities he expected to find in his province and was disappointed whenever a fellow provincial lacked them. It seemed proper and natural that Nova Scotians should be unimportant, but unnatural for them to be cheap, and Evelyn's remarks grated on his sensibilities. Men like her father faced danger every day in the foggiest and stormiest tract of the entire Atlantic, and apart from the Scandinavians they were almost the only seamen still left under sail. "He's been gassed or something. . . . He never made any money. . . ." Wain felt personally hurt by these remarks. On the other hand there was little he could do about it. To find a satisfactory mistress in Nova Scotia was difficult and in this respect Evelyn was admirable; her poverty had made her shrewd, and in her eagerness to escape from it she was willing to do nearly anything he wished. After all these months, no one in the office seemed to suspect their relationship, and he was prepared to give her some credit for this.

"Will you be coming around tonight?" she said, as he opened the door for her.

"Perhaps." He opened his wallet and gave her a five-dollar bill. "Here, go to a moving picture if you like. But you'd better be back by nine-thirty. I may want to see you then."

Four o'Clock The living room of the house where Jim and Mary Fraser lived in Prince's Lodge was like an album of their lives. It was quiet, simple and spacious; it never lacked the odor of wood smoke and it managed to preserve something of the freshness of the forest on the edge of which it was built. The room was dominated by a huge hearth made of stones removed from the excavation of the house itself, and its ceiling was supported by beechwood beams cut from the forest. A moose head with fourteen points in its antlers stared glassily from above the mantel.

Although it was the room of a man who liked to live out of doors and of a woman who enjoyed making him comfortable, the photographs hanging from the walls showed that Jim Fraser was not a professional sportsman. There were pictures of him as a mining engineer in South Africa, pictures of galleries in the actual mines in the Rand, pictures of him in uniform, pictures of the mess of the Royal Canadian Regiment and a framed drawing of the company in bivouac before Paardeberg. There were also snapshots of the Wains in dreary family groups and one of Mary herself looking gaunt and awkward in blouse and bloomers, lunging with a fencing foil at a dummy which still hung in the gymnasium of her old school.

Now it was early evening. Darkness would soon convert the unshuttered windows that looked on Bedford Basin to mirrors reflecting the warmth and ease within. Had anyone been able to look into the room from the outside, it would have seemed like an oasis of yellow light in the brooding and heavy darkness of the forest and the paler, slightly ominous sky to the eastward over the Basin. Angus Murray and Jim Fraser lounged in easy chairs on either side of the hearth and Penny was on her knees before it, playing with Jean. Mary's hands moved in quick, birdlike gestures as she cleared away the dishes.

All afternoon Penny had been watching Murray quietly. He had not wished to accompany her to Prince's Lodge; for a time during lunch she had been afraid that her plan to entice him out here would miscarry. But once here he had surprised her, for she discovered that he loved children, and the presence of Jean had made him feel immediately at home with the Frasers. In turn, they had been charmed by his ease with their adopted daughter. Earlier in the afternoon they had gone walking through the woods, Jean perched on Murray's good shoulder and Penny moving alongside to steady her. The forest was silent and empty in the hush before snow, and filled with daylight like a ruined house. A weasel had chased a rabbit across the path in front of them, and beside a pond in the heart of the wood they had come upon the tracks of a moose. Penny had never seen Murray appear so peaceful, and the mood had remained.

"You ought to settle down in the country when the war's over." Jim was on his favorite subject now. "Look at the cost of maintaining a practice in a place like Montreal or Toronto! You'd be doing as well with two thousand a year in the country as with ten in places like that. And you'd enjoy yourself into the bargain."

Murray smiled. "There's not much doubt of that," he said. "I've often thought about it. By the way—you used to play tennis, didn't you?"

"Yes."

"Well, practising medicine is like playing tennis. It's the same game wherever you are but the players are different. You get more fun out of it in the small town but the champions play in the city. I guess we all kid ourselves we'd like to be champions."

Jean's attention suddenly wandered from the game she was playing with Penny. She turned to Murray, spreading her arms wide, and cried out, "Water!"

"But the water was frozen and that made it ice."

"No. Water."

Jim gave Murray an inquiring glance and stopped filling his pipe. Murray laughed. "She's right, you know. Where some animal had holed the ice on the edge of that heart-shaped pond the water was black as a pit. I wonder how a two-year-old can notice a thing like that?"

Jean was tumbling on the carpet now, trying to avoid Penny's attempt to tidy her ruffled hair. "Somefing in mouf," she said.

"Who had something in his mouth?" Penny finally captured her. "You mean your father's pipe?"

"Oh, so she's back on that again!" Mary said. "She can't seem to forget it. Jim went off with her a week ago and when they came around one of those big boulders they nearly ran into a deer. It had a piece of fungus in its mouth. She's been excited about it ever since."

"It's a wonder she hasn't been pointing out the ships in the Basin," Jim added. "That's how she's learning to count. Right now there are far too many in, but when they're no more than a few she can generally add them up after a fashion."

Jean now became clamorous for a story and Penny tried to quiet her.

"She's a lot more sense than we have," Mary said. "It's half an hour past her bedtime." She turned to Murray. "Penny tells her a bedtime story whenever she comes out here. She never forgets and she usually has a new one. She'll be spoiled if we don't look out."

"Nobody believes you, Mary." Penny swung Jean towards the door. "Come on up with us, Angus. I'm putting her to bed. This is a job you ought to be good at."

Murray followed them upstairs to the nursery, a tinted room the color of an apple blossom in the light of the lamp. Penny moved quietly about, undressing the sleepy baby and humming to herself as she hung up the discarded clothes. Murray sat quietly and watched, feeling well content. The afternoon had been one of those respites in time during which a man feels that although no outward event has occurred, something intangible has taken root in himself.

Now Jean was tucked into her cot and Penny was bending over her, beginning the evening tale. "When the winter comes and Jean goes out in the woods, she can't see a thing but the white blanket of snow that covers everything. But underneath the snow there are all sorts of things happening. The rabbits have cities in the ground with tunnels all made like little streets and big holes where they live, warm like you are now, until the spring comes and the snow melts. And the squirrels live all tucked up in the trunks of the trees and every time they get hungry, all they have to do is go downstairs in the tree and bring up the acorns we saw them gathering this fall. And if you go a long way back in the woods, away back behind all the ponds and on the other side of the ridge where the sun goes down, there you'll find a place where the snow is tramped down into streets with high walls higher than this room, and that's where the moose and the deer live in the winter."

"Bees and bears, Aunt Penny?"

"Oh, when the snow falls they just go sound asleep and they never wake up at all, not till after it all melts away." She paused; the child's eyes were closed. "And all winter long the cruel animals go hungry, because the gentle ones are safe and can't be found. . . ." Jean was asleep and Penny's voice tailed off to a whisper. She rose and picked up the lamp and turned to Murray. "It's silly. I don't know where I get all that nonsense but she likes it and I suppose it won't do her any harm. Tell me—what do you think of her?"

He got to his feet. "It's hard to say. I've got a weakness for all children, I guess. So naturally I like this one." He took the lamp and held it high while she tucked in a loose corner of blanket. "Where did they get her?"

"In Montreal." She looked closely at him, then back to the cot. "I think she's going to resemble Mary, don't you?"

"Why should she? She's adopted."

"The Wain characteristics are pretty self-assertive."

"I can't see environment doing that much. Did your aunt know Jean's parents?"

"Very well."

Murray's eyebrows went up in mild inquiry, but he did not seem vitally interested. Penny's hair was golden brown in the light falling over it and there were deep shadows under the cheek bones and lips. When he lowered the lamp the dim glow of the burning wick encased her figure from the waist upwards and accentuated the swell of her full breasts and the plane of her chest branching into the shoulders.

"It's funny," she said, "how people change and still stay just the same as long as they live. I remember when Jean was an infant. She couldn't do anything but lie on her back and blink at the light and cry whenever she was hungry, but even then I knew what she'd be like when she grew older. Stubborn, and curious about everything. Even Mary realizes she has more natural charm than any of her other relatives."

"That's right. . . . You *were* in Montreal when they adopted her. That's when you were taking your technical training, wasn't it?"

"More or less." The light quivered as her hand holding the lamp began to tremble. "Oh, Angus—you're not usually so guileless!"

"What are you talking about?"

"Are you going to make me say it? I've been trying to tell you"—her voice broke—"Jean—Jean is my daughter."

Murray stared at her, his face frozen into immobility, and in the uncertain light she was unable to detect any change of expression about his eyes.

"I'm very proud of her," she said.

He remained silent, standing stiffly with the fingers of his left hand automatically manipulating those of his right, his shoulders slightly stooped and his breath heavy in his twisted nose.

Suddenly her face flushed with disappointment. "I'll not bore you any longer. Neil was Jean's father. I'm not ashamed of it. But I had to give her up all the same. I gave her up forever when Jim and Mary Fraser adopted her."

"I . . . look here . . ."

He hesitated and his voice stuck in his throat. And Penny, her eyes wet with humiliation as the memory of nearly three years of secrecy and abnegation exploded inside her brain, trembled so that she could hardly control her voice. "Never mind. You needn't feel you have to say anything." With quick strides she went to the door, carrying the lamp in her right hand, and Murray followed silently. "A train leaves in a few minutes, and I'm going back to town. You needn't take it unless you wish. At least there'll be several cars on it. You don't—"

"Penny . . ."

She rushed down the stairs without listening and Murray followed as slowly as he could, his left fingers still manipulating the stiff ones of his right hand.

Jim met them at the bottom of the steps. "Well, did you get initiated into nursery tactics?"

"I've got to go now," Penny said shortly. "Jean's asleep. There's no need for anyone to come with me."

"But you've still . . ." Mary stopped as she saw the flush on Penny's cheeks, and ended weakly, "Wouldn't you like us to go to the station with you, dear?"

"No, of course not. . . . Oh, Mary, I didn't mean to sound like that. I'm—I just remembered . . ."

"She's really very tired, Mrs. Fraser," Murray interrupted quietly.

Penny had her coat on by this time and was standing in front of the mirror to adjust her hat. Murray took his greatcoat from its hook and slipped his cap carelessly over the thinning hair on the back of his head. He looked almost raffish, standing there with his coat open and his helmet at an angle.

"Are you coming?" Penny's voice was so cold it shocked Jim Fraser, but he could think of nothing to say and quietly opened the door. "There's a later train than this," Penny went on to Murray. "Why don't you wait for it?"

"I'm coming now," Murray said.

He turned to Jim and Mary and thanked each of them for the afternoon. Then he followed Penny down the path to the road, and they walked in silence to the gate opening on the platform that served Prince's Lodge as a station. The two stood like show-window dummies, waiting for the train to arrive.

The sky was bright with stars. Orion and Sirius stood over the forest, and the Bear, stretching a long arm to the northwest, rested above the Basin. The forest was hushed on the verge of winter storms, and the Basin, walled by darkness and illuminated by the stars, seemed filled to capacity with ships awaiting convoy. Their riding lights flickered like a swarm of fireflies motionless in a void. Here Murray sensed an atomic quietness balanced at the core of constant change, of forces eternal and temporal about to radiate into areas where they would be drowned in a welter of predestined and uncontrollable motion. The cold air was fresh with the smell of evergreens and of salt water, and in the far west there remained, like a tiny island burning with distant fire, a sliver of cloud still reflecting a glow from the sunken sun.

To Penny, standing aloof and silent a few yards from Murray's elbow, the scene had the moving quality of all the beauty she had witnessed in the past three years and been unable to enjoy. Occasionally she stole a glance at Murray's profile, but he gave her no evidence that he was conscious of her presence. He was the only human being besides Jim and Mary who knew her secret. She had looked forward eagerly to being able to tell him. And now he was standing beside her, with nothing to say.

The train hooted from the nearest curve and its searchlight came into view, sending the shadows of trees circling away from the sunken tracks. It ground to a stop and they boarded an empty car, Penny first and Murray following, handing their tickets to the conductor as they entered. She sat in the seat next to the door, and Murray dropped down beside her. The train ground on, gaining momentum.

Then Penny was aware that Murray's hand was on her own and she turned slowly to face him. In bewilderment she realized that his eyes were wet.

"Penny . . ." His voice was thick and he had to clear his throat. . . . "Will you still marry me?"

She stared at him.

"Aren't you the guileless one now, my dear?" he went on. "I love you very much, you know."

"Oh, Angus!" Her lips parted and she turned back to the blank window, her left hand clenched against her mouth, her right spasmodically closing on Murray's. He said nothing more as he watched the back of her head, waiting for her to gather in the tears and face him again. The train swung heavily on a curve, and the two figures swayed right and then left in unison.

"You're so decent, Angus." Her hat had become pushed back on her forehead and she looked a little girl who has just discovered that a major catastrophe can be only a minor incident to grown-ups. "And I'm so terribly fond of you. I think you and I . . . But do you mind if we don't settle anything tonight? In a day or two, when I've finished the job I'm working on now . . ."

"Whenever you like, my dear. I'll always be around, and I've learned to wait."

She yielded to an inner amusement. "Now you see I'm not exactly the girl everyone thinks I am, aren't you afraid I might hurt *your* reputation?"

"I've always been able to see what kind of girl you are, though I didn't know a good many of the details. They only improve the picture."

"There are more if you want to know them."

"Why should I?"

"Father and the rest of the family have never cared what I did, and when I returned from Montreal I had reason to be thankful for it. If they noticed any difference they blamed it on my job."

The train stopped at Rockingham and moved on again.

"You see, Neil didn't know anything about Jean before he was killed," she went on, as though explaining something to herself. "He was going into action for the first time just before she was born."

"Didn't you ever tell him?"

"No. What was the use? He'd only have worried."

"Why didn't you get married in the first place?"

"We were first cousins."

"What of it? Not even the Church of England Prayer Book says cousins can't marry."

"No, but my father did. He hated him, more . . ."

The conductor opened the door at the end of the car and spat sibilantly into the spittoon between the two end seats, then lurched halfway down the aisle and peered out a window. The train was rattling through outlying freight yards, still on the edge of the Basin.

"Mighty big convoy building up out there," said the conductor. "Makes this run more interesting than it used to be, the war does."

He paused for encouragement, and receiving none, passed into the next coach.

"There's one thing I can't understand," Murray said. "Why in hell did Neil have to enlist in your father's battalion?"

"He didn't. He was transferred just before he sailed. You know yourself it wasn't a Nova Scotian battalion father commanded."

"I see." Murray made no pretence of his amazed admiration. "And I suppose you thought of that, too, and wouldn't let him take on that added responsibility!"

"Why not? He really wanted to marry me, even then. But it would have been so unfair to him. How could I make his existence as one of father's subordinates worse than it was bound to be, anyway?"

"So your father hated him as much as all that!"

The train swung around the last elbow of the Basin and ran along the Narrows and into town, past shipyards and dockyards, finally coming to rest in the North Street Station. Its exhaust crashed ryhthmically in the confined space and its smoke mounted seventy feet to the canopy of heavy glass that covered the platform like a sheet of dirty ice.

Penny felt drained of all emotions, tired but peaceful, and she wanted more than anything else at the moment to be alone. She wanted to be at her desk in the Shipyards for a few hours, alone with the absolute and unquestioning simplicity of figures and the docile beauty of white lines on blue paper. She pulled her hat back over her eyes, and once again she was the capable technician.

"If you don't mind, Angus, I'd like very much to go back to work for a while this evening. It's not late, and there are a good many things pressing to be done. Thank you for giving me this afternoon."

"You're a great girl, Penny," he replied. "If you'll take a taxi, I'll go on to the hotel and leave you. But I'll still be around."

He left her standing at the end of the platform, watching him walk away.

Five o'Clock Without remembering how he had come to be there, Neil Macrae found himself skirting the high iron railings of the Public Gardens, peering inside in order to avert his face from passers-by. The Gardens were locked for the winter and it was difficult to see through the fence, but he found himself remembering what they were like between spring and autumn, when the townspeople walked their paths as though they owned them. The whole town was transformed in summer. The streets of the South End were long tunnels of trees, elms and maples and limes. No matter how hot the day had been, it was always cool in the Gardens after sunset, and they were crowded with sailors and marines, walking their girls and stopping to look at the flowers. There were beds of delphinium and larkspur, intermingled with snapdragon and edged with candytuft; formal beds of rose begonia and lobelia; and hundreds of strange and rare old trees with their botanical names stamped on metal disks on their trunks. English swans and Canada geese swam about in the pond at the center of the Gardens, and when darkness fell and the keepers had whistled home the crowds, the birds could be heard honking and calling for blocks away.

He walked up the flank of the Gardens until he reached the open corner at one side of the Citadel. Here the wind was unobstructed and it was cold. He drew his scarf more tightly around his throat. His muscles were tired with long walking, but the strange sense of peace grew as he watched the sun roll over the line of trees by the Wanderers' Grounds and disappear in fire. Darkness descended in successive waves to the ground, street lights flickered on, and the splintered clouds in the west shook loose one by one from the turmoil of the sunset and began their drift to sea. Even as he stood and watched, the colors were dying and by the time he had reached Spring Garden Road again it was dark.

As he continued his walking of the pavements he felt at last that they belonged to him, and that Halifax, for all its shabbiness, was a good place to call his home. The life he had led in Europe and England these past two years had been worse than an emptiness. It was as though he had been able to feel the old continent tearing out its own entrails as the ancient civilizations had done before it. There was no help there. For almost the first time in his life, he fully realized what being a Canadian meant. It was a heritage he had no intention of losing.

He stopped at a corner to wait for a tram, and his eyes reached above the roofs to the sky. Stars were visible, and a quarter moon. The sun had rolled on beyond Nova Scotia into the west. Now it was setting over Montreal and sending the shadow of the mountain deep into the valleys of Sherbrooke Street and Peel; it was turning the frozen St. Lawrence crimson and lining it with the blue shadows of the trees and buildings along its banks, while all the time the deep water poured seaward under the ice, draining off the Great Lakes into the Atlantic. Now the prairies were endless plains of glittering, bluish snow over which the wind passed in a firm and continuous flux, packing the drifts down hard over the wheat seeds frozen into the alluvial earth. Now in the Rockies the peaks were gleaming obelisks in the mid-afternoon. The railway line, that tenuous thread which bound Canada to both the great oceans and made her a nation, lay with one end in the darkness of Nova Scotia and the other in the flush of a British Columbia noon.

Under the excitement of this idea his throat became constricted and he had a furious desire for expression: this anomalous land, this sprawling waste of timber and rock and water where the only living sounds were the footfalls of animals or the fantastic laughter of a loon, this empty tract of primordial silences and winds and erosions and shifting colors, this beadlike string of crude towns and cities tied by nothing but railway tracks, this nation undiscovered by the rest of the world and unknown to itself, these people neither American nor English, nor even sure what they wanted to be, this unborn mightiness, this question mark, this future for himself, and for God knew how many millions of mankind!

The tram came and he boarded it. Then he sat quite still looking sideways out the window to keep his face away from the passengers, as the car bore him north to his lodgings.

Six o'Clock After Murray had left her, Penny remained standing at the end of the platform. The sense of relief she felt was so new and wonderful that it was good to be alone in order to enjoy it. She bought an evening paper at the newsstand and glanced over the headlines, and finding nothing of much interest, tucked it under her arm and strolled idly about the station, watching the people come and go and listening to the cries of the porters and the bellowing of cab drivers massed behind a railing at the street entrance, bidding for fares. She no longer had any wish to return to her office; just to be alone here amid the flow of people was sufficient to rest her. The train from the Annapolis Valley arrived with its minuscule red engine making a great clatter from the cylinders, and she watched the passengers come down the platform towards the concourse.

"Why, Penny Wain—what are you doing here?"

A uniformed man her own age was facing her, a bag in his hand and a wide smile on his tanned face. "Billy—I could ask you the same question."

"That would be too long a story." He set the bag down. "I got back from France three months ago and I'm still around. My family moved to Bridgetown and I've been down there on leave."

She remembered it had been in her own garden that she had last seen Billy Andrews. He had been one of Neil's closer friends, and on a July day years ago the three of them had gone sailing together, putting out from the Yacht Squadron in the early afternoon and returning late for supper. She had prepared scrambled eggs and bacon and tea, and afterward they had gone out to the garden and sat in the summerhouse and talked on in the dark until the moon rose and whitened the leaves of the trees. She remembered how Neil had sat there on the stone bench, scratching patterns with his fingernail on the lichen that dusted the stone, the night air liquid-cool and fragrant from her grandfather's lime trees. Billy had said how lovely it was in Halifax in summertime. It was hardly an exaggeration; the garden had possessed a graciousness common to so many places and things before 1914. As she remembered it now and saw again the details of the scene, it occurred to her it might have happened as easily beside the Yellow River in a remote dynasty when mandarins moved in dark kimonos, praising the flower beds and the vines and talking of wisdom.

Did Billy understand that no one mentioned Neil's name in Halifax any more? Was this why he looked so courteously ill-at-ease? She said, "It's been ages since you were in our house."

"It's been quite a while, hasn't it?" He still sounded awkwardly embarrassed. "As a matter of fact, I'm married now."

"Congratulations! Is your wife in town with you?"

"She's in England. That's the devil of it."

"I hope I'll meet her sometime."

"Yes. She'd like to know you—I'm sure she would."

She looked at him directly. "You weren't in Neil's battalion, I suppose?"

"Who?" The smile left his face and he flushed slightly. "No, I was with the Twenty-fifth."

So he knows, too, she thought; like all the rest of them, he knows something I don't, but won't tell. She forced herself to sound casual. "You didn't happen to see him over there, I suppose?"

"No, I heard he was—Jerry got his number, I heard. Terribly bad luck!"

She put her hand on his arm and addressed him with the easy familiarity one uses towards an old friend. "I wish you'd look me up while you're in town. I see few enough familiar faces these days."

"Righto! I'd love to."

Billy had picked up a clipped, English way of speaking. She remembered he had always been an amiable boy, and unconsciously quick to mirror his environment. Probably his wife was English. "I'll be expecting you," she said. "I mean that, too."

"Rather!" He hesitated and looked over his shoulder. "But as a matter of fact, I'm not going to be here more than another day. It was awfully nice seeing you, Penelope."

He saluted, smiled formally, and sloped off towards the street entrance, not once looking back. And as Penny followed at a discreet distance she was sorry she had met him. She walked slowly down the street, allowing several southbound trams to pass her, and did not stop until she had reached the noisy corner of Buckingham Street, where two tram lines intersected.

A pair of Clydesdales pulling a sloven laden with casks of salt pork were out of control at the corner, and three men were trying to catch the bridles of the plunging horses. Their hooves crashed and struck sparks on the pavement, traffic was stalled and the driver of a northbound tram was jangling his bell angrily while the teamster shouted and lashed his horses. Loafers moved from lamp posts and store fronts to get a closer look.

The scene was a fairly common one in the steep and narrow streets of Halifax, and Penny watched with slight curiosity. The trolley of the tram had slipped off its overhead wire, and as the woman conductor tried to replace it, the lights in the car flashed on and off and the figures of the passengers inside flickered in alternate darkness and light. Finally the trolley gripped and the tram lights burned steadily.

When Penny saw him, he was sitting by one of the central windows of the tram, his chin in the heel of his hand, his hat on the back of his head, his eyes looking at nothing. She recognized the familiar posture and glanced away, closing her lips tightly. When would this trick of the imagination stop? It had happened so many times before. She would recognize the back of his neck or the swing of his arms or the set of his ears or his manner of walking straight ahead through a crowd; sometimes she would even hear his voice and turn sharply around to find its source. These occasions had never lasted for more than a few seconds but they had always unnerved her. During the last few months they had been less frequent; meeting Billy must have caused it this time, or the peculiar effect of the lights flashing on and off in the car and the bizarre shouting of the teamster.

She looked down at the ground while she waited for the feeling of limpness to leave her limbs. It was worse than silly to get this way over nothing; it might even become dangerous if it continued. The tram was about ready to move on and the crowd was dispersing. Everything seemed normal again. And then she looked up once more.

When she cried his name, her voice was drowned by the renewed shouting of the teamster and the clawing of the horses' hooves as they dragged the sloven past. She leaped into the street, but before she could reach the tram it gave a violent jerk and started forward. Someone got in her way; she felt a powerful hand grip her shoulder and wrench her backward, and heard a man's voice scolding her for carelessness. The sloven had rounded the corner at last and the horses would have surged down on her if she hadn't jumped quickly.

"For Jesus' sake, lady, watch your step!"

She stared around into a stranger's open mouth, full of bad teeth.

"Lucky thing for you I got you that time! What do you think them horses were doing out there?"

Why was she waiting while this man talked nonsense? The tram was already across the intersection heading north at full speed. She began to push along the pavement, elbowing pedestrians out of her way until she was able to cross the street. Then she began running frantically, hoping that at the next corner the tram would stop for passengers. But the stretch the car was traveling had no regular stop for nearly two hundred yards, and the vehicle was rocking with speed as the driver let full power into the wheels. By the time it slowed down again she was far behind and breathless. Perhaps he was getting off now. It was an important intersection. Perhaps he would have disappeared before she could reach it. People stared at her as she ran forward. Her skirt and coat hampered her movement, and her lungs, unused to heavy exercise, choked from the effort. She reached the intersection and looked up and down, but in the dim light she could recognize no one. She stopped still, gasping and choking for breath and trying to think what to do.

Then she saw a taxi standing across the street waiting for passing fare. She crossed to it and climbed in and told the driver to proceed slowly north. Her methodical brain had subconsciously recorded the number of the tram and now she remembered it and told the driver. "It can't be more than five blocks ahead of you," she said. "There's no other tram behind it."

"Yes, ma'am." The driver let in the clutch. "That car's only got another mile before it reaches the end of its run. Then it reverses and comes back. We can't help catching it, if that's all you want."

As the taxi moved north, Penny kept looking out of the windows on both sides and scanning the sidewalks. This had always been a poorly lit district, and since the war it had become as dark as a country road. She could see no one she recognized. Several trams rattled past on their way south, but they were not the right ones. It was nearly fifteen minutes before the driver slowed at a corner and pointed to an approaching headlight. "That's likely the one you want, miss," he said.

Penny paid the man off with one hand while she hailed the approaching car with the other. When it drew to a stop she saw it was empty. The driver was hidden behind a curtain at the front and the girl conductor was standing by the back door beside her ticket machine. Penny got on and paid her fare, looked quickly into the face of the girl and said, "Did you see a man—a young man—I don't think he was very well dressed? Did he get off somewhere along here on your way north?"

"I didn't notice," the girl said.

"But you must have! There weren't more than a dozen people on the car. Try to think—please!"

The girl made an effort, but before she could find anything to say the car stopped again and three more people got on board. Penny went forward to a seat and watched the girl make change. As soon as the new passengers were seated she came up the aisle and stopped by Penny's seat.

"A lot of people got off at Cornwallis Street," she said.

"Was there a young man left on board after that?"

"A few more got off around the dockyard. Before that there was some that left at the station. There was only one passenger after we passed the dockyard, I remember."

"Was he young? Darkish—perhaps not very well shaved?"

The girl shook her head. "I don't think so," she said.

Then Penny realized that she herself was unable to say whether the figure she had seen was in uniform or not. She had only received the quickest of impressions, and now she began to have doubts. Surely if it had been Neil he would have been wearing a uniform, and the girl would certainly have remembered a soldier among her passengers.

"Were there any officers on the car?" she asked.

"No, I'm sure of that. There weren't even any sailors."

Penny felt her heart beginning to labor. Of course, if Neil were alive and in disgrace he would be a deserter and would not dare wear a uniform. She looked quickly at the girl and said, "Thanks, thanks very much." The girl left her and retreated to the rear platform, and as the car ran south she kept calling out names of familiar streets. Penny sat still and listened to the sing-song voice and heard the clicking of the ticket machine, and finally she began to relax. It had been a mistake, like all the other times she had fancied she had seen Neil on the streets. It had been some man with a posture resembling his, nothing more. Her case was certainly not unique; she knew a woman in Halifax whose son had been killed nearly three years ago and yet the woman was convinced that only last summer she had seen the boy leaning over the rail of the Dartmouth ferry. Not even the fact that she had searched the decks and found nothing had shaken her conviction. Penny breathed deeply. Surely if Neil were in Halifax she would have heard from him. She could not endure the thought that he was alive anywhere and had not come to her.

Then the withering feeling returned as she remembered her father and the things people had whispered about Neil Macrae for the past two years. She remembered Murray's unwillingness to talk and the sudden embarrassment of Billy Andrews only half an hour ago. But Angus, at least, would have told her if Neil was alive. He could never have brought himself to lie about a thing like that. She had been so sure of his sincerity that his answers had finally dispelled any lingering hope that Neil might still be living, in spite of everything.

The tram stopped at the foot of her street and she got off and began to climb the hill. It was silent and cold and empty on this street where she had lived all her life. The air cooled her brain and slowed her thoughts and her heart to a normal pace. As she began to calculate the situation she thanked God for this gift which never failed her, this merciful power within herself that enabled her to spill cold water over her brain and make it lucid in moments of crisis.

She moved slowly up the hill under the bare branches of the trees until she reached the red house at the crest. A thin wind moaned in the eaves and the empty branches, and faint lines of light ringed the cracks in the shutters. Her father was home, had eaten dinner and was probably annoyed because she was still out. Roddie was home, and was using her absence as an excuse not to do his homework.

She looked at the front door. That heavy rectangle of oak weighted with its brass knocker was a symbol. Her family had shut her in from the world when she was young; it had shut her out from itself when she had ceased being a child. Her body straightened, became erect and rigid, as though to counteract the trembling sensation in her spine which now was spreading to her hands, her knees and her shoulders.

In that instant she knew unmistakably that Neil Macrae was alive and that she had seen him. She realized this beyond the power of any logic to confute it. Her eyes were trained to recognize what was placed before them; they had often tried to fool her, but after sober consideration, they had never cheated her in her whole life.

The quivering in her limbs subsided. She drew a deep breath of damp air and slipped her hands into the pockets of her coat. And then she felt saturated with anger and determination. No one had ever had the kindness to give her an honest account of what had happened to Neil that day or night in Flanders when they hinted that his cowardice had ruined her father's career in the army. The family had whispered their obscure remarks, and after Jean's birth she had been too shaken and apprehensive to ask many questions. But Neil was alive now and she knew it. He was back in Halifax, and not all the coldness and pride of her father could keep her from compelling him to answer her questions tonight. She closed the door loudly behind her as she entered the house.

WEDNESDAY

Another fine morning, and Neil Macrae was wakened out of a nightmare by the reverberations of steamer horns sounding in different notes, one after the other. He lurched from bed and looked out. There in the harbor, large and unreal in their proximity, the ships of a convoy were following each other in line out of the Basin and through the Narrows to the Stream, then to the harbor gates and the open sea. The window of his room commanded a long stretch of the harbor and held five ships in view. The convoy moved slowly, each vessel keeping station about three hundred yards behind the one immediately in front, so that during the half-hour he watched there were always five ships visible.

They were merchantmen of all the standard sizes and designs, representing half a dozen countries. Subconsciously he judged each with a professional eye and condemned them all. Long ago he had decided that the standard designs of most tramp ships were wrong. Builders were so conservative they still insisted on setting the funnel in the exact center of the vessel. A coal burner made a direct draft necessary, but now that the navy was burning oil exclusively in its new ships, coal would soon be dropped from all ocean-going craft, and something more utilitarian could be designed if anyone were willing to do it.

He remembered a sketch he had made years ago for a lumber carrier. He had set the bridge and mast far forward over wide bows and a shortened forecastle, and the funnel had been placed astern, just forward of the poop. This left the whole midships free for cargo, with derricks on forecastle and forward of the poop free to load without fouling obstructions on the decks.

His freighter had carried the gross tonnage of a medium-sized liner, though most tramp steamers today were under five thousand tons and many were no bigger than coasters. Yet each required a crew substantially as large as that necessary to work a ship twice the size.

He left the window and poured water from a cracked jug into a basin and plunged his face into it, feeling the bristles of his beard grate against his hands as he rubbed. He splashed water over his naked chest and shoulders and toweled them, and then he shaved in cold water and sat on the edge of the bed with his chin in his hands and a cigarette in the corner of his mouth.

There was a dead rat somewhere in the walls. In this ramshackle house of ten rooms there was everywhere the sour odor of corners which had never seen sunlight or a mop, and of thirty inhabitants who slept in their underclothes. His own room, no better than a cupboard in the attic, was one of three usually rented to sailors waiting in port for another ship. At the moment he was the only lodger. He looked at the floor. It was made of softwood boards, dark gray with the impressed dirt of fifty years. Outside his door, the hall and stairwells were loud with the noise of children playing.

He wondered what complacent individual in the South End owned this house. He remembered someone having once said that if a man wants a profit from property he must own something in the slums, because the poor make their own repairs, and twelve renters paying twenty dollars a month are worth more than five paying fifty.

He dressed and got out of the place as quickly as he could. He bought a paper on the corner and walked in the direction of the railway station for breakfast. AMERICA TO HAVE TEN MILLION SOLDIERS WITHIN TWO YEARS—and already there were six million from the Empire, seven from France, fourteen from Germany, God knew how many in Russia, all these in addition to the dead. His mind swung to the time when all these men would return home, ants swarming the surface of a globe in which most of the anthills have been wrecked, a million sergeants with no more sections to command.

The gloomy slum buildings of the North End depressed him this morning and he had a distorted image of himself as a Gulliver in this Lilliput, wrenching the roofs off houses to discover how many myriads of creatures swarmed underneath and never saw the light. For this was the disgraceful thing about Halifax, the hurting and humiliating thing about his town, that here, backed by millions of acres of space, there should be slums like these and people dull and docile enough to inhabit them. Children, ill-dressed and half-dressed, brawled about this district with dirty faces and blank eyes. The houses were like cracker boxes standing in rows on a shelf. In some cases the foundations were so cockeyed it looked as though the houses they supported might tip over and sprawl into the street. Their cracked timbers were painted chocolate or cocoa brown, and these drab colors absorbed all the light that entered the streets and made them seem even narrower and dirtier and meaner than they actually were.

Sometimes he passed an open doorway, and the interior made him shudder: plastered walls, sticks of furniture that looked like rubbish, everything greasy and hand-touched, sour smells issuing into the streets. In this section of Halifax the noises never ceased all the twenty-four hours of the day. It was a shock to realize how little he had known of the North End. When he had lived here, he had always avoided the district, and by avoiding it, had contrived to blink its existence.

It was a relief to enter the station and find it alive with people, brilliant with sunshine filtered through the glass roof and roaring with steam exhausted from four locomotives which stood panting in front of their cars . . . the Sydney train, the Saint John Express, the Dominion Atlantic from the Valley, a local train from the nearer villages. He folded the newspaper under his arm and entered the restaurant where he found a seat in the corner farthest from the door.

"Mind if I sit here? Place is crowded this morning."

He looked up sharply, and with a start recognized the numeral of his old battalion on the cap of a private soldier. For a frozen second he stared at the face, then his muscles relaxed and he eased back in his chair. He had never seen this man in his life.

"Sit down." He passed over the paper. "Want a read of this?"

"Don't mind if I do. Thanks."

The waitress took their orders and the two men kept their privacy until Neil had finished eating his eggs. Then the soldier said, "You look like you were just demobbed. What was your outfit?"

"Toronto Highlanders." The lie was quick enough for anybody. "You been back long?"

"Coupla months. Hanging around hospitals. Guess you know all about that yourself. Got a job?"

"Not yet."

"I bet it ain't so easy, getting what a guy wants. Well, I guess you get a pension, though."

"Some."

"A lot of guys, they're in such a hurry to get out of the army they don't get themselves checked up proper. Now take me, for instance. I'm making sure of mine. A lot of guys, they're going to find themselves without any pension, take it from me."

The waitress took the man's cup and refilled it with coffee, and he went on eating heartily, talking through mouthfuls of food. "You know, those doctors sure want to keep the finger on a fella. I'm supposed to hang around town till they get through checking on me, see. But I fooled them yesterday. Went down to Truro to see the old lady. That train goes so goddam slow I thought I was going to be late. I got another board inside an hour."

"You'll have plenty of time," Neil said. He shifted his plate and his voice was sharp. "I used to know some fellows in your outfit."

"Yeah, who?"

"Big Alec MacKenzie—know anyone of that name?"

"Sure, everyone knew Big Alec."

"Where is he now—in France?"

"No, Alec got smashed up. Not real bad, but—you know, like you and me. Just about right."

"Is he home now?"

"Sure, he's been back quite a while."

Neil's fingers opened and closed with quick, nervous gestures and he had to clench his fists under the table to keep his hands still. "Where's he now?" he said.

"I guess he's around." The man stopped in the middle of a bite. "Funny thing you asking that. I saw Alec a week ago."

"Here? In town?"

"Sure. I wasn't talking to him long. You know, just met him around."

"Is he under examination, or something like that?"

"Not on your life, he's got a job. He's doing all right, too. Got his old lady and kids in town. Foreman on one of the wharves, he said."

"Yes? Which one?"

"Don't remember that exactly, though he did tell me."

"Is he at Campbell's? Smith's, maybe?"

"I don't remember."

"Maybe he's at Pier Two?" Neil went on. "Furness-Withy?"

"No, it wasn't one of them."

"Wain's?"

The man sat upright, grinning with sudden pleasure. "Say, that's the one! You must know your way around this town. Alec's been working at Wain's on to a year, he said. I ought to have remembered a name like that. His boss used to be colonel of our outfit."

"Isn't he still colonel?"

"No, there was some sort of balls-up and he got sent home. Happened before I went over. I was a replacement."

Neil was breathing heavily and he passed his hand over his forehead, bringing it away moist. He was grateful that the man was so absorbed in his food. Geoffrey Wain was home; Alec was home. That they should now be found in the same place seemed such an inevitability that he wondered why he hadn't guessed it long ago.

The man finished his breakfast and wiped his mouth. "You run into Big Alec in France, you said?"

"Yes."

"Then maybe you were in some of those big attacks before I got there. They must have been pretty bad. When I first went into the line I remember the boys were sore."

"I only saw Alec around the base," Neil said. "I never knew what happened to his outfit."

"I guess no one else did, either, the way the boys used to talk. For a while they had hardly any officers left. Well, it was better when I was with them, though it wasn't any picnic."

"Maybe the new colonel was better?"

"Maybe. The boys didn't have anything against Wain, though."

When the soldier left, Neil picked up the paper and began turning the pages. Now there was no if and no maybe, for Alec had remembered or he had forgotten, and a word would decide it. As Neil realized this, the back of his throat felt dry and parched even while the moisture from under his armpits seemed to be spreading through his shirt until the linen clung coldly to his skin. "Hell!" he muttered, and rose to pay his check.

He walked with exaggerated deliberation through the station waiting room to the information desk and asked for a city directory. While the girl was looking for it, he admitted to himself that during the past few weeks he had so dreaded the possibility of disappointment that he had almost been afraid to meet Big Alec at all. Otherwise he would have remembered that the name might be in the directory, even if it was not in the phone book. He thumbed through the pages, a quarter of which seemed to be covered with Macs. There was an Alexander MacKenzie on a South End street; that was not his man, for the district was too prosperous. There was another in the North End, but the directory said he was a schoolboy. He snapped the book shut. "When was this directory made up?" he asked the girl.

"It's this year's."

"I'm looking for a man who's been in town just about a year."

She shook her head. "His name wouldn't be in there. A lot of newcomers are in town these days and we get a lot of inquiries."

"I see." He put up his coat collar and began walking toward the waterfront, and when he reached the dock area, turned south in the direction of Wain's Wharf.

The old firm seemed busy this morning. Through the archway he could see slovens unloading crates and sacks, and there was a great activity of workmen all over the wharf. He hunched his head into his collar and lounged through the arch. On his right was the doorway leading to Geoffrey Wain's office, directly in front were the shed and the slovens, with horses dropping dung on the timbers of the wharf and rattling their harness and bits as they tossed their heads or were maneuvered about by their drivers.

MacKenzie was not in sight, and Neil realized that if he was here at all he would probably be working inside the shed. He dared not enter. If any of Wain's old workers were still around he would be recognized immediately. A teamster left his wagon and lumbered across the yard, and Neil spoke as the man was about to enter the door leading to the office stairs.

"Does a man called Alec MacKenzie work here?"

The man jerked his thumb over his shoulder. "Alec's in the shed," he said. "Know where his house is?"

"No."

The man walked on up the stairs, leaving the door open behind him. Then Neil heard a familiar voice.

"Miss Phillips, I'm expecting a caller. Tell him to wait. I'll be right back."

Neil turned and faded through the archway to the street, his eyes darting like an animal's from side to side. But there was no escape this way, either. Coming down the hill facing the wharf entrance was a familiar figure in uniform, Angus Murray heading straight for the wharf and apparently in a hurry. Neil turned his head aside and moved hastily back into the middle of the slovens and horses on the wharf. Murray entered the archway without noticing him, and finally Neil gained the street.

He was condemned to wait again and the thought enraged him. He had suffered too much and too long, and unless there was a reckoning soon, his existence would become a disgrace to itself. Wain was back, comfortable and secure; Halifax was drifting through the war in smug and profitable self-satisfaction, unconscious of the realities he knew. The old men like Wain had been willing to have this war because they were bored with themselves, and now they fancied they were in control of a wonderful new age.

For him, the dreary army routine had given place to a phantasmal existence of hospitals and cities away from the front but still a part of the war, an experience in which nothing had been real but loneliness and nothing knowledge but statistics and newsprint. To continue like this indefinitely would turn him into a ghastly, groping automaton who would ultimately accept an invalid psychosis as a substitute for real life. Another two years of it would finish even the courage necessary for suicide.

He walked on toward the South End, muttering to himself, careless of the whole town recognizing him. To be anonymous in Halifax was worse than wandering unknown through London or Liverpool, for there were people here who knew him, even some who had loved him once. He came to a decision. Why wait to find Alec MacKenzie? There was another person he wanted to see even more.

Ten o'Clock At this hour of the morning Geoffrey Wain's office was filled with sunshine so brilliant that the nickel on the edges of Miss Phillips' typewriter flashed a spot back and forth across the ceiling as the carrier traveled with the lines of the letter she was writing. Murray leaned back in the only comfortable chair and smoked a pipe, speculatively appraising Evelyn Phillips at work. She paid no obvious attention to him, but he knew she was aware of his attention and possibly of some of his thoughts, and he admired her detachment. Her adolescent figure seemed to him more piquant than attractive, but he acknowledged its interest for experiment as he recollected that his own experience had never included a woman so tiny.

After nearly a quarter of an hour, Wain returned full of apologies for being late and motioned Miss Phillips to leave them alone. She picked up her papers and went to the inner office behind the frosted glass, and almost immediately the sound of another typewriter joined the chorus of three already at work there.

"You seem pretty busy down here," Murray said. "I must say I like the establishment. It doesn't look like an office at all."

"Well, it hasn't changed much in the last hundred years," Wain said. "I hope that's some of my tobacco you're smoking?"

"Don't worry, it is. To have access to tobacco and cigars like yours must make the West Indian trade pretty attractive."

"It's about the only thing that does. I can't say this business ever interested me much."

Murray smiled politely. He was curious, but by no means concerned, to discover why his presence had been requested here this morning.

"My daughter speaks to me a great deal about you," Wain said.

"So?" Murray did not believe it. "I hope what she says isn't too boring."

Wain produced a perfunctory smile. "I'll be very frank with you, if you don't mind. Penelope has begun to worry me. Since her mother's death our house has been pretty lonely. I'm too busy to have many people in, myself. And–" There was a momentary silence during which he seemed not so much embarrassed as at a temporary loss for a sequence of words which would cause him the least bother. "By the way, I'm glad to see your arm finally out of its splint. That's splendid!"

The irrelevancy made Murray laugh. "I doubt if the arm agrees with you. The finger joints still ache like hell."

"But it's good to know it's improving. After all, you and I are the sole survivors of our original battalion mess."

"I never thought of that," Murray said reflectively.

Wain's hesitation had resolved itself. "Frankly," he said, "I've asked you here on a personal and delicate matter. I hope you'll take what I say in the spirit it's intended. The fact is, I want you to do me a favor. I have a feeling you'll be helping yourself as well. You'll certainly be helping Penelope."

Murray indicated that he was listening.

"You know, our family has been here so long it's supposed to have a certain social position in the town. In the eyes of a lot of people I fancy we're snobs. But you know, yourself, that if a family has gained prominence it can't avoid its responsibilities. It's got to maintain itself or go under and lose everything. Now, a situation has arisen——" He stopped abruptly, and Murray had the impression that he had been giving away more than he had intended.

"Is Penelope having any difficulty?" Murray asked.

Wain opened a handkerchief. "I'm afraid she may get herself into an unholy mess. I admit I'm fairly worried about it. As you know, she's in some respects an exceptional sort of girl. She's also a wilful one. I've always respected her for it, and more or less allowed her to go her own way. The consequences involved now are far more serious than she can understand."

The colonel blew his nose loudly. "To put it bluntly, she insists she saw her cousin Neil Macrae last night—on a tram and out of uniform."

"What!" Murray started so abruptly the pipe fell out of his mouth. "Macrae—alive!"

"You can appreciate what that may mean to all of us."

"But—man, it's impossible! He's dead. Besides, I was with Penelope last night myself."

"She says it was after you left her. The tram, I believe, was northbound on Barrington Street."

"You sound as if you actually believed she really saw him."

"I do."

"But you virtually certified his death yourself."

"Yes, I did. But did anyone see the body? Missing, believed killed—that was the wording in the casualty list. You were Battalion M.O. Did you see the body?"

"No, but I saw a hole the size of a church door where you'd had him put a few hours before."

"And therefore we both assumed he was killed." Wain shook his head. "Funny things can happen in a bombardment on a dark night. We went down the line the next evening. I wish I could remember the name of that North-Country battalion that relieved us. They might have an interesting story to tell."

"Then you really believe the boy's alive?"

"I don't definitely believe anything. I merely think it's quite probable."

"But for God's sake——"

"Murray—you know my daughter pretty well. Do you think she's hysterical?"

"No."

"When she spoke to me last night, she was absolutely positive."

Murray scowled at the bowl of his empty pipe. It now began to occur to him to wonder at Wain's purpose in singling him out as an audience for this story. "Look here," he said, "I think you're exaggerating everything. It's an obvious case of hallucination. The war has provided hundreds of examples like it."

"I've naturally thought of that," Wain said.

"Well?"

"If any other woman but my daughter had told me this I'd have dismissed it at once."

Murray put the pipe in his pocket and got restlessly to his feet. He could see the panorama of the harbor spreading in the winter sunshine and the ships of the convoy passing down the Stream towards the sea. "Granted then that he's alive," he said slowly, "what of it?"

He turned, the two men faced each other, and Wain's nostrils dilated.

"I have no intention of giving him another opportunity to make trouble for me and my family," Wain said.

Murray resumed his seat and crossed his legs calmly. There was an emergency, and the emergency was Penny's.

"You are aware that your daughter's in love with the boy, of course?" he said.

"What does she know about a thing like that?" The anger in Wain's voice was undisguised and unpleasant, and he seemed to realize it for he added more quietly, "The boy used to appeal to her sense of pity. She's warm-hearted, I suppose. The sort who's apt to think that every wastrel is the helpless victim of circumstances or villains, and needs her support."

"But your nephew was hardly a wastrel, was he?"

"No, that's overstating it. But he was completely impractical. Like a lot of the Highland Scotch he was shiftless unless he had everything his own way. Not that he didn't have ability, mind you. He could have had a wonderful future, but he'd never be interested in anything he'd get paid for. No one was willing to finance him while he experimented on ship designs that looked like vessels from Mars. Penny was a sheltered girl, and because he always had the gift of the gab, he imposed on her. As if that wasn't enough, he was her first cousin."

"I gather she's been told that." In a spurt of dislike he could not control, Murray jabbed out, "I take it you just didn't like him. But the English aristocracy have a habit of marrying their own cousins, so I don't see what objection a family like yours could have to doing the same."

Coming from anyone else, this would have been hard for Wain to take; from Murray it was almost unendurable, and the man made it worse by watching calmly as Wain closed his jaws to avoid a retort.

"It never was a question of marriage," Wain said finally. "I saw to that. But he was always unsettling us. That's why I sent him to school in Montreal. He put ideas into her head and he had plenty of empty ones. I never bothered to find out, but I suppose he was a socialist, as well." Suddenly aware that he was giving a lot more than he was receiving, Wain lowered his voice and added indifferently, "It was a thoroughly unpleasant situation for everybody, and I haven't any intention of seeing it resumed."

"Might I ask," Murray said, "what Penny thinks about all this now?"

"She's too upset to know what she thinks."

"I can understand that. There's another thing—would you mind being specific about what all this has to do with me?"

"I should have presumed that anything connected with my daughter would be of concern to you."

"What do you mean?"

Wain set his spreading hands on the desk, observing carefully the powerful fingers like talons. "I'm no longer your colonel," he said quietly. "I'm well aware that your affairs are no concern of mine. But my daughter's are. And when a man your age—and with your reputation, Murray—is paying open attention to her—just what am I supposed to think?"

"What you damn well please!" Murray was on his feet. "If that's all, I think I'll say good morning."

Wain's lips parted and the teeth shone brightly under the black bristles of his mustache. Murray realized that the expression was a smile.

"Please, Major! Pay me the compliment of realizing that I'm not quite as stupid and conventional as you seem to assume. I merely mentioned that I knew you were interested in Penelope, that's all. Let's reach an agreement before you go."

Murray grunted and resumed his seat, crossing his legs. "It would be a hell of a lot easier if you'd quit trying to be subtle with me," he said. "I know damn well what you meant."

Wain passed his fingers over the cleft in his chin. "Let's assume for the time being that Neil Macrae is in Halifax. What effect is that going to have on all of us?"

"You tell me," Murray said, "what effect it's going to have on you. That's all you're thinking about, isn't it?"

"I was thinking of the effect it would have on my daughter."

"Well, I can help you there, in case you don't know already. It would be the most wonderful thing that's happened to her in years."

"Even if it means he will now be shot by a firing squad?"

"What? You——"

"He's still subject to court-martial, you know. What slight chance he might have had to escape sentence is gone now. He's made himself a deserter with a record against his name."

"You'd actually do a thing like that to your own nephew?"

"It would be easier," Wain said with pretended weariness, "if people would avoid the habit of looking for a villain in situations which are merely confused. I suppose I ought to feel insulted by your attitude, but frankly, I don't. I want you to understand me, that's all. I haven't the slightest chance of stopping anything that happens to Neil Macrae if he's found here. The first military policeman he meets will arrest him on the spot—if he knows who he is, I mean. Military law will do the rest. But at the same time, I won't be able to avoid connection with the case. I'll be summoned as a witness. You understand me? *I'd* have to be the chief witness against him! And in Halifax!" He leaned back in his chair and surveyed Murray coolly. "That would be a pretty picture for Penelope to carry through life, don't you think? Her cousin convicted and shot for cowardice with her father the chief witness against him!"

Murray slumped back in his chair and passed a hand over his flushed face. At last Wain had managed to convince him; although he knew that Penny's father would be delighted to see Neil Macrae destroyed, he also realized that his picture of the situation was probably accurate. If Neil were discovered, these things would happen.

"You probably have still more to say," he answered at length, in a low voice. "I'm listening."

Wain tapped his fingers decisively on the desk and Murray was able to catch a flicker of satisfaction relaxing the muscles of the older man's expression.

"In the first place, there must be no court-martial."

"If what you say is true, how can it be avoided?"

"I'll tell you. We must first find the boy. Once he's found–by us–I'm fairly certain things can be fixed. Now, he won't be in a hotel where he's likely to be recognized. He isn't with any of his relations. Why he's here at all, I don't know, but I'm afraid he may try to see Penelope. If he meets her before we can reach him––"

Murray shut his eyes. "Go on, I know what you mean."

"It's my guess he's gone to a boarding house. Some cheap place in the North End, probably. There aren't many and I'm having them all checked. That's one advantage of the war. You can give orders without a parcel of fools asking why."

"Why do you think you need me in this?"

"When we find him, I want you to talk to him."

"Why not talk to him yourself?"

"Considering everything, I don't think there'd be much point in that."

"Probably not. Well, what do I say to him?"

"Remember that we must avoid a court-martial. The only way that can be done is for him to leave the country at once. Try to persuade him that no matter what sense of grievance he may feel he hasn't a chance if he remains here. Try––"

"Grievance?" Murray interrupted sharply. "What do you mean by that?"

"Nothing definite. I suppose he feels the world is against him, that's all. He ought to. The world *is* against him."

"All right, go on."

"He could easily lose himself if he went to the States. And with the opportunities over there, he might still have a decent future. He's probably traveling under an assumed name. Tell him to keep it. And one thing more" –again an irreconcilable anger flared into Wain's voice–"tell him if he ever sets foot inside Nova Scotia again, or communicates with my daughter in any way, I'll see to it that the law takes its course with him."

Murray did not move; he sat blinking in the sunlight streaming in through the long window.

Wain became impatient. "In all fairness to me, isn't that the most decent thing I can do under the circumstances?"

"I don't know," Murray said slowly. There was a moment of silence during which the ticking clock was audible. Then he blinked again. "If that's your only message," he said, "you'd better see him yourself."

He unfolded his long legs and got to his feet, put his hands deep into his pockets and walked over to the window, where he stood in silence for nearly a minute, looking down on the wharf and the slovens unloading at the end of the shed. The air whistled audibly through his crooked nostrils as he breathed, and behind his back Wain's fingers drumming on the desk were like an obbligato to the muffled clatter of the typewriters in the other room. Finally he turned and said, "Does Penny know you're seeing me this morning?"

"Naturally not."

Murray's manner became decisive. "You've told me a lot, Wain, but I don't feel I've heard anything that really matters. Suppose you go back and fill in the gaps?"

Wain's only change of expression was a fixity in the muscles of his face; the movement was slight, but it transformed his appearance. "Just what are you suggesting? I don't like the inference."

"I'm suggesting nothing. I'm telling you I'll have to hear a lot more before I'll have any part in this mess."

"I'm sorry," Wain said. "I should have apologized for mixing you up in what, after all, is a family affair. I seem to have been mistaken. I had thought your interest in my daughter—or your ambitions, to put it bluntly—would have been enough to make you willing to assist."

Murray laughed shortly and shook his head. "We'd better stick to facts. You and I are so different we'd never understand each other in a million years. Come on—what's the real problem? It isn't just Penny's welfare. What is it?"

Wain's lips parted in another smile, and Murray was mildly astonished to see that the man seemed relieved. The impression was corroborated when Wain's chin lifted in a quick laugh.

"You know, Murray, maybe you and I can understand each other better than you think. It's a matter of getting used to things that are taboo in Halifax. It's a matter of admitting them—of admitting them to one's self. You imply that I'm thinking of myself. I am. And as I've always assumed that your motives with regard to Penny were not—shall we say, the motives of a twenty-two-year-old boy—I don't see why we can't reach an understanding."

"Go on," Murray said.

"Evidently you realize that you have some bargaining power, and have sensibly decided to use it. On the whole, I think you can. You may or may not be fond of my daughter, but she has attractions other than herself. Money, for instance. You're no longer young. And with your injured arm"—he glanced pointedly—"as well as with your past record—in short, if Neil Macrae stays dead, I'd be the first to wish you success with Penelope."

Murray was silent. Then he tapped his nose and broke into a broad grin. "You know—I can't remember when I've been so blandly insulted. One thing I'm curious about—did you know you were insulting me, or didn't you?"

Wain said nothing, but the drumming of his fingers on the desk indicated that his patience had almost run out.

"Never mind about my marrying Penny," Murray said. "What's your personal motive in wanting to get Macrae out of town?"

"I've given it."

Murray shook his head. "No. You see, I just can't believe that your affection for your daughter or your regard for your precious family is so strong. It was through him you lost your command, wasn't it?"

However great Wain's growing resentment and humiliation might be, he contrived to keep it out of his voice when he answered the ringing telephone. His answers to the queries from the other end of the line were succinct and crisp, and when he replaced the receiver on its hook he continued to talk to Murray with no change of tone.

"Yes, I have a personal motive. Everybody has . . . The other night you asked how long I thought the war was going to last. I said three years and I had good reason for the estimate. That means we're now exactly in the middle of it." He looked up to make sure that Murray was attending. "People around here seem to think this war's merely a matter of beating the Germans. I don't. I think it's the first stage of a revolution. Now then—what state will the world be in after three more years like the last ones?"

"What's all this to do with Neil Macrae?"

"It has a lot to do with my plans, which that young fool can spoil by getting himself arrested. After this war the entire world will be bankrupt. It has already become a military society for purposes of the war. Do you think it will slip back into the old mold again? After this war, anyone outside the army or navy will be a nobody. Therefore the services offer the only sure future an ambitious man can hope to have." His voice rose. "I've counted on that, Murray, and I intend to be in on it. I'm not going to have any two-by-four scandal stop me. I got word only yesterday that I'm to be reinstated in overseas service—but this time I shall be on the staff." His clenched knuckles rapped the desk. "I've wasted a whole lifetime in this hole of a town. Everything in this damn country is second-rate. It always is, in a colony. Now I'm going to get away from it for good. You've asked me for my motive and there it is. You can think what you like and be damned to you."

"If you mean all that," Murray said, "I think you're crazy. Hell, I'm a major myself, and the idea of becoming a colonel like you wouldn't get me excited. Of course, you might become a brigadier, and after that they might make you a major general and . . ."

"You can think what you like of my ability," Wain said. "The general staff will be the judges of it."

"Yes," Murray said with a yawn, "maybe they will, at that. You know, the only thing in all this rigmarole that makes any sense to me is that at this particular moment you're all excited about a staff job, and that Neil Macrae has something on you. I should have supposed that if he were successfully court-martialed, your position would be strengthened with the staff. But he'd talk at the court-martial, and that seems to be the rub. How about explaining a little more?"

Wain sighed. "You seem determined to make a mountain out of a molehill. Don't you know how an officer gets onto the staff?"

"No, I guess I was never interested enough to find out."

"Well"—Wain hesitated in distaste—"a man has to have the qualifications, naturally. But influence is very important. Some show of politics is often necessary, especially on this side of the water."

"So the dead rat under the family floor is beginning to smell at last! You not only don't want the boy court-martialed. You don't even dare let him get in calling distance of a court."

"You don't know what you're talking about."

"Young Macrae was arrested on your orders, wasn't he? And a court-martial was never held, was it?" He got up and began to pace the floor. "Your version of the story has spread all over the place, Wain. People have come to take it for granted. Neil Macrae disobeyed your orders when he retired, and half the battalion was wiped out. But I don't remember hearing his side of the story. Where were you that day? If I remember rightly, you lost touch with the whole lot of us. A fat chance you'd have of collaring a staff job if all that stuff came to light in an investigation!"

Wain rose to his feet and the two men faced each other. Both were trembling, Murray with the excitement of an idea, Wain with fury.

"You're hysterical, Murray, and you're being a fool! If you'd done more thinking and less talking in your life, you'd have a little more money in your pocket today."

"I'm doing plenty of thinking right now."

With a great effort, Wain relaxed sufficiently to turn away and resume his seat. When he spoke again, his voice had a sound of weary exasperation.

"I suppose I ought to show you the door," he said. "If there was anyone else——" He shrugged his shoulders—"You seem to have forgotten several things, Major. It was I who committed Macrae for court-martial. In the light of that, I can't understand your suspicion that I have anything to fear from what he might say. It is merely impolitic for me to have a scandal at the present moment. Macrae would be convicted, all right. He disobeyed a written order. Do you think I'd court-martial a man who could produce a signed order from me that would acquit him?"

"What was the order? Something impossible?"

"It would help if you wouldn't persist in regarding me a scoundrel, Murray."

"What was the order?" Murray said.

"I was cut off from the front by the enemy's barrage. You remember that, don't you?"

"I remember the barrage. My dressing station was in the middle of it."

"Very well. The lines were destroyed, the adjutant was wounded. I sent a runner ahead with a message to the senior officer in charge at the front line. The order was to advance immediately on the second objective. That was a low ridge a quarter of a mile in advance of where the battalion then was. It would have cost some casualties——"

"It certainly would!"

"At least it would have saved the attack from collapsing. Besides that, a retirement into an area selected by the enemy for a counter-barrage would have been the worst possible move, and that was precisely what Macrae did. Why my corporal had to encounter my nephew, of all the junior officers in the battalion, and give *him* the message, I don't know, but—"

"You ought to," Murray interrupted. "The senior officers were all dead by then."

"Anyway, the order was flatly disobeyed. It was the most flagrant case of loss of nerve—or plain cowardice—I ever encountered."

Murray leaned back and stroked his bald spot. He found himself remembering an old tag about the man who convicted himself by constant explanation. But at the same time, he was forced to admit that Wain's story hung together and that every detail seemed to be accurate. His recollection of the affair had cleared, and the remembrance of that afternoon in Flanders filled him with a weary and hopeless anger, a disgust with the fundamental stupidity of men like Wain, with the premises on which their lives and actions rested, with the past few years and his own part in them. That particular attack had been a military crime, but he knew it was futile to waste one's self in generalities about it. The back areas of France were littered with execution notices of men who had broken down in the face of similar staff orders, and yet the war went on and no British soldiers were in revolt against their generals. They wanted to beat the Germans more than to save their own lives. It was easy to criticize the high command for incompetence, but a waste to attack their values, for society shared them through and through.

"If I've been making a fool of myself," he said finally, "I apologize."

"Very well." Wain straightened in his chair. "Let's waste no more time misunderstanding each other. Will you see the boy and tell him what I've told you?"

"I suppose so." Murray was hesitant and added gloomily, "But first I'd like to know why Neil Macrae has returned to Halifax."

"Animals always come back to familiar places. For all we know, he may have been here some time, living a life of his own and no one else the wiser. But I'd prefer you to save Penelope the necessity of running into him again. A meeting with her would probably start him into the open, and his execution would hardly improve her state of mind."

"All right," Murray said. "Tell me where he is and I'll see him. At least he has the right to tell someone his side of the story before he leaves." He looked sharply at Wain, but there was no mistaking the fact that the older man was confident. "And when he has left," Murray went on, "do you think Penny can be persuaded that she was mistaken about seeing him that night?"

"She can be—by you. Or"—Wain made a gesture of indifference—"she'll eventually realize he wasn't worth bothering about, anyway. Once she's safely married she'll forget all about him."

Murray got to his feet abruptly. "And then you'll be safe from whatever's bothering you. God damn you, you're the first man that ever tried to bribe me. I'll not forget it."

"An appeal to common sense is hardly a bribe. Our interests in the case differ, that's all."

Wain picked up some papers and affected to be interested in their contents. Of all the men Murray had ever met, this one seemed able to present the hardest shell to others. But Murray had no illusions about him; he knew that underneath the urbane exterior the older man was seething with anger and wounded pride, with humiliation at the steps necessary to advance his career, with outrage over the need of disclosing so much of his private affairs to a stranger.

He picked up his military cap and set it carelessly on the side of his head. As he turned to leave he muttered, "At least your notion of a military dictatorship in this country is a lot of balls."

"I'll let you know whenever the boy is located," Wain said without looking up. "I suppose you can be found at your hotel?"

Murray left the office without another word. It was a relief to reach the wharf and the biting odor of salt on the blown air, and see the workmen unloading the wagons by the shed. A pack of cumulus cloud was building up over the land across the harbor and the wind was hauling toward the south. He strolled down the wharf to watch the men, and their calm and regular movements soothed him.

He smiled inwardly at himself. It was strange that he, whom most people regarded as a waster and an outsider, should all his life have tried to do the right thing by others. He rarely got any credit for his motives, even from himself. He knew he was not stupid in the ordinary sense of the word; his stupidity was emotional rather than intellectual, and he had no illusions about the harm he had consistently done himself. At the moment he had no clear idea what he was going to do. He was positive that Wain had told him the legal truth, and he was equally sure that it would be a ghastly mess for everyone if Penny encountered Neil Macrae now. Even if Neil were in the clear, it would not be an enviable situation. Too much had happened to each of them these past three years, and it had happened to them separately. Neil would never be able to understand or appreciate what Penny had gone through, and now that she was professionally successful, he would find her changed. In this particular, Geoffrey Wain seemed entirely right; Neil and Penny must be kept apart.

He turned and began to stroll back along the wharf. It was useless to argue with himself about a matter of which he knew so little. He knew nothing whatever of Neil Macrae; he cared nothing about Wain. If he were to do anything in this situation it must be done for Penny's sake, and so he must find out as soon as possible what she had really said to her father the previous night, if it could be done without revealing his purpose.

He took a last look down the wharf before turning about, and then double-checked what he saw. An enormous man was coming out of the warehouse with a sheaf of papers in his hand, and the figure was familiar. There was no mistaking the face; it was Big Alec MacKenzie, Wain's former corporal. MacKenzie moved on to the shed, and after a few moments Murray walked back to Water Street.

"I wonder," he said to himself, "why that particular man happens to be working here?"

Two o'Clock The winter sunlight was like a net thrown over the frozen garden behind the old red house. In the living room Penny lay on the chesterfield while her father's Persian cat, an aloof cloud of black fur with enormous yellow eyes, played with a ball of khaki wool which had fallen on the floor. Work had been out of the question for her today after a sleepless night, and now she was grateful to be alone, her father in his office, Roddie at school, Sadie given an unexpected afternoon off.

One refrain jogged endlessly through her mind: Neil was alive, Neil still was, and the war had not killed the only eager human being she had ever known. Now she could let herself remember, but the inhibitions she had imposed upon her mind for three years were difficult to shake off. That last night together in Montreal, how shy and delicate he had been the first time she lay beside him and then how his habitual eagerness had made him forget everything except that he wanted her, and she had closed her eyes and left the lead to him as she had always done before, and through her mind had floated the words, "into thy hands I commend my spirit." And then he was gone, and she was left with Jean growing within her, and the pain and terror of bringing a child into the world so that no one should know its identity and existence suddenly became formidable with nothing to control it but courage, and endless discipline.

Now he was alive again. That meant she was no longer alone. But so many leaves had dropped from the calendar since that June day by the St. Lawrence. How would Neil be able to recognize the woman she had become, or even want her again? Now that the requirements of her profession had made her critical, would she be able to discover again her need for a man whom judgment told her was careless and impetuous and overconfident of his own ability to shape the world according to his own design?

The cat had finally tangled himself inextricably in the ball of wool, and with a baffled and desperate dignity was trying to get free. But for two years he had been alive without writing her a word; he had been in trouble and failed to ask her help; he had come home, but not to her. Oh, Neil—why couldn't you have let me know? Just something, so I could have known and talked with you no matter where you were!

She checked her emotion ruthlessly. The problem was not limited to themselves. There were Jean and Mary and Jim Fraser; there was even Angus Murray. And above all, there was her father. She thought she would never as long as she lived forget the look on her father's face when she had told him she had seen Neil Macrae alive in Halifax.

The cat rolled over, clawing frantically. Whenever he extricated himself from one loop he involved himself in another. She watched him idly. There were too many problems to solve now. Only one was urgent, and that was to save Neil from arrest, to get him out of Halifax before he was caught.

The cat made a few more efforts to free himself and then twisted his paws loose and sat down with the wool encircling his shoulders and legs and belly and, with such dignity as he could still retain, began to wash his face. She wondered if Angus Murray could help her. She would have to tell him that Neil was alive. The more she thought about it, the more sure she was that he was the only person she dared approach. She rose from the chesterfield and picked up the cat, removing the strands from his body. Then she resumed her seat, and the animal stalked out of the room with its tail in the air.

The door bell rang and she decided to ignore it. When it sounded a second time, she regretted her decision to let Sadie go and went out into the hall to answer it.

Neither of them moved or spoke. Neil's enlarged eyes stared defiantly out of a strained and lined face. The fan of crinkles away from his eyes, furrowed in the past by much spontaneous laughter, were merely marks now, unnoticeable among the deeper lines cut like gashes into the thin flesh of his face. His clothes were cheap and stained and shabby, and his shoes scuffed and run down. But out of the astonishment of seeing him on the doorstep she felt a quick lift of hope, for though his face was lacerated by worry and suffering, it had not entirely lost its familiar aspect of negligent confidence.

She saw him gulp, and then he said, "I happened to know your father would be out this afternoon," and without waiting for her to answer, he passed by her into the hall.

She closed the door and followed him silently into the living room, standing still inside the doorway as he stopped in front of the map of Jamaica.

"My God, is that thing still here?"

"Neil!"

She forced the word out, and at the sound of her voice he flashed about. She could see his face muscles loosen and his Adam's apple leap convulsively. Everything in the room blurred, and then she was in his arms, feeling his hands clutching her and slipping quickly over her back and loins and shoulders. He tried to lift her, but knowing his intention, she moved with his body and they lay on the chesterfield. It was minutes before his hands were still.

The clock struck a quarter-hour and he sat up abruptly. His face was flushed but its lines were easier now; they were more diffuse, though the eyes were still strange. They seemed to be constantly staring. He stretched out his hand and touched the white lock running along her temple.

"You didn't have this before."

She shook her head.

"You're still so lovely, Penny."

"Am I, Neil?"

His large eyes ran over the lines of her body and back again to her face. He made a quick movement as if to touch her again, but checked himself.

"God, things are in a mess! I mustn't let myself think of you like this, now!"

She touched his hand, picked it up and traced the length of his fingers. It seemed necessary to maintain a physical contact. His hands were rough, and some of the fingernails were broken. "Neil," she said, "you didn't come back just to tell me that?"

"As a matter of fact, I didn't come back to tell you anything. I'm here to square some accounts. It's a pity I wasn't bright enough to have started long ago, but that's the way it is now."

She watched his face more closely. Some of the old scorn was still in his voice, but little of the enthusiasm. She was hurt by the tone of defiance. How much of it was permanent and how much was caused by his determination to crush back his physical desire for her? There was no mistaking that he wanted her. She had the feeling that his eyes stared right through her clothes and lingered on her body. His desire underlay everything he was saying, and after a while it conditioned her own hearing of his words.

But there was something else in his mind much stronger than bodily eagerness, and its presence was just as obvious. It was something new between them; she did not know what it was.

"Why not tell me about it, Neil?" she said quietly.

"I'd like to." The words were decisive, but almost immediately his expression flicked back to a cautious tension. "But I can't yet. If things turn out all right . . ." He got up and ran his eyes quickly over the mantelpiece. "Have you got any fags around here?"

"I'll see."

She crossed to a table and opened one of its drawers and returned with a large box.

"Three Castles? Your father still does himself well. I've been glad enough of a Woodbine lately." He lit the cigarette and held it critically away, ironically admiring the fine white ash.

"We thought you'd been killed, Neil."

He looked away and dragged heavily on the cigarette.

"I heard other things, too, but I didn't believe them," she went on. She tried to keep emotion out of her voice but it was no use; the overtones that stole into her quiet words made them more bitter than an accusation. "Why didn't you write to me? I loved you when you went away."

He stared at her while the cigarette burned in his fingers. Then he slumped back on the chesterfield and buried his face in his hands, and his shoulders shook as he broke into terrible silent sobs.

Penny sat quietly with his head hard and warm against her breasts, and for several moments she was still. Then she laid her arm over his shoulders and pressed him against her body.

"Don't touch me, for God's sake!" He twisted away. "I shouldn't have come, only I couldn't stand it any longer thinking you might be here. Can't you see it nearly killed me not to be able to write you a single line? I've been alone all this time. I haven't heard my own name spoken in two years. They were going to shoot me, Penny—do you think I could have told you a thing like that? It's bad enough having to say it now." He swallowed and his face twisted as he looked away from her. "Oh, God—it's impossible! Here you are—living in your father's house, everything the same, nothing different! He'd still have me shot if he knew I was alive where he could get his hands on me."

She watched him as he crossed the room to the window and jerked the curtains apart. "The garden!" He turned and faced her again. "I'll tell you this much, Penny. I didn't come back to see you. I came to see your father—your father and one other man. And nothing on earth is going to stop me."

Now she knew. Her father *was* responsible. Whatever had happened, Neil was being killed by the burden in his mind.

"I don't know what father has done to you," she said. "I don't know anything that happened over there. But whatever it is, can't *I* help you?" She hesitated. "Have you—have you any chance of proving your case?"

He looked at her sharply, almost with hostility. "What do you mean—prove my case? What has your father told you?"

He sat down beside her again and she leaned softly against his shoulder. "Darling—what does it matter now? Oh, Neil—can't you see I love you still?"

He winced away again. "You've got to let me alone in this. It's something I've got to do myself." His eyes were boring into her, examining, scrutinizing. Then he said sharply, "You aren't particularly surprised to see me."

"I knew you were alive."

"How? Who told you?"

"Yesterday evening I saw you—you were on a tram going north. I followed it in a taxi, but by the time I caught up you weren't on it."

"Does anyone else know I'm here?"

She hesitated.

"Did you tell your father?"

"Yes—I had to."

"My God, I might have known!" His eyes lashed her. "For the love of Christ, Penny, of all the people in this world, why did you have to tell him?"

"Oh, Neil!" The look on his face was intolerable and it was an effort not to hide from it. "What else could I have done? Things have happened to me, too. You're not the only one who's been alone. I've been awfully alone. When I saw you last night and realized you'd stayed away from me for some reason . . . Neil, I had to find out why. I was going crazy."

"Well, did you?"

"No."

He got up and moved around the room, looking at familiar objects without recognition. Finally he dropped into an armchair opposite her, and after moving in a sudden convulsion, his face became quite calm. It was only then that she realized he had been shell-shocked. The knowledge seemed good; at least it gave a reason for a change that otherwise would have been unaccountable.

"You couldn't help it," he said. "I don't suppose it was much fun to discover I was alive and hadn't let you know. And I don't suppose it's been pleasant living with all the hyenas in the family prowling around you." He gave a curious laugh and seemed genuinely amused. "Tell me, what did Aunt Maria say when she heard the sad news of my demise?"

"Do you really want to know?"

"I've often wondered. Honestly, I have."

"Well, at first she seemed to think you'd fallen in the line of duty and that was so gratifying to her patriotism she said quite nice things about you. What she thinks now I don't know and don't care. Neil—please tell me something. Haven't you any better clothes than those you're wearing?"

"No," he said, suddenly cheerful.

"Then let me get you some. Have you enough money? I don't want to pry, but——"

"To hell with all that, it doesn't matter! I've got enough for the time being and my clothes will do. I suppose you've been wondering why I'm no longer in uniform. It's a long story and you'll have to wait to hear it later. Tell me, is Uncle Alfred still alive?"

"Of course. And Mary and Jim are living in Prince's Lodge now."

"Whatever made them leave Montreal?"

"That's a long story, too."

The desire to tell him about Jean was overpowering. Hundreds of times, lying awake at night, she had imagined meetings with Neil and planned how she would tell him and what he would say. Now she bit her tongue to keep it quiet.

He smiled at her then, almost in the old way, as his tenseness relaxed. "I haven't asked much about you. You aren't married, are you?"

"Of course not."

"What have you been doing with yourself all this time?"

"I'm working."

"Where, in your father's office?"

"No, in the Shipyards."

"Learn stenography?"

"I learned enough mechanical engineering to design a boat."

"You did *what?*"

"Don't be so surprised. You taught me, didn't you?" She smiled shyly. "I'm supposed to be quite good at it."

"I'll be damned! My young Penny a ship designer!" But he was not taking it seriously. "I saw they were expanding a lot down there. What is it—usual stuff? Buy a few blueprints from the Clydebank and try not to make too many mistakes in following them?"

"I suppose so."

"It must be dull as hell."

"I've done a few small craft of my own."

"You don't happen to be working with the local genius who designed that craft I read about in the paper today?"

"I—in what paper?"

"You know what I'm talking about. Penny—you're blushing! I read the details——" He opened his mouth and stared at her in astonishment. "Jesus Christ! It was *you!*"

She was uncertain whether his reaction showed amazement, jealousy or commendation; possibly a little of all three. While he continued to stare at her the phone rang and she left to answer it.

"Hello, Penny," said the voice on the other end of the wire. "I'm on my way over to see you."

"Oh, Angus, please! Not now. Any other time, but not now."

"I'm not going to stop to explain why, but it's important. Your father had me in his office today and blew the gaff. I've got to see you right away."

"Wait a minute." She rose from the phone and closed the door softly between the living room and the hall. She was frightened, but as usual the state of alarm made her appear outwardly more calm. "You can't come now. Just tell me what he said. That will have to do."

"I can't tell you over the phone. No matter what you say, I'm coming over."

"Wait a moment, Angus." She dropped her voice to a whisper. "Can you hear me now?"

"Yes, but——"

"Neil's here. He's in the living room—now."

Murray swore. She heard the air whistling in his nostrils, and over the wire the sound was more strident than usual. After a moment he said quietly, "I'm still coming. Keep him there till I arrive."

"But that's impossible. He's in trouble."

"Are you telling me?"

"But can't you——"

"No, I can't. I have an idea you may be as much a babe in the woods as he is, and he seems a champion in that class, walking right into your father's house." He paused. "What's the matter, don't you trust me?"

She breathed deeply and repeated his question over in her mind. Did she trust Angus Murray in a situation like this? For that matter, did she trust anyone in the world besides herself? "Yes," she said finally, "I think I do. But I still don't want you here this afternoon."

His voice rose angrily. "You little fool, you don't know what you're talking about. You've been keeping this to yourself so long you've lost all sense of proportion. I spent more than an hour with your father. He means business. There are angles in this case you don't know the first thing about, and maybe Neil doesn't either. If nothing else will hold him there, tell him I just found out your father's in line for a staff job. He ought to know enough about the army to understand it's not a good idea for a youngster to try to buck that lot in wartime."

Penny hesitated, again calculating. "All right, I'll tell him. Will you be long?"

"No more than five minutes," Murray said.

She put the receiver up and sat still on the chair with her hands folded in her lap. She might have been quietly resting there with her own thoughts. Then she walked slowly back to the living room and opened the door. Neil was standing with his legs apart in the middle of the carpet staring at her.

"What's the secret?" he said.

She smiled. "I'm going to make you some tea. Nobody will be home the rest of the afternoon, so we may as well be comfortable."

"To hell with tea!" He blocked her passage to the dining room. "Who was that on the phone, your father?"

"Of course not!"

"I've got to know. Was it important?"

"Yes, Neil, perhaps it was. Do sit down. For heaven's sake," she suddenly exploded at him, "what do you think I'm made of? I want some tea and you need it, too, whether you know it or not."

"Who was it?"

"You're just as stubborn as you ever were. Come on out to the kitchen and I'll tell you. Did you ever meet Major Angus Murray?"

"He was a captain when I saw him last. What's he to you?"

She picked up an old Sheffield tray from a walnut sideboard in the dining room and carried it with her to the kitchen. Then she filled the kettle and set it on the coal stove, opening the draft and lifting the lid to stir the fire.

"What's Angus Murray to do with you?" he persisted.

"He'll be here in a few minutes."

"The hell he will!" Violent alarm flashed across his face and he gripped her arm fiercely. "Penny, what's the idea?"

"He just called up to say he had something important to tell me. I told him to come over. Now get out of my way and let me make the tea. Everything's going to be all right."

"All right!" He dropped her arm. "He was my Battalion M.O."

Neil had not changed as much as she had feared; he was still impetuous, still explosive and oblivious to what other people might be thinking.

While she measured tea in a pot he slumped down on a kitchen chair, straddled it and leaned his folded arms across its back. "I'm sorry, Penny," he said. "You're right. I'm a damned fool. But why does Murray have to come around here just now? I can't stay long. Couldn't he come some other time?"

"He's coming to see you, among other things."

"Oh!"

The quiet, distant sound of his voice saying this single word startled her and she set the teapot down. In the instant his face had grown older, it had drawn into itself and become shrewd and brooding. She felt as though a door had been shut in her face.

"Well, my dear," he said, getting up quietly, "I must be on my way. Apparently I haven't yet learned to be careful enough."

"Meaning?"

"This is where you live. You can ask whom you please to the house. But my plans are too important to be ruined now."

"Neil"–she put her hand on his arm, holding him–"Neil, look at me. I know what I'm doing."

They stood quite still, watching each other, and then his eyes wavered and he turned away as a puzzled expression spread over his face. She knew then that if she chose she had the power in his present condition to control him. Something not even he understood had happened to him since entering the house. The responsibility frightened her.

Again he seemed to be calculating, yet it was evident to her that something beyond himself had made up his mind for him. He pulled in a deep breath like a sigh. "All right," he said, "I don't know what you want, but I'll stay and see."

During the past year Penny had met a large variety of men, some of them important, some officials who held far more power than the public guessed. It had been necessary for her to study them and estimate their aims and the forces that moved them. And now as she studied Neil in the same fashion and heard in her own mind the overtones of his reply, she was relieved. It was not the answer of a weak man, or one with a persecution mania.

The kettle began to hum. She set out cups and saucers on the tray and cakes on a plate, and led him back to the living room. "I've something else to tell you," she said quietly. "Angus Murray wants me to marry him."

"Oh, he does!"

"I've not agreed," she said. "But . . . we both thought you were dead."

"It's all right with me."

"And when you meet him, please——"

"Don't worry, I'll behave. I've nothing against Murray. As a matter of fact, he seemed a decent egg, in spite of his reputation for drink. You certainly know how to pick men, don't you? First me, then——" He fingered some magazines piled on a table. "By the way, this isn't an irrelevant question. How's your father keeping?"

"Much the same, I think."

"Still beastly to you?"

"He never was–to me."

He grunted. "You know bloody well he was–but of course, always the officer and gentleman about it. How's his military career making out?"

"He was transferred from France and he's been a transportation officer here for the past year and a half."

Neil grunted again. "Good job for him. I'm glad somebody remembered he had an expert knowledge of train schedules and clearance papers. Well, he was an expensive officer in France. It's a comfort to know there's at least one megalomaniac brought back here where he can't do any harm."

"Do you really think he's that?"

"Don't you?"

"Of course. I didn't know you saw it, too."

"One learns—especially from personal experience."

"Angus just told me something he thought would interest you. Father's been offered a job overseas again—on the staff, this time."

Neil sniffed. "I can't see that altering anything." Then he added reflectively, "On the other hand . . . I see what Murray means. Has the appointment been confirmed yet?"

"I don't think so."

Neil looked relieved, but he made no further comment. The bell rang, and Murray was in the hall before Penny could reach the door. She met him on the threshold, his coat and hat still on, and they looked quickly into each other's eyes.

Neil was on his feet, aloof and careful. The two men shook hands formally, and then Murray removed his cap and coat, laid them on a chair and sat down. Neil remained standing as he had been, his elbow high on the mantel and his back straight. Murray took a cigarette out of the box Penny handed him, lit it and cleared his throat loudly. Then Penny sat down and there was an awkward silence.

Murray surveyed the burning end of his cigarette, took a few more draws on it and laid it on an ash tray before he lifted his eyes to Neil. "I'm going to be frank, Macrae. I'm sorry you found Penny and I'm sorry you're here now. But since you are here, we might as well make the best of it. Have you been in town long?"

"Does it make any difference?"

"No, not particularly. I'd like to know, just the same."

"About four days."

"Where have you been staying?"

"Why should I tell you that?"

Murray rubbed his nose and grinned wryly. "I suppose it's not easy for you to understand that my general idea is to help you out. God knows I don't want to mix up in your affairs. But I'm afraid so many other people are mixed up in them now you've got to get used to the idea they aren't private any more. The important thing is to understand what the situation is. Then we can figure out what to do."

Neil was obviously angry now. "I didn't come here to talk about my affairs to anyone. I came to see Penny. And if you don't mind my saying so, it's none of your business and I don't want your help."

"Sorry," said Murray. "I don't particularly want to help you, either. I just happen to be mixed up in this, that's all. Colonel Wain has given me a message for you. He asked me to find you and say that he doesn't want you in town. In fact, if you don't get out of Canada immediately, he says he'll prosecute you to the limit."

Penny's indrawn breath was audible, and Murray suddenly felt embarrassed. Neil gave a short laugh, but made no further comment.

"I'm remembering what this means to Penny, you know," Murray said.

Neil folded his arms and stared at the far wall.

"You've had a raw deal, Macrae," Murray said. "Don't misunderstand me, I know more about it than you think. I don't want to interfere with you but it looks as though I can't help it." He stopped to catch Neil's eye. "I wonder if you realize just how high the cards are stacked against you?"

"I think I do."

"Well . . . a man can't come back from oblivion and expect to be ignored. You've got to give some sort of account of yourself."

Neil said nothing, but continued in stubborn silence to lean sideways against the mantel and stare without interest at the map of Jamaica.

"Neil," Penny said, "please don't stand in your own light."

He turned derisively and surveyed first Murray and then Penny through a cloud of blue smoke; then he eyed the end of his cigarette and stared into the fire. Penny looked from Neil to Murray and back again, and she felt an irrelevant awareness of the mystery of human attraction, for both these men who loved her had more in common than they knew. Murray was older; failure had made him wiser and more philosophical, and because he had given up the fight long ago, he was now content to understand life and to leave its control to others. Neil was still defiant, and she guessed that he would always be a harder man than Murray. Yet the two regarded things and people from much the same standpoint, and they valued the same attributes in those they met. She knew they could never become enemies and wondered if Neil realized this, as Murray appeared to have done already.

"Where were you," Neil spoke slowly to Murray, "the night I was supposed to have been killed?"

"In a dressing station near the front line."

"Did you see any of the attack that afternoon?"

"I saw some of the results of it."

"Competent performance, didn't you think?"

"I've seen worse."

"You know bloody well you never saw worse. I'm saying this for Penny's sake, mind you, not for yours. Since it's obvious I wasn't killed that night, I suppose she has a right to know what actually did happen. Our colonel was distressed about the failure of his battalion and accused me of ruining the attack he'd planned so carefully. He put me under guard"—Neil's lips twisted unpleasantly—"as soon as he found out where his orders had landed us—as well as himself. Sometime in the night a German heavy landed on top of the dugout and it was several weeks before I woke up sufficiently to know who I was. By that time I was in a hospital somewhere in England with my thigh in a cast and a pretty case of shell shock. My identity disk had been lost and I was registered as one Private Harry Bowman of an East Lancashire regiment——"

"That's right," Murray interrupted quietly, "the East Lancashires did relieve us that time."

Penny knew Neil was watching her, but she kept her eyes on her own hands clasped in her lap.

"As an alternative to certain court-martial I decided to remain Harry Bowman indefinitely. Apparently the fellow had no near relatives—at least, I never heard from any of them. So it wasn't as difficult as it might have been."

"Quite a coincidence!" Murray said.

"You can believe it or not," Neil said without a change of expression. "I'm talking to Penny."

Penny raised her eyes and Neil looked into the fire again. She felt warm sympathy for the older man. She knew how much he hated involvement with others; he had shown her last night how deeply he had committed himself to her. Now he had to deal with a situation which would be painful for anyone. He would act justly because he could not act otherwise; but underneath everything he did or said would be the sure knowledge that he would either lose her entirely or be forced to see her suffer. She watched his lean face, shadowed by his twisted nose, and knew she had never seen him behaving so true to his own nature as he was at this moment.

"I don't disbelieve you," Murray said thoughtfully. "I think I believe everything you've said. But my personal opinions don't count. You'll have to vindicate yourself to a military court if you intend to stay here and resume your identity."

Penny's eyes shifted back to Neil. If he didn't soon say something positive she felt she could not stand being in the room with him.

"Were you discharged as Private Harry Bowman?" Murray asked.

"Yes."

"Then—surely you realize you can't stay here where everyone knows you?"

"That remains to be seen."

"I wish you wouldn't be so difficult. Military police are searching for you at this moment."

"Are they?" But the information produced an effect, for Neil's face lost its derisive composure. "The colonel's work again?"

Penny rose and left the room, and the two men watched her go. When they were alone, Murray leaned forward and tapped his cigarette into the hearth, then sat back in his chair, waiting.

"It's not easy," Neil said finally, "to speak of Penny's father like this."

"No," Murray said. "But if it helps, I agree with your opinion of him."

Neil's face showed a trace of a smile, and the obstinate expression faded out of it. "For two years," he said, "I've dreamed of the day I'd be able to smash that man. Now I don't want to do it. I don't want to, because all hatred is merely self-hatred. And I don't want Penny mixed up in a scandal."

"Wain doesn't want a scandal any more than you do," Murray said. "He'd let the case stay buried if you'd agree to leave the country for good."

"I'll bet he would!" Neil filled his lungs with tobacco smoke and coughed harshly. Again he seemed to be calculating, and as he did so his wide eyes remained fixed on Murray. "You were born in Nova Scotia, weren't you?"

"Yes, in Cape Breton."

"Then listen. I'm going to tell you something." He hesitated, and his voice softened as he continued. "There's a man I used to know here. He comes from the north shore—Guysborough County. He was born in a house with two rooms set in a barren clearing among the rocks. He never went to school. But he learned how to make boats. When he was a young man he crossed over to Tancook Island and studied how they built those light shore craft over there. He never was particularly good at building, so he went to sea and finally he became a master. He still is one, if he's living. He can take a ship along these coasts in fog so thick he can't see across his own deck, and he can take it inside the ledges because he knows every breaker from Cape North to Cape Sable by its sound. He's been doing that forty years and his keel has never kissed bottom yet. There's no use telling you his name, for you've never heard it. Judged by standards along these shores, he's not even particularly good. There are dozens more can do the same thing."

The black cat rubbed against his legs. "I'll tell you something else. My father was born in a little village in Cape Breton—like yourself, I guess. He never had much schooling but the Bible. But he learned to build ships, too, and he happened to be more than good. He might have been as good as MacKay if he'd lived earlier. But hardly anyone ever heard of him, either. And when he died, it wasn't in Nova Scotia. It was in Boston, where they've long ago forgotten how to breed seamen or build a ship. What I'm trying to say is . . . . this province is my home."

Murray continued to look into the fire.

"So you see," Neil went on, "Wain can't avoid a scandal. He let himself in for it the day he put me under guard in France."

"Then you intend to stay in Halifax?"

"For as long as I please."

"I see." Murray sighed. "I wish I knew what to say. Wain's case sounds pretty formidable." He rubbed out his cigarette and got wearily to his feet. "My presence here is superfluous unless you care to tell me where you stand," he said. "You'll need more than plain evidence. I don't mean to imply the trial will be rigged, but things will just be so much harder for you once Wain's on the staff. At the moment I haven't the slightest idea whether you have any evidence on your side or not. As the case stands, it seems to be this: you disobeyed your colonel's order in open battle. Regardless of whether it was a good order or not, you've made things infinitely worse by living under an assumed name. In the eyes of any court, that would amount to a frank confession of guilt."

Neil laughed harshly. "Do you think Wain could bring himself to murder me?"

"Don't be ridiculous!"

Murray looked exasperated, but Neil kept his ironical grin.

"If a scandal were to break now," Neil said, "he'd not get on the staff if the war lasted a hundred years. His military reputation would stink even if I was convicted. So it would be logical for him to dispose of me at once, don't you think? And what could be easier—seeing I'm supposed to be dead already?"

"For God's sake stop being dramatic!"

Neil shrugged. "I may be able to prove I didn't disobey his orders after all."

"You still have the signed order he sent you?"

"No, it was lost. But another man who was in the line that day read it, and he may remember it verbatim. Moreover, I've at last found out where that particular man is." He threw away the stub of his cigarette and picked another out of the box. "My God—you should have seen the order that damned fool sent! I couldn't have obeyed one part without automatically disobeying the other, and both parts were stupid."

"Is that all your case rests on?"

"Isn't it enough?"

"Two years ago I'd have said it was ample. But you've let things go too long. And there's your assumed name. It amounts to desertion."

"I couldn't have acted sooner. The man who read that message was reported missing just after I was. It was only a month ago—by a chance encounter in a London hotel—that I met someone who told me he'd been wounded and sent back home." His face twisted. "Life wasn't exactly sweet, living in London all that time and trying to fake a Lancashire accent. I was afraid to open my mouth. And to make matters worse I couldn't get any kind of regular job with that damned Bowman's record hanging around my neck. He was a plumber."

"Well." Murray got up and began to move about the room. The close air of the house seemed to be dulling his brain. "They've still got you for desertion. If I'm not mistaken, Wain will have you arrested and charged with that. In which case you mightn't even be allowed to tell your story."

"I'm medically unfit for further service."

"That would be an extenuation if you could prove it. But damn it, Macrae—there's your assumed name!"

"Haven't you heard of cases of loss of memory?"

"Will the hospital in England certify you as a victim of amnesia?"

"I don't know."

Murray drummed the floor with his foot and cleared his throat. "I hate to say this, but there seems to me only one thing to do. You and Wain will have to agree to compromise. The case can be explained away if you both co-operate in the explaining."

Neil folded his arms. "That's impossible," he said.

"Why is it? I'm sure Wain would agree."

"But I wouldn't. He's blackened my name all over the province to save his own reputation. I intend to live in Canada, Murray. I haven't the slightest intention of emigrating to the States or stewing in my own juice in England. It's going to hurt Penny. It's likely to hurt several other people, but there's no other way. If Wain tries to cover up that day's business now, people will only say he's used his influence to whitewash me. Don't forget—I happen to be his nephew, too."

Penny announced her approach from the kitchen by rattling the dishes on the tray she carried, and Murray with instinctive politeness held the door open for her. He noticed that her hands were unsteady as she set the tray on the table. Her eyes met his, dumbly interrogative, and a pang of loneliness went through him. He helped her set out the cups and saucers on the table.

"We're in need of tea," he said with a quiet smile. "I think everything is going to be all right."

Neil remained motionless in Wain's long chair as she poured milk into the three cups and picked up the teapot. "Do you want to tell me, Neil?"

He said nothing and looked the other way.

"Perhaps it will be easier if you get the story from me," Murray said.

Neil got to his feet, staring at the stream of pouring tea. "I'm leaving now," he said. "Penny, will you come to the door with me?"

She followed him into the hall and watched him pick up his worn overcoat and put it on. He tried to grin at her, but the attempt collapsed when he saw the tears in her eyes. The fingers of one of his hands reached out to caress the lock of white hair, and then both arms went around her. "I like it," he murmured. "It's what that scrubby brown head of yours always needed."

"It's not scrubby."

"Never mind, it's brown—a dull color."

"Neil, will you be gone long this time?"

"No, this time I promise I won't." His hands slid along her back. "God—if you knew how you feel to me! Be honest—do you really want to see me again?"

Her only response was the searching of her fingers along the line of his hair behind his head. This hard, unbreakable substance in him! He had always had it and never would lose it, not even if it crushed him and everyone in the world he loved.

He released her and saw that she was crying, and his eyes passing over her body noticed for the first time the dress she was wearing. "For God's sake," he said, "that outfit looks like hell on you!"

"All right, I won't wear it any more." She smiled and dried her eyes. "Let me know this time where you are?"

"Tomorrow," he said. "I promise."

He kissed her quickly and closed the door behind him with a slam, and she heard the rattle of his heels as he hurried down the steps.

When she went back to the living room she found Murray holding a cup of tea ready poured for her, but she disregarded it and sat down on the chesterfield with her hands clasped so hard their knuckles turned white. She sat there staring into the fire. She wished Jean were here. She wished it were tomorrow.

"Angus," she said, "has he really got a chance?"

"I think so."

"What can I do?"

"I don't think you need do anything." Murray seemed to be speaking to himself. "That boy's not so rash as you think. He told me a lot, but there wasn't a word I could have used against him if I'd wanted to."

Nine-thirty P.M. A growing moon, pale as the inside of an oyster shell, hung over the forests and harbors of Nova Scotia, and in this nocturnal glimmer the edges of the province were bounded by a wavering flicker of grayish white, where the sea broke over the rocks of the coast. On all the solitary points thrusting out into the Atlantic, into the Fundy or the Gulf of St. Lawrence, lighthouses winked or gleamed like fixed stars. Such fishing boats and small craft as still worked after dark were now black shadows rising and falling to the lift of the groundswell as they glided home to their village coves. The highways were empty and dark, and the windows of the farmhouses gave no light but that reflected from the moon. In the north of the province, around the Sydneys, pouring slag flared against the sky and turned the harbor into a pool of ruddy fire, while the blast furnaces trembled under the pressure of armament production. In all other parts of Nova Scotia, silence gripped the land like a tangible force, for in only two of its counties was there the noise of a great city or factory, or the rush of traffic over a road.

In Halifax that night, all work at the docks had ceased. A few ships lay in the Stream, and in the Basin a great cluster of freighters pulled at their anchor chains as the incoming tide swung them. Only a few streets had bound over much life from the day. The rest were becoming empty and dark, splashed only at corners by the bluish flicker of arc lamps, and in some sections the few pedestrians abroad had to walk carefully to avoid stumbling on the uneven surface of the sidewalks.

The North End had the lifeless, brooding atmosphere common to districts where most of the inhabitants are manual workers who rise and go to bed early, whose only relaxation is to sit on doorsteps in summer and in winter about a kitchen stove. It was an extensive area, spreading fanwise from the northerly slopes of the Citadel to the Narrows and Richmond Bluff, overlooking Bedford Basin. The wooden houses crowded each other like packing boxes left out in the weather for years. And in the far North End, beyond the Shipyards at the Narrows, a few streets plunged at headlong angles to the wooden jetties that still survived in that part of the waterfront. On the steepest of these streets, in the ground floor of a chocolate-colored frame house, Big Alec MacKenzie lived with his wife, his daughter, and his two growing boys.

The dinner dishes were washed and the dish cloths hung against the copper boiler to dry. Alec was seated on a wooden chair beside the kitchen table with his shirt open at the neck, his shoes off, and his feet in heavy army socks that made them look like enormous khaki sponges. A glass containing a mixture of rum and water was half-hidden in one of his hands, but he seemed to have forgotten it was there, for he had been sitting all of ten minutes without moving. The stove in the corner was burning high and all the windows were shut. The hot air of the room had an odor of dishwater and cabbage and the fumes of Alec's pipe. Like most poor folk in northern countries, the MacKenzies hoarded what warmth they had. The plastered walls of the kitchen were bare except for a large calendar donated by a grocery store. They were stained and yellow as naphtha in the glare of the unshaded lamp which stood in the center of the table, giving Alec light to read his paper and enabling Annie, his wife, to see the socks she was knitting.

Although Alec's huge frame was still, relaxed by a day's work and quiet in its very nature, it was possible to detect a vague restlessness, an uneasy sense of insecurity and disharmony, in the lines of his face. There was no evident cause for this; both he and his wife had reason to feel satisfied with the past year. Alec's wounds had been only serious enough to secure his discharge from the army, and his new job at Wain's was bringing him good money for the first time in his life. His two boys were at school, and his grown daughter, Norah, had learned to be a typist and was now earning, too. Later than usual, Alec's family had begun to follow the traditional pattern of Nova Scotia Highlanders. They had consciously given up the land and the fisheries for a life in the towns.

Yet Alec was missing things he had never thought about before: shadows traveling the steep hills of the Cape Breton shoreline; pockets of mist white as fleece in the sunshine along the braes opposite Boulardarie; a feeling that time did not matter much, a sense that when a man planted a field or built a boat he did so to meet a season and not a time-table; a habit of rising with the sun instead of an Ingersoll alarm clock. In an indefinite way, Alec realized that he and his wife were at the close of an era and their children were entering a new one.

His eldest son came in from the parlor where he had been finishing his home work and sat down by the stove. Norman was a tall, high-shouldered boy of fifteen, with red hair and sandy skin. "Do you want coal up from the cellar, Father?" he said.

Alec turned slowly and looked at an exercise book and pencil in the boy's hands. "You keep on with the mathematics. That's more important than coal."

"I've finished. I don't know why I find it easy, but it never seems to take any time. Next term we're starting physics. That may be harder."

"Indeed!"

"Mr. Cross says if I keep on being able to do maths I may become a scientist." He came over with his books and set them on the table. Then he opened a scribbler and displayed a page of his work. The geometrical figures were as neat as a blueprint. "Look, Father—I'll show you. It's as simple! One thing leads right into another. You always know just where you are with it."

He began explaining the problem he had solved, and his father tried painfully to follow him. Finally Alec shook his head. "It must take a terrible smart man to be understanding things like that. I remember a boat-builder back in Cape Breton. He could plan a real big boat all the way from the truck to the kelson and do it all on paper. He never used a model at all. Now me, I have to see a thing. And I can't see the mathematics."

"It's just a kind of knack." Norman put the book aside quickly for fear his father would think he were boasting. His voice had lost its native Gaelic accent; Halifax had flattened it out. "I wish I could remember things in history as well."

Alec looked more interested. "Now that would be something I could understand. You were telling me the other night about them Romans and some of the things they used to do then, and I got to thinking, and it was easy to see why they did them. People don't seem to change much, no matter where they are. And I guess they always had corporals, even in the old days."

Norman closed his books and went down the rough wooden stairs to the basement where he could be heard shoveling coal into a scuttle. Alec took a sip of the rum and water and went back to reading the paper, which he did slowly, following the lines of print with his thumb and index finger. His wife rocked back and forth in her chair, silent, heavy and absorbed, her eyes fixed on her knitting. Presently Norman came up with the coal and set it beside the stove, looked around and asked his father if there were any more chores. Then he kissed his mother good night, shook hands with Alec and went off to join his younger brother in the double bed they shared. Norah had not come home yet; she had gone to the movies with a soldier from the garrison who was courting her.

"Well," Alec said after many minutes, "it's a fine thing coming to Halifax for the children. Think what could have happened to Norman without the education."

"Indeed!" Annie said.

After this there were no sounds from the room except the draft in the stove and the clicking of the knitting needles and the occasional creak of a board over their heads as the family of Newfoundlanders who lived in the upper flat moved over the floor.

The room was still silent when Neil Macrae found the house in the darkness and knocked on the door of the storm porch.

That night Geoffrey Wain telephoned home to say that he would be working until morning, making preparations for a sudden influx of troops from the west. He then presented himself at Evelyn Phillips' flat in the North End and informed her he intended to spend the night.

This was something he had never done before. Although there was a double bed in Evelyn's bedroom she had never expected him to stay in it longer than an hour or two, and Wain had never given any indication that he considered this length of time insufficient. Indeed he had never, in the strict sense of the word, slept with any woman but his wife. There was something repugnant to him in the idea of lying unconscious and exposed to others, especially to a person he considered his inferior.

He owned nothing in the flat. He had given Evelyn the necessary money to furnish the rooms, but had refrained from offering any suggestions as to the manner in which it was to be done. He felt that if he betrayed a personal interest in her taste, either in clothes or furniture, it would be an admission that he regarded her place as a home of his own, as well as an invitation to her to consider that their present arrangement might become permanent. And so the appointments of the flat were cheap and gaudy, although the offensive details were numerous enough to cancel out their individual powers of disturbing him.

It was part of Wain's pleasure to allow Evelyn to manage the initial stages of their meetings according to her own desires, for her vulgarity and childishness sometimes enabled him to feel that in her presence he had adopted a new personality. Now he sat in her only armchair, smoking a cigar and waiting for her to emerge from the bedroom. For the moment he was able to consign the resurrection of Neil Macrae to a remote corner of his mind. Its influence was not sufficient to spoil his anticipation of pleasure, but it was at the same time enough to upset his customary feeling of security. And so he comforted himself with the reflection that by the time the war ended, familiar conventions would be broken down entirely, and a new age would be at hand of power and vulgarity without limitation, in which the prizes would not be won by the qualified but by the cunning and the unscrupulous. It would be an age which would accept most of the values Evelyn held now. It would change everything, and it would soon be here. He recognized its approach without regret and without approval.

Evelyn came from the bedroom, wearing a silk kimono tight about the waist and hips and open at the neck. With what she considered a whorish candor, she had reworked the lines of this garment so that it cupped her breasts separately, pointing them in such a manner that his eyes could rest on no other part of her person. Her black hair was brushed sleekly away from her forehead and she had secured it by a blue ribbon knotted into a wide bow on the top of her head. This was Evelyn's touch—the little girl's ribbon and the accentuated, pear-shaped breasts. She lay down on the davenport in front of the fire and half closed her eyes, looking at Wain from under her lashes. And Wain watched her. She was so small, so delicate, yet was capable of such tensity of body and fixity of expression, of such smoldering, expanding but yielding hatred! An odor of perfume, cheap and cloying, pervaded the room as he moved towards her.

That night in Prince's Lodge after Jean had been put to bed, Jim and Mary Fraser sat before the fire and talked. The birch logs crackled and shadows plunged and flickered along the white wainscoting of their living room, and in the far corners the floor was cold. The shutters were open and the water of the Basin was burnished by the moon, while stars rode on the rim of the hills along the horizon.

"Nothing matters in the world but chance," Jim was saying. "I can't remember a single thing that ever happened to me that wasn't an accident."

"You mean to say that was why you married me?"

"That was because you had a rich father, which was an accident so far as you were concerned." He tapped his game leg. "Look at this—if I hadn't wanted that pipeful of tobacco and picked that particular moment to cross a line of fire, a Boer never would have hit it. Look at the way Jean came into this house."

Mary frowned. "Do you think Angus Murray would make a good husband for Penny? He seems so much older."

"Could be worse. Let's see—he's about as much older than Penny as I'm older than you."

"Oh, Jim! You're younger than he is right now."

Jim laughed and stretched his arms. "What was Geoffrey like when he was young?"

"It's funny, I can't remember. He's always seemed the same age."

"What kick does he get out of life, anyway? Well, I suppose Penny could have a worse father. At least he leaves her alone. My dear, you have a dreadful family."

"Some of us aren't so bad."

"That's just another accident." He got to his feet and yawned again, kicked a log deeper into the hearth and set the screen in front of it. "We have a rendezvous in bed, remember? That's something else I've never been able to understand—why I like to go to bed with a woman who has aunts and uncles and brothers like yours." He pulled her to her feet and put a heavy arm about her thin shoulders, and after a feeble show of resistance she smiled at him.

"We need sleep," she said. "We've got to get up for that early train into town."

"That's why you need me first," he said.

A small troop of cavalry had been detailed to patrol the streets to watch for windows emitting light. There was no good reason for this order except the uneasy state of the official mind, which had resigned itself to the strategic failure of Passchendaele and another winter of war. A handful of men on horses went through the dark streets at a slow trot and occasionally one of them blew a bugle.

Maria Wain heard the bugle and the trotting horses and opened her shutters to look out. The troop halted and a man got off his horse, crossed the sidewalk and rang her door bell. When they had gone, Alfred Wain, asleep in his armchair before the fire, stirred and sniffed. "Maria, what was that?"

"Soldiers. They said we had a light showing."

"Humbug!" he said, and closed his eyes again.

An hour later, Penelope and Roddie Wain heard the horses' feet and Roddie was careful to turn out his bedroom light before peering out. He looked down on the caps and shoulders of the horsemen trotting past and saw the glint of moonlight on the bugle of the boy riding beside the leader. After they had passed, he came downstairs with wide eyes to find his sister.

Penelope, tired and worried and unable to sleep herself, told him to go back to bed; then, discovering that he would be certain not to sleep in any case, she made him produce his schoolbooks and went over his lessons one by one until they were all checked and Roddie was heavy-eyed. She then went up to his bedroom and tucked him in and sat on the edge of his bed listening while he talked about the war. He could hardly remember when it had begun, but he horrified her with his precise and detailed knowledge of it. He could repeat from memory the tonnage and gunnage of every vessel in the navy and was looking forward to six years from now when he would be old enough to enlist. She had noticed that every one of his school scribblers had a picture of a soldier or a sailor on the cover, or a British bulldog standing on a white ensign draped over the stern of a battleship while a Canadian beaver crouched in the corner and sharpened its teeth. As she heard him talk, she marveled at the skill of the propagandists. Living in a great nation virtually guaranteed by the United States, the present crop of publicists seemed determined to convince Canadians that their happiness would be lost forever if they should aspire to anything higher than a position in the butler's pantry of the British Empire.

Roddie finally showed signs of sleepiness and she left him alone. The house was still now, so still she could hear in every room the ticking of its many clocks, but over everything seemed to throb the overtones of Neil's voice.

All that night the streets of Halifax remained dark and empty of traffic, and the whole town, this clearing in a forest fronting the sea, was utterly silent. Yet a panorama of history, vital and in the main unperceived, flowed through the minds of the seventy thousand people who at that moment inhabited the region marked on the map as Halifax peninsula.

In beds down the long wards of military hospitals lay hundreds of Canadians, some suffering, some bored, some asleep. They had gone to France from the prairies and the west coast, from Ontario and Quebec and the

Maritimes, and soon they were going to be discharged back to the cities and the solitudes. Just as soon as they were well enough to exist without help they would be going home. But the war had altered the vision of them all, breaking some and healing the gashes it had made in others by enlarging their consciousness. They could never be the same again, nor could the land they had returned to inhabit.

On the ships anchored in Bedford Basin, men were talking in most of the languages of the Indo-European and Slavonic systems, playing cards and telling each other how it was in the places thousands of miles away from which they had come. Here in Bedford Basin, if thought had any meaning at all, Stockholm and Haugesund existed, and Rotterdam, Antwerp, Lisbon, Genoa, Marseilles, Odessa and Cape Town. There were Lascars from Calcutta and Bombay, Latin Americans from Rio and Montevideo, Yankees from Boston, sailors from all the ports and havens of England. They were on ships anchored in an indentation of the coast of Nova Scotia, and they knew that one in every five of the ships was doomed to destruction. They wished they were in a port where there were lights and music and women, where a man could raise a thirst and forget the unreality of his skill; they wished they were almost any place in the world except here, bounded by the stars and the empty, inviolate North American forest surrounding them.

In the lighted offices of the Dockyard and the stately rooms of Admiralty House, and in various unnamed buildings along the waterfront, uniformed men on night duty were at work, tabulating orders and registering information. The official wireless crackled incessantly, and N.C.O. messengers came and went from the wireless room, delivering slips of paper to various officers. Incoming messages were read and filed, and notes of the movements of enemy submarines were emendated in the light of later knowledge. Intelligence knew that a German submarine had just stolen out of the Bay of Biscay and was heading for Hell's Hole, that another was lying on the bottom near Queenstown waiting for the destroyers to go away, that still another was moving westward towards the shipping lane that passed Cape Race. They knew that a small British squadron was advancing into the Atlantic to meet a convoy at a secret rendezvous. The information was noted, tables and charts were checked and positions of shipping revised; minor alterations in projected courses were planned.

And in the consciousness of thousands of the generality of citizens who were still awake there lurked as their constant companion a brooding anxiety they rarely uttered, for they pictured sons, brothers, husbands, fathers, sweethearts somewhere in the lines about Arras or Ypres, and yet all were thankful that they were still able to be worried and that another day had passed without the receipt of a private letter from His Majesty.

The war had changed these people, too, but only slightly; it had merely splashed over their lives a little of the hatreds and miseries of the great cities, for quite unwittingly they lived tonight as they had done for years, with their thoughts and actions mainly determined by the habits they had inherited from their forefathers, from the Loyalists who had come here generations ago from the United States because they preferred King George to the new freedom, from the English who had settled in Halifax when their time of service in the garrison was up, from the Irish who had escaped the potato famine seventy years ago, from the Highlanders who had lost their clans at Culloden. They lived in Halifax in an anomalous permanency, still tied to England, suffering when she did but rarely partaking of her prosperities, unreconciled to being Americans or even Canadians, content for the moment to let their status drift with events, convinced that in being Nova Scotians they possessed a peculiar cause for satisfaction, an excellence which no one had ever troubled to define because no one outside the province believed it existed, and everyone on the inside took it for granted.

In Big Alec's kitchen, after Annie had gone to bed and left Neil Macrae alone with her husband, the two men talked quietly together. Neil's manner was calm, and Alec's face, after recovering from a momentary astonishment when he saw that Neil was alive, had resumed its former immobility. If he realized that helping Neil might cost him his job at Wain's, he gave no indication of it by expression or words.

"This is my situation, then," Neil said. "I shall probably have to call on you to testify for me. Would you do that?"

Alec's heavy face was serious, but he did not try to avoid the issue. He sat perfectly still with his knees apart and a hand spread open on his thigh. The other hand still clutched a half-empty glass. "You would be meaning that message Colonel Wain gave me that day?" he said.

"Yes." Neil looked directly at him. "I know it's asking a lot. It may mean you'll lose your job."

"That's as may be."

This was what he had returned home to get. He had counted on Alec's honesty and clannishness to compel him to speak the truth. It had been his great advantage, and if Alec had shown any hesitation he had been prepared to play on his character with all the force he could bring to bear. But besides this, there was a still more subtle interplay of emotion in Neil's mind. Alec and he stemmed from the same roots; now it was almost as if Alec were about to help him vindicate his father for years of humiliation suffered at the hands of the Wains, as though the fundamental strains in his own nature were for once to be successful over the environment which had previously thwarted them.

This momentary feeling of triumph disappeared as quickly as it had arisen, leaving him cold again, and calculating. "Alec, we've got to be precise about this. Do you remember how long you were with Colonel Wain that afternoon? How long was it between zero and the time he handed you that message to take up to the front?"

"That would be about four hours. It would be maybe four hours exactly."

"And all that time the colonel had no contact with the rest of the battalion?"

"Not quite all that time. But for about three hours he didn't know where in hell you were."

"So he sent you forward as a runner with an order? When you reached the front line you found I was the senior officer surviving and you gave me the message?"

Alec nodded.

"I read it and said it was contradictory. Then, before putting my interpretation of it into effect, I ordered you to commit the message to memory—is that right?"

Alec nodded again.

"Now—can you still swear to its exact reading?"

Neil leaned forward in his chair while Alec took a swallow of the rum, and thought slowly. His throat muscles contracted as the rum passed through to the stomach. Then he nodded. "I can swear. The order went this way: 'Establish contact with Imperial brigade on the right, then attack second objective immediately.' That would have been the hill right in front of us." Alec breathed heavily. "My God, but that was a bad day for all of us. After I put that message to memory you sent me back with a reply. I didn't read the reply but it made Colonel Wain awful angry when *he* read it."

Neil let the breath slowly pour out through his clenched teeth as he got up to ease the strain of waiting to hear his sentence pronounced. Now that Alec had finally spoken, the whole matter seemed to have lost stature and become almost trivial. And yet the scene of that afternoon had recurred to Neil's mind so often that every detail of it had seared itself into his consciousness. Now it recurred again, but this time the events seemed slighter, as though they had lost their heat. His sensation was similar to that of a man reading a newspaper years after its printing.

He saw himself crouching in a ditch tired and sweating, and then Alec appearing covered with mud and handing him the message. He read it and saw at once it could not be executed in its entirety. Owing to the direction of advance there was at that moment no Imperial brigade on the right. The flank was in the air. The Imperials could be seen firing from a ridge a quarter of a mile to the rear and nearly six hundred yards to the right. To advance directly on the second objective, as Wain was ordering, would have increased the gap on the right flank to almost a mile. On the other hand, to establish contact with the English brigade involved a withdrawal on the diagonal. Withdrawal meant the failure of the day's operation; but advance meant probable annihilation and the certainty of a successful enemy counterattack.

This was the situation. He knew it and Wain didn't. Whoever had planned the attack had failed to take into account the nature of the terrain, for the general line of advance had been along two sides of a gentle slope, the Canadians on the left and the English on the right, and in the course of action they had lost touch. The slope had divided them further, and the resistance had been much more severe than the staff had anticipated. The whole plan of the attack was faulty, and no front-line officers were to blame. Neither Neil nor anyone else had known at the time that the suggestion for this attack had been Wain's and that his superiors had reluctantly agreed to try it out.

When the day's operation was over and the battalion had returned to its original jumping-off position, someone had to be blamed for such a useless failure. No one could have been more aware of this than Wain himself. When Big Alec brought him Neil's message that he was retiring, his own ignorance of the true position of his men made it impossible for him to realize that to establish contact with the Imperials involved retirement. All he could see was disgrace and failure, and it was easier to blame someone else than to admit that the whole operation had been rash and ill-prepared. For a time he was convinced that a subordinate had ruined his plans by deliberate disobedience; the fact that the subordinate happened to be a nephew whom he had always hated did not improve his disposition or his judgment.

Yet on that smoky day, Wain's moods altered fast. By the time he had reached the front line and had seen for himself the extent of the casualties and heard the men cursing as they crouched under a violent counter-bombardment, his anger disappeared and his fright amounted to panic. He had visions of dismissal for incompetence. A hasty roll-call was taken and showed that he had already lost nearly all his officers. Darkness fell and he was alone in a dugout with the earth shaking around him, and war was now neither a game nor a profession, but something he couldn't control or understand.

It was only then that he had ordered Neil's arrest. Because the counter-bombardment was so severe, the prisoner had been placed in a dugout in the second line, under guard. When the news arrived the next day that his nephew had been killed, Wain hardly knew whether to be glad or sorry. Neil had admitted to him that he no longer had the written order; he had passed it on to the officer of the next platoon, and this officer was now lying dead in the German lines. With Neil dead, Wain had no chance of shifting the blame and proving to his superiors it was not his.

As the tangled events of that day passed through Neil's mind it seemed to him that he had become two persons, himself and his uncle Geoffrey Wain. He had re-examined the case so often that he had been able to see it from Wain's point of view as clearly as from his own. And now he was weary of it. He was impatient to have it settled. It no longer had meaning. It bored him.

He resumed his seat and looked at Big Alec again. "Did the colonel ever refer to the business again—after he thought I was dead?"

"No," Alec reflected. "But he seemed to be remembering it."

"I bet he did. What about yourself? I heard you'd been taken prisoner. That's why I never tried to get in touch with you before this."

Alec smiled shyly. "I was, but it was not for very long. I had to hit a German fella awful hard one night. I have often wondered what happened to him."

"I thought you'd been wounded?"

"Indeed I was. But it was a bullet. I was hit on my way back to our own lines."

Conversation lagged between them and Neil found himself trying to resist the conviction that chance and preposterous accident had complete control of a man's life. It had been an accident that Alec had given him the message in the first place, an accident that the shell had blown up the dugout where Wain had confined him, an accident that at the very moment he had first tried to contact Alec the big man was supposed to be a prisoner of war. The final chance had occurred a month ago when he had stepped into the lobby of the Regent Palace Hotel in London to avoid a shower of rain and had run into the soldier on leave who told him that Alec was not only alive but back in Canada.

And yet not even this evidence was able to convince him that his life's continuance was as problematic as a fly's. Rather it seemed the final degradation of war that it could make a man's life appear so.

Angus Murray was drunk. The walls of the room, the tables and chairs and the picture of the dead duck surged like the sea, flowing against his eyeballs and ebbing away with a motion so steady it destroyed everything but his thoughts, and from these it removed the pain. Whenever he said anything, his words seemed to stand like an entity in the air until someone grasped them and removed their existence. The place was dirty, and three hours ago Murray had been able to smell it.

Across from him, sitting sideways on the edge of a wooden chair with one fleshy arm leaning on the table, was a woman his own age.

"Why the hell don't you fix this place up, Mamie?" Only he knew how drunk he was. "It looks something awful."

"I do all right. Maybe I fix it up and then the cops'll only have me out of it."

"That's not the right attitude, not the right attitude. You ought to keep a home here."

"These fellas that come in off the ships, they don't know any better."

"You don't like us, Mamie—or do you?"

"Why should I like these fellas?"

Murray sighed and leaned back into such a sprawl that the woman got up to steady his balance, but with an easy swing forward he recovered himself. "Where did you say you come from, Mamie?"

"What's it to you where I come from?"

"I'm not one that just asks."

Her face softened a trifle, but she got it back to its usual vacancy with what looked like a flurry of embarrassment. "You don't really want to know, do you?"

"Of course."

"Aw, go back to your wife, Major. She'll talk about herself."

He laughed soundlessly, shaking his head, and his bloodshot eyes blurred with moisture. "Thought you'd know better, thought a woman like you'd know a man better than that."

"Why, ain't you?"

"Married? Don't make me laugh!"

"You were once, though. That's something I always know about a man."

"What's the matter—touchy about your professional reputation? Look at me! Think any woman'd want to marry me?"

"Holy Mary, I guess you're speaking the truth for once."

"All right. Now tell me."

"Why?"

"I asked you, didn't I?"

"There's nothing about me a man like you would want to know. I guess I've made some money lately, that's all." She laid her hand over his, but his senses were so deadened he did not feel it. "Why do you come around here, Major?"

"Hell, you ought to know."

"You don't get anything out of it. Those girls of mine, they aren't any good. The trouble is they don't seem to care. They don't like it themselves. Sometimes, maybe a nice young fella comes along and one of them—Major, they don't give a man anything."

"Lord, we have toiled all night and caught nothing—that's more than most whorehouses can tell their customers."

She looked annoyed. "You haven't got any need to get to talking that way. What's the matter with you educated fellas, anyway? Why can't you leave things the way they are?"

"Though I speak with the tongues of men and of angels and have not charity"—his voice broke—"Mamie, you're a good girl. You must have been born that way. You don't mean anyone any harm. You just want us all to be one big happy family. Were you born here, Mamie?"

"I told you."

"I've forgotten. And then you went away to the Boston States, eh?"

"Shut up, can't you?"

"And then some fella you thought was pretty good ran out on you and back you came. Just like me. What do you think of this country, Mamie? Everyone comes and goes around here, eh? So, like the wanderer, the sun gone down, darkness be over me, my rest a stone—that's your Nova Scotian, if you've the eye to see it. Wanderers. Looking all over the continent for a future. But they always come back. That's the point to remember, they always come back to the roots, like you and me. When you were a girl you had the Gaelic, didn't you?"

"What are you talking about? I'm Irish!"

"What's the difference? From the lone sheiling in the misty island, mountains divide us and a waste of seas——"

"How's your hand, Major? Better now it's out of a splint?"

He lifted his right hand and surveyed it as it swam before his eyes, and the fingers moved stiffly as he worked the muscles.

"It's looking just fine," she said.

"Do you really care what it looks like?"

"Of course I do."

"The last operation it did was on an eye. Couldn't have done that without two hands. The trouble with this war, it's become too natural. We're all getting used to it. What I say——"

"A fine, clever man like you! You ought to have a wife and children."

"Know any good women, Mamie?"

"Sure, of course I do."

"No, you and me are alike. We wanted something different every time. You might as well admit it, Mamie. When you were a girl you were curious about every man you saw. You wanted to see what he'd be like, didn't you? Well, look at us now. You run a whorehouse and I come to it."

She got up and put an arm about his shoulders, lifting him to his feet. He stood upright with ease and watched her, his long body swaying but his feet in perfect balance, his whole face distorted by a vague and senseless grin. "What keeps you going, Mamie? Money?"

"Well, I guess money's something you know where you are with. I do all right, I tell you." She looked away from him and added sullenly, "I got a couple of kids. They're living in the country, too."

"That's the thing to do with them! Make everyone live in the country and there won't be any more of these goddam wars. Or maybe there won't." He looked at his hands again. "Listen, Mamie, this war hasn't finished me yet. I can still operate, understand? I've got a natural pair of hands that can do almost anything I tell them. Not original, mind you, but once I see a demonstration I can do it. Sometimes better than the demonstrator. Take a mastoid, for instance—a good radical mastoid. I can——"

"Aw, Major, go on home. What do you have to tell me all this for?"

"Who in God's name else have I got to tell it to? One of your girls? One of those morons that hang around the hotel and talk about a war they've never seen? You know it's all a swindle, don't you?"

"I don't know what you're talking about."

"You know there's no resurrection from the dead, don't you? Ever since the first Easter, if a man's dead he's stayed dead, hasn't he? All right. A man falls in love with a girl. He dies. The girl nearly dies with grief but she gets over it, she gets mended again somehow and now she's a young woman with a mind that's old—old, Mamie, like mine, but with a young body. She's too old for any of the kids her own age. She's what I want, isn't she? She's someone I can marry without it being a dirty joke, isn't she? Good

Christ, if we have to live through all this misery, why can't a young girl marry a man old enough to show her the road? Someone old enough to appreciate what her youth is worth?"

"Major, you're talking too loud. Please now—I don't want to have any trouble. You used to be one of the steady ones. You never used to get this way on me."

"I've seen a man that's risen from the dead."

"Get out—please!"

"But that's not the part that really matters. Maybe—maybe I've got to send him away again, see? Maybe I've got to make him a wanderer. Jesus Christ, he may turn into a second edition of myself. Only he won't have the right kind of toughness, he won't be able to take it. People like you and me—we've got our pride. We can see what smashes us, so it can never smash us really. *Cogito, ergo sum!*"

He put an arm about her waist and guided her toward the stairway leading up to the rooms of the second floor. "When the barbarians entered the empire they came gradually and no one believed they would really succeed. First one province, then another, one city and then another, and people always said there were plenty of other cities left to take the place of the lost ones. But all the dykes gave way in the end, Mamie. These big cities, these places like Boston you thought was so fine—watch them empty themselves when the invasions come! Watch the big hotels grow cobwebs. Watch the great liners disappear from the seas. Then there'll be fishing boats in Halifax, nothing but fishing boats. And the women of Lunenburg and Cape Breton will bring up the looms from the cellars!"

She shook free and watched him closely. And then she smiled, and the wrinkles appeared suddenly about her eyes, and for the first time that evening her face looked kindly, as it must have once when she was a generous and pretty girl.

"Come on up with me, then. You poor fellow—I'll spend the night with you. When I like a man I can make him forget a lot of things. You'd be surprised."

"No," he said.

"Come on." Her voice was almost eager. "I want you."

"It's too close in here. It smells."

She shrugged her shoulders and crossed the room to the hat rack. Her voice was business-like when she spoke again. "Then let me help you on with your coat. It's getting cold out—a lot colder than you think." But her softened mood still remained underneath the professional exterior, for she laughed and said in a strange voice, "I can still remember my old dad on winter nights the way he used to come in from the barn with his whiskers frozen. 'Mamie,' he'd say, 'it's cold enough to freeze something mighty important off a brass monkey.' That was his little joke."

Murray reeled towards the door. "It's been a devil of a night, Mamie, but I guess it wasn't your fault. How much do I owe you?"

"Forget it, you don't owe me anything. Hell, you were too drunk to run up any bill tonight."

When Murray reached his room in the hotel his head was clearing. He sat down and leaned over the arm of his easy chair, fighting back the nausea as his eyes ran along the backs of the books which were always a part of his belongings. There were some ninety volumes on medicine in the finest bindings he had been able to obtain, ranging from a worn Gray's *Anatomy* to the latest publications in his own specialty. But these did not interest him as much as the ones which were almost falling apart from use, the books he had acquired at college, which were always news to him. Years ago they had enabled him to fancy himself a part of a wonderful and enormous heritage, but now their titles made a poignant ring in his mind like the remembrance of a bell heard in childhood from a cathedral which the years of a technical era had blindly emptied.

Plato's *Republic*, the *Nicomachaean Ethics*, Rashdall's *Theory of Good and Evil*, Horace and Catullus, Thucydides, Shakespeare and Milton—these and the others crowded through his vision as he hung wearily over the arm of his chair, a man grown suddenly old, with the bar of hope broken in his brain. "I'm glad I know about them," he said to himself. "In spite of everything, I'm glad of that."

"So you knew my father!" Neil was saying an hour later. "Alec, you're almost the only person I've met in years who did know him."

"When he went away from Cape Breton we soon heard he was doing fine. First it was Halifax and then we heard it was Boston. I remember a rich man came up to South Gut St. Ann's with his yacht and asked did John Macrae come from this village. And Hector Gillies—that was Donald's son that used to have the gristmill on the Margaree road—he went to Boston and worked as a joiner there, and he heard about John Macrae, too. Your father could handle his tools light and easy, just like a woman handles a needle."

There was silence between them and an alarm clock over the stove ticked clamorously.

"When this trouble with me is over," Neil said, "what about your chances of another job in Halifax?"

"Indeed, I do not know."

"You still have your land in Cape Breton?"

"Yes, but there's terrible poor prices on fish."

"Why the devil should a man like Geoffrey Wain inherit the earth?" Neil's eyes widened with excitement again. "It's firms like his that have ruined the fishermen in the province. I'd like to see——"

Alec laid a huge hand on his wrist and smiled. "Now, Mr. Macrae, you're not a fisherman yourself and you don't have to worry about the prices. And I do not think it pays to have ideas like that, moreover. It makes it harder. I do not understand very much, but I always have known what it is I have to do next, and if I lose the job at Wain's there will be another one somewhere else. We are told that the Lord will provide, and there would be no use whatever in going to church if a man cannot believe a thing as easy as that."

"That's all very well. But the Lord also helps those that help themselves."

Alec got slowly to his feet. "You must sleep here tonight, Mr. Macrae. Your father has slept with us many a time at home."

Neil felt restless and suddenly ill-at-ease. "Alec, I'm afraid I'm only bringing trouble into your house. I'm terribly sorry."

"Indeed, it's not yourself that would be bringing the trouble but the trouble that would be finding its own way. Your father was one of our own people. And there would be no use in arguing against a thing like that, whatever. So you don't have to explain and you don't have to be thanking me, either."

He led the way to a prim little room he called the parlor. Among other relics of the past century, it contained a sofa of horsehair. "I'm sorry there's nothing better in the house for you than this," he said. "But your mind is easy now and you should rest well."

Alone in the parlor, Neil tried to fall asleep. His name and his future were now secure, but how he could reconcile either with Penny or with her father he did not know. Sleep came to him before the course of future plans could be formulated.

When dawn finally lightened over the Eastern Passage, only lookouts on the ships, intelligence men at the Dockyard, and night watchmen at warehouses and the railway station were awake and abroad to see it. Not a breeze stirred. A veil of mist rose from the surface of the harbor and spread like a pool into the lower streets of the town, where it lay until the sun rose and turned it into a trillion points of flashing light.

THURSDAY

Seven-thirty A.M. After the sun rose, the whole landscape shone. The rays of light, first red, then orange, then shining gold like the heart of a fire, poured from the seaward horizon into the harbor and lit up the mist which lay like a liquid over the flat water. The drops of moisture flashed like quicksilver. And through this mist moved the shapes of two vessels, one a British cruiser, the other a freighter with a lean funnel and a high bow, a bulging, sordid, nondescript vessel brought to Halifax by the war.

The men of the cruiser's bridge could see nothing in the Stream but the funnels of a few ships, for the morning mist concealed the hulls. The town itself had a false nobility in this light, a counterfeit of the mist and the sunrise, for only its contours were distinguishable. Sparks of light leaped off the weather vane of St. Mary's Cathedral and the rising shield of the Citadel was bathed in a golden sheen. Two ferryboats were crossing the harbor so smoothly their movement seemed miraculous, as though it were derived from a cause outside themselves, for with hulls invisible, their funnels and decks appeared to be sliding effortlessly along the top of the mist. On the surface of the ground the night frost was thawing out, but the air was still cold enough to make noses wet. There was little smoke, for the town had not yet begun to work.

Underneath the mist was a disconnected, various life that in a warmer climate or another town might have sufficed to make its people intense and excitable. A battalion was standing to at the Armories. Thousands of men and women were waking with thoughts of the war. Boys were wheeling out bicycles over lawns and gardens stiff with hoarfrost, to ride down to the waterfront and see what new thing the war might have brought on that day. Workers in flat cloth caps, no collars or ties, were striding along to docks and warehouses and foundries and shipyards, hitting the pavements hard with their heels and leaning backwards to check their pace on the steep cross-streets. A long freight train loaded with wheat from Saskatchewan crawled slowly around the corner of Richmond Bluff, the promontory that concealed most of Bedford Basin from the harbor. The train passed the Dockyard and moved on under the lee of another hill crowded with tumble-down houses, until it reached the big shed of Pier Two. There it choked, panted a second, and rested.

By far the most of the town rested, too, for it was the habit of workers' wives to give their husbands breakfast and return to bed, and it was also rare to see a prosperous man in his office before nine. But whistles were blowing, and the *Morning Chronicle* was being bawled from street corners and tossed into doorways, and soon Haligonians would be reading about how hungry the Germans were, and about Cambrai and Bourlon Wood, which the communiqués were still calling victories long after the conscripts broke and the Guards stood, and fought, and died in their tracks.

The stillness of the harbor was shattered by a heavy rumble as the British cruiser dropped anchor a little south of the Dockyard, the fathoms of steel thundered down the hawse. The outgoing tide chafed the stern and swung her bow toward the north, and she lay there lean and gray and cruel, pointing straight at the Narrows. The mist quivered and broke as the air grew warmer, then in a flurry of breeze the wraiths climbed toward the sun. Seagulls that had followed the cruiser into port came to rest on the water, and with a creaking of blocks a gangplank dropped over the warship's side. The officer of the watch stood by to receive a pair of officials who already were approaching in a launch from the Dockyard jetty.

Angus Murray woke early and bathed his sore eyes with a solution of water and boracic acid, and then dressed and brushed his thinning hair carefully down on his scalp. His veins were still quick with alcohol and his skin felt stiff, but his stomach was quiet and there was no headache. Indeed, he was seeing everything very clearly, seeing himself and his world without benefit of intoxication or self-pity, and for the first time in many years a vision of the truth failed to make him afraid.

He ate a quick breakfast and left the hotel immediately, and forcing his flabby muscles to work, sweated up the hill toward the Citadel, past cross-street after cross-street, meeting people with washed faces on their way to work. He walked until he had reached the footpath circling the moat on the hilltop.

Spread below him, the town lay with the mist concealing every ugly thing, and the splendor of its outline seemed the most perfect, natural composition he had ever seen. He thought now that a man could only know the meaning of peace when he no longer reached after the torment of hope. He had lost Penny, with whom there might have been happiness. Now there was no need to argue or justify himself any more; unhappiness could no longer have meaning, for there was no longer anything positive for him to be unhappy about. There was nothing to worry him. Last night he had relinquished the last thread of ambition which had held worries tight in his mind. But the beauty of the world remained and he found himself able to enjoy it; it stayed a constant in spite of all mankind's hideous attempts to master it.

With eyes blinking in the light he surveyed Halifax fanning away under its bare trees from the rounded base of the Citadel. Almost every street and building held for him a fragment of personal history dating back to the time, twenty-seven years ago, when he had first come as a boy, raw from the farm, to Dalhousie College. The faces of classmates crossed his memory: some were successful in the upper provinces or the States; one was famous; few were left in Nova Scotia.

Even as he watched, the mist was dissolving, and glancing down to the harbor, he saw the British cruiser coasting in to her anchorage. The incisive outline of the ship seemed to emphasize and sharpen the essential helplessness of all small places in the world to resist the impact of the outer world. Murray sighed. The town throbbed with the war, and the people in their hearts were not sorry. They welcomed it the way a doctor welcomes the prospect of a dangerous operation which he alone can perform, for England could not fight the war without this town. The great cities which made the wars and sought to circumvent the nature of things could not do without Halifax now.

He took hold of his injured hand and began to manipulate the fingers. They were stiff with the morning cold, but it was obvious they were recovering and soon would be fit for work. He would still have his trade. That would have to be enough from now on.

He glanced at his watch and saw it was nearly eight o'clock, and then began walking down the slope of the hill to the streets. His mind filled with recollections of the scene between himself and Penny and Neil Macrae the previous afternoon. This brought back his conversation with Geoffrey Wain, and then he remembered how he had seen Big Alec MacKenzie come out of the shed on Wain's Wharf. A sudden thought struck him. In what company of the battalion had Alec served? Methodically he checked a mental list of the old N.C.O.'s of the battalion, but could not place him. Then a scene in France flashed into his mind: himself standing by the door of a farmhouse and Geoffrey Wain inside at a table with Big Alec standing beside him. "God damn it!" He quickened his step involuntarily. "So *that's* why Wain remembered to give MacKenzie a job!"

He went straight down the steep street toward Wain's Wharf. The colonel himself would not be there so early, but his foreman might be around any time now. He walked boldly through the arch and continued along the wharf to the central shed. Its door was open and the interior was piled high with crates and barrels and it smelled of raw lumber. No ships were alongside and only a few men seemed to be working. He approached a thin man who was sitting in stolid silence on an upturned hogshead, smoking a clay pipe and spitting in occasional long arcs over the curb of the wharf into the water.

"Is MacKenzie here yet?" Murray said.

"No."

"When do you expect him?"

The man fumbled under a jersey and pulled out a watch. "Mebbe half an hour." He replaced the watch and spat again. "Ain't much work to be done today. Mebbe he don't arrive till later."

"Where does he live?"

The man gave the number of the house and the name of the street; then, as though seeing for the first time that he was addressing an officer, he got off the hogshead and touched his cap. "Do you know where that street is, sir?"

"Yes," said Murray, "I know."

He went up to Barrington Street and boarded a tram, and he did not get off until it had reached the end of its northward run.

The mounting sun flashed into Penny's bedroom and struck her pillow, then crept to her face and across her eyelids. She wakened and blinked, looked at the clock and sat upright with a jerk, her eyes hurting and her limbs numb with nervous exhaustion. It seemed only a few minutes since she had last seen the clock. That had been at four in the morning.

She lay back on the pillow and closed her eyes. She could hardly remember what it had been like in the old days before the war when existence had been relatively simple and people had not found it necessary to live on short-term credits. She had gone through a ridiculous life during these past few years, trying to outwit the Almighty by handing over her daughter to a kindly uncle and aunt, pretending that her sole ambition was to succeed in a man's profession. She thought of the design of her launch, that neat blueprint on which she had spent so much work, the long research that had preceded the formulation of the plan. She remembered how indulgently the engineers and regular designers had smiled at her, then the change to unconscious resentment as they realized she was as good as themselves, then the grudging admiration when finally they were forced to admit that her work had a quality theirs could not equal. So now the Admiralty in London wanted to use a craft of her design, of Penelope Wain's, who had lived most of her life in Halifax. No wonder Angus Murray had been amazed. No wonder Neil had not credited it.

Familiar sounds were in her ears. She heard Roddie's footsteps on the stairs as he went down for breakfast and then the noise of the front door opening. That would be Roddie getting the morning paper from the front porch. The headlines, the war, insanity past human comprehension projected into newsprint and constituting a new world there! Two years ago it had been possible to look forward to the time the war would end. Now it seemed not to matter when the guns stopped. If everyone were as tired as she, they would be unable to do anything but lie torpid and wait for the next calamity to overtake them.

She sighed and turned over, burying her face in the pillow. Had the strain of the past three years been entirely senseless? A woman could reach a point in which want of normal things became so chronic that her organism rebelled against a change from the familiar privations. Neil was alive and well; he was even sanguine. The war had bruised him but he had not broken under it. It had not even made him forget her. The lack was not in Neil, but in herself. She was like a starving person suddenly confronted with food and unable to consume it, and as she remembered his eagerness she was frightened by the prospect he offered her. After all this time she would never be able to equal his desire.

Footsteps again sounded on the stairs and there was a knock on the door of her bedroom. Sadie announced that she had overslept. She answered briefly and got out of bed, went to the bathroom and plunged her face in cold water. She looked up and saw herself lined and frowning. "You're tired out," she told herself. No, it was much more than merely being tired. There were too many tangled threads to be sorted out. Neil's case was simple compared to hers. She hardly dared contemplate the confusion into which she had landed her life: Neil and her father, Neil and herself and Jean—ever since Jean's birth she had longed for the sight of his face when he first saw his daughter. How could she tell him about Jean now? Jean no longer belonged to her.

The force of habit reasserted itself and she straightened her back and tried to arrange her thoughts for the coming day. One thing at a time. That was what everyone was telling himself nowadays.

She went down to breakfast and found Roddie looking self-satisfied behind the paper. Usually he had to peek at its headlines in the scant moments when his father held the paper up in order to turn the pages. He gave his sister a searching look and set the *Chronicle* down beside his plate. "Where's father?" he said.

"He had to work all night."

"Why?"

"I don't know." She felt she could keep the balance in this house no longer. "He's simply—he's busy, that's all."

"Is it about the war?"

"I suppose so."

"Tell me, Penny. I won't let on to a soul."

"You'd better go off to school or you'll be late. Do you remember your lessons?"

"I should hope so, after what you put me through last night!" He pointed to the clock and grinned. "Somebody else better hurry today. I bet they give it to you when you get down there late. Or doesn't being late matter when a person gets old?"

Sadie brought in half a grapefruit, two slices of toast and a pot of tea. She ate quickly and went to the kitchen to check orders and give Sadie instructions for the day. When she returned to put on her hat and coat, she saw Roddie in the living room still buried behind the paper, and the sight of him sitting with his feet on the chesterfield exasperated her. "Will you never do anything unless you're made to? Get out and go to school!"

He got up, startled by her vehemence. "Gee, Penny——"

But Penny did not wait to listen to his excuses and went out, slamming the door behind her. If nothing delayed the tram on its run to the North End she would probably reach the Shipyards a few minutes before nine.

To Geoffrey Wain, the sunlight coming in through Evelyn's faded lace curtains and splashing over the crocus-colored eiderdown on her bed was vaguely insulting. He sat up and rubbed his eyes, and then looked at the girl beside him. Evelyn had fallen asleep naked, too lazy to put on the nightgown she had discarded over the side of the bed. She was still asleep and the cold air reaching her skin as he lifted the bedclothes raised a pattern of goose pimples. She stirred uneasily. The deadness of expression caused by sleep robbed her of all attractiveness. Her slightness which last night had appeared so provocative now seemed a defect. She was so thin that her breastbones were like ranges of mountains rising against her white skin. After a night of sleep, her breath had an odor of acetone which displeased him, too, although it never occurred to him that in this respect he was the greater offender.

With a jerk he swung out of bed, and the movement woke Evelyn. She opened her eyes and surveyed his back, but when he turned to look at her again she closed them. He crossed to the window and surveyed a prospect of untidy backyards and a couple of garbage men wheeling barrels toward the lane beside the house. He stretched and entered the bathroom.

As he shaved, he decided that a night like the one past would never occur again. Evelyn stood for disorder, for the state of mind which is prepared to let everything take its course, and she spoiled his dreams of greatness. He had discovered that while it was possible to enjoy Evelyn for a few minutes without losing prestige in his own eyes, he was incapable of spending a night with her in bed without admitting, tacitly and inwardly, that she was necessary to him.

Eight-fifteen o'Clock Jim and Mary Fraser ate breakfast together in sunlight so bright it dazzled their eyes, for their breakfast nook overlooked the Basin, which now angled the reflected beams of the sun directly at them. After eating they watched Jean set out up the forest path with the maid for her morning's outing. Then they put on their hats and coats and went down the road to the station to catch the local train into town.

The unwonted brilliance of the day and the quietness of the air delighted Mary, and she began to speak of returning home for a lighter coat. "It's almost like Indian summer," she said.

Jim looked at the treetops, motionless in the still air, and then he sniffed loudly. "There's east in that wind."

"Nonsense, there isn't any wind at all."

They were still arguing good-naturedly when they boarded the train for Halifax.

There was now only one vessel moving north towards the upper harbor, the French munition ship *Mont Blanc*. An ugly craft of little more than three thousand tons, she was indistinguishable from thousands of similar vessels which came and went during these days. She was inward bound, heading for Bedford Basin to await convoy. Moving very slowly, she had crawled through the opened submarine net and now was on her way up the Stream, past the breakwater, George's Island, and then the South End docks. She had been laded a week ago in New York with a cargo consigned to a French port, but only her crew, the Admiralty authorities, and the captain of the British cruiser in port to command the convoy, knew what her main cargo was.

Men on the motionless ships in the Stream watched her pass and showed no interest. The previous day they had all received orders not to move until further notification, but none had been told they were giving sea-room to a floating bomb.

The cruiser's captain came on deck to watch the *Mont Blanc* pass and estimate the speed she would be able to produce. He was about the only person in the vicinity of Halifax to take any overt notice of her passage up the harbor.

The *Mont Blanc* moved so slowly that her bow seemed to push rather than cut the water as she crept past the cruiser. The pilot was proceeding cautiously and the cruiser's captain observed this with satisfaction. What was not so satisfactory to him was the manner in which the cargo was stowed. Her foredeck was piled with metal canisters, one on top of the other, held down with guy ropes and braced at the sides by an improvised skeleton of planks. The canisters and visible parts of the deck glistened patchily with oil. The after deck was clear and some sailors in dungarees were lounging there out of the wind.

"I wonder what she's got in *those* things?" the captain muttered to his Number One. "Petrol?"

"More likely lubricating oil, I should think, sir."

"I doubt it. She's not a tanker, after all. Might be benzol from the color of it. How much speed would you say she's got in her?"

"Ten knots at the most, I'd say."

"Doubt if it's even that. I wish they'd realize that a munition ship ought to be faster than the general run of ships. I can't have a cargo like that keeping station with the rest of them. She's got to cruise on the fringe and she needs about three extra knots to do it."

But the *Mont Blanc* glided on up the harbor with little sound or evidence of motion except for a ripple at the bows and a thin wake. She was low in the water and slightly down by the head. A very sloppily laded ship, the cruiser's captain decided. She passed awkwardly onward, the pilot pulling her out to the exact center of the channel as the harbor narrowed. The tricolor flapped feebly from her stern as she floated in, and as she reached the entrance to the Narrows, bells sounded in the engine room calling for a still further reduction in speed.

Eight-forty o'Clock Big Alec MacKenzie was putting on his hat to leave for work when Murray knocked on the door of his storm porch. Too courteous to show surprise, he admitted his visitor and offered to help him off with his coat. Murray declined. And at that moment Neil appeared from the back room, flushed with annoyance.

"Murray—what the devil are you doing here?"

Alec looked from one man to the other in bewilderment.

"You're a little late," Neil said. "I've already found my witness. So you can go back and tell Wain to go to blazes."

"I haven't been seeing Wain," Murray said. He looked inquiringly at Alec. "Could you spare a few minutes, MacKenzie? I've just come from the wharf, and I can tell you there's no need for you to get down there for another hour. Wain isn't expected till late and the watchman told me there was nothing to do."

"Look here, Murray," Neil interrupted. "Wherever I go you seem to be around. What's the idea? I thought I told you yesterday what I intended to do."

Murray glanced at Alec and made a slight clicking sound with his tongue. "Please don't think I'm intruding, MacKenzie. I saw you at Wain's Wharf yesterday, and this morning I guessed you were the man Mr. Macrae had come home to find. As I didn't know where to locate him this morning, I came to you instead." He turned to Neil. "I may be able to help both of you, if you're willing to let me."

"How?"

"That's what I'm here to tell you. Wain, yourself, and I are the only survivors of the original battalion mess. Think a minute, Macrae. When your case is called, I'm certain to be made a witness. Won't it be easier if we confer first?"

Neil hesitated; Alec looked from one to the other with a grave and expressionless face.

"All right," Neil said. "Let's get done with it."

The *Mont Blanc* was now in the Narrows and a detail of men went into her chains to unship the anchor. It would be dropped as soon as she reached her appointed station in the Basin. A hundred yards to port were the Shipyards and another hundred yards off the port bow was the blunt contour of Richmond Bluff; to starboard the shore sloped gently into a barren of spruce scrub. During the two minutes it took the *Mont Blanc* to glide through this strait, most of Bedford Basin and nearly all its flotilla of anchored freighters were hidden from her behind the rise of Richmond Bluff.

Around the projection of this hill, less than fifty fathoms off the port bow of the incoming *Mont Blanc*, another vessel suddenly appeared heading for the open sea. She flew the Norwegian flag, and to the startled pilot of the munitioner the name *Imo* was plainly visible beside the hawse. She was moving at half-speed and listing gently to port as she made the sharp turn out of the Basin to strike the channel of the Narrows. And so listing, with white water surging away from her forefoot, she swept across the path of the *Mont Blanc*, exposing a gaunt flank labeled in giant letters BELGIAN RELIEF. Then she straightened and pointed her bow directly at the forequarter of the munitioner. Only at that moment did the men on the *Imo's* bridge appear to realize that another vessel stood directly in their path.

Staccato orders broke from the bridge of the *Mont Blanc* as the two ships moved toward a single point. Bells jangled and megaphoned shouts came from both bridges. The ships sheered in the same direction, then sheered back again. With a violent shock, the bow of the *Imo* struck the plates of the *Mont Blanc* and went grinding a third of the way through the deck and the forward hold. A shower of sparks splashed out from the screaming metal. The canisters on the deck of the *Mont Blanc* broke loose from their bindings and some of them tumbled and burst open. Then the vessels heeled away with engines reversed and the water boiling out from their screws as the propellers braked them to a standstill. They sprawled sideways across the Narrows, the *Mont Blanc* veering in toward the Halifax shore, the *Imo* spinning about with steerageway lost entirely. Finally she drifted toward the opposite shore.

For a fraction of a second there was intense silence. Then smoke appeared out of the shattered deck of the *Mont Blanc*, followed by a racing film of flame. The men on the bridge looked at each other. Scattered shouts broke from the stern and the engine-room bells jangled again. Orders were half drowned by a scream of rusty metal as some sailors amidships followed their own inclination and twisted the davits around to lower a boat. The scurry of feet grew louder as more sailors began to pour out through the hatches onto the deck. An officer ran forward with a hose, but before he could connect it his men were ready to abandon ship.

The film of flame raced and whitened, then it became deeper like an opaque and fulminant liquid, then swept over the canisters of benzol and increased to a roaring tide of heat. Black smoke billowed and rolled and engulfed the ship, which began to drift with the outgoing tide and swing in toward the graving dock of the Shipyards. The fire trembled and leaped in a body at the bridge, driving the captain and pilot aft, and there they stood helplessly while the tarry smoke surrounded them in greasy folds and the metal of the deck began to glow under their feet. Both men glanced downward. Underneath that metal lay leashed an incalculable energy, and the bonds which checked it were melting with every second the thermometers mounted in the hold. A half-million pounds of trinitrotoluol and twenty-three hundred tons of picric acid lay there in the darkness under the plates, while the fire above and below the deck converted the hollow shell of the vessel into a bake-oven.

If the captain had wished to scuttle the ship at that moment it would have been impossible to do so, for the heat between decks would have roasted alive any man who tried to reach the sea cocks. By this time the entire crew was in the lifeboat. The officers followed, and the boat was rowed frantically toward the wooded slope opposite Halifax. There, by lying flat among the trees, the sailors hoped they would have a chance when their ship blew up. By the time they had beached the boat, the foredeck of the *Mont Blanc* was a shaking rampart of fire, and black smoke pouring from it screened the Halifax waterfront from their eyes. The sailors broke and ran for the shelter of the woods.

By this time men were running out of dock sheds and warehouses and offices along the entire waterfront to watch the burning ship. None of them knew she was a gigantic bomb. She had now come so close to the Shipyards that she menaced the graving dock. Fire launches cut out from a pier farther south and headed for the Narrows. Signal flags fluttered from the Dockyard and the yardarms of ships lying in the Stream, some of which were already weighing anchor. The captain of the British cruiser piped all hands and called for volunteers to scuttle the *Mont Blanc;* a few minutes later the cruiser's launch was on its way to the Narrows with two officers and a number of ratings. By the time they reached the burning ship her plates were so hot that the sea water lapping the plimsoll line was simmering.

The *Mont Blanc* had become the center of a static tableau. Her plates began to glow red and the swollen air inside her hold heated the cargo rapidly towards the detonation point. Launches from the harbor fire department surrounded her like midges and the water from their hoses arched up with infinite delicacy as they curved into the rolling smoke. The *Imo*, futile and forgotten, was still trying to claw her way off the farther shore.

Twenty minutes after the collision there was no one along the entire waterfront who was unaware that a ship was on fire in the harbor. The jetties and docks near the Narrows were crowded with people watching the show, and yet no warning of danger was given. At that particular moment there was no adequate centralized authority in Halifax to give a warning, and the few people who knew the nature of the *Mont Blanc's* cargo had no means of notifying the town or spreading the alarm, and no comfort beyond the thought that trinitrotoluol can stand an almost unlimited heat provided there is no fulminate or explosive gas to detonate it.

Bells in the town struck the hour of nine, and by this time nearly all normal activity along the waterfront had been suspended. A tug had managed to grapple the *Mont Blanc* and was towing her with imperceptible movement away from the Shipyards back into the channel of the Narrows. Bluejackets from the cruiser had found the bosun's ladder left by the fleeing crew, and with flesh shrinking from the heat, were going over the side. Fire launches surrounded her. There was a static concentration, an intense expectancy in the faces of the firemen playing the hoses, a rhythmic reverberation in the beat of the flames, a gush from the hose nozzles and a steady hiss of scalding water. Everything else for miles around seemed motionless and silent.

Then a needle of flaming gas, thin as the mast and of a brilliance unbelievably intense, shot through the deck of the *Mont Blanc* near the funnel and flashed more than two hundred feet toward the sky. The firemen were thrown back and their hoses jumped suddenly out of control and slashed the air with S-shaped designs. There were a few helpless shouts. Then all movement and life about the ship were encompassed in a sound beyond hearing as the *Mont Blanc* opened up.

Nine-five o'Clock Three forces were simultaneously created by the energy of the exploding ship, an earthquake, an air concussion, and a tidal wave. These forces rushed away from the Narrows with a velocity varying in accordance with the nature of the medium in which they worked. It took only a few seconds for the earthquake to spend itself and three minutes for the air expansion to slow down to a gale. The tidal wave traveled for hours before the last traces of it were swallowed in the open Atlantic.

When the shock struck the earth, the rigid ironstone and granite base of Halifax peninsula rocked and reverberated, pavements split and houses swayed as the earth trembled. Sixty miles away in the town of Truro windows broke and glass fell to the ground, tinkling in the stillness of the streets. But the ironstone was solid and when the shock had passed, it resumed its immobility.

The pressure of the exploding chemicals smashed against the town with the rigidity and force of driving steel. Solid and unbreathable, the forced wall of air struck against Fort Needham and Richmond Bluff and shaved them clean, smashed with one gigantic blow the North End of Halifax and destroyed it, telescoping houses or lifting them from their foundations, snapping trees and lamp posts, and twisting iron rails into writhing, metal snakes; breaking buildings and sweeping the fragments of their wreckage for hundreds of yards in its course. It advanced two miles southward, shattering every flimsy house in its path, and within thirty seconds encountered the long, shield-like slope of the Citadel which rose before it.

Then, for the first time since it was fortified, the Citadel was able to defend at least a part of the town. The air wall smote it and was deflected in three directions. Thus some of its violence shot skyward at a twenty-degree angle and spent itself in space. The rest had to pour around the roots of the hill before closing in on the town for another rush forward. A minute after the detonation, the pressure was advancing through the South End. But now its power was diminished and its velocity was barely twice that of a tornado. Trees tossed and doors broke inward, windows split into driving arrows of glass which buried themselves deep in interior walls. Here the houses, after swaying and cracking, were still on their foundations when the pressure had passed.

Underneath the keel of the *Mont Blanc* the water opened and the harbor bottom was deepened twenty feet along the channel of the Narrows. And then the displaced water began to drive outward, rising against the town and lifting ships and wreckage over the sides of the docks. It boiled over the shores and climbed the hill as far as the third cross-street, carrying with it the wreckage of small boats, fragments of fish, and somewhere, lost in thousands of tons of hissing brine, the bodies of men. The wave moved in a gigantic bore down the Stream to the sea, rolling some ships under and lifting others high on its crest, while anchor chains cracked like guns as the violent thrust snapped them. Less than ten minutes after the detonation, it boiled over the breakwater off the park and advanced on McNab's Island, where it burst with a roar greater than a winter storm. And then the central volume of the wave rolled on to sea, high and arching and white at the top, its back glossy like the plumage of a bird. Hours later it lifted under the keel of a steamer far out in the Atlantic and the captain, feeling his vessel heave, thought he had struck a floating mine.

But long before this, the explosion had become manifest in new forms over Halifax. More than two thousand tons of red hot steel, splintered fragments of the *Mont Blanc*, fell like meteors from the sky into which they had been hurled a few seconds before. The ship's anchor soared over the peninsula and descended through a roof on the other side of the Northwest Arm three miles away. For a few seconds the harbor was dotted white with a maze of splashes, and the decks of raddled ships rang with reverberations and clangs as fragments struck them.

Over the North End of Halifax, immediately after the passage of the first pressure, the tormented air was laced with tongues of flame which roared and exploded out of the atmosphere, lashing downwards like myriad blow torches as millions of cubic feet of gas took fire and exploded. The atmosphere went white-hot. It grew mottled, then fell to the streets like a crimson curtain. Almost before the last fragments of steel had ceased to fall, the wreckage of the wooden houses in the North End had begun to burn. And if there were any ruins which failed to ignite from falling flames, they began to burn from the fires in their own stoves, onto which they had collapsed.

Over this part of the town, rising in the shape of a typhoon from the Narrows and extending five miles into the sky, was poised a cloud formed by the exhausted gases. It hung still for many minutes, white, glossy as an ermine's back, serenely aloof. It cast its shadow over twenty miles of forest land behind Bedford Basin.

Nine-ten o'Clock The locomotive was still panting. Little puffs of dust spurted out from the piles of rubble and broken glass about its wheels and fell in a powder on Jim Fraser's face as he lay on his back. What had a few minutes before been a dirty roof of glass was now a pall of smoke dissolving into open sky. Sunlight shot through breaches in the brick and cement wall of the station like searchlights cutting paths through darkness, and the dust of shattered mortar danced in it.

He heard a groan and tried to move. Instantly an agony racked him as though a saw had been drawn across the bones of his spine. He tried to lift his hands but they were helpless. There was a film over his eyes and he shook his head to clear it away. Where was Mary? It was going to snow tonight, it was going to be a very cold winter. What had happened? The shock of concussion and the unbearable noise of the station falling—and that heavy glass roof, thousands of spikes and arrows of glass hurtling nearly seventy feet to the platforms!

The film momentarily cleared from his eyes and he saw bubbles of blood breaking and forming and breaking again. They were directly in front of him. They came from his own mouth. What was that triangle beyond? The square on the hypotenuse of a right-angle triangle equals the sum of the squares on the other two sides. He tried to lift his hand again and saw another bubble break. He was wet through. Where did the apex of that triangle end? That glass triangle with the smoke smudge on its face?

The locomotive continued to pant and stir the dust. It was easier to remember now where he was. He had been passing the driver's cab heading for the newsstand at the end of the platform and Mary had been hoping he would not buy a paper because she hated hearing the war news.

"Mary—what the devil has happened?"

Silence, except for the panting of the engine, except for a queer sound somewhere in his own chest. Silence; the sort of silence that is all a man's own when he is falling asleep and hears the street noises of a strange city pass the window of his hotel.

The film cleared from his eyes again. The triangle of glass was an arrow and its apex was buried in the lung beside his heart. What a way to die, bleeding to death in North Street Station beside an idle locomotive!

He twisted his head and the pain nearly blinded him, but he saw Mary and knew that her eyes were closed and her face composed under a film of dust. Her hat was over one ear and the feather on its side flicked back and forth under the impact of the engine's exhaust. He heard a faintly hoarse sound which seemed to be his own voice calling her name; something stirred beside him and he saw her head waver through the haze, then turn over and settle like a cut flower on its stalk. Somewhere nearby a large sheet of broken glass toppled over with a puny, tinkling sound.

These things Jim Fraser perceived with a peculiar and distant curiosity before his vision darkened and all perception ceased. The locomotive continued to pant and blow dust over his face. And at the same time billions of motes of pulverized mortar began to float down through the sunbeams and settle over all the human beings who had been in the North Street Station when it crumbled.

Roddie Wain sat himself down very carefully on a cement curb fifty yards from the grounds of his school and left his bicycle sprawling in the street before him. Everything was utterly silent. Now that the great wind had passed, there was no movement except for a pendulum-like waver in the leafless branches of trees as they swayed slowly back and forth through shorter arcs to equilibrium. What had caused that monstrous, roaring crash, the spasmodic sound of unknown objects whizzing through the air, and then the triple lines of windowpanes in his school disappearing inward in a tornado of wind that had punched him in the back and knocked him off his bicycle and landed him here beside the curb?

He looked at his bare knees. Both were cut and bruised by the fall from the bicycle. He looked at the school. Nothing moved in it. And suddenly he smiled. It wouldn't matter being late for school now, not after all this had happened.

He heard a clatter of hooves and saw a milk wagon coming towards him down the street with the horse in panic, tossing his mane, and the tall, box-shaped wagon swaying from side to side and scattering milk bottles right and left from its open doors. The bottles broke on the pavement and the milk foamed out and spread in blue-white patches, but the horse came galloping straight on and a driving hoof plunged through the spokes of Roddie's bicycle wheel. The bicycle was pulled upright as the hoof tore clear and the horse stumbled; then the following wagon smashed the bicycle down again as it passed over it, and the wagon went on down the street leaving Roddie's machine ruined.

"Hey—look out where you're going!" He was on his feet, shouting. But almost immediately he closed his mouth again. The wagon had no driver. He watched it sway down the road and finally turn turtle as the horse, instinctively following its regular beat, turned a corner at top speed. He looked at his shattered bicycle and his first sensation was one of bewildered relief.

Penny could not say this accident was his fault. It was going to take a lot of explaining, but Penny always believed him when he spoke the truth.

He dragged the bicycle out of the street and along the sidewalk to the school grounds, and there he leaned it against the trunk of a young maple tree. Now perhaps he could find out what had caused such a peculiar disturbance in the nature of things. Everyone in the school must be afraid to come outside to look, and this gave him the advantage over them all. He observed far to the north a huge white cloud shining in the sun. It had not been there a few moments before. Then he caught sight of a twisted object sticking out of the withered circle of lawn in front of the main door of the school and crossed the wide schoolyard to examine it. It looked like a jagged piece of metal weighing about twenty pounds, and he saw that the grass about it was blackened as though by fire. He bent to touch it but drew his finger away at once; the metal was as hot as a stove-lid. He stared and wondered if it was one of those meteorites he had heard about in school a few weeks ago.

Then the front doors of the school were suddenly thrown open and the children came running out in the regular lines of a fire drill. Some of them were cut and bleeding. A wave of nausea swept over him as he saw a tiny spike of glass protruding from a small boy's cheek. He waited until his own class reached the yard, hoping that no one would observe him. Willie Moffat was the last boy out and he slipped over and stood beside him. "What's happened?" he whispered.

Willie paid no attention to him. The whole school seemed to be dumb.

"Is the school on fire or something?"

He asked this question in a louder voice, but no one told him the answer. Then he saw that the teachers were following the boys to the yard and that the principal was being supported by one of them, blood streaming from a gash in his forehead. Mr. Jackson, the assistant principal, a stiff man of middle age, marched to the front of the yard and said in a loud voice:

"You will all stand here until we find out what has happened. There is no need for alarm. Those who have been cut by glass will leave the ranks at once and go down to the basement. They will wait there until a doctor comes."

Having said this, Mr. Jackson stood with his hands behind his back like a soldier at ease, keeping the herd of children to their discipline while the injured ones left the lines and entered the basement.

"Guess there'll be no more school today."

Willie Moffat had found his tongue. Everyone heard him and then all the rest of the children began to talk together and their voices rose in a hysterical clamor.

"Quiet—that boy there!" Mr. Jackson bellowed and started forward to the front line, seized a youngster by the arm and led him apart to one of the maple trees which lined the separation of the schoolyard from the street.

"Stand there until you learn to be quiet when you're told! There'll be no more talking. School is not dismissed."

"Old bugger!" Roddie muttered.

He was shorter than any of the boys in the line immediately in front of him and the open door was directly at his back. None of the teachers could see him. He stepped cautiously backward, moving on the balls of his feet and keeping his eyes front and his shoulders squared. Then, feeling his heels touch the steps, he turned and bent double and disappeared into the school.

The big entrance hall was empty and his feet echoed as he ran through it to a classroom at the back of the building. He paused on the threshold in amazement and considerable awe. Every window was broken and the shattered glass was lying in crumbled fragments on the floor or sticking like spits out of the blackboard and walls. A plaster bust of Sir Wilfrid Laurier had a spike of glass six inches long protruding from its mouth and the effect was obscenely bizarre.

"Gee!" Roddie whispered.

He tiptoed over the broken glass on the floor and looked out the empty casement. No one was in sight on this side and it was a drop of only six feet to the ground. He cleared the window sill of glass with his handkerchief and dropped over, then ran for the fence at the back and clambered into a neighboring garden. He ran quietly through this and along a path beside the house until he reached the street. Then he paused to straighten his tie before setting out for the center of town.

The street was empty of traffic and the sidewalks still had no pedestrians. Every window he passed was blown in and the houses on the south side of the street had lost their doors as well. He reached an intersection and saw a tram halfway down the block, stalled and windowless, with no one attending it. He shivered and continued walking. He passed the car and continued into the next block before turning to head east for Barrington Street. One of the houses on this corner was vacant, and only this morning on his way to school he had observed plasterers at work behind its unshuttered windows. He looked up curiously. There were no windows left now and the ceilings inside had fallen to the floor.

Then he heard a low moaning behind him and stood still, trying to locate its source. No one was in sight and yet the moaning continued. It seemed to be issuing from the drain by the corner. He crossed the grass and then he saw a bundle lying there in a pool of blood. It was one of the plasterers in overalls that were now soaked and red. The man's jugular was severed. Even as Roddie watched, his legs shaking under him, the moaning stopped.

He turned and tried to run, but his knees were too weak. So he turned his back on the gutter and leaned against an iron fence. There was a sudden roar from the street and a truck tore past with a man sitting on the tailboard clutching his face with both hands and blood coming out from between his fingers. Then suddenly the empty street became crowded with people, as though the truck had summoned them. Women poured out from shattered doorways and rushed into the streets with aprons flying, and a confused shouting, wild and exciting and dangerous, began to rise about him. He wanted to escape. He wanted to be back in school again. He wanted Mr. Jackson to punish him. He wished anything would happen to break the continuance of this horrible mystery, this paradox of silence and sudden death and the awful women who now were screaming hysterically and clutching one another and asking what had happened.

Neil Macrae could see nothing but a blazing light behind his own eyes and could hear nothing but the thunder of explosions in his head. He was reeling around and stumbling over objects which he did not know were in his way. His mouth was opening and closing without making any sound. Things were hitting him from every direction. Even the solid earth was smashing at the soles of his feet. The blazing whiteness at the heart of the explosion, the whirling nose of the approaching shell, my own number inscribed in German on its nose, *nummer sieben hundert tausend acht hundert*—

He felt something sting his cheek and heard, as from a great distance, Angus Murray's voice. "Snap out of it! You're not hurt—come on out of it!"

Murray slapped his face again, sharply; under the eye and across the nose.

"What in hell's the matter?"

He did not hear Murray's shouted answer, but the roar of the explosion was lessening now; it was like the echo of a cannon shot reverberating among distant mountains. He opened his eyes. "What's happened—a dump gone up?"

Murray's voice seemed excessively loud. "That ship must have been filled with munitions."

The immediate landscape, wildly distorted and irregular, looked like floating wreckage seen from the porthole of a heaving ship. Neil moved toward something solid protruding from the ground and sat on it. But immediately he leaped up with a yelp of pain. It was a section of Alec MacKenzie's stove, still hot from the morning fire.

He felt Murray's arm across his shoulder.

"There's nothing the matter with you. You're an old soldier. When that ship went up you went flat on your face. Dove right off the doorstep into the street. Now—do you remember?"

"Yes, I remember now."

"We've got to dig Alec out—he's buried under the house somewhere. His wife's there, too."

Neil smelled smoke and the acrid stench of an unfamiliar gas. Murray's twisted face lengthened and shortened in front of his eyes and then gradually quivered into steadiness as he recovered his focus. Murray was covered with dirt and his coat and uniform were torn, but he was uninjured. The street had disappeared. It was almost impossible to tell where the MacKenzie house had begun or ended. Every building in a space of three hundred acres had been smashed and hardly a single wall was standing. Alec's house had no intact planking larger than a door; it was split to kindlings and deluged with a fine dust of pulverized plaster. The main roof beam stood upright, straight as a flagpole in the heart of the wreckage, and by some vagary of the shock, the horsehair sofa on which Neil had spent the night was standing on its four legs on top of an upturned bathtub which had been hurled through the toppling wall of a neighbor's house and now was resting twenty yards from its original position.

"Alec—where are you, MacKenzie?" Murray was already looking under broken beams and trying to heave some of the loose timber free. Neil's eyes ranged dizzily over the slope of the hill. It was a devastation more appalling than anything he had witnessed in France. The wooden houses had been punched inward and split apart, some of them had been hurled hundreds of feet; furniture, clothing and human bodies were littered in swathes and patches among this debris. The trees and lamp posts lining the street had disappeared, some of them uprooted and flung, others shorn or snapped jaggedly and lying where they fell, still others tangled with the general wreckage.

"Where are we, in front of the house or behind it?" Murray was looking in bewilderment at the wreckage.

Then Neil remembered that he and Murray and Alec had just been leaving the house, Murray and himself on the sidewalk and Alec still indoors.

"The place is catching fire! We've got to get a move on!"

"I'm all right now," Neil said. Where had these flames come from? With a sound like bracken igniting in thousands of camp fires, the entire North End was taking fire. He felt sore places on his scalp and along the back of his neck and saw that Murray's hair was singed. The flames—they had come from the sky, sharp torches spouting downward out of the atmosphere. But the fire was on the ground now. A flame three feet high was crackling in the wreckage of Alec's house.

Murray lifted his arms and let them fall limply to his sides. He turned back wearily to the wreckage to see if some of it could be cleared away.

Neil's ears were now hearing separate sounds and distinguishing them, the crackling of the flames and the cries of hidden voices, women and children screaming from under smoking heaps of timber and plaster and bricks. From a pile of rubble twenty feet off he saw a human hand wave feebly, then sink back and be still. And blackened figures were emerging everywhere, some of them crouching in the ruins and others crawling clear on hands and knees. They were like ants suddenly scrambling into daylight after their hill has been overturned. They were like soldiers crawling out of shelters into the smoking, heaving earth after a bombardment has passed.

Then suddenly he felt all right. It was as though the prospect of shock had torn at his nerves all these months and now he found his nerves better than he had hoped. The most appalling shock a mind could conceive had come and passed and he was all right. He leaped forward to the edge of the flames, and Murray grunted as he reached his side.

"I think he's under here. Help me lift this beam. Bloody hand of mine's useless."

Neil bent and heaved on the beam but it would not give. Some of the side wall still pinned it at one end. He picked up a heavy board that once had been a door jamb, inserted it under the beam and pressed. The beam yielded, lifted a few inches and slithered to one side, making a triangular gap four feet across at its base. Neil crawled through the aperture; his legs slipped and he dropped on all fours to the cellar floor. The place was filled with smoke and dust and he could see nothing. He shouted once and heard an answering groan. Then Murray's muffled voice came down from above. "Don't get yourself trapped down there!"

The dust was choking him and wherever he moved he stumbled over something. He reached in his pocket and pulled out a match and struck it against the seat of his pants. Immediately an arrow of flame darted away from him; there was a quick flash and shock and a noise like thunder. Gas escaping from a broken main had entered the foundation and formed pockets in the wreckage and his match had touched off the train. The ruins jerked upward and separated, then settled back noisily with a sound of cracking wood. Something knocked him to his knees but he was not hurt. As he rose, he saw patches of daylight above him and realized that the exploding gas had scattered some of the wreckage.

"What the hell are you doing down there?"

He heard Murray's voice, near and urgent, shouting from above, and squirmed out through a jumble of planks, tearing his clothes and his skin. He was almost back at the street level and Murray was sweating at the same plank they had tried to lever before. Then a low moan sounded near them and when Neil had cleared out a few loose boards he saw Alec's face.

The big man was crouching like Samson, with spread arms holding apart two beams which crossed over his shoulders like a pair of shears. His face was distorted and the sweat was already washing a tide of dust down to his neck. He moved his head and seemed to be nodding towards something under his feet. Murray came over and together he and Neil pressed the beams farther apart. Then Neil crouched and got into the space between Alec's legs and found Annie lying there unconscious. Getting his feet under her armpits and lying on his back, he pulled backwards with his elbows as props until he had drawn her clear. There was no visible wound on her body and she was still breathing.

Then he turned to help Murray and for a second the two men were immobile as they strained on the beams which sheared down on Alec's shoulders. All around them the ruins were on fire and the flames were already close about Murray's legs. Neil finally gave a lurch forward and the shears yielded. As they slithered sideways off Alec's back, the big man's face twisted and he gave a low cry, and then fell forward insensible. "God," Murray muttered. "There was a spike in one of those beams! It got his lung."

They pulled Alec and his wife clear of the fire and Murray cut the coat off Alec's back with a piece of broken glass. It was a deep wound and the blood looked arterial. Murray gestured towards Annie and Neil bent and tore off her skirt. Murray ripped it into sections and made a pad which he bound across the wounded back with Alec's own belt. Then he sat back on his haunches and rubbed the sweat off his forehead. "If we move him we'll probably kill him. If we leave him here, he'll burn. Oh, Christ—is there anything on wheels around here?"

Neil sat still and panted. Figures of stunned and wounded people were crawling and stumbling in and out of foundations and ruins, appearing and disappearing in the smoke. There was no sense or direction in their movements and their number never seemed to change. He shook his head and coughed. "Where's the nearest hospital?" he said.

"God knows if any hospitals are left."

"Most of these houses have a wheelbarrow. If we could find a whole one it would be better than nothing." Neil got up and skirted the flaming ruins to what had been the backyard. There, filled with rubble, was a wheelbarrow. He pulled it around to where Murray crouched beside Alec and Annie. "If we make a door fast to the top of this we can carry them both."

"Both? Who do you think you are—Samson?"

"The slope of the hill will be with us." He knocked the sides off the barrow and laid the former front door of the MacKenzie house across its floor and handles, and while he was balancing it Murray got up and foraged the street for something to secure it to the barrow's frame. There was no need of looking far, for the street was littered with torn sheets and blankets and wires. They lashed both Alec and his wife to the door, and Neil lifted the handles of the barrow while Murray steadied it at the side.

If the ground had been level they never could have managed it, for Alec and Annie totaled more than three hundred pounds; but the hill was so steep that the barrow rolled forward under its own weight. There were dead bodies of horses and human beings lying in the street, and so much debris that Murray constantly had to go forward to clear a path. Once they passed a burning fire engine lying upside down with its wheels still rotating. By the time they had covered the length of three blocks they were in a crowd of other survivors going out in the same direction. The way improved as they neared the harbor, for on these lower levels there were patches where the explosion had simply swept the ground clean. Finally they reached a tram line and stopped.

Here they first got an idea of the magnitude of what had occurred. Broken ships and the remnants of jetties were piled like driftwood on both sides of the harbor and the water had the appearance of a river after a log jam has broken. The cruiser moored at the Dockyard might just have come out of heavy action, for it was shorn of its masts and its upper works were bent and twisted. A lumber schooner had been blown out of existence and some of its cargo was now on the warship's foredeck, where sailors were heaving logs over the sides. Smoke was rising from the shell of a foundry and there were heavy fires at the Shipyards, although the metal cranes and the gantries and the shorings of the graving dock still seemed intact. Looking farther down the slope they saw wet ground and puddles left by the tidal wave and long runnels of dirty salt water trickling back to the harbor, and row-boats and launches lying broken in the street.

Murray bent over Alec's head and waited to catch the sound of his breath. "He's tough," he said. "He's still with us."

Neil took his bearings and realized they were on the northerly continuation of Barrington Street. It was already crowded. The dead and wounded were being laid out on the remnants of the sidewalk and policemen whose injuries were not severe already had the crowd in control. Smoke eddied and baffled in the windless air and the noise of coughing was mingled with the phantasmal cries of the wounded. Neil noticed the inordinate number of eye- and face-wounds caused by flying glass. Almost everyone he saw was hurt, and there were so many stretcher cases that an artillery brigade would not have had the transport necessary to evacuate them. He looked at Murray, then at the wheelbarrow. "We've got to get something else. Wait here till I take a look around."

He pushed his way ahead through the crowd until he reached the next cross-street. He looked both ways and saw what he wanted. An empty delivery truck was just around the corner, standing on two wheels with the foot spike of a lamp post plunged through the van behind the driver's seat and the post itself supporting the car. It was almost perfectly balanced, and a single heavy shove sent it lurching back on all four wheels. The foot spike tore clear, leaving a wide gash in the van's tin side, but that and a broken windshield seemed the extent of its damage. He reached in and turned the key, set the throttle and spark and went in front to crank. The motor was warm and roared immediately, and then he got in and backed the truck down to the main street.

Annie recovered consciousness as they shifted her, but she was too weak to stand and they swung her over the tailboard and laid her inside. One of the policemen helped them shift Alec on the door, and after he was safely stowed, a line formed behind the truck and began lifting other wounded inside. Murray stowed them crosswise, bending their knees to make them fit. Two walking cases were allowed on the seat in front before Neil finally got the truck under way.

It took over half an hour to make three miles, for they were stopped on every block by people carrying wounded. Murray stuck his head out each time through the hole left by the spike and shouted that there was no more room. Sometimes Neil had to stop to clear wreckage out of the way, and the going continued bad until they reached the bend where Lockman Street becomes one with Barrington. Here there was nothing to stop them but the congestion, for while buildings were battered and windowless, they were still on their foundations, and there were no fires.

They began to meet ambulances and private cars running fast to the north, and once a military car hurried by with a soldier in the back shouting directions through a megaphone. When they finally reached the hospital they found the driveway and streets about it lined with trucks, private cars, garbage carts, bread wagons, slovens and, at rare intervals, an ambulance. A chain of volunteers lifted the wounded out of these vehicles onto stretchers and doors and anything flat that would hold their weight. Alec was still breathing when a pair of internes carried him in.

Neil was about to turn the car about and head north for another load when he realized that Murray had entered the hospital. He moved out of line to make room for incomers and parked the car fifty yards around a corner, then went back to the hospital. It was a large military establishment with acres of ward space. The windows were blown in, but this was the only visible damage it had received.

He reached into his pocket and took out cigarettes, surveying the package as though its survival were a miracle. His shirt was wet with sweat but he felt no fatigue, and his hands were steady. A doctor came running up the drive with an instrument bag in his hand, glanced at him and said, "Hello, Neil," and hurried on. Neil blinked. It was only then that he realized that he no longer cared who recognized him. Even though he was still subject to court-martial, his personal danger had ceased to matter.

Then he remembered Penny and ran up the steps of the hospital. Murray, pushing his way out with a large bottle of colorless liquid in either hand, met him in the vestibule. "Chloroform and ether—ready mixed," he said. "Let's get going."

"Where's Penny?" Neil said.

Murray looked at him sharply and began to run down the steps without answering. Neil followed. "I said, where's Penny?"

They reached the truck and Neil started the engine. "Penny said something yesterday about having a job in the Shipyards. Is that a fact?"

"Yes. It is."

"Then we'd better go and get her."

"Listen"—Murray set the bottles on the seat and laid a hand on Neil's knee—"I'm supposed to be a doctor and a quarter of the population of this town is wounded. Camp Hill is the largest hospital this side of Montreal and it's filling up already."

Neil swallowed and stared through the windshield.

"In the first place, you'd never find her. She's being looked after by someone else if she's been hurt. Meanwhile I'm going to turn the Wain house into a hospital and you've got to help me. The military are already commandeering the public buildings in the South End, but it's my guess not even those will hold the overflow."

Neil put the truck about without answering and ran fast along the back streets. He reached the old red house within five minutes and was across the sidewalk and up the steps before he saw that the front windows had been blown in.

Aunt Maria met them in the hall. She was standing with beads of sweat at the roots of her wiry gray hair and a dustpan and broom in either hand. She stared at Neil and stiffened, then her eyes went large and her bosom expanded, but she stood her ground and the dustpan and broom were clenched more tightly than ever. "God bless my soul!" she said.

"Never mind being surprised," Neil snapped at her. "Where's Penny?"

"You!" She flushed angrily. "You stay away from me!"

There was something immortal about Aunt Maria's power to irritate him; it survived even the explosion.

Murray stepped between them. "All right, Neil!" he said, and turned to Aunt Maria. "Mrs. Wain, I have authority to turn this house into a hospital. I need your help. I want all the furniture cleared out and beds set up in every room but the kitchen and bathrooms and library. Go to the neighbors and take all the beds they'll let you have. We'll need a lot of pans and hot water, so keep up a big fire in the stove. I'll use the dining room to operate and I'll want it ready inside an hour."

She began to shake the broom and dustpan at them and her mouth widened at the corners and increased to a rounded cavern as she tried to think of something to say. Neil pushed by her and ran upstairs, and some of the breath wheezed out of her as she turned to stare after him.

"The report of your nephew's death was exaggerated, Mrs. Wain," Murray said. "As you see, he's quite himself again."

"God bless my soul!" she said.

"I have no doubt He will, but—did you take in what I just told you or do I have to go all over it again?"

With an amused and grudging admiration, Murray watched her fight for poise. And at last she saved it. "What's all this nonsense about?" she said.

"An ammunition ship blew up in the Narrows. It's pretty bad in the North End."

"They had no right to bring a ship like that through the town."

Neil came running down the stairs and stopped long enough on his way to the door to glare at his aunt. "Penny left for the Shipyards this morning. Why the devil couldn't you have told me?" He turned to Murray. "Come on! We're wasting time."

Murray gestured to him to keep quiet. "Mrs. Wain—I'm counting on you as one of the most efficient women in Halifax. Please now—this is no laughing matter."

She pointed at Neil, standing impatiently in the doorway, grinding his heel on some broken glass. "What are you doing here? What do you mean —you—you——"

"Mrs. Wain!" Murray interrupted loudly. "Save the family quarrel till later. You're under orders now. When I return, I expect to find beds in every room in this house."

He followed Neil out to the truck, and almost immediately they were charging down the hill toward Barrington Street. When Neil headed north it was like steering a canoe upstream against a torrent.

"That bitch!" Neil said.

"She can't hear you," Murray said. "Take it easy."

"I abhor the sight of her."

"Forget it." Murray suddenly laughed. "That old woman's going to be in her element in the next hour. I bet she loots the beds out of every house on the street."

"She isn't funny," Neil said. His fingers drummed on the wheel. "God—if Penny was in the Shipyards, that boat blew right into her face!"

"Do you want me to go with you?"

Neil looked at him quickly. "She might be hurt."

"All right. Stop at my hotel on the way. If the place is still standing my instruments are there."

Neil turned into Hollis Street and found the going just as bad. After fifteen minutes of stopping and starting, all movement forward bogged down in a traffic jam at the corner of Duke Street.

"It's hopeless," Murray said, and got out. "The hotel's just a block away. I'll be right back."

Neil went around to the back of the truck and probed the tank with a yardstick he had found behind the seat. There was only an inch of gasoline; probably enough for another twelve miles. He climbed in again and lit a cigarette.

By this time the streets had become like the channels of slow, solid-moving rivers. Sidewalks on both sides were so crowded no one could move at a faster pace than a slow walk, and the long columns of pedestrians presented a ghastly spectacle: women with torn clothes, men helping wounded, children staggering along with blood unwiped from hands and faces, people pushing baby carriages and wheelbarrows. Down the center of the street crawled a line of carts and trucks and ambulances heading south, while the northbound vehicles stood still in a packed and throbbing line, with horses champing and horns sounding and men standing on running boards and shouting to the cars ahead.

Neil saw a military car stalled alongside him with an officer shouting something through a megaphone at the crowd. No one seemed to pay the slightest attention. Neil recognized the officer and remembered they had once played tennis together. He got out and crossed the street, putting a foot on the running board of the military car.

"What's it all about, Dan? What are you telling them?"

The officer looked around without surprise. "Hullo, Neil. Powder magazine's on fire in the Wellington Barracks. I'm trying to make these people get a move on in the other direction."

"That's nice. What's the chance of getting the fire out before it goes up?"

"About even." The soldier driving the car was sounding a horn and the officer had to shout over the noise. He looked incongruously neat sitting there with his uniform all brushed and pressed and his cap jaunty over his left ear. "Well, if it does go up, we won't have to worry about this bloody traffic. Going north?"

"Yes."

"Then get off this street. It's solid."

His car started forward and he slumped back with a jerk. Neil went back to his truck and found Murray climbing in the other side with a doctor's bag in his hand and his cap on the back of his head.

"You ought to see that hotel," Murray said. "Jesus!"

"We've got to get onto another street. Hold tight a minute." He backed against the radiator of the car behind him. The driver stuck his head out the window and cursed, but Neil pivoted the truck and ground out the man's right headlamp, then turned sideways. There was a momentary break in the traffic on the other side of the street, and with horn going he plunged into it and stopped with his bonnet across the sidewalk and through the shattered windows of a store. Then he backed around once more and headed south. "We've got to get around on the other side of the Citadel. By the way—I just heard the magazine's on fire in the Barracks."

Eventually Neil maneuvered until the truck was on the grass on the western slope of the Citadel, for every one of the streets skirting its base was jammed. Under the grass the ground was hard and the tires gripped and the car plunged upward along the uneven surface with the pan bumping every time the wheels hit a hole. They continued until they were three-quarters of the way to the top, moving on a long diagonal and heading consistently north. Then Neil straightened the wheels and began to descend the long northerly slope toward one of the minor streets where the traffic was lighter.

From this height the catastrophe took on a cosmic aspect. The whole population seemed to be moving, and it was difficult to believe that Halifax could have held so many people. Far to the north the sky was a rolling mountain of smoke, shot through with flashes of fire. Twisting veils of lighter smoke rose in puffs from the nearer streets, hiding their details until they looked like tunnels fuming after the passage of a train. The air shook with a steady, low-toned vibration: the roar of distant fires and the softer rumble of the nearer traffic. The slopes of the Citadel itself were dotted black with people, and the hill was like an island, for the stream of traffic circumscribing its base had no end or beginning but flowed like a lazy river drifting out of the smoke and winding southward along the channels of least resistance.

"You don't look like a shell-shocked man to me," Murray suddenly said.

Neil glanced sideways in surprise. "Why do you say that?"

"I thought you'd been shell-shocked in France."

"I was. But I feel fine now." They were nearing the bottom of the hill and the truck was swaying drunkenly. "Watch for the ditch. Here we go!"

The machine bounced and broke its muffler, gave a vicious heave forward, and crashed over an earthen sidewalk into the street. Neil bullied his way across it through the traffic and immediately entered a narrow and smoke-ridden thoroughfare pointing north. This whole district seemed to have been evacuated and gaping windows and fallen walls revealed the contents of every house they passed. The smoke grew thicker block by block and there were isolated fires with no one to attend them. Neil heard Murray coughing beside him. They began to bounce over wreckage in the road, and once a figure staggered out of a whirl of smoke in front of them and disappeared. And then it was hot and the fires were all around them. Neil slowed down and put up the side window, to find that its glass had been shattered. "I suppose the Shipyards are somewhere beyond this?" he said.

Murray nodded and stared ahead at the road, and they went on. The wheels kept lifting and falling over burning planks and broken masonry, and the roar of the fires was almost drowned out by the thunder of their own exhaust. Finally they turned east and ran downhill until they crossed a tram line. Neil stopped the car at the curb and got out. Through thinning smoke he could see the twisted funnels of the cruiser at the Dockyard, and the harbor shaking behind waves of heat and drifting smoke and dust. The Shipyards lay at the foot of an embankment directly below him. Sailors from the Dockyard were clearing debris and the dead were already laid out under sail cloth in a double line on the packed cinders of the yard.

Eleven-thirty o'Clock Everything was suddenly quiet and the air smelled clean. From where Penny was lying, she could make out her father's Persian cat as it arched its back and yawned. Sunlight was pallid along the bark of the lime trees in the garden. Not a muscle stirred in her body; she lay quieter than she ever did when she was asleep. A voice seemed to whisper in her head, "I can't fight any more, I can't keep it up any more, I don't care any more what happens." Pain gnawed at her left eye, but it was so steady and unchanging that she hardly noticed it.

Whatever had to be done in the house would have to be done by someone else now. She was past caring. The whole place seemed full of strangers this morning. She could hear the sound of heels moving ceaselessly overhead, and Murray's voice rising and falling as he talked to Sadie in the kitchen, and Aunt Maria speaking at the top of her voice to someone in the hall. It was all queer; it was a revolution in the nature of things; it was probably a part of the war. But none of it seemed to matter.

She opened her right eye and raised herself slightly on one elbow. She was on that old sofa they always set up in the garden in summer and kept in the storeroom in winter. So that was where Neil and Murray had laid her when they carried her in! How could those two men have found it? A shiver shook her body and she huddled back on the sofa and closed her eye as she remembered the concussion of the explosion, the sudden stab of glass into her face, the floor lurching and heaving like a ship breaking up on a rocky shore, the atrocious, cracking roar as the building broke from its foundations and shifted with indifference, crumbling out from under the ceiling and slithering down and inward with a noise like hard, unmuffled thunder. When had that happened? How long ago since Neil and Murray had shouted from what seemed such a great distance and she had pulled a hand loose, somehow, to answer them?

"How's everything now?" Neil was bending over her, his face dirty but smiling. Strange . . . whenever they were together he always seemed the stronger; it was only when they were separated that she felt in command of herself. She tried to smile back, but the cheek tightening up under the eye hurt too much. A noise was bothering her. It was an insistent, rhythmic series of abrupt crescendos. "What's that?" she said, her face wincing.

"Aunt Maria's having fun. She's got a crowd of women in there tearing up sheets to use for bandages. We've turned this place into a hospital. You're the first patient."

"Oh!" She felt his hand fondling her right cheek and passing over her hair. Then he lifted the handkerchief from her eye and she watched his face alter as he saw the wound. "Do I look awful?"

He shook his head; his face blurred and his voice came from a long distance. "You'll soon be as good as ever. But I wish Uncle Alfred could see his wife today. The way she's welcoming strange men who come to the door, you'd think she was madam of a whorehouse."

"Darling!" But she seemed to lose sight and sound of him. The morning Jean was delivered, the trees on Mount Royal were covered with late spring snow that was bluish white and shone in the sun. Each time I came out of the chloroform I thought how cold those trees must be, and I thought of rabbits hopping about their boles. Never mind about the rabbits, the doctor said. There aren't any left on Mount Royal these days. You haven't a thing to worry about. You must make an effort—just once more, now—there, that's better! "—Neil!"

Her voice was urgent. A face blurred lower over her own. She had to speak to him now, she had to ask him something. She must find out if he liked children.

"Penny!" That wasn't Neil's voice. The blurred face was familiar, but it wasn't Neil's. Where had he gone? How long had she been here alone?

"You must make an effort, Penny. I've got to do an operation on that eye of yours. It's nothing to worry about, but I can't leave it untended or you'll lose the sight of it."

She sighed and grew limp. Neil had gone away again as usual. He was always going away. Always, as long as they lived, he would be going away. Now it was only Angus standing over her, wearing a white outfit that looked like a nightshirt. He had lifted the handkerchief from her face and was washing the skin about her eye.

"It's what I thought," he said. "The iris is prolapsed. The lid is cut as well. Does it pain badly?"

"I don't know," she said. "Please, Angus—I'm so tired."

"Yes, Penny—I know."

"What happened this morning?"

"Hasn't anyone told you? A munition ship blew up in the Narrows and knocked hell out of Halifax."

"Oh, yes, that ship. They wanted me— What is it I'm supposed to do now?"

"You'll have to sit up for a few minutes, my dear. Just put your arms about my neck and we'll soon have you comfortable."

"Does it matter that much? Can't you let it go?"

His face blurred again and she felt herself sinking back into a tide of weariness, a lapping darkness that enveloped but never touched her, a nothingness.

Murray bit his lip and frowned, then replaced the bandage lightly over Penny's eye and looked about the room. In the last hour Aunt Maria and her women had transformed it. A deal table stood under bright lights in the middle of the floor and his instruments were set out neatly on a small stand beside it. Bandages were piled on the dresser. All he needed now was an experienced person to assist him, and Aunt Maria had even promised him that. "Mrs. Wain," he called. A chair was knocked over in the next room, and then she came in followed by a buxom woman her own age who was wearing a white dress and apron and tying a veil over her hair.

"This is Mrs. Stevens," Aunt Maria said. "She's been a nurse and she'd like to help us." She bent over her niece, but Penny neither moved nor recognized her. "Poor child! We might have known a thing like this would happen to her—working in a place no woman ever ought to have been."

Murray appraised Mrs. Stevens and felt reassured when he saw her cross to the stand and pass her eye over the instruments. "Have you had operating-room experience?"

"Yes."

"This is an iridectomy." He nodded toward Penny's limp body. "She's pretty well exhausted. You'll have to steady her."

Between them they lifted Penny and set her in position under the lights. She revived with the movement and opened her eyes. Murray surveyed her critically and turned to her aunt. "Mrs. Wain—if I knew another man who was free and competent to do this operation I'd give him the case. You know that, I presume?"

"I'm not a fool, Dr. Murray. Can I help?"

"No, thank you. It will be better if Mrs. Stevens assists."

"Very well." She hesitated, then looked directly at him. "I have every confidence in you, Doctor."

Murray nodded. He had heard this remark hundreds of times, but the words took on a ridiculous meaning as they came from Aunt Maria. She left the room, closing the door behind her. He reflected that the explosion had been one thing Aunt Maria hadn't been able to bully out of the way.

Now there was no chance of turning back. His hand would have to do its work, and if it failed, no one would be able to repair the damage. His forehead was moist with sweat as he anesthetized and washed out the conjunctival sac. Then he paused for the anesthetic to take effect and observed that Mrs. Stevens had laid out the instruments in their proper order. This was good, for if he broke down she might be of some help to him. From another point of view it was bad because she would know enough to be critical. His fingers drummed the table nervously. To hell with her, he thought. Me—worrying about what a nurse may think!

She handed him the deWecker's scissors and he took them with his right hand and tested the strength and steadiness of his fingers. The movement hurt exceedingly, but the fingers were able to apply pressure and close the blades firmly. It would be a short operation. He had done dozens of prolapsed irises and used to think nothing of them. The trouble was that one had to use several instruments simultaneously. He had done it without help several times in France and he would do it now. He would be able to accomplish most of the preliminary work with his good hand and that would rest the weak one. There was a faint smile around his mouth as he inserted a speculum into the eye and secured the lids with a pair of fixation forceps. Penny stirred and tensed herself.

"Good girl!" he murmured. "Just a few moments now, and it will be over."

Noon Neil entered the military hospital and pushed through a noisy crowd until he reached a captain seated behind a reception desk at the far end of a long corridor. The man's florid face and white mustache were familiar, but since the explosion Neil thought he had seen a dozen faces he knew, faces which looked older and subtly changed, but he rarely remembered the names that belonged with them. He did not recall this man's name now. The captain dismissed an orderly and looked up with a harried expression. Neil asked blandly if the hospital would let him have some medical supplies. The captain's eyes opened wide and so did his mouth and he was about to say something unpleasant, but his mouth remained fixed. Then he found his voice. "My God, Macrae—did this explosion blow the hinges off hell? When did you come alive?"

"Last night, if it matters. How about letting me have a dozen hypodermic syringes and some morphine?"

"Are you crazy?"

Neil sat on the edge of the desk, blocking the approach of an orderly. "Major Murray sent me over. He's setting up an emergency hospital in Colonel Wain's house and it's filling up already."

The captain stared. "*Murray—Angus* Murray?"

"I'm not fooling. He says his hand's fit again. If you'd seen what I've seen this morning you'd know this hospital will be turning them away before afternoon."

"We're nearly full already," the captain said, and frowned. "What kind of work is Murray planning to do over there?"

Neil looked disgusted. "Is that a sensible question?"

"No." The older man grunted and pressed a button. A dozen people were waiting for his attention. "You can have whatever you want provided we've got it to spare. I'll have an orderly take you to the quartermaster's stores. And tell Murray to keep in touch with me—if he can stay sober. I want to know the whereabouts of every medical man in town."

Twenty minutes later, as Neil arrived with the supplies he had been given, he met Murray and Penny coming out of the dining room into the hall. Murray was supporting her, and his eyes flashed a signal for aid. A pad held by a bandage was over her left eye and her face was pallid. Either she did not see Neil or was too weak to show it.

"It's all right," Murray said as Neil came over. "She's only exhausted. Help her upstairs, will you?"

Neil handed Murray the package of supplies and picked Penny up in his arms. Holding her there, surprised at her lightness, he glanced at Murray and the two men appeared to be examining and re-appraising each other. Months seemed to have passed since the previous afternoon.

"How's your hand?" Neil said.

"It seems to have been adequate."

Penny stirred in Neil's arms and tried to turn her head. Without saying anything more he carried her upstairs. His leg flinched but was equal to the task, and he got her into her room without difficulty.

When he set her down in her own wide bed she lay thankfully; the walls surged against her consciousness, receded and flowed inwards again. Jean's face appeared in the darkness, then Mary's and then her father's; they circled about silently through the soft noises of her mind, through the welling waters of her exhaustion, and what they would do to her in the future or she to them no longer seemed of much importance. "I'm so tired!" she whispered.

"Of course you are. Poor darling—all you have to do is rest now. It's all over and you're going to be well in no time. I know you are."

That was Neil's voice. How could he know? He was outside her now, outside in the light of the sun, vigorous and confident and concerned with his own problems. Herself . . . what she had tried to do and the things that still remained to be done . . . these were no part of him. They never could be a part of anyone so confident and hard and sure.

She felt his hand stroking her own and moved a finger lightly to let him know she was conscious of his presence. Oh, Neil . . . don't leave me here. . . . I'm so lonely, and I mustn't ever let anyone know. . . .

When he saw that she was asleep he drew an afghan over her and went down to the dining room, where he found Murray cleaning up for another patient. "Was it really successful?" he said.

"Yes. Her eye's going to be as good as ever in a few weeks." Murray's voice was defiant, answering a deep-seated hesitation in his own mind.

"Thanks to you," Neil said, looking directly at him. "The military hospital's full already," he went on hurriedly. "The captain I met over there asked you to keep in touch with him."

Murray nodded. "You'd better bring your next truckload here. I can handle them now. If you find any stray doctors we can use them, too."

Neil left him readjusting the lights of the dining room. He went into the library, ignoring the women who had commandeered it to sort and roll bandages they were making from old linen. He searched until he found a box of his uncle's choice cigarettes and filled his case with them. Then he passed the box among the women without explanation, and when they all refused by nods or stares, he lit a cigarette and emptied the remainder of the box into his pockets. As he puffed the rich Turkish tobacco he wondered what Wain would say when he returned and discovered him in the house, but he spent little time in speculation. They would inevitably meet soon, and circumstances would have to settle the conversation between them.

He went to the street and looked over the truck, examining the tires and lifting the bonnet to make sure no wires were loose. The engine had missed frequently when he drove it down from the North End, but there was nothing superficial the matter with it. Probably the plugs were dirty. The car's essential need at that moment was gasoline.

He climbed into the driver's seat and looked at his watch. It was nearly half-past twelve: a little over three hours since the ship had blown up. During that time Halifax had come to look like a city caught in the fulcrum of a battle. It was already evident that there would be neither doctors nor hospitals enough to handle the situation, for all the younger surgeons were on active service in England or France.

Had the explosion occurred in the South End, at the tip of the peninsula, the refugees could have moved back into the province; special trains would already be carrying them to inland towns and the congestion would disappear before evening. But the threads tying Halifax to the continent were never more than a single main highway, a railway track, and a string of telegraph wires. And all these had gone out through the bottleneck of the North End. The explosion had blown the town in on itself, and if a strong wind should fan the flames southward, they would have a good chance of ultimately driving the remainder of the population into the sea.

Neil poked his head out of the car to look for chimney smoke to tell him the lay of the wind. There was a thin drift from the east. That meant the South End was safe unless the magazine blew up in Wellington Barracks. But an east wind always brought bad weather, and if it continued in its present quarter there would be rain before nightfall; if it shifted to the northeast there would be snow. Already the sky had a grayish tinge and the sunlight was filtered. Neil grunted; the dullness in the atmosphere was not caused entirely by smoke.

He released the brake and allowed the car to run down the hill, letting in the clutch so the engine could start itself. He would have to leave Penny in Murray's care and hope for the best. Already he had forgotten about Geoffrey Wain, and whether or not Alec MacKenzie would be able to testify in his behalf. He remembered a garage on a street near the foot of the hill and drove to it. The doors were wide open and no one was about. A torn-down engine was lying on a floor hard and black with oil, and there were tools spread around on a work bench. He hunted around until he found a barrel of gasoline in a corner and drew off three bucketfuls for his tank, pouring them in through a funnel. As he was about to leave, he noticed a map of the city tacked on the wall over the work bench and took it down. With a pencil he marked a double line about the area he knew to have been totally destroyed. Between this line and the Citadel most of the houses had been evacuated but were still on their foundations. South of the Citadel nothing much had been destroyed but plaster, windows and doors. On the whole, the catastrophe had been respectful to the middle classes.

He thrust another of Geoffrey Wain's Turkish cigarettes into the corner of his mouth, lit it and frowned through the wreathing smoke at the map. Even though the town was already under military authority, the work of evacuation still lacked system. From what he had seen, people were leaping to do the first thing that occurred to them as individuals, and no one had begun to organize the flow of wounded into the South End.

The map showed five main arteries running from the North End to the south: one of these passed along the waterfront with several bad bottlenecks on the way, another was Barrington Street and its extension, two more passed the roots of the Citadel, the fifth lay farther west. Between these main streets was a network of shorter ones, and owing to the oval shape of the peninsula some of them were not straight. Where each of these main arteries led out of the fire belt, clearing stations had been extemporized, but these would never suffice to evacuate such a broad area. There ought to be a station at every corner in the North End, all the way along the line of the fire. Otherwise the same ground would be worked by different parties and hundreds of lives would be lost as a result of time wasted.

On his way back to the North End, Neil tried to plan a way in which he could be of most effective use. He was stopped by a section of soldiers who wanted to commandeer his truck, and there was much argument before he convinced the sergeant in charge of the party that he was himself an officer and had no intention of yielding it. After five minutes of bluff and some minor intimidation, Neil had his way and drove off with a dozen men piled in behind him.

He explained his program in detail to the sergeant who was sitting beside him on the front seat. "We're going to set up a clearing station on the edge of the fire belt and as soon as we find a good place, you've got to organize your men into search parties. We'll commandeer any private vehicles we meet—along with their drivers. I don't suppose we can do anything now but evacuate wounded, but later on doctors are bound to get through to us from some of the other towns. Then maybe we can do some field-dressing on the spot."

The sergeant nodded; he said he was on leave from France and knew the military routine in his sleep. Then he became talkative and wanted to know if Neil thought the Germans were responsible for the explosion. "My lieutenant, he thinks it's German spies, all right. He's mighty sore at Jerry. Funny thing, though. I met a fella that swore he heard shells in the air this morning. Maybe there's something in it, at that."

"Did *you* hear any shells?"

"No, sir, but queer stuff sure has happened. They say the master of one of them ships out there in the harbor was blown a clear mile and woke up naked on the top of Fort Needham. They say the angle of the hill was the same as the course he was taking through the air and he just sort of skidded to a stop along the ground. Nothing left on him but boots and cuffs." The sergeant spat out the window. "I'd sure like to meet that fella and ask what it felt like."

The smoke grew thicker and they had to stop at a corner where trucks, slovens and delivery wagons were jammed so tight none of them had room to turn around.

"Another thing I heard," the sergeant said. "A fella told me when that ship went up he lay flat on the ground and when he looked up he saw a whole procession of people sailing through the air over him. First it was a naked woman, and then it was an old man looking sort of bowed over, and then it was a dory with a couple of fishermen sitting in it holding the oars just like they were when they blew out of the water."

"Get out behind," Neil said, "and tell the driver behind to back up. If he's not going anywhere in particular, tell him to follow me."

By the time Neil reached the fire belt he was heading a caravan of five trucks and two wagons. Smoke swirled around them but the flames were lower than they had been an hour ago, and most of the fire seemed to be lying along the ground. Much of the wood had already burned to cinder and individual foundations were like isolated garbage heaps with smoke winding up from the charred embers and bricks lying on them. The hideousness of the scene was heightened by foul smells issuing from it, and as Neil's nose contracted, he decided that some of the odors wouldn't bear analysis. A few people were poking about helplessly in the wreck of a house fifty yards away, but otherwise the district was deserted. Some dead were on the street, one almost under the wheels of the truck; the body of a woman oscillated slowly from the only lamp post standing on the block. She had been thrown against its top, and the cross-beam had skewered her bunched clothes and held them. The only house within sight which could afford any shelter was a ruined fish market. Neil got out to inspect it: the upper floor had fallen on one side and held on the other, so the structure now was roughly the shape of a triangle. Hundreds of haddock, cod, halibut and mackerel lay on the sloping counters spitted by glass and powdered by dust.

Neil called the sergeant. "Those counters will have to do for places to rest the wounded. Get your men in here and clean it up. And don't throw the fish away. Half the town is going to be hungry soon and we may find a way of sending them south."

Two o'Clock The military who had taken charge of Halifax had finally been forced to admit that for the time being the town could rely on nothing but itself. Telegraph riggers had gone out through the fires of the North End and repaired some of the wires running along the shore of the Basin, but the distance between Halifax and other cities of Canada was so great it was obvious that no help could arrive that day. It would take twenty-four hours at least for a train to arrive from Montreal or Boston and twelve hours for help to come from Saint John or Sydney.

This was only one difficulty. The principal railway yard had been blown to pieces and only a few live locomotives had been found. Cars were shunted in from the suburban yard and a hospital train sent up the line to Truro. All organization had to extemporize and depend on inexperienced individuals and impaired facilities. No one yet knew the extent of the casualties, and as the cars and trucks kept pouring into the South End, estimates had to be changed hourly. The Citadel and Commons were black with people driven from their homes. They lay or sat on the grass and built fires to keep warm, and even after the danger of a second explosion had passed with the quenching of the fire in Wellington Barracks, most of them refused to move. Halifax was now like a countryside after a dam has burst and flooded it; sediment was beginning to settle and familiar channels were becoming discernible.

By early afternoon, individual citizens were establishing food kitchens in churches and private homes, and units of the Army Service Corps set up so many tents on the Commons that the area looked like a military camp. Martial law was proclaimed, but so far as anyone knew, nothing had been looted but a brewery. As the afternoon wore on, crowds began to shift from the Citadel and the situation seemed more controllable. Halifax was cashing in on a century of unconscious self-discipline. Yet there was no end to the processions of wounded coming out of the North End. They kept dragging steadily out of the smoke, moving more slowly as the horses grew tired but always flowing on in a sort of weary perpetual motion, with drivers crouched silently on their seats and the heads of horses drooping lower after each journey. Cars and trucks which had run out of gasoline were stalled on all the principal northbound streets.

Roddie Wain had spent the morning prowling around the South End, after his fright had developed into a sense of importance. This was the real thing, and he was in on it. As it didn't occur to him that anyone he knew might have been injured, he went home only when he felt hungry. As he approached the house, he decided that its appearance was on the whole satisfactory. It was just sufficiently damaged to look as though it had played its part in events.

He went in by the back door and found the kitchen stove covered with pots of boiling water. Sadie was moving about doing unusual tasks and wearing a scared face, and he heard peculiar sounds coming from the dining room. He slipped across the floor and opened the door to look, then closed it with a jerk.

"What are they doing in there?" he said to Sadie. "All those lights and someone lying on the table?"

"Get out of my way," Sadie said. Then recognizing him, "Master Roddie —you should have been back long ago! Miss Penny, she's just 'ad a hoperation and Dr. Murray an' 'em's making the 'ouse hinto a 'ospital and you should've tol' somebody where you was."

"Where's Penny now?"

There was no answer, so he ran up the back stairs and stared at the unrecognizable place the upper hall had become. It was crowded with cots and bundles of people were lying on them; women in white aprons were moving about and two men were carrying a girl up the front stairs on a stretcher. He edged along unnoticed until he reached his own bedroom, where he found three women with bandaged faces lying on cots. Then he went to Penny's room, and in the first moment it was a relief to see her. He noticed that she was asleep, and this seemed strange. He approached the bed and saw that one of her eyes was bandaged.

She stirred as he bent over her bed. "Roddie—is it you?"

"Gosh, Penny—I didn't know." He peered gingerly. "Is it bad?"

"I've been so worried about you!" Her voice was weak and expressionless. "Where have you been?"

"In school."

"Oh, Roddie—why do you have to tell me something like that? Listen—you'll have to find a place to sleep and eat. Go to Uncle Alfred's. Everything here——" Her voice tailed off.

Roddie looked at her for nearly a minute, then drew in his breath in a quick and nervous gasp and slid out of the room on tiptoe.

Aunt Maria encountered him in the upper hall. "Bless my soul, what are you doing here? Are you hurt?"

"No, I was just——"

"Get along with you! This minute! Go over to our house and get something to eat. The idea of you being here! Get along. You'll have to sleep over there tonight, too."

"Is—is Penny all right?"

"She's just tired. Now don't you worry about her. Her eye was cut, that's all."

"Where's father?"

"How do I know where your father is? He's probably with the military somewhere. Everybody's doing things they've never done before. Now get along with you and stop asking questions."

Roddie went out the front door and watched an empty truck start off down the hill. He was sure the stains on its running board must be blood.

When he reached his Uncle Alfred's house he found a queue of refugees waiting at the front door for food, and so he went around to the back, intending to enter by the kitchen porch. He discovered his uncle puttering among the frozen flower beds. The old man looked up when he saw Roddie and coughed.

"Where's your father?" he said.

"Nobody ever knows that."

"They never should have allowed this to happen. I'm going to talk to your father about it. Not a pane of glass in the front of the house! I don't know what's going to become of us all. Your aunt's sent a bevy of women in here and they've turned me upside down. There's no good in that." He coughed again, and he looked bowed and old to Roddie as he stood there talking in bewilderment. "What are you here for?" he added.

"Aunt Maria told me to come here to get something to eat."

Uncle Alfred waved toward the back door and shook his head. "House full of strangers. All the rag, tag and bobtail of the town. I can't even get a policeman to see they don't steal."

"Our house is a hospital now," Roddie said. "Have you got a soup kitchen here?"

"Soup kitchen? Stuff! Go and get something to eat."

Roddie soon discovered that members of his aunt's chapter of the Imperial Order of the Daughters of the Empire had commandeered the entire house. One of them mistook him for a refugee and gave him cold ham and potatoes on a paper plate in the kitchen, and while he ate, she asked solicitous questions about himself and his parents. Roddie decided to oblige her, and she listened with horrified fascination while he told her that his father was buried in Flanders and his brother drowned at sea and his mother lost somewhere in the debris of the North End. Everything was going well until she asked where he had lived. He tried to remember the name of a street in the far North End and found he didn't know any. So he bolted his food and got out while she was attending to someone else.

From here he went to Willie Moffat's house. Willie lived on a street that had been fashionable seventy years ago but now had a dubious character. Half its houses had been divided into cheap flats and the remainder were occupied by mechanics, stevedores, railwaymen and clerks. One brown house in the center of the block, a dreary mansion of three stories and great girth, was inhabited by two old maids no one ever saw. They were rumored to have a hundred thousand dollars in the bank; as they also owned an apple tree, Roddie and Willie had frequently visited their backyard during the autumn.

Willie announced that he had just eaten his lunch, and this was easily credible since traces of bread and molasses were left on his face. He was now sweeping broken glass out the front door onto the sidewalk.

"Where have you been to?" he said. "You missed something."

"I've been around."

"Bet you haven't been up to the North End."

"I bet I have."

"I bet I saw more dead people than you did."

"Go on, I saw the explosion and that's more than you did. I can prove it, too. You were in school when it happened and I wasn't."

Willie put the broom inside the porch. The front door had been blown in and Roddie heard Mrs. Moffat's voice calling to her son to look for a hammer and nails to fix it.

Willie disregarded her. "I been looking for you all morning," he said. "I need some men to help me. I'm going to get a horse and team and I'm going to get up to the North End and get working."

"Where can you get a horse and team from?"

"Never mind." Mrs. Moffat's voice rose again and Willie cocked an ear cautiously. "Come on, or the Old Lady'll keep us hanging around here all day."

Roddie followed him to the back of the house and over the fence to a neighbor's yard. There was a small stable in the corner, a pile of manure against the fence and the sound of a horse moving in a stall inside the barn.

"Old Swicker's horse!" Willie said in a whisper. "He's not been around all day. Maybe he got killed or something."

"Where's the wagon?"

"He keeps a sloven inside with the horse." Willie looked truculent. "You're in on this, see! You better not forget that."

"Who's forgetting it?" Roddie said.

Willie looked over his shoulder and quickly unlatched the door and entered the stable. The horse shuffled in its stall and neighed, lifting its neck and showing teeth.

"Chuck the nag some hay while I get the harness," Willie said. "Old Swicker don't feed him right."

Roddie pitchforked some hay into the stall and lifted the shafts of the medium-sized sloven which occupied most of the barn.

"What does Old Swicker do?" he said.

"He drives this cart around," Willie said.

Unlatching the gate of the stall, Willie approached the horse diffidently, but the animal had his head down in the hay and made no movement whatever while they fitted on the collar. Then they backed him out of the stall and between the shafts, and after ten minutes' experimenting, they completed the harnessing and drove off, Willie swinging the whip while Roddie glanced over his shoulder to make sure no one observed them.

"I guess Old Swicker's dead," Willie said, as they headed north.

They were soon in the middle of heavy traffic, and a policeman directed them west. After twenty minutes they passed between the Citadel and the Commons and then they were in streets where the houses were uninhabitable and the smoke hung heavy. All the southbound vehicles they passed were loaded with wounded. It was not long before they saw a man lying dead by the curb.

Roddie had a recurrence of fright. "Look!" he said.

Willie gave the body a casual glance. "That's nothing. You wait till we get nearer. I bet none of the fellas in the school see what we're going to see when we get nearer."

The horse balked several times as the smoke thickened and Willie laid into him with the whip. The animal whimpered and walked on. Finally they stopped in line behind a long row of vehicles and waited. A sergeant approached, giving directions to the drivers, and when he reached them he was on the point of repeating his order. Then he looked more closely. "Who the hell let you kids up here?" he shouted. "Get back where you came from."

"We been sent up," Willie said.

"Come on—get out of it! You're being sent back right now." There were two men in the cart ahead and he called to them. "You guys there—one of you take this cart. Couple of kids swiped it somewhere and I'm sending them back home."

A thin-faced man with a dirty cap over one ear and a roll-neck sweater came up and pushed Willie off the driver's box. Roddie climbed down too.

"Go on, son," he said. "Beat it!"

"You better look out," Willie said to the sergeant, and pointed to Roddie. "His Old Man's a colonel."

The sergeant paid no attention and passed on to the vehicles that had pulled up behind them. Willie stared glumly after him. The column started to move and the thin-faced man drove their cart along with it. Roddie and Willie watched him go, and then began walking south.

"What's going to happen to Swicker's horse?" Roddie said.

"Gee, I never thought of that!" Willie took a match out of his pocket and began to chew it. "We never swiped it. That sergeant and the guy did. And don't you forget you were in on it, either."

"Who's forgetting it?" Roddie said.

They walked slowly southward, looking into gaping doors and battered interiors as they passed. Once they entered the empty shell of a house and tried to go upstairs but found the steps had fallen in. Roddie wandered out to the kitchen and saw the remains of a breakfast laid out on a table dusted over by plaster and glittering with sparks of broken glass. When he came back to the front room he found Willie opening a drawer filled with silver.

"Finders keepers," Willie said.

Roddie felt uneasy. "This is different," he said.

"How do you mean, it's different? I found it, didn't I?"

"The soldiers get you for it. They call it loot and they shoot looters."

Willie slammed the drawer shut. "I don't give a bugger for the cops, but the soldiers are different." He returned to the street by clambering over the remains of a fallen wall, Roddie following. "Come on, let's do something. Let's go downtown and see what's happening."

They turned east and walked for nearly a mile. At the foot of the hill they saw several carts and wagons drawn up before a grimy stone building and soldiers and workmen lifting long, heavy bundles across the sidewalk and carrying them in. They tried to enter the door and were turned back by a policeman. "Get out of here. This is a morgue. It's no place for you."

A woman standing behind the constable whispered something in the man's ear and his expression changed. He put an arm about Roddie's shoulder and led him into a vestibule. "What's your name, sonny?" he said.

Roddie gave it and the woman, overhearing, smiled. "Are you Colonel Wain's little boy?"

Roddie winced. "Yes," he admitted.

"Then you have nothing to worry about. Is your friend—looking for somebody?"

"My father was taken prisoner," Willie said with satisfaction. "The Germans treat him something terrible."

The policeman's face had become serious and he was trying to attract the woman's attention. Failing to do so, he interrupted gruffly. "Son, was Mr. Fraser of Prince's Lodge your uncle?"

"Yes." Roddie suddenly was frightened and wanted to run away, but the policeman's eyes magnetized him. When he looked at the strange woman he felt still more uncomfortable. "Why? What's happened to Uncle Jim?"

"You must be very brave," the woman said.

Roddie said nothing.

"Your aunt and uncle were brought here this morning. They were found in the North Street Station."

"Are they—are they dead?"

The woman nodded.

"Perhaps the boy ought to make the identification?" the policeman said.

"That's been done already."

Roddie's lips quivered. "I've got to go now, I guess."

"You're a brave boy," the woman said. "And will you remember something? Tell your father we'd appreciate it if he'd come down here as soon as he can. There are papers to be signed—he'll understand."

Roddie blundered down the steps and Willie followed him silently. He liked his uncle and was fond of his Aunt Mary, but it was no sense of bereavement that caused his present emotion. Rather it was the abrupt and ruthless impingement of the unseen and the incalculable into his own life, the realization that what had happened today was not an adventure but a catastrophe.

"Gee," Willie said, "that's tough. Well, they can't talk about Swicker's horse now, not after what's happened to you they can't."

Roddie did not answer and they began their homeward walk in silence. They cut west toward the Citadel and then they were aware that it was getting cold.

"Gosh," Willie said, "you should've gone into that place. I bet it was full of dead bodies and corpses and things. I'd like to see a corpse. Gee, we only saw one all day!"

But Willie's heart did not appear to be in his words, for by the time they reached the hill they were both uncomfortable with cold and apprehension. The stream of traffic on the roads about the Citadel had the same consistency as before, but now all adventure had gone out of the sight of it and the people huddled together on the trucks and carts looked miserable and hungry, and this was not a vision transported from France or Serbia or some country that was never immune to such things, but an actual occurrence in Halifax. The sky was grayish brown in the east and a wind had risen. It moaned now and stirred the frozen branches of the trees. As they raised their faces to the sky they felt the wind sting; for a moment the air looked misty and then it solidified rapidly and they saw it was snow. It slanted down in a thin, wiry mist, hardly visible as it struck the ground but intensely cold and constantly building up its body. The gray air whitened and began to swirl. As they neared home, the rising wind had pegged itself in the northeast and had begun to drive. The streets were shiny black bands on a white sheet and the sky was darkening into early night. The wind eddying in alleyways took on a fuller tone and howled like a homesick dog.

At the front door of the old red house they watched a soldier come out and get into an empty truck. He looked at the sky and buttoned the collar of his greatcoat. "That's the last straw," he muttered, and drove away.

Five o'Clock Angus Murray's back was aching and the fingers and wrists of his right hand had become numb. He fumbled as he adjusted a dressing and the nurse had to help him. Finally the bandage was secured and the patient lifted off the table and carried from the room on a stretcher. Almost immediately the door opened again and another limp form was brought in and laid on the table. Murray and the nurse looked at each other.

"Don't you think you'd better rest, Doctor?" she said. "You haven't stopped for six hours."

Murray spread out his right hand under the lamp; it had begun to swell again and the joints were so stiff he could hardly control them. He looked at the patient: another bad eye case, another hard decision whether to excise the eye or take a chance and try to save it. He looked up at the nurse again. "How many are waiting, do you know?"

"I'll see."

She returned almost immediately. "Mrs. Wain says there are twenty urgent cases waiting operation now and almost thirty needing minor attention."

Murray made a clicking noise with his tongue and looked at his hand again. "I've got to get some help," he said.

The lines on his face were deep gashes and his eyelids were red. As he turned, he had to reach out to the table for support and he waited there a moment, bent over with both hands resting on the flat surface of the table. Then he readjusted his head lamp and examined the patient's eye. He swabbed away the blood and shook his head. Three hours ago, he thought, it might have been possible to save this man's sight. It was a double accident for him to have been brought here now.

"Stand by for a few moments, Mrs. Stevens. I'm going to get a cup of tea."

He picked his way through the crowded hall to the library, found it empty and quiet, and slumped down in an armchair, closing his eyes. "What a surgeon!" he muttered aloud to himself. "Conking out after six hours!"

"Drink this, Doctor."

He stretched out his hand automatically. Aunt Maria was standing beside him with a cup of tea, extended like an ultimatum. He grinned feebly. "Thanks."

She watched him as he drank. Her face was flushed with work, but the experiences of the day had done little to change its expression. It was, therefore, a surprise to Murray when she said, "There's no sense in not talking about it—you've done wonders today, Doctor."

"Who—me?" He laughed shortly and glanced at his sore hand. "I've merely overrated myself—as usual." But the hot tea had revived him and he got to his feet. "Thanks for the lift. You know"—he laughed again—"you're not so formidable as I thought. Well, maybe this hand will hold out an hour longer but that's about its limit."

"Nonsense!" Aunt Maria said sharply. "I won't hear of you going back to operate any more."

"Won't you, Mrs. Wain?" Murray tried to grin once more. It was many months since he and Neil Macrae had lifted Big Alec and his wife out of the ruins of their home. It was an age since yesterday. "Who's going to take my place?"

"I've arranged for that. Special trains are being run in from Truro and I've sent two soldiers to meet them. I told them to bring doctors here as soon as they arrived—at least three."

"But the regular hospitals will be short-handed, too."

"If this isn't a hospital I don't know what to call it. Anyway, I'm positive you'll get help shortly."

Murray sat down in the chair again and closed his eyes. He had never been fond of hard work and after six months of idleness and alcohol his physical condition was hardly normal. The floor was swaying like a hammock under his feet and his right arm throbbed with pain. He wondered if he was falling asleep. Was his life always to be a series of dreary vacuums capped by violent crises? Why did he have to be so goddamned philosophical at a time like this? Neil Macrae didn't waste time generalizing. Or did he? And what do I care what he does with his spare time? I am a reed, but I am greater than those things that destroy me. I am a thinking reed. My boredom and my defeats are therefore more significant than the excitements and victories of others because I recognize them for what they are. At least they're significant to me.

He opened his eyes and discovered Aunt Maria in front of him again. This time she held a glass in her hand.

"Here," she said. "You need something stronger than tea. Drink this."

He sniffed and observed that it was brandy. Aunt Maria's face was impassive under her wiry gray pompadour as he drank it down. "That's much better," he said. He pulled himself up and cast his eye over Wain's library of inherited and unread books. "Has the colonel returned yet?"

"No. Now I hope you'll stay here and rest. I thought the brandy——"

There was a knock at the door and she crossed to open it. A soldier entered with snow on his shoulders and stood at attention until Murray signed to him to be easy. He was followed by three elderly men, each carrying a medical bag. Murray recognized none of them, he had no idea of their qualifications or abilities, but at least they seemed to be of the profession.

He rose to shake hands. "You can start in immediately, gentlemen," he said. "You can see for yourself what we're up against."

The doctors took off their coats without more than a few murmurs and opened their bags in unison. Murray observed the supply of instruments and was relieved to note that two of the men were surgeons.

"How did you get into town?" he said. "I thought the line was up?"

"They stopped the train outside—Fairview, I think they call the place. Your two men didn't give us much chance of doing anything but accompanying them. We expected to go to the military hospital or at least to the General."

"There'll be plenty to do here," Murray grunted.

"It looks like it," the second doctor said.

As Murray passed through the hall to the dining room with the three men following, he heard an unconscious suspiration of relief from the suffering bundles on the floor. It was a strangely exhilarating sound, and it annoyed him to realize that he was moved by it. He left the two surgeons in the dining room and directed the third upstairs, then returned to a desk Aunt Maria had set up in the back corner of the lower hall. There a woman was keeping a record of the casualties and he checked it over rapidly. With three men besides himself working, it was likely that the present number of patients would receive attention before midnight.

He straightened and complimented the woman on the precision of her work, and as he was about to return to the dining room he saw Roddie standing by himself just inside the front door. The boy beckoned to him and Murray went over to see what he wanted. Roddie's eyes filled with tears and his throat seemed caught by a sudden constriction and he reached up and clutched Murray by the arm.

"Well, well—what is it now? You're not hurt, are you, Roddie?"

Roddie shook his head and clung tighter.

"Is it Penny?" Murray said. "She's going to be all right, you know."

"No." Roddie's face was haunted by fear of something he did not even begin to understand. "Aunt Mary and Uncle Jim—they're dead. They were in the station."

"Good God!"

An older man should never show alarm to a youngster, Murray tried to tell himself, and he put a hand on the boy's shoulder and guided him through the hall to the kitchen. "I suppose—I don't suppose Jean was with them?"

Roddie gave him a puzzled look as though he could not think who Jean was; then, remembering, he shook his head and the tears retreated from his eyes. "How long is this going to last, sir?" he said.

"What do you mean, Roddie?"

"I don't know, I guess. I mean—how long before things are going to be like they used to be?"

Murray smiled gently and shook his head. "We'd better not worry about things like that, do you think? After all, who'd like things to stay the same forever?"

"I never thought of that," Roddie said.

Midnight It was dark when Penny woke. Her uncovered eye tried to estimate her surroundings, but her room had become an ominous and unfamiliar place. Three cots had been set up close to her bed and three strange bodies were outlined under the blankets. A lamp set on a table near the door had been covered with a green cloth and it gave the room an eerie luminosity. The shadows it cast were faintly rigid on the floor and walls. The room was cold. Outside, the wind howled and there were angry spurts of snow against the beaverboard someone had nailed across the broken windows. Under a particularly heavy impact of wind the whole house trembled and swayed gently like a ship bending to the motion of the sea.

She propped herself on one elbow, and then swung her feet to the floor. Except for her dress and shoes, she was still wearing everything she had put on that morning—was it that morning? She was wide awake now. The events of the day crashed through her mind and for the first time she realized clearly what had happened. Halifax, and with it the rigid, automatic life of her family's hierarchy, had been blown wide apart.

She stood still, shivering. Where was Jean? Had she been frightened when the ship blew up? Had the expanding air struck with equal violence to the northwest? As the crow flew, Prince's Lodge would be less than four miles from the Narrows. Perhaps the house at Prince's Lodge had been flattened, too? The expansion would have had a clear pathway across the Basin. But Richmond Bluff would have diverted its violence. There were also contours in the shore of the Basin itself which would lend Jim Fraser's house protection. There were the trees between it and the road.

She went softly to her closet and opened the door. The old hinges creaked and a woman on one of the cots stirred and moaned. Penny felt among the clothes hangers until she found a warm dress, drew it out and pulled it on.

The sleeping woman groaned more loudly and turned over. Penny waited until her breathing became regular. Then she felt for her slippers in their familiar place, pushed her feet into them and tiptoed out of the room, closing the door behind her.

The house was like a cathedral at a Watchnight service, for all the lights were carefully shaded; a low, rustling sound pervaded the still air, and it was not the echo of the wind outside. As she moved among the cots to the stairhead, a figure crouched by a desk lamp rose and came to meet her, its shadow gigantic on the ceiling.

"Where are you going?" It was one of the nurses she had seen earlier in the day. As she recognized Penny, she added more quietly, "You should be in bed, Miss Wain."

"I'm better now. Is anyone awake downstairs?"

"Some of the doctors are still working in the dining room. Your aunt has gone to the next house to rest. There's a terrible storm outside."

"What time is it?"

"A little after midnight."

Penny went down the stairs and found that the cots in the lower hall were empty. She saw a light under the library door and turned the knob without knocking. Murray, his face haggard and his eyes red, was nodding in an armchair and she saw with amazement that an open book was lying across his thighs. She looked over his shoulder and read the title of one of Balzac's novels. There had been a set in the library as long as she could remember. She let herself down into another chair, but as the springs creaked, Murray opened his eyes.

"Yes?" he said. Then, recognizing her, he started up. "For God's sake, what are you doing out of bed?"

"I'm sorry I wakened you."

"I wasn't asleep." He yawned, and as he stood up the book fell to the floor. "I've been giving your father's library a little exercise. It needed it. How does your eye feel now?"

"I'd forgotten about it."

Murray pulled a battered packet of cigarettes out of his pocket and lit one. "Mouth like the bottom of a rusty can and I'm still smoking," he muttered. "What's the matter with you? Why didn't you stay in bed?"

"I couldn't. Did you ever wake up in your own room and find queer sounds and strange women in it?"

"Plenty of times. Once I even thought there was a green tiger, but I wasn't sure. Still, I know what you mean."

"Where's Roddie?" she said.

"I persuaded him to go with his aunt to sleep next door. He spent several hours this evening working at the furnace. Are you warm?"

"Yes. Is Neil all right?"

"I haven't seen him since noon, but he seemed better able to look after himself than most of us."

"Angus—I just thought of something and I'm terribly frightened. Do you think—have you heard anything about Jean? Or Mary and Jim? They were coming into town today—or yesterday or whenever it was."

Would this day never come to an end? Midnight, a ruined city buried under the snow, and here was one more crisis he was required to face. Was all the rest of the twentieth century going to be a continuance of this alternation between boredom and violence?

Murray picked the Balzac off the floor and sat back with it closed in his hand. "Jean's all right," he said. "Jim and Mary must have left her at the Lodge with the maid. They were alone when they were found."

"What do you mean?"

He faced her with as much detachment as he could. God damn people like Penny with that tense calm like still water under pressure! The idea that he might have married her appalled him now. That calm, that potential energy in the girl would annihilate him if he ever had to live with it. A stubborn, imaginative, violent man like Neil Macrae would be just the sort to make her do whatever he wanted, make her forget to think, force her into the pattern of his own life without even knowing he was doing it. The next time he thought of getting married, Murray decided, he'd hunt someone capable of hysterics.

"Jim and Mary are dead, Penny," he said quietly. "They were in North Street Station when the ship blew up. I doubt if anyone in the station survived."

Penny received the information exactly as Murray had known she would. She sat up very straight, her backbone rigid and the clenched fingers of her right hand set hard against her lips. She said nothing and made no sound.

Murray got up and looked away. He was too tired to find relief in physical activity, but anything was better than sitting still and watching her insuperable control. He moved to the window and remembered that it was covered with beaverboard. Then he turned back and started forward. Penny had fainted.

All that night the storm grew and the wind drove steadily harder out of the northwest. The wind shattered the snow high in the air, and when the flakes reached the ground they had the consistency of sand. Horses and men traveling north moved with hanging heads into the gale that lashed the snow against them and drove it into the horses' eyes and embedded frozen particles in the men's collars and clothing. The temperature dropped steadily and by early morning it was not far above zero. Wagon wheels began to stick in drifts and soon only the heaviest trucks were able to smash through. Many horses had become too tired to pull and their owners had to stable them for the night. Some men had found sleighs, and after dark there was much activity as the wheels were stripped off slovens and replaced by runners.

The snow fell invisibly in the darkest night anyone in Halifax could remember, for the gas lights that illuminated the streets were not burning.

In most of the North End there was total blackness, apart from the glimmer reflected from the snow around the occasional glow of a lingering fire. The streets circumscribing the base of the Citadel were outlined by lights that bobbed dimly behind the curtain of falling snow in endlessly moving chains. These were the lanterns and hurricane lamps that swung from the shafts of the sleighs coming and going from the North End. In the South End, most of the windows had been covered by beaverboard or planks or blankets nailed on the inside, and few gave out any light. Here and there at street corners the police had hung out red lanterns.

Now the whole city was quiet. By early morning the rescue workers were too tired or hungry to speak, and there was nothing to hear but the wind and the hiss of sleigh runners gliding over the streets and the constant whisper of falling snow.

The blackened ruins of the North End were buried in drifts and gradually they quenched the remaining surface fires. Yet heat lingered in the foundations and melted the snow which lay directly over them, so that steam rose cold and humid and foul-smelling from that section of the town. Some of the rescuers probing the ruins for human life tried to work in the dark, but most of them had lanterns, and these flickered back and forth through the fire belt as men kept doggedly at work.

When dawn broke, Fort Needham looked like a long whale-back, pocked with hundreds of hummocks, gray with sooty snow. But a fume of steam rose from the whole of it and blew southwest in the gale, and the thin line of men working methodically across it appeared like the vanguard of an attacking army stopped in its tracks and digging in under fire.

The ships in the Basin were still awaiting convoy and the storm hid most of them. In the dawn the harbor was bleak and steel-colored, extending into the whitened land like a scimitar with broken edges, stained by fragments of debris drifting with the tide.

FRIDAY

Midnight Neil and the sergeant stood up to their calves in snow and checked the file of men returning with stretchers to the dressing station. Most of the stretchers were empty, but a few held prostrate forms. Two hurricane lamps swung from nails in the ruined building at their back, creaking in the wind. Shadows of the approaching soldiers plunged forward in the snow. Behind them, at the rear of the shelter, a cluster of lanterns made a patch of yellow light, and in the center of it a silent little doctor was dressing a man's wounds.

The soldiers filed in and set down the stretchers, all of them sooty as colliers from the blackened foundations in which they had been working for thirty-six hours. "All this lot seems to be dead," one of them said.

Bending wearily, Neil lifted the blanket from each of the four still forms, flashed his torch into the eyes and raised the lids. When he had completed the examination he took off his cap and beat the snow from it, passed a hand through his hair and sat down on an upturned box. "After the doctor's made sure they're dead you'd better take them out to the sleigh," he said.

The soldiers made no reply. One of them sat down on the floor but the others remained standing with arms limp and shoulders bowed over with exhaustion.

"There's only one sleigh, sir." The sergeant's voice seemed to explode out of the silence.

"That's all you need, isn't it?"

"I told you a while back that horse was too tired to pull," the sergeant said.

"Oh."

Neil got up and flexed his knees, one thigh stiff and devoid of all feeling, pulled his cap over his eyes and went outside. The silent persistence of the falling snow irritated him, as though the flakes had been a swarm of flies. He flashed his torch about and saw the sleigh in the middle of the street, with the horse crouched on the ground between the shafts. He slapped the animal's shoulder, then kicked it gently in the ribs. There was no response. "He'll freeze to death if we leave him out like this."

No one answered him. He looked back at the shadows of the soldiers in the shelter, but none of them moved. Perhaps they had not heard him; perhaps they were too tired to care any more what he said. After the panic and excitement of yesterday their work had descended to a killing routine of digging in the frozen earth, heaving away fallen beams, and clearing foundations. The longer they worked, the fewer bodies they found; but because they always found one here and another there, the work had to continue. Most of the bodies brought in within the last six hours had been dead a long while, and all were frozen stiff. The men had not slept the night before and had taken little food. The fish they had found in the market had been sent off to a community kitchen in the South End.

Neil felt mechanically in the pocket of his overcoat for a cigarette before realizing that he had smoked his last one hours ago. He moved slowly back to the shelter. His nerves were numb with exhaustion, but the cessation of physical work was followed by no relaxation. His mind was abnormally active and it refused to allow him to rest.

This was his own city; it had been in North America that this had happened. For more than a century and a half Halifax had existed without violence. Yesterday, within a few minutes, he had seen it cease to be a city. It occurred to him how solitary an organism Halifax had been, a diminutive cage of streets and houses illumined after dark, an oval of rocky soil surrounded by sea and forests. Now in the North End nothing remained but snow and anonymous death, nothing but whitened ruins, no lights but an occasional lantern flickering in the darkness. There had been one splendid, full-throated bellow of power: the earth had trembled, houses fallen, fires arisen. There had been a few hours of brave and passionate cooperation of human beings laboring in a single cause; then a mechanical routine; then exhaustion and hunger; then finally the primal solitude of snow drifting like sand over the ruins, of snow obscuring the quick and the dead and all the hideousness of carnage, of handfuls of men too tired to speak standing mutely in a ruined house with their heads and shoulders and hanging arms casting long shadows in the light of hurricane lamps.

He listened. There was no sound but the interminable hiss of the blizzard. He flashed his torch once more down the snow-filled depression that had been a street; nothing moved across the beam but the unending spangles of white. He coughed and buried his chin in his collar, and realized that his whole body was feeble from cold and that his coat was too thin for such weather. He returned to the shelter.

"Sergeant–" The man's head rotated in his direction. "There's nothing else to do tonight. March the men out."

They must have heard what he said, but they did not move.

"They're too tired to march, sir," the sergeant said.

In the back of the shelter the doctor had finished examining the last bodies brought in. "All dead," he said. "We might as well give up for the night."

One of the soldiers moved slightly. "I saw a small furniture store about five blocks south," he said. "Some of their stuff was still whole. Might be a place to sleep."

"Had the roof fallen?" Neil said.

"I don't know."

Neil shook the sergeant by the shoulder. "This is no place to spend the night. Get your men out of here. If we head south we're bound to find somewhere for them to rest."

The instinct to obey reasserted itself and the sergeant came slowly into action. A thought flashed through Neil's mind: I've just learned something. When a man's too tired to eat or speak he's still willing to obey.

"Come on, men!" the sergeant said. "Out of it! You heard what the captain said–get a move on, you there!"

The men shuffled out to the street, instinctively maintaining some form of order, and they went off through the snow with the sergeant leading and Neil and the doctor bringing up the rear. Neil carried one lantern, the sergeant another; the rest of the lamps had been extinguished and left in the shelter. Their stumbling march continued for over a quarter of a mile before one of the soldiers touched the sergeant's elbow. "This looks like the place," he said.

They scrambled through what had been a show window and the sergeant lifted his lantern to look at the interior of the store. Snow had drifted in, the roof had fallen at the back and most of the furniture was damaged. In the middle of the floor were three brass beds littered with glass and plaster. The sergeant pulled a coverlet off the nearest one and flicked it into the air. There was a rattle of falling glass, and then he flung it over the foot of the bed and sat down, feeling the blanket with dirty fingers. "Sheets and everything! Bloody place's like a hotel!"

Neil looked at the beds. There were twelve men besides himself and the doctor, and the beds would hold four each, if necessary. In a corner he found a small sofa lying on its side and dragged it out. "Want to try sleeping on this?" he said to the doctor.

The doctor sighed. He was a thin, nervous little man, obviously beyond initiative of his own. "What about yourself?" He hesitated, looking at Neil with weary admiration. "You've been on your feet nearly two days."

"I can't sleep now," Neil said. "I've got to see someone in the South End and I might as well start on my way."

The men rolled into the beds without even troubling to take off their boots. Neil went back to the street and trudged southward, the lantern swinging in his hand. The image of a strange girl who still was Penny filled his mind and excluded everything else. He was conscious of wanting to get back to her more than anything else, and he began to imagine what it would be like to be lying with her now, both of them warm and smoothly naked, in bed alone in the dark with the sound of the snow on the outer windowpanes.

But Penny had been wounded. He had almost forgotten that. And Murray . . . was he still working, or was he asleep now, too? Were they all going to forget about what had happened, now there was nothing more to be done and the snow hid so much of it? It was difficult to imagine that anyone else was still alive anywhere in Halifax, this district was so desolate and abandoned.

He held up the lantern and looked at his watch; it was nearly one o'clock. Surely Penny would be asleep now. Murray had said the wound was not serious, but it had required a delicate operation just the same. Odd chap, Murray. He plodded on with the wind driving the snow against his back. The explosion had played tricks with this block. Some of the houses were in total ruin while their neighbors seemed untouched except for broken windows, but the snow had drifted into all alike and they had become caverns through which the wind moaned. Penny had changed. It was difficult to grasp just how she had changed, but something alien had taken root in her mind and whatever it was, it was all her own. She had no intention of sharing it with him. That white lock of hair—that startlingly beautiful stripe retiring over the left temple from the forehead, white from the scalp! He had never meant to fall in love with his own cousin. Not with Penny, of all people.

He remembered the night he returned from his first year in the technical college at Boston. He remembered her face as she caught his look, her eyes dropping as she flushed in alarmed surprise, the immediate knowledge that there was a secret between them and no use denying its existence, the garden after dark and the soft feel of her cheek against his own. He had wanted her even then but had not dared admit it. The old childhood affection and easiness were too good to lose. And afterwards, alone in his room watching the moonlight on the familiar wall, he had known that she was awake in her room also. That was two years before the war; the night in Montreal had merely been a culmination.

He reached a corner and the snow swirled about him like a cape. The blizzard seemed endless; the gale had been blowing for thirty hours and now was stronger than ever. It was as though all the snow of Labrador had blown across the estuary of the St. Lawrence in an enormous migration to the Gulf Stream. His feet clogged in the drifts and his old wound ached, his mind was overcrowded with the dismal and shocking images which had charged it during the past forty hours, and yet he discovered in himself a sort of weary elation. The bitterness of his exile was quite extinguished. No matter what happened to him in the future he would always be able to tell himself that he had survived worse things in the past. *Forsan et haec olim meminisse iuvabit.* Only one who had experienced ultimate things could comprehend the greatness of that line.

He continued walking through the blizzard, his feet dragging in the drifted snow, but the sense of elation did not leave him. He was alone in this desolation and ruin and nothing seemed to matter but a new feeling of enormous and unreasonable joy. He was no longer a wanderer. He had come home and seen his city almost destroyed, yet he knew beyond any doubt that the war was not all powerful. It was not going to do to Canada what it had done to Europe. When it ended, there would be madness in the Old World. Men would be unable to look at each other without contempt and despair. How many in Europe would have the will power to live naturally under such an intolerable burden of guilt as theirs would be? The war was no accident, but the logical result of their own lives, the inevitable consummation of a willingness to frustrate others at any cost, to smash what they could not equal or understand.

And yet he and his countrymen had been a part of it. Why should Canada escape the results? There were thousands of dead Canadians and hundreds of thousands of living ones fighting over there now. Yes, but though a part of the war, they were innocent of the cause of it. They were explorers of an alien scene; they were adventurers, idealists, mercenaries, or merely followers of the herd. But no matter what the Canadians did over there, they were not living out the sociological results of their own lives when they crawled through the trenches of France. The war might be Canada's catastrophe, but it was not her tragedy; just as this explosion in Halifax was catastrophic but not tragic. And maybe when the wars and revolutions were ended, Canada would begin to live; maybe instead of being pulled eastward by Britain she would herself pull Britain clear of decay and give her a new birth. For that Britain would not endure into the future was unthinkable; she would endure, even if the United States were finally compelled to accept her destiny and balance a world which the Europeans were bent on destroying because they knew in their hearts they had lost it.

Suddenly, like a blow on the back of the neck, physical exhaustion struck him. He could never walk through this heavy snow all the way to the old red house tonight. He peered at the buildings he was passing. They were empty and windowless, but in much better condition than the places he had left a half-mile back. Some of them looked as though they had been punched in by a colossal fist, most were awry on their foundations, but almost any one of them would give shelter from the storm. He thrust his lantern through a casement and saw the snow-covered ruin of a living room. He continued to the next house, and the next. The snow had drifted knee-deep into the ground floors of all these places, for the window sashes were all set low and now were on a dead level with the drifts in the street. After five more minutes of searching he entered a doorway and the lantern disclosed a flight of steps. He tested them, and finding them firm, went up to the second floor. The door at the top of the stairs was open and he entered a narrow hall. The floor was dry and carpeted and the lantern showed lumps of plaster which had fallen from the ceiling. A telephone stood on a table and a small stained-glass window set high above it was intact. A strong wind was blowing from the back of the house and he went down the hall to investigate its source. The floor suddenly began to bend and sway under his feet and he saw there were great cracks between it and the supporting walls. Moving carefully, he turned into a doorway and stopped still, for empty space yawned at his feet and cold air was eddying into his face. The roof and upper half of the back wall had been blown down, and only by a vagary of the shock had the front half of the building been left standing. He crouched and held the lantern so that its light went down into the chasm. It revealed a welter of beams, of plaster and furniture caught in a trap by the lower half of the back wall. Little snow had entered, for it was the southwest side of the house. By all the normal logic of force, this side ought to have been the one spared.

His lantern began to flicker and he noticed that the edges of the wick were red. When he shook it there was no answering sound of splashing oil. He swore, and the light dimmed and went out. He took the electric torch from his pocket and as he flashed it down into the ruins he thought he saw the outline of a human body protruding from the rubble. He fixed the beam on the spot and isolated a head and a pair of shoulders in the circle of light. He replaced the torch in his pocket, lowered himself over the broken edge of the floor, and dropped. As his hands plunged forward for balance they touched something soft and smooth and cold. He flashed on the torch again and saw that it was a girl's body, entirely naked and exposed. It looked pathetically frail, stretched there in this senseless confusion, but the sight of it was more incongruous than shocking. He played the torch about towards the form that had first drawn his attention, lying face down. He was about to commence the weary routine of digging these corpses out of the debris when he realized that without the lantern he would have only one hand free for the work. The job of composing these strangers for their journey to the morgue would have to wait for the morning.

As he was trying to find a foothold to climb back, a plank broke loose and the man's face was revealed. Neil stood staring as the beam of the torch fell on the frozen, familiar features of Geoffrey Wain. His fingers slipped from the switch and he was in darkness, his knees shaking and the tired blood throbbing through his temples.

SATURDAY

Four-thirty P.M. The snow had ceased to fall, the wind had hauled to the southeast and was pouring inland from the sea under a sky that glistened like wet lead. The boarded windows of the South End looked raw against the lusterless volume of new snow. Occasionally, when the wind opened seams in the roof of cloud, there were brief splashes of watery sunshine and the fresh flakes glittered, but almost immediately the roof would close again. The streets were deep in drifts and gashed darkly by the marks of horses, sleighs and human feet, and in the downtown districts people shuffled aimlessly through uncleared sidewalks past boarded and half-empty stores, their overcoats appearing so black against the dreary whiteness of the streets and the sooty red bricks of the battered buildings that they all seemed to be in mourning.

The town was silent as a sick man too miserable to move. No trams jangled their bells at corners, there were no sudden sounds of motor horns. The snow was too deep for any car lighter than a truck with chains or a military camion to negotiate it, and many of these had already skidded on the hills and stalled in strange positions. The ships in the Basin remained at anchor; there seemed no life on them and no one gave them a thought. They had become a part of the landscape.

Angus Murray walked down Spring Garden Road, keeping to the middle of the street and watching nothing but his own steps. No one spoke to him, and if he recognized any of the people who passed he gave no sign. Since Wednesday morning he had not had more than six hours' sleep, and although the strain and fatigue and the constant throbbing of his injured arm bowed his shoulders and made him appear like an old man, he was too nervy to want to rest. He wanted more than anything to be alone, he wanted to see something that had not been maimed or destroyed; above all, he wanted to think and to have time to recover the only thing he had left in the world, the sense of his own personality.

He walked as far as the waterfront, perspiring with the exercise, and then continued south until he reached the outskirts of the Park. It was solitary enough here. The wind had whipped the shore so fiercely that most of the road was clear and the drifts had accumulated seven feet high among the trees to leeward. The sea wall was covered by a thin crust of ice through which individual stones were clearly visible, like bricks under whitewash. George's Island was encased in snow and crusted around the edges; on McNab's the trunks and branches of trees scarred the whiteness like a labyrinth of black wires. The harbor was opaque, and wraiths of steam crawled here and there over its surface.

Murray wondered what Halifax would have been like today had there been no explosion before the snow. He pulled a newspaper from his pocket and sat down on the smooth ice crust of the sea wall. The war had been relegated to the back pages. Passchendaele seemed to have petered out and there would be little news from Europe before the spring. If there had been no explosion, people in Halifax would now be telling each other what an awful storm it had been and prophesying the worst winter in memory. Geoffrey Wain would have learned that his plans for military glory had been upset and that the hidden resentments of his past life were not worth the bill which had accumulated through the years. And Neil himself, after keeping a hold on life for so long by the hope of revenge and vindication, might now be discovering that in the process he had changed too much to care for those things he had a right to enjoy.

Murray folded the paper and laid it on the sea wall, then shifted his position and sat on it. Perhaps Neil might still make that discovery. From the little he had seen of Penny and Neil together, he had been unable to find any real common denominator between them. Since the explosion they had hardly seen each other; when Murray had left the Wain house two hours ago they had both been asleep.

He crossed his legs and looked at the landscape; for the moment there was nothing more important for him to do. The town had plenty of doctors now. They had come in on special trains from every town in Nova Scotia, from New Brunswick and Montreal, even from Boston. A major he had just been talking with at the military hospital had expressed fear of an epidemic, but Murray was not inclined to take him seriously. Supplies were needed, and there was a distinct shortage of food, but that condition could hardly last for long. It was rumored that the Americans were going to send a relief ship from Boston, loaded with food, clothes, glass and medical supplies. It was a strange characteristic Murray had often observed in Americans, that nothing ever excited them quite so much as the repairing of a disaster, provided it were big enough.

Murray was as motionless as a part of the landscape, his chin sunk in his collar and a fur cap pulled down over his ears. During the past three days he had done good work, and he knew it. He had done better than even his incurable personal optimism had fancied possible. Since Thursday he had performed eleven operations without assistance and done the dressing for nearly fifty more. He had improvised a hospital which had handled nearly two hundred cases and he had seen to it that the work was good. He reflected on this record without pride but with definite satisfaction. Many doctors in Halifax had done more and were still at it, but if they were sensible they would rest now. There were enough fresh men to take their places and weather the emergency.

A solitary tramp ship had entered the submarine gates and was moving up to the Basin, and the sight of it reminded Murray again of his own part in the war. Just three years ago, almost to the day, he had sailed out of this harbor for Europe and had leaned over the rail of the trooper to watch every familiar angle of shoreline recede from view. So now the glorious adventure was in its fourth winter! Three years had passed and left him an old man. Was this feeling the culmination of a process induced by the war alone? He hardly thought so. Last week he had not felt this way. It was something more personal than an abstract disgust with the war, a revolution more profound than his immediate fatigue. He knew quite simply that the remainder of his life was going to be different from his past. He would never again crave excitement for its own sake, and the thought of alcohol or accessible women had lost any power they once possessed to modify his actions. The explosion, his experience with Penny and Neil and Geoffrey Wain, were undoubtedly connected with this development in himself, but the immediate link he could not discern. The only thing he knew definitely was that the microscopic society in Halifax of which he had felt, even though inadvertently, a part, had been blown to pieces and his own function in it had ceased to exist. Penny no longer needed him. Geoffrey Wain was dead. Alec MacKenzie had died only two hours ago. No one else in this town would even notice his absence.

Murray's twisted face yielded to a slight smile. The catastrophe which had torn Halifax had revealed nothing about its inhabitants that he had not known or guessed anyway. It had merely accentuated their ingrained characteristics. He smiled again as he tried to decide whether or not he really liked Neil Macrae. The boy had his points, but care for details was certainly not one of them. He had apparently forgotten already his original purpose in returning to Halifax. The explosion had been merely a release for his violent natural energy. He had done excellent work, and few others had shown equal resourcefulness. But while Neil had been busy in the North End with his dressing station, Alec MacKenzie was slowly dying in the military hospital. Neil had forgotten all about him; had it not been for Murray's own initiative, Alec would have died without giving the vital testimony.

Once again the wind was building up to gale strength. It swept raw and cold off the sea and stung Murray's face and pierced the thick wool of his greatcoat so that he had to rise and begin moving back to town. His eyes left the harbor and wandered among the iced tree trunks of the Park, and the sight of those gnarled, familiar boughs gave him a melancholy pleasure. He remembered a day very like this when he had arrived home for Christmas after his first term in college. There was no road to his father's valley in those days; it had been necessary to go from Sydney by a small coaster which brought mail and provisions to the Cape Breton outports twice weekly. He had left the ship at the jetty and walked the river road three miles to his father's house, arriving just about this time in the afternoon, shortly before dark. His father had taken him out to the barn to cut a sirloin off the frozen carcass of beef that hung there for the winter, and he could still remember the whiteness of the old man's mustache, his soft voice asking questions about college and the life in the city, his gruff manner as he tried to conceal his pride in the fact that his son Angus had the brains to secure a better life than had been possible for his parents.

A better life? If the old man were alive now he would probably still say so, even though in most people's eyes and often in his own Angus Murray was a failure. It was too easy to be sentimental and tell one's self that the pioneers were superior. Murray never shared the current bourgeois view that to be acquainted with the world's culture was a handicap for which a man should apologize. His father had been better integrated than he, but the only choice that had ever confronted the old man was whether to work hard and have a good farm, or take things easy and keep just above starvation level. He had chosen to work hard. Inheriting fifty acres of fairly good earth on the farthest eastern tip of North America, he had cleared a hundred more. He had taken some of the timber to a sawmill up the stream and had it shaped into planks for the larger barns he had built with his own hands. He had educated two sons and sent a daughter to high school. But his children were all he had been able to give the world, and they were his only continuity.

Murray had returned to the little valley just before he went across in 1914. The house had not been painted for twenty years and a stranger lived in it, the land was untidy and one of the barns was not being used, and when he walked up the slope from the river he saw the fences running into a stand of young spruce, and realized that nearly fifty acres of his father's clearings had already reverted to forest.

Why was he remembering all this now? Because only two hours ago he had been at Alec MacKenzie's bedside watching the big man die. His presence had been a peculiar comfort to Alec, for it had made him feel that he was dying, not in the crowded ward of a military hospital, but among his own people. Alec's village had been about thirty miles from the valley where Murray was born. He spoke like Murray's own father, he had the same aspirations, he had lived on into an era he could not understand; he, too, had left the world nothing but a family assured of a better life than his own.

To Murray, the death of an individual was an insignificant event unless it could be reconciled with a pattern possessing a wider meaning. He was still capable of being moved by a village funeral, by the sight of a whole community standing about the grave of someone who had been a part of the lives of them all. But death in a great city seemed to him much like death in the war, an atomic life extinguished finally by an enormous process which had always been its enemy.

The wind began to swing the frozen branches of the trees, gathering a powder of snow from their bark and lifting it howling backward through the woods. It was going to be a bad winter in Halifax, with schools working in double shifts, hospitals jammed, doctors working to the exhaustion point, thousands living in emergency tenements with insufficient heat and no privacy, and the unspeakable hideousness of wreckage left in every street as a reminder of what had happened to everybody. Perhaps it was fanciful to look for any pattern here; the explosion had been blind in its selection. Perhaps if there were a pattern at all it had been here all the time, and it had required this upheaval to enable him to see it.

He turned away from the wind and tried to walk more quickly. There was Geoffrey Wain, the descendant of military colonists who had remained essentially a colonist himself, never really believing that anything above the second-rate could exist in Canada, a man who had not thought it necessary to lick the boots of the English but had merely taken it for granted that they mattered and Canadians didn't. There was Alec MacKenzie, the primitive man who had lived just long enough to bridge the gap out of the pioneering era and save his children from becoming anachronisms. There were Penny and Neil Macrae, two people who could seem at home almost anywhere, who had inherited as a matter of course and in their own country the urbane and technical heritage of both Europe and the eastern United States. And there was himself, caught somewhere between the two extremes, intellectually gripped by the new and emotionally held by the old, too restless to remain at peace on the land and too contemptuous of bourgeois values to feel at ease in any city.

We're the ones who make Canada what she is today, Murray thought, neither one thing nor the other, neither a colony nor an independent nation, neither English nor American. And yet, clearly, the future is obvious, for England and America can't continue to live without each other much longer. Canada must therefore remain as she is, noncommittal, until the day she becomes the keystone to hold the world together.

Yet it was characteristic of Murray that before he reached the Wain house he had dismissed these ideas as too artificial to entertain seriously. His skepticism was already accusing the positive side of his nature for inventing an explanation of something which did not exist out of words unrelated to anything in his own experience. He yawned with fatigue as he entered the door and smelled the odor of disinfectant. Then he saw Aunt Maria, as inexhaustible as a machine, walking heavily down the front stairs to meet him.

"Penny's awake," she said, "and she seems to want you for something. For goodness' sake, Major, take off that wet coat first. She's in the library."

Murray found Penny balancing a teacup on the edge of an armchair. She had brushed out her hair and put on a tweed suit which made her hips look broad, and the pleasant composition of her features was ruined by the patch over her wounded eye. But in spite of this, there could be no doubt that she was on the way to recovery.

"Hello," he said. "You look as though you'd had a good sleep. When did you get up?"

"I've been getting up at all hours. First it was dawn. And then I got up when Neil came in." She put the cup down and crossed to the table to pour tea for Murray. "I guess I'm up for good now."

The listlessness of her voice surprised him. He took the cup she handed him and drank the tea standing, then sat down in an armchair opposite her. The heat of the room was increasing his drowsiness and he was about ready to fall asleep. He wished it were a month from now. He wished Penny were well again. He wished he did not have to think of so many things all at once.

"Neil still asleep?" he said.

"Yes, he's sound."

"I suppose they've told you?"

"About father? Yes."

Murray closed his eyes and sighed heavily. He hoped sincerely no one had told her of the circumstances in which the body had been found. "Things seem to have piled up, don't they?" he said slowly, as though fumbling for words. "The physical shocks—spectacular, I suppose—but they're easier to take than—than a lot of things." He opened his eyes and saw her looking at him intently. "Try not to have any regrets, my dear."

"Regrets? Why do you say that, Angus?"

"Nothing." He shrugged his shoulders. "A lot has happened in a little while, that's all."

"Maybe I should have—regrets, as you say. But I don't seem to feel anything. What's the matter with me? Am I still in a stupor?"

He knew that if Penny harbored any sensation of sorrow it would not be caused by her father's death, but by his life and the knowledge that he had done little with it that anyone wished to remember. So much the better if she felt empty of emotion now. Once more, he wished it were next month. But there was a routine to go through: Penny must grow accustomed to the idea that her father was dead and that Neil was to be accounted for again, to convalesce from a slight wound and a violent shock, to the cessation of her regular work until the Shipyards were repaired. Like everyone else in Halifax, she would have to spend the winter in a town hideous with destruction in which more than a quarter of the population were mourners.

He sighed and passed his hand over his eyes. It would be a great medical discovery if people could be put to sleep or hibernation for the duration of such a period. The whole world would need a sort of acclimatization drug when this war was over, but they wouldn't get it. They would have to live in the ruins for quite a while.

"Don't worry, Penny. You can't expect to feel otherwise. You've had a hell of a few days."

Her voice continued toneless. "But nothing seems to matter. Other people cry, or look as though they wanted to. I don't want to do anything."

"Not even to see Jean?"

She moved a foot back and forth, and her answer was more disturbing because neither her face nor her voice altered. "I've schooled myself to think of Jean as my niece for two years. I've never let myself imagine her a part of my own life." Her shoulders moved slightly as though to resist an advancing hand. "After all this time—Neil has never so much as . . . wondered. Now—I don't know—I hardly want to tell him at all."

"Why do you resent his not asking?"

"I know it's silly—why should I? I don't suppose there's any reason to expect a man to wonder about a thing like that."

Murray smiled slightly. "If you think he's forgotten, you know less about men than you imagine." His expression changed. "Where is he now?"

"He's asleep next door. Another explosion wouldn't wake him."

"He needs all the sleep he can get. After another few hours he'll wake up hungry. And then he'll eat like a horse. After that he'll want you. If you take my advice, you'll leave everything to him. He's got survival value. So have you, for that matter, but you've been drawing a lot of checks on it for quite a while."

Her lips quivered slightly as she watched Murray's tired face grow animated again. She wondered where his vitality came from. Neil was like that too, apparently exhausted one minute and full of vigor the next; only Neil's body was never still while Murray seldom moved.

"You've been awfully good to me, Angus. It's funny—I can't believe I've known you only a few months. You seem a part of the family—though that's not saying much, considering the family. But now I can't imagine not having you here."

"Don't let your Aunt Maria hear you say that," Murray said absently. He reached into his breast pocket and took out a long envelope. He looked at it a moment and then handed it to her. "You'd better read this. It concerns you as much as it does Neil."

She opened the envelope slowly and spread out a sheet of official hospital note paper covered with Murray's awkward handwriting and Alec MacKenzie's large and wavering signature at the bottom. There were two other signatures besides Alec's, witnessing the document.

She looked up at him. "What is it? I don't understand."

"You know why Neil came home so mysteriously, don't you? Why he was afraid of recognition?"

"Oh!" she said quickly.

Murray watched her bend over the paper and saw her fingers clench as she read it through. He had spent a full half-hour of the morning working out the wording of that document, but the only words that mattered were those quoting the message Geoffrey Wain had handed to MacKenzie that afternoon in the middle of the battle, and Alec's signature testifying to their authenticity as placed on this paper. It still seemed incredible to Murray that Neil could be so careless as to ignore the necessity of getting such a document. Alec had not forgotten. He had been so weak he could hardly move, but he had insisted on signing the paper before he died.

Penny looked up, her face colorless. "Did Neil know you were doing this?"

"No, he was too tired when he came in. I didn't bother to tell him."

"But you—you weren't too tired!" She buried her face in her hands and Murray moved awkwardly over to the arm of her chair and put his hand on her shoulder. She started to her feet and her eyes swept the room wildly.

"This—this house! I can't ever live in it again! That's it. Where shall I go, Angus? I want to get away from Halifax and everyone connected with it."

Murray smiled and let himself down into the chair he had just left. "I felt like that once, too. The house? Well, maybe. But Halifax? Nova Scotia?" He shook his head and closed his eyes, and then he almost forgot her presence in the room. Nothing but a short time to sleep, and then he would be moving out for good. There was a sound in the air, a plangent ringing that seemed to be in the walls. "I'd forgotten the wind had shifted to the southeast. The harbor bells are at it again. I suppose they'd still be ringing if everyone of us here were dead."

His mind clouded. He saw green trees under the sun and heard locusts shrilling at high noon and there was no more snow because it was midsummer; the hay wains were coming up the hill and after sunset the sea-run salmon would be rising in the river.

MONDAY NIGHT

Eight o'Clock It had stormed again over the week-end with rain and sleet, and then the blizzard had renewed itself and turned the atmosphere into a flux of dry snow drifting with a gentle motion out of the east. Now, for the first time in days, the night sky was clear. Everything was buried under shimmering snow so delicately clean that it seemed as though nature had conspired to conceal the misbegotten effects of human ingenuity. The peninsula of Halifax was a white shield curving upwards under the sharp-edged stars. The patches of harbor visible where the streets ended at the foot of the hill shone like sections of a river moving in moonlight and flicked by a breeze.

Penny closed the house door behind her and followed Neil across the snow-filled sidewalk to a military truck parked with engine running on the slope of the hill. A soldier inside opened the door and they entered, Neil sitting next to the driver with his knees straddling the gears, Penny on the outside.

"You're sure you can get through to the train?" Neil said.

The soldier let in the clutch and the car slipped forward with a cushioned movement through the deep wool of the snow. "The main street's pretty well beaten down now," he said. "We can try, anyway."

The car surged down the hill in an uncanny silence and the rear wheels slithered widely as they swerved into the beaten level of Barrington Street. It would be almost impossible to return up that hill, Penny thought; and then she realized with a sense of shock that she had left home for the last time. The house would be there for years to come. Spring would revive the flowers in the garden, and by the Queen's Birthday the creeper would have covered the stone wall, and by mid-June the cones of the chestnut blossoms would be nodding by the upper windows. But the familiar intimacy of the house would never return. Her father, the most untouchable man she had ever known, had been capriciously extinguished, and it was as though something profoundly improper had occurred without any adequate reason beyond the physical fact that two ships had met at a point where only one should have been.

She looked sideways as they passed one of the emergency street lights just installed, and saw Neil's profile clearly etched for a second; then it merged with the darkness again, and she was left with the impression of a man who seemed strange and unknown. The lines of his face were like sweeping arcs bound over an enormous spring of energy. They were tense and concentrated. She was tied to this man, and the realization made her shiver. She was a prisoner of his maleness because once she had wanted him and he had refused to forget it.

Turning, and seeing her eyes on him, he slipped his arm about her shoulder and pressed her closely against his side.

"Are you all right?"

"Yes," she said.

"Seems funny, going out to the suburbs at a time like this. Prince's Lodge was just a few houses on the edge of the woods the last time I saw it."

"I suppose it still is."

"This youngster of Jim and Mary's—how old did you say she was?"

"Just about two years." Penny waited for him to make some other comment, but none came. "She can talk a little."

"Is that remarkable at two?"

"Oh, yes."

She felt she must cry out if Neil said nothing more. He had not even asked why she was so anxious to go out to Prince's Lodge immediately after the storm, when it would have been reasonable to wait awhile or to send someone else to bring Jean into town. He had asked her no serious questions at all since that first afternoon when she had admitted him to the house. Now when he spoke to the soldier his voice sounded indifferent and practical.

"Is that the Shipyards down there?"

The soldier's reply came back carelessly. "What's left of it. It gets worse farther north. You'll have to walk through a lot of junk to reach the train. That ship blew right into the middle of the railroad yard. It ain't pretty."

The car bumped onward and the Shipyards slipped by in the darkness on their right. They drove slowly on through the darkened street, past scattered groups of tired men and women, past sleighs and slovens dragging wearily to the south, and on their left was a dreadful area of emptiness with incongruous bulges projecting along the slope where a few days ago thousands of people had lived.

Neil's hand tightened on her shoulder. He looked down and she saw his teeth as he smiled and then felt his chin harsh on the line where her hair met her forehead.

"This is a good town," he said. "Professional soldiers could have been demoralized by a lot less than these people have taken."

Everything he said seemed to frustrate her. "Neil—" she began.

"Yes, Penny."

"Neil—did you ever think——"

Here in the jolting truck, crawling through the darkness along the slope of Fort Needham, she was no more capable of telling him about Jean than when she had been in the oppressive atmosphere of her own home, with patients filling the upstairs rooms and Roddie and Aunt Maria hanging on every scrap of conversation that passed between them.

"Are you sure you're all right?" His voice was anxious. "Maybe we should go back? If the child has managed to get along all this time without us, another day or so won't make any difference."

"No. No, let's go on. We've got to."

She was in the current now. She had been in it ever since that night in Montreal, except that by synthetic action she had tried to pretend she was safe on dry land, safe with the accumulated weight of her environment to support her. She could see nothing clearly ahead. To force one's self on into the darkness, to keep one's integrity as one moved—this was all that mattered because this was all there was left.

Neil's hand was hard against her upper arm. She tried to visualize something of the welter out of which he had perserved himself. She saw him trying to make himself a cog in the machine of the army. She saw him lying like a dead man alone on a patch of tormented earth. She heard the sound of his footsteps echoing bleakly as he wandered like a fugitive through strange cities in England.

Then she knew that it was inevitable for him and Jean and herself to go on together, even if they could do nothing better than preserve themselves blindly for a future she felt to be epitomized by the events of the past few days. She was too much of a scientist to forget that titanic forces once let loose are slow in coming to rest again. Did Neil have any idea what confronted him? By nature he would fight indefinitely to achieve a human significance in an age where the products of human ingenuity made mockery of the men who had created them. He would fight because nothing yet had been too big for his courage. And perhaps he would gain his significance, just as within the last few days he had achieved his dignity.

She relaxed against his shoulder and tried to rest. Then out of the blackness enfolding the landscape they saw the glow of an engine's fire box and the flickering of moving lanterns, and finally they came in view of a string of coaches with their lighted windows drawing a long line around a gentle curve.

"It's almost like a wrecked ship!"

"A train in the middle of all this!" Neil's voice was eager. "When there are no trains to take people away from the messes they make—then you'll know the lights have gone out for sure."

The truck came to a standstill and the soldier pointed down the embankment to the tracks. "That's your way, sir. The path's been beaten down some since suppertime. I guess the lady'll make it easy enough."

Neil thanked him and jumped to the ground after Penny. They made their way through a confusion of tracks, overturned and gutted box cars and uprooted sleepers. This yard had been almost totally destroyed, but the snow had buried the worst remnants of the carnage and the moon gave the scene a false peace. The greater constellations were only a little dimmed by the moon, and their lights were hard and clear; the Bear hung over the Basin, Orion at their backs was mounting toward its zenith.

Neil laughed suddenly. "Remember the old tobogganing parties we used to have on the golf links? Do the kids still do it?"

"Oh, Neil!"

"What's the matter?"

"What a thing to think of now!"

"It's not that bad. Some things never change."

"But people do. I've seen the war changing them all the time."

"Maybe that's a good thing." He pulled her strongly forward as she sank into a deep hole in the snow.

"Neil, I'm so tired. I can't think any more about what may happen now."

"Yes, I know. Being tired is the worst part of things like this."

They reached the train and he left her while he picked his way forward to find the conductor. Then he was back almost immediately. "Standing room," he said. "We leave in a few minutes. Let's wait here till they start."

They stood at the rear of the train watching the opposite shore slope up from the black surface of the Narrows. Penny knew that in his own way he was trying to find means of assuring her that she was no longer alone.

He breathed deeply and smiled. "This air—it smells so damned clean! God, it's good to be back! Over on the other side I sometimes thought I could smell the future, but as soon as I got to thinking about it I couldn't tell the future from the past. I wonder how many people realize how fast they're breaking up over there? It's not a decline and fall. It's just one bloody smash."

"Do you think we're much better here?"

"Better? I didn't mean that. But I'm damn well sure we're different. The trouble with us is, we've been taught to think we're pioneers. We ended that phase long ago, and now we don't know what we are. I tell you, if Canada ever gets to understand what her job in this world really is—well, unless she does, she'll never be a nation at all. She'll just have to look on at the rest of the world committing suicide."

Penny made no answer, but continued to stare into the darkness over the Narrows. Neil knew next to nothing of his own country. He had never been able to see how it was virtually owned by people like her father, the old men who were content to let it continue second-rate indefinitely, looting its wealth while they talked about its infinite opportunities. And meanwhile the ones like Neil, the generous ones who had believed the myth that this was a young man's country, were being killed like fools thousands of miles away in a foreign world.

The conductor came down the line swinging a lantern. "You folks better get aboard," he said. "We're starting."

Every car in the train was crowded. Some were ordinary day coaches, but the majority were old-fashioned colonist cars generally used to transport harvesters and settlers to the West at cheap rates. These had board seats padded with black leather and backs which could be lowered so that passengers could sleep flat with their clothes on and their heads on their kits. The backs of the seats were down now, and wounded lay on either side of the aisles. In each car there was a single nurse.

Neil drew Penny into the door of the rearmost coach and they stood just inside the corner by the drinking-water tank. The interior of the car was in half-light and most of the prone forms seemed asleep.

"Neil—apart from the trouble you were in—why are you so glad to be back? What makes you think you'll find things so much better over here?"

There was a muffled blast from the locomotive's whistle; the engine passed a gentle shudder from coach to coach and the whole train began to move forward.

"A man has to think he hasn't got a country before he knows what having one means," he said.

He looked down the car and saw the lines of quiet bodies sway gently with the train's motion. Why was he glad to be back? It was so much more than a man could ever put into words. It was more than the idea that he was young enough to see a great country move into its destiny. It was what he felt inside himself, as a Canadian who had lived both in the United States and England. Canada at present was called a nation only because a few laws had been passed and a railway line sent from one coast to the other. In returning home he knew that he was doing more than coming back to familiar surroundings. For better or worse he was entering the future, he was identifying himself with the still-hidden forces which were doomed to shape humanity as certainly as the tiny states of Europe had shaped the past. Canada was still hesitant, was still ham-strung by men with the mentality of Geoffrey Wain. But if there were enough Canadians like himself, half-American and half-English, then the day was inevitable when the halves would join and his country would become the central arch which united the new order.

The train swung through a long arc and he saw the bodies of the wounded slide gently to the right as the force of the curve pulled them. They were outside Halifax now, going around the foot of Richmond Bluff.

"How long does it take to get to Prince's Lodge?" he said.

"Ordinarily we'd be there in less than ten minutes."

The statement tightened the muscles of her throat. She tried to look at Neil but was unable to keep her eyes on his. She felt his fingers on her wrist as he stood swaying with the train, and with the hundreds of wounded they surged on into the darkness of the continent, wheels clicking over the joints and the echo racketing back from the rock-face. In a few minutes the train slowed at Prince's Lodge.

They paused on the narrow, snow-banked platform and watched the lights of the coaches disappear around the next curve and heard the dying echoes of the whistle reverberating through the forest. A slight wind out of the northwest dragged down the gully of the track, bringing with it the fresh smell of balsam. There were no lights anywhere, but under the moon and stars the snow gleamed faintly out of the woods. Everything was utterly silent.

Suddenly Penny required his tenderness so greatly that it was as though all her life she had been starving for it. She wanted him to take her in his arms and hold her as he had done that unbelievable night in Montreal when nothing had existed but sounds in the darkness and the sense that each of them had been born for that moment. All this she wanted, but the habit of restraint, the cold control she had trained herself to acquire, was still unbreakable.

Neil made no effort to move up the road. He stood watching her, then came close and his fingers touched her hair where it escaped over her temples. He gave a sudden smile, and all strain vanished from his face.

"Wise Penelope! That's what Odysseus said to his wife when he got home. I don't think he ever told her he loved her. He probably knew the words would sound too small."

Tears welled up in her eyes and receded without overflowing, and her fingers closed over his. He looked over her head to the patch of moonlight that broke and shivered in the center of the Basin, and heard in the branches of the forest behind him the slight tremor of a rising wind.

RIGMAROLE

Morley Callaghan

After they had come in from the party, Jeff Hilton, the advertising man, looked up and saw his young wife, Mathilde, standing there beaming at him. She seemed to him to be glowing from the memory of many whispered conversations with young men who had been anxious to touch her hand or her arm; she smiled and went on dreaming and her wide dark eyes grew soft with tenderness. She began to hum as she walked over to the window and stood there looking down at the street in the early winter night; and as Jeff went on watching her he kept resenting that she should have had such a good time at a party that he had found so dull. She had left him alone a lot, but he had always remained aware of the admiration she aroused in the young men around her. And now she turned, all warm and glowing, and burst out, "Didn't you like the party, Jeff?"

"It was a lousy party," he said vindictively. "I'm fed up with that crowd. No one ever has anything new or bright to say. They've all gone a little stale."

Mathilde tried to stop smiling, but her dark, ardent face still glowed with warmth as she stood there with her hands clasped in front of her. Though Jeff went on talking with a kind of good-humored disgust his earnest face began to show such a desolate loneliness that she suddenly felt guilty; she longed to offer up to him all the tenderness, all the delight it had been so enchanting to have in her since the party. "I had an awfully good time," she said. "But I kept my eye on you. I know who you were with. Were you watching me, Jeff?" and she rushed over to him and threw herself on his lap and began to kiss him and rub her hand through his hair, laughing all the time like a little girl. "Did you think I was flirting? Did you think I laughed and whispered too much? Don't you love people to think I'm pretty?"

But Jeff, who had such a dull time, felt only that she was trying to console him and make him feel good; so he said irritably, "You don't need to feel you neglected me. Don't feel guilty. Nobody ever has to worry about me trailing you around. You can feel free."

"Jeff," she said very softly, "I don't want to feel free. I don't feel free now."

"Sure you do. You'd be the first to complain if you didn't."

"Didn't you worry a little about me once tonight, Jeff?"

"Listen here, Mathilde," he said shortly, "jealous men are the greatest bores in the world."

"Jeff, put your arms around me."

"What's the matter with you? You don't need to mollify me or feel guilty because you had a good time. Surely we've got beyond that."

"I wasn't trying to mollify you," she said, looking quite lost, and she began to show in her face much of that curious discontent he had felt growing in her the last three months. She was pouting like a child and she had the shame of one whose innocent gift has been rejected curtly, and then she went away from him awkwardly and curled herself up on the couch, almost crouching, her eyes hardening as she stared at him.

After a while he said, "You're childish, Mathilde. Why are you sitting there as if you hate me?" But he began to feel helpless against her silent, unreasonable and secret anger. "These last few months you've become about as unreasonable as a sick woman. What on earth is the matter with you?" he said. And he got up and paced up and down and his voice rose as he went on questioning her, but every time he passed the couch where she was crouching he became more disturbed by the passionate restlessness he felt in her.

So he tried to laugh and he said, "This is a lot of nonsense, Mathilde," and he sat down beside her. In a rough, good-natured way he tried to pull her against him. When she pushed him away he stared at her for a long time till at last he began to desire her, and again he put his arm around her, and again she pushed him away. Then he lost his temper; he threw his arms around her and held her down while he tried to caress her. "Stop it, stop it, Jeff!" she cried. "Haven't you got any sense at all? Doesn't it mean anything to you that you didn't want me near you a few minutes ago? What do you think I am?" As she pulled away roughly she was really pleading with him to see that she was struggling to hold on to something he had been destroying carelessly month after month. "Doesn't it mean anything?" she asked.

"There you go," he said. "Why can't you be direct about things instead of sentimental?"

"Because I don't want things that way," she said. And then she cried passionately, "You can't touch me whenever you like. You can't do that to me just when you feel like it," and her eyes were full of tears as if at last she had touched the true source of all her disappointment.

But he grabbed hold of her, held her a moment to show he could possess her, then pushed her away. "I'm not a little boy playing that old game," he shouted. "We've been married three years. Why all the rigmarole?" and he expressed the rage that was growing in him by banging her on the knee with his fist.

"Oh, you've hurt me," she said, holding the spot. "Why did you do that?" and she began to cry a little. "That ends it. You'll never hit me again," she said.

"Damn it all, I didn't hit you."

"You did. Oh, dear, you did! That settles it. I'll not stay around here! I'll not stay another night! I'm going now!"

"Go ahead. Do what you want to."

"Don't worry. I'll soon be gone," she said, and with tears streaming from her eyes she ran into the bedroom. He stood gloomily at the door with his arms folded across his chest. He watched her pull out drawers, toss dresses into a suitcase, sweep silver at random from the top of the dresser. Sometimes she stopped to press her fists against her eyes. He began to feel so distressed, watching, that he shouted at last, "I won't stand for this stupid exhibition!" and he jumped at her and flung his arms around her and squeezed her as though he would crush forever the unreasonable revolt in her soul. Then he grew ashamed and said, "I won't stop you, and I won't stay and watch this stupid performance either. I'm going out." And when he left her she was still pulling out dresser drawers.

As soon as Jeff walked along the street from the apartment house on that early winter night he began to feel that he really had not left that room at all, that wherever he walked, wherever he went, he would still be pulled back there to the room to watch her, and when he went into the corner tavern to have a glass of beer he sat there mopping his forehead and thinking, "Not just when I want, not just when I feel like it! I can't go on with that stuff when we're so used to each other. I'd feel stupid."

In the crowded tavern men and women leaned close together and whispered and while he listened Jeff kept hearing her voice beneath the murmuring voices and the clink of glasses and seeing her face in the smoke of the tavern, and as he looked around a dreadful fear kept growing in him that whatever was warm and vital among people was being pushed out of his reach; and then he couldn't stop himself from getting up and hurrying back to the apartment house.

He saw her coming out wearing her brown coat, and her felt hat was pulled down over her eyes. She was carrying her bag. A taxi was waiting. In a foolish way, to hide his eagerness, he smiled and said, "May I take the bag for you, madam?" He even made a little bow.

"No, thanks," she said, and she swayed the bag away from his outstretched hand, looking at him in that shy pleading way.

"Are you sure you wouldn't like me to take it?"

"Quite sure," she said.

"All right," he said politely, and he stood there trying to smile while she got into the cab, and when the cab actually moved off along the street, he stood there, worried and unbelieving, feeling there was no place to go.

But he went into the apartment and as he wandered aimlessly into the bedroom and looked at the empty dresser drawers his loneliness deepened, and he thought, "I tried to use some common sense anyway. She'll come back. If I went on struggling with her like that all the time I'd never be able to hold my job. I'll bet a million dollars she'll be back."

And he waited and was desolate remembering the shy pleading look in her eyes as she swayed the bag away from him on the sidewalk, and he listened for every small sound from the street, the stairs and the door; and when at last he heard the key turning in the lock he jumped up triumphantly and rushed to meet her.

She came in quietly with a timid, apologetic smile, and as she pulled off her hat she said in a bantering tone, "What were you doing, Jeff? What was keeping you up till this hour?"

"Waiting for you, of course."

"You mean you missed me?"

"Sure I missed you. You know I did, too," he said. He helped her off with her coat, begged her to sit down, rushed to the icebox to get a snack for them and his face kept showing all of his childish triumph. She was delighted to be waited on in this different way. Every time the broad smile came on his face she asked, "What are you laughing at, Jeff?"

"How does it feel to be free?" was all he said.

But when they were going to bed and she had buried her dark head in the pillow she began to cry brokenly, and no matter how he coaxed her, or how gently he spoke she would not be quiet. "Aren't we happy now, Mathilde? Isn't it all over now," he kept on saying.

"No, I'm not happy. I can't bear it," she said.

"You can't bear what?"

"The way you let me go. No matter what happened I didn't think you'd ever let me go. You wouldn't have done it two years ago."

"But you wanted to go, Mathilde, and if I thought you wanted to . . ."

"Two years ago you would have made me come back. You would have been afraid of losing me."

"I knew you'd come back like a homing pigeon."

"Yes, you were so sure of it. You were so very sure," she said, and then she put her hands over her face and she turned her head away, mumbling, "I'm silly. I guess I sound silly. I guess I don't know what I want," and he could only see the back of her neck and her hand moving over her cheek.

As he walked around the bed, looking at her, he thought, "Why didn't I stop her? Why can't she see that knowing we love each other is better than worrying that we don't," but he began to feel terribly afraid. "Nobody loves insecurity," he said, knowing his words sounded weak and apologetic. For a while he watched her, then went to speak, but he found himself shyly fumbling what seemed to be old words; so he stood there, silent, with his love becoming an ache, for it seemed a terrible thing that such words should sound strange just because they had grown used to each other. Then he knew that his fear had been that he would never be able to express all the feeling he had for her. And all he said was, "I had a glass of beer at the corner and I began to feel terrible."

"Did you?" she said without looking up.

"I think I know what you've been missing," he said.

"Yes," she said.

"I couldn't stay away from here," he said. "I felt you'd be pulled back too."

She looked up at him timidly for though the words he used were neither new, nor warm, nor strange, she began to feel his awkward shyness, she began almost to hear him thinking. "What happens that you can't keep showing your love when it's so strong in you?" She just waited there and grew shy too, and the feeling between them at that moment seemed so much deeper than any earlier time of impulse and sudden joy.

MRS. GOLIGHTLY AND THE FIRST CONVENTION

Ethel Wilson

Mrs. Golightly was a shy woman. She lived in Vancouver. Her husband, Tommy Golightly, was not shy. He was personable and easy to like. He was a consulting engineer who was consulted a great deal by engineering firms, construction firms, logging firms in particular, any firm that seemed to have problems connected with traction. When he was not being consulted he played golf, tennis, or bridge according to whether the season was spring, summer, autumn or winter. Any time that was left over he spent with his wife and three small children of whom he was very fond. When he was with them, it seemed that that was what he liked best. He was a very extroverted sort of man, easy and likeable, and his little wife was so shy that it just was not fair. But what can you do?

At the period of which I write, Conventions had not begun to take their now-accepted place in life on the North American continent. I am speaking of Conventions with a capital C. Conventions with a small c have, of course, always been with us, but not as conspicuously now as formerly. In those days, when a man said rather importantly I am going to a Convention, someone was quite liable to ask What is a Convention? Everyone seemed to think that they must be quite a good thing, which of course they are. We now take them for granted.

Now Mr. Golightly was admirably adapted to going to Conventions. His memory for names and faces was good; he liked people, both in crowds and separately; he collected acquaintances who rapidly became friends. Everyone liked him.

One day he came home and said to his wife, How would you like a trip to California?

Mrs. Golightly gave a little gasp. Her face lighted up and she said, Oh Tom . . . !

There's a Western and Middle Western Convention meeting at Del Monte the first week of March, and you and I are going down, said Mr. Golightly.

Mrs. Golightly's face clouded and she said in quite a different tone and with great alarm, Oh Tom . . . !

Well what? said her husband.

REPRINTED BY PERMISSION OF OXFORD UNIVERSITY PRESS FROM *Canadian Short Stories*, EDITED BY ROBERT WEAVER AND HELEN JAMES.

Mrs. Golightly began the sort of hesitation that so easily overcame her. Well, Tom, she said, I'd have to get a hat, and I suppose a suit and a dinner dress, and Emmeline isn't very good to leave with the children and you know I'm no good with crowds and people, I never know what to say, and—

Well, *get* a new hat, said her husband, get one of those hats I see women wearing with long quills on. And *get* a new dress. Get *twenty* new dresses. And Emmeline's *fine* with the children and what you need's a change and I'm the only one in my profession invited from British Columbia. You get a hat with the longest feather in town and a nice dinner dress! Mr. Golightly looked fondly at his wife and saw with new eyes that she appeared anxious and not quite as pretty as she sometimes was. He kissed her and she promised that she would get the new hat, but he did not know how terrified she was of the Convention and all the crowds of people, and that she suffered at the very thought of going. She could get along all right at home, but small talk with strangers—oh poor Mrs. Golightly. These things certainly are not fair. However, she got the dress, and a new hat with the longest quill in town. She spent a long time at the hairdresser's; and how pretty she looked and how disturbed she felt! I'll break the quill every time I get into the car, Tom, she said.

Non-*sense*, said her husband, and they set off in the car for California.

Mrs. Golightly travelled in an old knitted suit and a felt hat well pulled down on her head in observance of a theory which she had inherited from her mother that you must never wear good clothes when travelling. The night before arriving at Del Monte a car passing them at high speed sideswiped them ever so little, but the small damage and fuss that resulted from that delayed them a good deal. The result was that they got late to bed that night, slept little, rose early, and had to do three hundred miles before lunch. Mrs. Golightly began to feel very tired in spite of some mounting excitement, but this did not make her forget to ask her husband to stop at the outskirts of Del Monte so that she could take her new hat out of the bag and put it on. Mr. Golightly was delighted with the way his wife was joining in the spirit of the thing. Good girl, he said, which pleased her, and neither of them noticed that nothing looked right about Mrs. Golightly except her hat, and even smart hats, worn under those circumstances, look wrong.

How impressive it was to Mrs. Golightly, supported by her hat, to approach the portals of the fashionable Del Monte Hotel. Large cars reclined in rows, some sparkling, some dimmed by a film of dust, all of them costly. Radiant men and women, expensively dressed (the inheritors of the earth, evidently) strolled about without a care in the world, or basked on the patio, scrutinizing new arrivals with experienced eyes. Mrs. Golightly had already felt something formidably buoyant in the air of California, accustomed as she was to the mild, soft and (to tell the truth) sometimes deliciously drowsy air of the British Columbia coast. The air she breathed in California somehow alarmed her. Creatures customarily breathing this air must, she thought, by nature, be buoyant, self-confident—all the things that Mrs.

Golightly was not. Flowers bloomed, trees threw their shade, birds cleft the air, blue shone the sky, and Mrs. Golightly, dazzled, knocked her hat crooked as she got out of the car, and she caught the long quill on the door. She felt it snick. Oh, she thought, my darling quill!

No sooner had they alighted from their car, which was seized on all sides by hotel minions of great competence, than her husband was surrounded by prosperous men who said, Well Tom! And how's the boy! Say Tom this is great! And Tom turned from side to side greeting, expansive, the most popular man in view. Mrs. Golightly had no idea that Tom had so many business friends that loved him dearly. And then with one accord these prosperous men turned their kindly attention to Mrs. Golightly. It overwhelmed her but it really warmed her heart to feel that they were all so pleased that she had come, and that she had come so far, and although she felt shy, travel-worn and tired, she tried to do her best and her face shone sweetly with a desire to please.

Now, said the biggest of the men, the boys are waiting for you Tom. Up in one three three. Yes in one three three. And Mrs. Golightly I want you to meet Mrs. Allyman of the Ladies' Committee. Mrs. Allyman meet Mrs. Tom Golightly from British Columbia. Will you just register her please, we've planned a good time for the ladies, Tom . . . we'll take good care of Tom, Mrs. Golightly. And Mr. Golightly said, But my wife . . . and then a lot of people streamed in, and Tom and the other men said, Well, well, *well*, so here's Ed! Say Ed . . . the words streamed past Mrs. Golightly and Tom was lost to her view.

A lump that felt large came in her throat because she was so shy and Tom was not to be seen, but Mrs. Allyman was very kind and propelled her over to a group of ladies and said, Oh this is the lady from British Columbia, the name is Golightly isn't it? Mrs. Golightly I want you to meet Mrs. Finkel and Mrs. Connelly and Mrs. Magnus and pardon me I didn't catch the name Mrs. Sloper from Colorado. Oh there's the President's wife Mrs. Bagg. Well Mrs. Bagg did you locate Mr. Bagg after all, no doubt he's in one three three. Mrs. Golightly I'd like to have you meet Mrs. Bagg and Mrs. Simmons, Mrs. Bagg, Mrs. Finkel, Mrs. Bagg, and Mrs. Sloper, Mrs. Bagg. Mrs. Golightly is all the way from British Columbia, I think that's where you come from Mrs. Golightly? Mrs. Allyman, speaking continually, seemed to say all this in one breath. By the time that Mrs. Golightly's vision had cleared (although she felt rather dizzy), she saw that all these ladies were chic, and that they wore hats with very long quills, longer even than hers, which made her feel much more secure. However, her exhilaration was passing; she realized that she was quite tired, and she said, smiling sweetly, I *think* I'd better find my room. The hubbub in the hotel rotunda increased and increased.

When she reached her room she found that Tom had sent the bags up, and she thought she would unpack, and lie down for a bit to get rested, and then go down and have a quiet lunch. Perhaps she would see Tom somewhere. But first she went over to the window and looked out upon the incredible radiance of blue and green and gold, and the shine of the ethereal air. She looked at the great oak trees and the graceful mimosa trees and she thought, After I've tidied up and had some lunch I'll just go and sit under one of those beautiful mimosa trees and drink in this . . . this largesse of air and scent and beauty. Mrs. Golightly had never seen anything like it. The bright air dazzled her, and made her sad and gay. Just then the telephone rang. A man's strong and purposeful voice said, Pardon me, but may I speak to Tom?

Oh I'm sorry, said Mrs. Golightly, Tom's not here.

Can you tell me where I can get him? asked the voice very urgently.

I'm so sorry . . . faltered Mrs. Golightly.

Sorry to troub . . . said the voice and the telephone clicked off.

There. The Convention had invaded the bedroom, the azure sky, and the drifting grace of the mimosa tree outside the bedroom window.

I think, said Mrs. Golightly to herself, if I had a bath it would freshen me, I'm beginning to have a headache. She went into the bathroom and gazed with pleasure on its paleness and coolness and shiningness, on the lavish array of towels, and an uneven picture entered and left her mind of the bathroom at home, full, it seemed to her, of the essentials for cleaning and dosing a father and mother and three small children, non-stop. The peace! The peace of it! She lay in the hot water regarding idly and alternately the soap which floated agreeably upon the water, and the window through which she saw blue sky of an astonishing azure.

The telephone rang.

Is that Mrs. Goodman? purred a voice.

No, no, not Mrs. Goodman, said Mrs. Golightly, wrapped in a towel.

I'm *so* sorry, purred the voice.

Mrs. Golightly got thankfully into the bath and turned on some more hot water.

The telephone rang.

She scrambled out, Hello, hello?

There's a wire at the desk for Mr. Golightly, said a voice, shall we send it up?

Oh dear, oh dear, said Mrs. Golightly wrapped in a towel, well . . . not yet . . . not for half an hour.

Okay, said the voice.

She got back into the bath. She closed her eyes in disturbed and recovered bliss.

The telephone rang.

Hello, hello, said Mrs. Golightly plaintively, wrapped in a very damp towel.

Is that Mrs. Golightly? said a kind voice.

Yes, oh yes, agreed Mrs. Golightly.

Well, this is Mrs. Porter speaking and we'd be pleased if you'd join Mrs.

Bagg and Mrs. Wilkins and me in the Tap Room and meet some of the ladies and have a little drink before lunch.

Oh thank you, thank you, that will just be lovely, I'd love to, said Mrs. Golightly. Away went the sky, away went the birds, away went the bath, and away went the mimosa tree.

Well, that will be lovely, said Mrs. Porter, in about half an hour?

Oh thank you, thank you, that will be lovely . . . ! said Mrs. Golightly, repeating herself considerably.

She put on her new grey flannel suit which was only slightly rumpled, and straightened the tip of her quill as best she could. She patted her rather aching forehead with cold water and felt somewhat refreshed. She paid particular and delicate attention to her face, and left her room looking and feeling quite pretty but agitated.

When she got down to the Tap Room everyone was having Old-Fashioneds and a little woman in grey came up and said, Pardon me but are you Mrs. Golightly from British Columbia? Mrs. Golightly, I'd like to have you meet Mrs. Bagg (our President's wife) and Mrs. Gillingham from St. Louis, Mrs. Wilkins from Pasadena, Mrs. Golightly, Mrs. Finkel and—pardon me?—Mrs. Connelly and Mrs. Allyman of Los Angeles.

Mrs. Golightly felt confused, but she smiled at each lady in turn, saying How do you do, but neglected to remember or repeat their names because she was so inexperienced. She slipped into a chair and a waiter brought her an Old-Fashioned. She then looked round and tried hard to memorize the ladies nearly all of whom had stylish hats with tall quills on. Mrs. Bagg very smart. Mrs. Wilkins with pince-nez. Little Mrs. Porter in grey. Mrs. Simmons, Mrs. Connelly and Mrs. Finkel in short fur capes. Mrs. Finkel was lovely, of a gorgeous pale beauty. Mrs. Golightly sipped her Old-Fashioned and tried to feel very gay indeed. She and Mrs. Connelly who came from Chicago found that each had three small children, and before they had finished talking a waiter brought another Old-Fashioned. Then Mrs. Connelly had to speak to a lady on her other side, and Mrs. Golightly turned to the lady on her left. This lady was not talking to anyone but was quietly sipping her Old-Fashioned. By this time Mrs. Golightly was feeling unusually bold and responsible, and quite like a woman of the world. She thought to herself, Come now, everyone is being so lovely and trying to make everyone feel at home, and I must try too.

So she said to the strange lady, I don't think we met, did we? My name is Mrs. Golightly and I come from British Columbia. And the lady said, I'm pleased to meet you. I'm Mrs. Gampish and I come from Toledo, Ohio. And Mrs. Golightly said, Oh isn't this a beautiful hotel and wouldn't you like to see the gardens, and then somehow everyone was moving.

When Mrs. Golightly got up she felt as free as air, but as if she was stepping a little high. When they reached the luncheon table there must have been about a hundred ladies and of course everyone was talking. Mrs. Golightly was seated between two perfectly charming people, Mrs. Carillo from Little Rock, Arkansas, and Mrs. Clark from Phoenix, Arizona. They both said what a cute English accent she had and she had to tell them because she was so truthful that she had never been to England. It was a little hard to talk as there was an orchestra and Mrs. Golightly and Mrs. Carillo and Mrs. Clark were seated just below the saxophones. Mrs. Golightly couldn't quite make out whether she had no headache at all, or the worst headache of her life. This is lovely, she thought as she smiled back at her shouting companions, but how nice it will be to go upstairs and lie down. Just for half an hour after lunch, before I go and sit under the mimosa tree.

But when the luncheon was over, Mrs. Wilkins clapped her hands and said, Now Ladies, cars are waiting at the door and we'll assemble in the lobby for the drive. And Mrs. Golightly said, Oh hadn't I better run upstairs and see whether my husband. . . . But Mrs. Wilkins said again, Now Ladies! So they all gathered in the lobby, and for one moment, one moment, Mrs. Golightly was still.

Oh, she thought, I feel awful, and I am so sleepy, and I feel a little queer. But she soon started smiling again, and they all got into motor cars.

She got into a nice car with some other ladies whom she did not know. They all had tall quills on their hats which made it awkward. Mrs. Golightly was the smallest and sat in the middle. She turned from side to side with great politeness. Flick, flick went the quills, smiting against each other. Well, we'd better introduce ourselves, she thought. But the lady on her right had already explained that she was Mrs. Johnson from Seattle, so she turned to her left and said to the other stranger, Do tell me your name? I'm Mrs. Golightly and I come from British Columbia.

The other lady said a little stiffly, Well, I'm Mrs. Gampish and I come from Toledo, Ohio, and Mrs. Golightly felt awful and said, Oh Mrs. Gampish, how stupid of me, we met in the Tap Room, of course! So *many* people!—Oh, it's quite all right, said Mrs. Gampish rather coldly. But she and Mrs. Johnson soon found that their husbands both had gastric ulcers and so they had a very very interesting conversation. Mrs. Golightly did not join in because she had nothing to offer in the way of an ulcer, as she and Tom and the children never seemed to be ill and the ladies did not appear to need sympathy. She dodged this way and that behind Mrs. Gampish and Mrs. Johnson, interfering with their quills, and peering at gleaming Spanish villas enfolded in green, blazing masses of flowers, a crash and white spume of breakers, a twisted Monterey pine—they all rushed dazzling past the car windows—villas, pines, ocean and all. If I were courageous or even tactful, thought Mrs. Golightly, I could ask to sit beside the window where I want to be, and these ladies could talk in comfort (the talk had moved from ulcers to their sons' fraternities) which is what they wish, but she knew that she was not skilful in such matters, and it would not do. Oh, she yearned, if I could ever be a woman of the world and achieve these simple matters!

Then all the cars stopped at a place called Point Lobos, and everybody got out.

Mrs. Golightly sped swiftly alone toward the cliffs. She stood on a high rock overlooking the vast ocean, and the wind roared and whistled about her. She took off her hat as the whistling, beating broken quill seemed to impede her. She looked down and could hardly believe the beauty that lay below her. Green ocean crashed and broke in towering spray on splintered rocky islets, on the cliffs where she stood, and into swirling, sucking, rock-bound bays and caves. In the translucent green waves played joyous bands of seals, so joyous that they filled her with rapture. Bellowing seals clambered upon the rocks, but the din of wind and ocean drowned their bellowing. The entrancement of sea and sky and wind and the strong playing bodies of the seals so transported Mrs. Golightly that she forgot to think, Oh I must tell the children, and how Tom would love this! She was one with the rapture of that beautiful unexpected moment. She felt someone beside her and turned. There was Mrs. Carillo with a shining face. They shouted at each other, laughing with joy, but could not hear each other, and stood arm in arm braced against the wind, looking down at the playing bands of seals.

As the party assembled again, Mrs. Golightly stepped aside and waited for Mrs. Gampish and Mrs. Johnson to get in first. Then she got in, and sat down beside the window. Conversation about Point Lobos and the seals became general, and Mrs. Johnson who was in the middle found herself turning from side to side, bending and catching her quill. They then became quiet, and the drive home was peaceful. I shall never forget, thought Mrs. Golightly, as the landscape and seascape flashed past her rather tired eyes, the glory of Point Lobos, and the strong bodies of the seals playing in the translucent water. Whatever happens to me on earth, I shall never never forget it.

When she arrived at the hotel she discovered that she was nearly dead with excitement and noise and fatigue and when Tom came in she said, because she was so simple and ignorant, Oh darling, can we have dinner somewhere quietly tonight, I must tell you about all those seals. And Tom looked quite shocked, and he said, Seals? But darling, aren't you having a good time? I was just talking to Mr. Bagg and he tells me that you made a great hit with his wife. This is a Convention you know, he said reprovingly, and you can't do *that* kind of thing! Seals indeed! Where's your program? Yes, Ladies' Dinner in the Jacobean Room, and I'll be at the Men's. And Mrs. Golightly said, Oh, Tom. . . . Yes, of course, I know, how stupid of me . . . I'm having the *loveliest* time, Tom, and we had the *loveliest* drive, and now I'm really going to have a proper bath and a rest before I dress. And Tom said, *Fine!* But can I have the bathroom first because . . . and then the telephone rang and Tom said, Yes? Yes, Al, what's that? In the Tap Room? In fifteen minutes? Make it twenty Al, I want to bath and change. Okay Al. . . . That was Al, dear. I'll have to hurry but you have a good rest. And then the telephone rang and it was Mrs. Wilkins and she said, Oh Mrs. Golightly will you join Mrs. Porter and me and some of the ladies in my room one seven five for cocktails at six o'clock. I do hope it won't rush you. One seven five. Oh that will be lovely.—Oh, yes, that will be lovely, said Mrs. Golightly. She put her hands to her face and then she took out her blue dinner dress and began pressing it, and away went the bath and away went the rest and away went the mimosa tree. And Tom came out of the bathroom and said, Why ever aren't you lying down. That's the trouble with you, you never will rest! Well so long darling, have a good time. And he went, and she finished pressing her dress and put it on.

The next time Mrs. Golightly saw Tom was downstairs in the hotel lobby as she waited with some of the other ladies to go into the ladies' dinner. Tom was in the middle of a group of men who walked down the centre of the lobby. They walked almost rolling with grandeur or something down the lobby, owning it, sufficient unto themselves, laughing together at their own private jokes and unaware of anyone else. But Mr. Golightly's eyes fell on his wife. He saw how pretty she looked and was delighted with her. He checked the flow of men down the lobby and stepped forward and said, Terry I want you to meet Mr. Flanagan, Bill this is my wife. And a lively and powerful small man seized Mrs. Golightly's hand and held it and looked admiringly at her and said, Well, Mrs. Golightly, I certainly am pleased to meet you. I've just got Tom here to promise that you and he will come and stay with Mrs. Flanagan and me this fall when the shooting's good up at our little place in Oregon—now, no argument, it's all settled, you're coming! What a genial host! It would be a pleasure to stay with Mr. Flanagan.

Tom beamed in a pleased way, and Mrs. Golightly's face sparkled with pleasure. Oh Mr. Flanagan, she said, how kind! Tom and I will just *love* to come. (Never a word or thought about What shall we do with the children —just We'd love to come.) So *that's* settled, said Mr. Flanagan breezily and the flow of men down the hotel lobby was resumed.

At dinner Mrs. Golightly sat beside a nice woman from San Francisco called Mrs. de Kay who had once lived in Toronto so of course they had a lot in common. Before dinner everyone had had one or two Old-Fashioneds, and as the mists cleared a bit, Mrs. Golightly had recognized Mrs. Bagg, Mrs. Connelly, dear Mrs. Carillo, and beautiful Mrs. Finkel. How lovely was Mrs. Finkel sitting in blonde serenity amidst the hubbub, in silence looking around her with happy gentle gaze. You could never forget Mrs. Finkel. Her face, her person, her repose, her shadowed eyes invited scrutiny. You gazed with admiration and sweetly she accepted your admiration. While all around her were vivacious, Mrs. Finkel sat still. But now Mrs. Finkel and Mrs. Carillo were far down the table and Mrs. Golightly conversed with Mrs. de Kay as one woman of the world to another. How well I'm coming along! she thought, and felt puffed up.

During the sweet course she became hot with shame! She had not spoken a word to the lady on her left who wore a red velvet dress. She turned in a gushing way and said to the lady in the red dress who, she realized, was not speaking to anyone at the moment. Isn't this a delightful dinner! We haven't had a chance of a word with each other, have we, and I don't believe we've met, but I'm Mrs. Golightly from British Columbia.

The lady in the red cut-velvet dress turned towards Mrs. Golightly and said clearly, I am Mrs. Gampish, and I come from Toledo, Ohio. Their eyes met.

Mrs. Golightly remained silent. Blushes flamed over her. She thought, This is, no doubt, some dreadful dream from which I shall soon awake. And still the chatter and clatter and music went on. Mrs. Golightly could not think of anything to say. Mrs. Gampish continued to eat her dessert. Mrs. Golightly attempted to smile in a society way, but it was no good, and she couldn't say a thing.

After dinner there was bridge and what do you suppose? Mrs. Golightly was set to play with Mrs. Magnus and Mrs. Finkel and Mrs. Gampish. Trembling a little, she stood up.

I think I will go to bed, she said. She could not bear to think of Mrs. Gampish being compelled to play bridge with her.

No, *I* shall go to bed, said Mrs. Gampish.

No, do let me go to bed, cried Mrs. Golightly, I simply insist on going to bed.

And *I* insist on going to bed too, said Mrs. Gampish firmly, in any case I have a headache. Mrs. Magnus and Mrs. Finkel looked on in amazement.

No no, I shall go to bed, said Mrs. Golightly in distress.

No, *I* shall go to bed, said Mrs. Gampish. It was very absurd.

Mrs. Bagg hurried up. Everything all set here? she said in a hostess voice.

Mrs. Gampish and Mrs. Golightly said, speaking together, I am going to bed.

Oh, don't *both* go to bed, pleaded Mrs. Bagg, unaware of any special feeling. If one of you must go to bed, do please one of you stay, and I will make the fourth.

Mrs. Golightly considered and acted quickly. If Mrs. Gampish *really* wants to go to bed, she said, timidly but with effect, I will stay . . . a slight headache . . . she said bravely, fluttering her fingers and batting her eyelashes which were rather long.

Mrs. Gampish did not argue any more. She said good night to the ladies, and left.

Oh do excuse me a minute, said Mrs. Golightly, flickering her eyelashes, and she caught Mrs. Gampish at the elevator. Mrs. Gampish looked at her with distaste.

I want to tell you, Mrs. Gampish, said Mrs. Golightly with true humility, and speaking very low, that I have never been to a Convention before, and I want to confess to you my stupidity. I am not really rude, only stupid and so shy although I have three children that I am truly in a whirl. Will you be able ever to forgive me? . . . It would be very kind of you if you feel that you could. Oh, please do try.

There was a silence between them as the elevators came and went. Then Mrs. Gampish gave a wan smile.

You are too earnest, my child, she said. (Oh how good you are! breathed

Mrs. Golightly.) I wouldn't myself know one person in this whole Convention—except Mrs. Finkel and no one could forget her, continued Mrs. Gampish, and I never knew you each time you told me who you were *until* you told me, so you needn't have worried. If you want to know why I'm going to bed, it's because I don't like bridge and anyway, I *do* have a headache.

Oh I'm so glad you *really* have a headache, no I mean I'm so sorry, and I think you're perfectly sweet, Mrs. Gampish, and if ever you come to Canada . . . and she saw the faintly amused smile of Mrs. Gampish going up in the elevator. Well I never, she said, but she felt happier.

She turned, and there was Tom hurrying past. Oh Tom, she called. He stopped.

Having a good time darling? he said in a hurry. D'you want to come to the meeting at Salt Lake City next year? and he smiled at her encouragingly.

Oh Tom, she said, I'd adore it! (What a changed life. Del Monte, Mr. Flanagan's shooting lodge, Salt Lake City, all in a minute, you might say.)

Well, well! said Tom in surprise and vanished.

On the way to her bedroom that night Mrs. Golightly met Mr. Flanagan walking very slowly down the hall.

How do you do Mr. Flanagan! said Mrs. Golightly gaily. She felt that he was already her host at his shooting lodge.

Mr. Flanagan stopped and looked at her seriously as from a great distance. It was obvious that he did not know her. How do you do, he said very carefully and with a glazed expression. Did we meet or did we meet. In any case, how do you do. And he continued walking with the utmost care down the corridor.

Oh . . . said Mrs. Golightly, her eyes wide open . . . oh. . . . It was probable that Mr. Flanagan invited everyone to the shooting lodge. The shooting lodge began to vanish like smoke.

When she entered the bedroom she saw that in her hurry before dinner she had not put her hat away. The quill was twice bent, and it dangled. She took scissors and cut it short. There, she thought, caressing and smoothing the feather, it looks all right, doesn't it? She had felt for a moment very low, disintegrated, but now as she sat on the bed in her blue dinner dress she thought, Mr. Flanagan isn't a bit afraid to be him and Mrs. Gampish isn't a bit afraid to be her and now I'm not a bit afraid to be me . . . at least, not much. As she looked down, smoothing her little short feather, a dreamy smile came on her face. Seals swam through the green waters of her mind. Mrs. Finkel passed and repassed in careless loveliness. Mrs. Gampish said austerely, Too earnest, my child, too earnest. The ghost of the mimosa tree drifted, drifted. Salt Lake City, she thought fondly . . . and then . . . where? . . . anticipation . . . a delicious fear . . . an unfamiliar pleasure.

Mrs. Golightly was moving out of the class for beginners. She is much more skilful now (How agile and confiding are her eyelashes!) and when her husband says, There's going to be a Convention in Mexico City (or Chilliwack or Trois Rivières), she says with delight, Oh *Tom* . . . !

A PRAIRIE VAGABOND

(*from* PIERRE AND HIS PEOPLE)

Sir Gilbert Parker

Little Hammer was not a success. He was a disappointment to the missionaries; the officials of the Hudson's Bay Company said he was "no good"; the Mounted Police kept an eye on him; the Crees and Blackfeet would have nothing to do with him; and the half-breeds were profane regarding him. But Little Hammer was oblivious to any depreciation of his merits, and would not be suppressed. He loved the Hudson's Bay Company's Post at Yellow Quill with an unwavering love; he ranged the half-breed hospitality of Red Deer River, regardless of it being thrown at him as he in turn threw it at his dog; he saluted Sergeant Gellatly with a familiar "*How!*" whenever he saw him; he borrowed *tabac* of the half-breed women, and, strange to say, paid it back—with other *tabac* got by daily petition, until his prayer was granted, at the H.B.C. Post. He knew neither shame nor defeat, but where women were concerned he kept his word, and was singularly humble. It was a woman that induced him to be baptized. The day after the ceremony he begged "the loan of a dollar for the love of God" from the missionary; and being refused, straightway, and for the only time it was known of him, delivered a rumbling torrent of half-breed profanity, mixed with the unusual oaths of the barracks. Then he walked away with great humility. There was no swagger about Little Hammer. He was simply unquenchable and continuous. He sometimes got drunk; but on such occasions he sat down, or lay down, in the most convenient place, and, like Caesar beside Pompey's statue, wrapped his mantle about his face and forgot the world. He was a vagabond Indian, abandoned yet self-contained, outcast yet gregarious. No social ostracism unnerved him, no threats of the H.B.C. officials moved him; and when in the winter of 187– he was driven from one place to another, starving and homeless, and came at last emaciated and nearly dead to the Post at Yellow Quill, he asked for food and shelter as if it were his right, and not as a mendicant.

One night, shortly after his reception and restoration, he was sitting in the store silently smoking the Company's *tabac*. Sergeant Gellatly entered. Little Hammer rose, offered his hand, and muttered, "*How!*"

The Sergeant thrust his hand aside, and said sharply, "Whin I take y'r hand, Little Hammer, it'll be to put a grip on y'r wrists that'll stay there til y'are in quarters out of which y'll come nayther winter nor summer. Put that in y'r pipe and smoke it, y'scamp!"

Little Hammer had a bad time at the Post that night. Lounging half-breeds reviled him; the H.B.C. officials rebuked him; and travellers who were coming and going shared in the derision, as foolish people do where one is brow-beaten by many. At last a trapper entered, whom seeing, Little Hammer drew his blanket up about his head. The trapper sat down very near Little Hammer, and began to smoke. He laid his *plug-tabac* and his knife on the counter beside him. Little Hammer reached over and took the knife, putting it swiftly within his blanket. The trapper saw the act, and, turning sharply on the Indian, called him a thief. Little Hammer chuckled strangely and said nothing; but his eyes peered sharply above the blanket. A laugh went round the store. In an instant the trapper, with a loud oath, caught at the Indian's throat; but as the blanket dropped back he gave a startled cry. There was the flash of a knife, and he fell back dead. Little Hammer stood above him, smiling, for a moment, and then, turning to Sergeant Gellatly, held out his arms silently for the handcuffs.

The next day two men were lost on the prairies. One was Sergeant Gellatly; the other was Little Hammer. The horses they rode travelled so close that the leg of the Indian crowded the leg of the white man; and the wilder the storm grew, the closer still they rode. A *poudre* day, with its steely air and fatal frost, was an ill thing in the world; but these entangling blasts, these wild curtains of snow, were desolating even unto death. The sun above was smothered; the earth beneath was trackless; the compass stood for loss all round.

What could Sergeant Gellatly expect, riding with a murderer on his left hand: a heathen that had sent a knife through the heart of one of the lords of the North? What should the gods do but frown, or the elements be at, but howling on their path? What should one hope for but that vengeance should be taken out of the hands of mortals, and be delivered to the angry spirits?

But if the gods were angry at the Indian, why should Sergeant Gellatly only sway to and fro, and now laugh recklessly, and now fall sleepily forward on the neck of his horse; while the Indian rode straight, and neither wavered nor wandered in mind, but at last slipped from his horse and walked beside the other? It was at this moment that the soldier heard, "Sergeant Gellatly, Sergeant Gellatly," called through the blast; and he thought it came from the skies, or from some other world. "Me darlin'," he said, "have y'come to me?" But the voice called again: "Sergeant Gellatly, keep awake! Keep awake! You sleep, you die; that's it. Holy. Yes. *How!*" Then he knew that it was Little Hammer calling in his ear, and shaking him; that the Indian was dragging him from his horse. . . . His revolver, where was it? He had forgotten . . . he nodded . . . nodded. But Little Hammer said: "Walk, Hell! You walk, yes"; and Little Hammer struck him again and again; but one arm of the Indian was under his shoulder and around him, and the voice was anxious and kind. Slowly it came to him that Little Hammer was keeping him alive against the will of the spirits—but why should they strike him instead of the Indian? Was there any sun in the world? Had there ever been? Or fire or heat anywhere, or anything but wind and snow in all God's universe? . . . Yes, there were bells ringing—soft bells of a village church; and there was incense burning—most sweet it was! And the coals in the censer—how beautiful! How comforting! He laughed with joy again, and he forgot how cold, how maliciously cold, he had been; he forgot how dreadful that hour was before he became warm; when he was pierced by myriad needles through the body, and there was an incredible aching at his heart.

And yet something kept thundering on his body, and a harsh voice shrieked at him, and there were many lights dancing over his shut eyes; and then curtains of darkness were dropped, and centuries of oblivion came, and his eyes opened to a comforting silence, and someone was putting brandy between his teeth and after a time he heard a voice say: "*Bien*, you see he was a murderer, but he save his captor. *Voilà*, such a heathen! But you will, all the same, bring him to justice—you call it that. But we shall see."

Then someone replied, and the words passed through an outer web of darkness and an inner haze of dreams, "The feet of Little Hammer were like wood on the floor when you brought the two in, Pretty Pierre—and lucky for them you found them. . . . The thing would read right in a book, but it's not according to the run of things up here, not by a damned sight!"

"Private Bradshaw," said the first voice again, "you do not know Little Hammer, nor that story of him. You wait for the trial. I have something to say. You think Little Hammer care for the prison, the rope? Ah, when a man wait five years to kill—so!—and it is done, he is glad sometimes when it is all over. Sergeant Gellatly there will wish he went to sleep for ever in the snow, if Little Hammer come to the rope. Yes, I think."

And Sergeant Gellatly's brain was so numbed that he did not grasp the meaning of the words, though he said them over and over again. . . . Was he dead? No, for his body was beating, beating . . . well, it didn't matter . . . nothing mattered . . . he was sinking to forgetfulness . . . sinking.

So, for hours, for weeks—it might have been for years—and then he woke, clear and knowing, to "the unnatural intolerable day"—it was that to him, with Little Hammer in prison. It was March when his memory and vigour vanished; it was May when he grasped the full remembrance of himself, and of that fight for life on the prairie: of the hands that smote him that he should not sleep; of Little Hammer the slayer, who had driven death back discomfited, and brought his captor safe to where his own captivity and punishment awaited him.

When Sergeant Gellatly appeared in court at the trial he refused to bear witness against Little Hammer. "D'ye think—does wan av y' think—that I'll speak a word agin the man—haythen or no haythen—that pulled me out of me tomb and put me betune the barrack quilts? Here's the stripes aff me arm, and to gaol I'll go; but for what wint before I clapt the iron on his wrists, good or avil, divil a word will I say. An' here's me left hand, and there's me right fut, and an eye of me too, that I'd part with, for the cause of him that's done a trick that your honour wouldn't do—and no shame to y' aither—and y'd been where Little Hammer was with me."

His honour did not reply immediately, but he looked meditatively at Little Hammer before he said quietly: "Perhaps not, perhaps not."

And Little Hammer, thinking he was expected to speak, drew his blanket up closely about him and grunted, "*How!*"

Pretty Pierre, the notorious half-breed, was then called. He kissed the Book, making the sign of the Cross swiftly as he did so, and unheeding the ironical, if hesitating, laughter in the court. Then he said: "*Bien,* I will tell you the story: the whole truth. I was in the Stony Plains. Little Hammer was 'good Injin' then. . . . Yes, *sacré!* it is a fool who smiles at that. I have kissed the Book. Damn! . . . He would be chief soon when old Two Tails die. He was proud, then, Little Hammer. He go not to the Post for drink; he sell not next year's furs for this year's rations; he shoot straight."

Here Little Hammer stood up and said: "There is too much talk. Let me be. It is all done. The sun is set—I care not—I have killed him"; and then he drew his blanket about his face and sat down.

But Pierre continued: "Yes, you killed him—quick, after five years—that is so; but you will not speak to say why. Then, I will speak. The Injins say Little Hammer will be great man; he will bring the tribes together; and all the time Little Hammer was strong and silent and wise. Then Brigley the trapper—well, he was a thief and a coward. He come to Little Hammer and say: 'I am hungry and tired.' Little Hammer give him food and sleep. He go away. *Bien,* he come back and say: 'It is far to go; I have no horse.' So Little Hammer give him a horse too. Then he come back once again in the night when Little Hammer was away, and before morning he go; but when Little Hammer return, there lay his bride—only an Injin girl, but his bride—dead! You see? Eh? No? Well, the Captain of the Post he says it was the same as Lucrece. *I* say it was like hell. It is not much to kill or to die—that is in the game; but that other, *mon Dieu!* Little Hammer, you see how he hide his head: not because he kill the Tarquin, that Brigley, but because he is a poor *vaurien* now, and he once was happy and had a wife. . . . What would you do, judge honourable? . . . Little Hammer, I shake your hand—so! *How!*"

But Little Hammer made no reply.

The judge sentenced Little Hammer to one month in gaol. He might have made it one thousand months—it would have been the same; for when, on the last morning of that month, they opened the door to set him free, he was gone! That is, the Little Hammer whom the high gods knew was gone; though an ill-nourished, self-strangled body was upright by the wall. The vagabond had paid his penalty, but desired no more of earth.

Upon the door was scratched the one word:

"*How!*"

THE WORKER IN SANDALWOOD

Marjorie Pickthall

I like to think of this as a true story, but you who read may please yourselves, siding either with the curé, who says Hyacinthe dreamed it all, and did the carving himself in his sleep, or with Madame. I am sure that Hyacinthe thinks it true, and so does Madame, but then she has the cabinet, with the little birds and the lilies carved at the corners. Monsieur le curé shrugs his patient shoulders; but then he is tainted with the infidelities of cities, good man, having been three times to Montreal, and once, in an electric car, to Saint Anne. He and Madame still talk it over whenever they meet, though it happened so many years ago, and each leaves the other forever unconvinced. Meanwhile the dust gathers in the infinite fine lines of the little birds' feathers, and softens the lily stamens where Madame's duster may not go; and the wood, ageing, takes on a golden gleam as of immemorial sunsets: that pale red wood, heavy with the scent of the ancient East; the wood that Hyacinthe loved.

It was the only wood of that kind which had ever been seen in Terminaison. Pierre L'Oreillard brought it into the workshop one morning; a small heavy bundle wrapped in sacking, and then in burlap, and then in fine soft cloths. He laid it on a pile of shavings, and unwrapped it carefully and a dim sweetness filled the dark shed and hung heavily in the thin winter sunbeams.

Pierre L'Oreillard rubbed the wood respectfully with his knobby fingers. "It is sandalwood," he explained to Hyacinthe, pride of knowledge making him expansive; "a most precious wood that grows in warm countries, thou great goblin. Smell it, *imbécile*. It is sweeter than cedar. It is to make a cabinet for the old Madame at the big house. Thy great hands shall smooth the wood, *nigaud*, and I–I, Pierre the cabinet-maker, shall render it beautiful." Then he went out, locking the door behind him.

When he was gone, Hyacinthe laid down his plane, blew on his stiff fingers, and shambled slowly over to the wood. He was a great clumsy boy of fourteen, dark-faced, very slow of speech, dull-eyed and uncared for. He was clumsy because it is impossible to move gracefully when you are growing very big and fast on quite insufficient food. He was dull-eyed because all eyes met his unlovingly; uncared for, because none knew the beauty of his soul. But his heavy young hands could carve simple things, like flowers and birds and beasts, to perfection, as the curé pointed out. Simon has a tobacco-jar, carved with pine-cones and squirrels, and the curé has a pipe whose bowl is the bloom of a moccasin-flower, that I have seen. But it is all very long ago.

And facts, in these lonely villages, easily become transfigured, touched upon their gray with a golden gleam.

"Thy hands shall smooth the wood, *nigaud*, and I shall render it beautiful," said Pierre L'Oreillard, and went off to drink brandy at the Cinq Chateaux.

Hyacinthe knew that the making of the cabinet would fall to him, as most of the other work did. He also touched the strange sweet wood, and at last laid his cheek against it, while the fragrance caught his breath. "How it is beautiful," said Hyacinthe, and for a moment his eyes glowed and he was happy. Then the light passed, and with bent head he shuffled back to his bench through a foam of white shavings curling almost to his knees.

"Madame perhaps will want the cabinet next week, for that is Christmas," said Hyacinthe, and fell to work harder than ever, though it was so cold in the shed that his breath hung like a little silver cloud and the steel stung his hands. There was a tiny window to his right, through which, when it was clear of frost, one looked on Terminaison, and that was cheerful and made one whistle. But to the left, through the chink of the ill-fitting door, there was nothing but the forest and the road dying away in it, and the trees moving heavily under the snow. Yet, from there came all Hyacinthe's dumb dreams and slow reluctant fancies, which he sometimes found himself able to tell —in wood, not in words.

Brandy was good at the Cinq Chateaux, and Pierre L'Oreillard gave Hyacinthe plenty of directions, but no further help with the cabinet.

"That is to be finished for Madame on the festival, *gros escargot!*" said he, cuffing Hyacinthe's ears furiously, "finished, and with a prettiness about the corners, hearest thou, *ourson?* I suffer from a delicacy of the constitution and a little feebleness in the legs on these days, so that I cannot handle the tools. I must leave this work to thee, *gacheur*. See it is done properly, and stand up and touch a hand to thy cap when I address thee, *orvet*, great slow-worm."

"Yes, monsieur," said Hyacinthe, wearily.

It is hard, when you do all the work, to be cuffed into the bargain, and fourteen is not very old. He went to work on the cabinet with slow, exquisite skill, but on the eve of Noel, he was still at work, and the cabinet unfinished. It meant a thrashing from Pierre if the morrow came and found it still unfinished, and Pierre's thrashings were cruel. But it was growing into a thing of perfection under his slow hands, and Hyacinthe would not hurry over it.

"Then work on it all night, and show it to me all completed in the morning, or thy bones shall mourn thy idleness," said Pierre with a flicker of his little eyes. And he shut Hyacinthe into the workshop with a smoky lamp, his tools, and the sandalwood cabinet.

It was nothing unusual. The boy had often been left before to finish a piece of work overnight while Pierre went off to his brandies. But this was Christmas Eve, and he was very tired. The cold crept into the shed until the scent of the sandalwood could not make him dream himself warm, and the roof cracked sullenly in the forest. There came upon Hyacinthe one of those awful, hopeless despairs that children know. It seemed to be a living presence that caught up his soul and crushed it in black hands. "In all the world, nothing!" said he, staring at the dull flame; "no place, no heart, no love! O kind God, is there a place, a love for me in another world?"

I cannot endure to think of Hyacinthe, poor lad, shut up despairing in the workshop with his loneliness, his cold, and his hunger, on the eve of Christmas. He was but an overgrown, unhappy child, and for unhappy children no aid, at this season, seems too divine for faith. So madame says, and she is very old and very wise. Hyacinthe even looked at the chisel in his hand, and thought that by a touch of that he might lose it all, all, and be at peace, somewhere not far from God; only it was forbidden. Then came the tears, and great sobs that sickened and deafened him, so that he scarcely heard the gentle rattling of the latch.

At least, I suppose it came then, but it may have been later. The story is all so vague here, so confused with fancies that have spoiled the first simplicity. I think that Hyacinthe must have gone to the door, opening it upon the still woods and the frosty stars, and the lad who stood outside must have said: "I see you are working late, comrade. May I come in?" or something like it.

Hyacinthe brushed his ragged sleeve across his eyes, and opened the door wider with a little nod to the other to enter. Those little lonely villages strung along the great river see strange wayfarers adrift inland from the sea. Hyacinthe said to himself that surely here was such a one.

Afterwards he told the curé that for a moment he had been bewildered. Dully blinking into the stranger's eyes, he lost for a flash the first impression of youth and received one of some incredible age or sadness. But this also passed and he knew that the wanderer's eyes were only quiet, very quiet, like the little pools in the wood where the wild does went to drink. As he turned within the door, smiling at Hyacinthe and shaking some snow from his fur cap, he did not seem more than sixteen or so.

"It is very cold outside," he said. "There is a big oak tree on the edge of the fields that has split in the frost and frightened all the little squirrels asleep there. Next year it will make an even better home for them. And see what I found close by!" He opened his fingers, and showed Hyacinthe a little sparrow lying unruffled in his palm.

"*Pauvrette!*" said the dull Hyacinthe.

"*Pauvrette!* Is it then dead?" He touched it with a gentle forefinger.

"No," answered the strange boy, "it is not dead. We'll put it here among the shavings, not far from the lamp, and it will be well by morning."

He smiled at Hyacinthe again, and the shambling lad felt dimly as if the scent of sandalwood had deepened, and the lamp-flame burned clearer. But the stranger's eyes were only quiet, quiet.

"Have you come far?" asked Hyacinthe. "It is a bad season for travelling, and the wolves are out in the woods."

"A long way," said the other; "a long, long way. I heard a child cry. . . ."

"There is no child here," answered Hyacinthe, shaking his head. "Monsieur L'Oreillard is not fond of children, he says they cost too much money. But if you have come far, you must be cold and hungry, and I have no food or fire. At the Cinq Chateaux you will find both!"

The stranger looked at him again with those quiet eyes, and Hyacinthe fancied his face was familiar. "I will stay here," he said, "you are very late at work and you are unhappy."

"Why, as to that," answered Hyacinthe, rubbing again at his cheeks and ashamed of his tears, "most of us are sad at one time or another, the good God knows. Stay here and welcome if it pleases you, and you may take a share of my bed, though it is no more than a pile of balsam boughs and an old blanket, in the loft. But I must work at this cabinet, for the drawer must be finished and the handles put on and these corners carved, all by the holy morning; or my wages will be paid with a stick."

"You have a hard master," put in the other boy, "if he would pay you with blows upon the feast of Noel."

"He is hard enough," said Hyacinthe; "but once he gave me a dinner of sausages and white wine, and once, in the summer, melons. If my eyes will stay open, I will finish this by morning, but indeed I am sleepy. Stay with me an hour or so, comrade, and talk to me of your wanderings, so that the time may pass more quickly."

"I will tell you of the country where I was a child," answered the stranger.

And while Hyacinthe worked, he told—of sunshine and dust; of the shadows of vine-leaves on the flat white walls of a house; of rosy doves on the flat roof; of the flowers that come in the spring, crimson and blue, and the white cyclamen in the shadow of the rocks; of the olive, the myrtle and almond; until Hyacinthe's slow fingers ceased working, and his sleepy eyes blinked wonderingly.

"See what you have done, comrade," he said at last; "you have told of such pretty things that I have done no work for an hour. And now the cabinet will never be finished, and I shall be beaten."

"Let me help you," smiled the other; "I also was bred a carpenter."

At first Hyacinthe would not, fearing to trust the sweet wood out of his own hands, but at length he allowed the stranger to fit in one of the little drawers, and so deftly was the work done, that Hyacinthe pounded his fists on the bench in admiration. "You have a pretty knack," he cried; "it seemed as if you did but hold the drawer in your hands a moment, and hey! ho! it jumped into its place!"

"Let me fit in the other little drawers, while you go and rest a while," said the wanderer. So Hyacinthe curled up among the shavings, and the stranger fell to work upon the little cabinet of sandalwood.

Here begins what the curé will have it is a dream within a dream. Sweetest of dreams was ever dreamed, if that is so. Sometimes I am forced to think with him, but again I see as clearly as with old Madame's eyes, that have not seen the earthly light for twenty years, and with her and Hyacinthe, I say "Credo."

Hyacinthe said that he lay upon the shavings in the sweetness of the sandalwood, and was very tired. He thought of the country where the stranger had been a boy; of the flowers on the hills; of the laughing leaves of aspen, and poplar; of the golden flowering anise and the golden sun upon the dusty roads, until he was warm. All the time through these pictures, as through a painted veil, he was aware of that other boy with the quiet eyes, at work upon the cabinet, smoothing, fitting, polishing. "He does better work than I," thought Hyacinthe, but he was not jealous. And again he thought, "It is growing towards morning. In a little while I will get up and help him." But he did not, for the dream of warmth and the smell of the sandalwood held him in a sweet drowse. Also he said that he thought the stranger was singing as he worked, for there seemed to be a sense of some music in the shed, though he could not tell whether it came from the other boy's lips, or from the shabby old tools as he used them, or from the stars. "The stars are much paler," thought Hyacinthe, "and soon it will be morning, and the corners are not carved yet. I must get up and help this kind one in a little moment. Only I am so tired, and the music and the sweetness seem to wrap me and fold me close, so that I may not move."

He lay without moving, and behind the forest there shone a pale glow of some indescribable colour that was neither green nor blue, while in Terminaison the church bells began to ring. "Day will soon be here!" thought Hyacinthe, immovable in that deep dream of his, "and with day will come Monsieur L'Oreillard and his stick. I must get up and help, for even yet the corners are not carved."

But he did not get up. Instead, he saw the stranger look at him again, smiling as if he loved him, and lay his brown finger lightly upon the four empty corners of the cabinet. And Hyacinthe saw the little squares of reddish wood ripple and heave and break, as little clouds when the wind goes through the sky. And out of them thrust forth little birds, and after them the lilies, for a moment living, but even while Hyacinthe looked, growing hard and reddish-brown and settling back into the sweet wood. Then the stranger smiled again, and laid all the tools neatly in order, and, opening the door quietly, went away into the woods.

Hyacinthe lay still among the shavings for a long time, and then he crept slowly to the door. The sun, not yet risen, set its first beams upon the delicate mist of frost afloat beneath the trees, and so all the world was aflame with splendid gold. Far away down the road a dim figure seemed to move amid the glory, but the glow and the splendour were such that Hyacinthe was blinded. His breath came sharply as the glow beat in great waves on the wretched shed; on the foam of shavings; on the cabinet with the little birds and the lilies carved at the corners.

He was too pure of heart to feel afraid. But, "Blessed be the Lord," whispered Hyacinthe, clasping his slow hands, "for He hath visited and redeemed His people. But who will believe?"

Then the sun of Christ's day rose gloriously, and the little sparrow came from his nest among the shavings and shook his wings to the light.

THE CZECH DOG

W. G. Hardy

She had been noticing him sitting in the corner, half hidden by a fern. Because she had been told that he was a Czech newly come to New York, and because he seemed alone and out of place and somewhat tense, she went over and tried to make conversation.

But the room was noisy with well-fed, charitable people, come together in this Red Cross rally, and now that she was near him she sensed emanating from him an unpredictable violence of protest. Trying to view the gathering as she supposed it must appear to him—the cocktails, the gay chatter, the complaints about gasoline rationing and the dearth of steaks—she thought she understood. So on impulse she said, keeping her voice even:

"Look, I ought to be home early. Will you be an excuse for me to go?"

He was well-bred. He picked up the cue without visible surprise. At her own door she hesitated, and then, stirred by sympathy, and at the same time interested in what kept this man taut and withdrawn, she asked him in.

It was no easier to talk when they were in her living-room. She dragged out of him that a month ago he had been flown out of Czechoslovakia to England, and that he was in America on something to do with supplies for the Underground in his country. But he would not enlarge on either point. So she said the obvious thing, hoping that it might get him started:

"It must be terrible in Czechoslovakia."

He nodded—and let it go at that. She looked at his mobile intellectual face, realizing that it was closed against her and wondering why. Just then her dog came into the room. It was a collie, a beautiful animal. She leaned forward and spoke to it, expecting it to come to her. But after a leisurely look around it ignored her, and, ears flat and half laughing with its mouth in the way dogs have, it walked deliberately over to the man, put its head on his knees, and looked up at him. He reached down and scratched behind the silky ears. She remarked with a certain measure of annoyance:

"You seem to be a person dogs like."

He glanced at her quickly. "Yes," he said. He thought a moment. Then, stroking the dog's head gently, he went on: "I know what you have been trying to do. It is kind of you. But it is of no use. Each of us has his own circle of experience into which no one else can enter."

REPRINTED BY PERMISSION OF THE AUTHOR. ORIGINALLY APPEARED IN *Tomorrow*, 1944.

She leaned back in her comfortable chair. "I am not sure that that is always true."

"I think so." He looked away from her and around at the room—the soft light, the pictures, the deep rugs, the graceful vases. The collie, perceiving that the man's attention was diverted, placed itself with dignity at his feet, and putting its head on its forepaws, watched him. "If I tell you that I, who was once a physician—well-to-do, respected, secure—lay on a floor, helpless, and was kicked and beaten, and then revived, and then beaten and kicked—hour after hour—it will only be words to you, because you cannot imagine that ever happening to your brother or your husband, or to anyone you know. Or if I say to you that my sister, as educated and as delicately brought up as you, is now in a German concentration camp, you will exclaim, 'How terrible!' It will not be actuality—a living actuality—because never in your life have you been, or will you be, in danger of that."

"I suppose we, here in America, must seem—untouched," she murmured, thinking of the meeting they had left and noticing how alive his face was now. "Yet some of us would like to understand."

He shrugged his shoulders. "To you, Freedom is still a careless dress. Forgive me, if I am rhetorical. If you had ever known what it is to cringe in your own country before an alien, to starve, to be helpless. As it is . . ." He stopped and looked around him again, as if searching. His eyes chanced on the collie at his feet. It stirred and made a whimpering, inquiring sound in its throat. He reached down to touch it, soothing it. Then he looked across at her hesitantly, almost shyly. "You have a dog, a dog that you love," he said. "If I were, perhaps, to tell you of another dog, a dog in Czechoslovakia . . . ?"

"Do."

"It was not much of a dog," he explained, sitting up. "It was only a little one, half—no, almost wholly—starved. But its manners were good. At one time it had been, I am sure, someone's pet, sleek, fat, probably impertinent. When I saw it, its coat was ragged and its ears were torn and its ribs were there to count.

"It was on the first morning that it found me. I was, you must understand, carrying a message for the Underground, and it was imperative that that message reach one man, the right man. At the very outset of my journey I was stopped by a patrol. They knocked me about. But I was disguised as a crippled peasant—and as you see, that was good, because I am crippled. Nor did I, who used to walk down the street and give way to no man—even as you in America—forget to be as cringing and as animal-like as the Nazis think a Czech in his own country should be. I begged on my knees. I wept. I went slobbering after my bit of bread when they flung it into the mud. One of them put a hob-nailed boot on my hand—this hand—when I had got hold of it, and laughed, and they all laughed and they let me go. I laughed, too, within myself. I had won, this time.

"But about the dog. I was travelling, you comprehend, between dusk and dawn. It was in the early morning, in a wooded part of my country where I had made myself a hiding-place, that it smelled me out. I cursed it. I flung sticks at it. But dogs know. It came crawling back to me, its tail between its legs, its eyes pleading. I ought to have kicked it away. We Czechs, you must understand, have been left only one possession—the will not to give in. We dare not have any other—except hate. So I ought to have kicked it, brutally, so that it would not come back. But it was lost and homeless and starving and did not comprehend why. It had done no wrong. I could not kick it. I said to myself:

" 'Cannot a Czech peasant have a dog with him?'

"I gave it the bit of bread. I let it curl up against me. That night, and the next night, I let it come with me. What food I got I shared with it. It was a good dog. It was so grateful to belong to someone again. And then during the third night I was crawling along a ditch. I was there, you understand, because I was in an area of Czechoslovakia where a Czech is shot at sight. But I was tired of the ditch and of the mud and water in it. I had seen no Germans. I had heard none. I said to myself that I would get out of the ditch. At that instant the dog growled, deep in its throat. I waited. A patrol came tramping by.

"When it had passed I patted the dog and praised it, and it wagged its tail and its whole body, and licked my hand. It was when it licked my hand that I realized how alone I had been, and for how long. I had been kicked and beaten. I had had other things done to me—things that leave you no—no dignity. I, who had once been prosperous and secure and free, had been compelled to stand by helpless in my own home while what was done to my wife was done. Something had died in me. But now it began to stir again. I, who for so long had had no part in any emotion but hate, felt that dog lick my hand. I hugged it. I hugged it to myself."

He paused, and she could see that his mind was a long way off. Sitting here in this secure, comfortable room, she tried to visualize the ditch and the darkness and this man, so quiet, so proud, so impeccably-mannered, down in the mud, hugging a half-starved dog. Yes, she could see the dog—poor thing. She glanced at her own collie. It was continuing to watch the man in complete oblivion of herself.

"And then?" she asked, more sharply than she realized.

The man roused himself. "Then? Oh, then we went on. Two nights later we came at last almost to the end of my journey, to the most crucial part of it, to a place where there was a cordon of sentries through which I must pass. In my other life I would have pronounced it impossible. But those Germans—so methodical that we of the Underground had been able to plot the exact time each sentry passed each post! I waited for the sentry to go by because I knew that then I would have exactly seven and one-half minutes before he returned, and that would be time enough, if I were quick.

"I crouched there in the darkness in a hollow, waiting. There was a certain triumph in me. For I felt now that I would get my message through, and then certain Nazis who had exercised lust and cruelty on helpless ones, and had laughed and thought there would be no reckoning, would find out that they were wrong.

"That was how I felt. I had my arm around the dog and it was warm against me, and we waited.

"But then the dog growled.

"It meant that the sentry was coming. But I was afraid that he might hear. I could not take chances. In that place, at the slightest hint of anything unusual, the orders of the sentries are not to investigate, but to call out the guard. If it were called and a search were made, I would be discovered and my message would not get through. I spoke quickly under my breath to the dog, bidding it be quiet.

"But it kept on growling.

"It was imperative, you must comprehend, that I get through with my message. But I had come to love this dog. I had no wife any longer, and no home and no sister. But I had this dog. And the dog had me. It was all either of us had left to us. So I took a chance. I whispered to it again, begging it to understand and to be still. How could it understand? This was one of the enemy coming—and I had praised it before. It growled louder, deep in its throat.

"I could hear the sentry now. My message had to get through. I leaped on that little, half-starved dog, gripping its body between my knees so that it could not move. I seized its throat with my fingers—these fingers. They are strong, these fingers. They have to be, because if we have no weapons and a man has to be killed. . . . So I squeezed—savagely.

"If only the sentry had gone right by. I prayed that he would go right by. But he took his time. He stopped. He lit a cigarette and took a puff or two and looked about him. Then he put out the cigarette and went on. I unloosed my fingers. If only the dog had been well-fed, strong—like this one here. It wasn't. And I—I had no time. I left it there. I went on."

He stopped speaking. She stirred in her chair. Her mind comprehended what the man was trying to tell her. But she kept seeing that dog, the dog which had trusted him. Her own dog, troubled by the sense of things about him, shifted its head and made that whimpering, questioning sound again. The man leaned down, and smiling in understanding, passed his fingers gently over the collie's head. She looked at those fingers. It was not this man's fault that in his fight for his country he had had to sacrifice everything—even pity. But—those fingers——

"Here, Drake," she said to the collie, getting abruptly to her feet. "Come here!"

The man rose, looked around for his hat and cane, and started for the door.

"Of course, it was a Czech dog," he said, as if to himself.

READ!

Lord Beaverbrook

To young men who complain of defects in their education I would give this message:

Never believe that success cannot come your way because of the manner of your education.

The nineteenth century made a god of education. Its eminent men placed learning as the foremost influence in life. Yet education imposed from without may be a hindrance rather than a help. The young man on the verge of life need not be discouraged by the fact that he has been denied the hallmark of a great university. Valuable, indeed, is the training offered to youth in these venerable establishments, but the inquiring mind may have escaped a grave danger; for if, in the impressionable period of youth, attention is given to one kind of knowledge it may be withdrawn from another.

The truth is that education is the fruit of temperament, not success the fruit of education. What a man draws into himself by his own natural volition is what counts, because it becomes a living part of himself.

Of course a child or an adult should learn what he can from teachers. I value formal education and I recommend university training. In these days of scholarships the bright, ambitious, and venturesome youth will make full use of the opportunities they afford. But if the student should find that he has genuine difficulty in learning lessons imposed upon him from above, let him not despair. He will be in good company. Did not the great Churchill almost break the hearts of his schoolmasters?

My own education was most rudimentary. It may be difficult for the modern mind to grasp life in the parish of Newcastle, New Brunswick, in the 'eighties–sparse patches of cultivation surrounded by the virgin forest and broken by the rush of an immense river. For half the year the land is in the iron grip of snow and frost, and the Miramichi is frozen right down to its estuary, so that "the rain was turned to a white dust, and the sea to a great green stone." In such conditions and in those days education lacked continuity.

Men and books have been my real school. Reading is the source of education and of style. Read what you like, not what somebody else tells you that you ought to like. That reading alone which becomes part of the reader's own mind and nature is valuable.

Read anything and read everything—just as a man with a sound digestion and a good appetite eats largely and indifferently of all that is set before him.

The process of selection and rejection—in other words, of taste—will come naturally to any man who has the right kind of brains in his head. Some books he will throw away; others he will read over again.

As a liking for the right kind of literature grows on a man, he unconsciously forms his mind and his taste and his style, and by a natural impulse, without forced growth, the whole world of letters is his.

There are, of course, certain special branches of education which many youths consider unnecessary equipment for a business career. Foremost among these are mathematics and foreign languages. Knowledge of the higher mathematics is not essential to a successful career; nonetheless, the type of mind that takes readily to mathematics is the kind that succeeds in the realm of industry and finance.

I regret that my business career was shaped on a continent that speaks one single language for commercial purposes from the Arctic Circle to the Gulf of Mexico. Foreign languages are, therefore, a sealed book to me.

If a man can properly appraise the value of something he does not possess, I would place a knowledge of languages high in the list of acquirements making for success.

But when all is said and done, the real education is the market place of the street. There the study of character enables the boy of judgment to develop an unholy proficiency in estimating the value of the currency of the realm.

Experience teaches that no man ought to be downcast in setting out on the adventure of life by a lack of formal knowledge.

The first Lord Birkenhead many years ago asked me where I was going to educate one of my sons. When I replied that I had not thought about the matter, and did not care, he was unable to repress his horror.

And yet the real reasons for such indifferences are deep rooted in my mind. A boy is master, and the only master, of his fortune. If he wants to succeed in literature, or in any other walk of life, he will read until he obtains by what he draws into himself that kind of trained perception that enables him to distinguish between good work and bad, just as the wine expert with his eyes shut knows the difference between a good and a bad glass of wine.

Neither may be able to give any reason for a verdict based on unconscious knowledge, but each will be right when he says, "Here I have written well," or "Here I have taken bad drink."

The message, therefore, is one of encouragement to young men who are determined to succeed in the affairs of the world and yet have not been through prep school and college. There is the danger that the prep school may turn out a boy to type—the individual turns out himself.

In the hour of action it is probable that the individual will defeat the type.

Style cannot be acquired except by reading for oneself. Nothing is of advantage in the art of learning to know a good cup of wine but the actual practice of drinking. Nothing can help in business except going in young, liking the game, and buying one's experience.

In a word, man is the creator, and not the sport, of his fate. He can triumph over his upbringing and, what is more, over himself. The lack of education in the formal sense need be no bar to advancement.

Every young man has his chance. But will he practice industry, economy, and moderation, avoid arrogance and panic, and know how to face depression with a stout heart? Even if he is a genius, will he take off with caution and soar with safety?

The secret of power is the method by which the fire of youth is translated into the knowledge of experience. I have suggested a short cut to that knowledge.

I once had youth, and now I have experience. I believe that youth can do anything if its desire for success is sufficiently strong to curb all other desires. I also believe that a few words of experience can teach youth how to avoid the pitfalls of commerce that wait for the most audacious spirits.

I write out of the conviction of my own experience.

JALNA

Mazo de la Roche

I. THE RAKE'S PROGRESS

Wakefield Whiteoak ran on and on, faster and faster, till he could run no farther. He did not know why he had suddenly increased his speed. He did not even know why he ran. When, out of breath, he threw himself face down on the new spring sod of the meadow, he completely forgot that he had been running at all, and lay, his cheek pressed against the tender grass, his heart thudding against his ribs, without a thought in his head. He was no more happy or unhappy than the April wind that raced across his body or the young grass that quivered with life beneath it. He was simply alive, young, and pressed by the need of violent exertion.

Looking down into the crowding spears of grass, he could see an ant hurrying eagerly, carrying a small white object. He placed his finger before it, wondering what it would think when it found its way blocked by this tall, forbidding tower. Ants were notoriously persevering. It would climb up his finger, perhaps, and run across his hand. No, before it touched his finger, it turned sharply aside and hurried off in a fresh direction. Again he blocked its path, but it would not climb the finger. He persisted. The ant withstood. Harried, anxious, still gripping its little white bundle, it was not to be inveigled or bullied into walking on human flesh. Yet how often ants had scrabbled over him when he had least wanted them! One had even run into his ear once and nearly set him crazy. In sudden anger, he sat up, nipped the ant between his thumb and forefinger, and placed it firmly on the back of his hand. The ant dropped its bundle and lay down on its back, kicking its legs in the air and twisting its body. It was apparently in extreme anguish. He threw it away, half in disgust, half in shame. He had spoiled the silly old ant's day for it. Perhaps it would die.

Briskly he began to search for it. Neither body nor bundle of ant was to be seen, but a robin, perched on a swinging branch of a wild cherry tree, burst into song. It filled the air with its rich throaty notes, tossing them on to the bright sunshine like ringing coins. Wakefield held an imaginary gun to his shoulder and took aim.

"Bang!" he shouted, but the robin went on singing just as though it had not been shot.

"Look here," complained Wakefield, "don't you know when you're dead? Dead birds don't sing, I tell you."

The robin flew from the cherry tree and alighted on the topmost twig of an elm, where it sang more loudly than ever to show how very much alive it was. Wakefield lay down again, his head on his arm. The moist sweet smell of the earth was in his nostrils; the sun beat warmly on his back. He was wondering now whether that big white cloud that he had seen sailing up from the south was overhead yet. He would lie still and count one hundred—no, a hundred was too much, too sustained a mental effort on a morning like this; he would count up to fifty. Then he would look up, and if the cloud were overhead he would—well, he didn't know what he would do, but it would be something terrific. Perhaps he would run at full speed to the creek and jump across, even if it were at the widest part. He pushed one hand into the pocket of his knickers and fingered his new agate marbles as he counted. A delicious drowsiness stole over him. A tender recollection of the lovely warm breakfast he had eaten filled him with peace. He wondered if it were still in his stomach, or had already changed into blood and bone and muscle. Such a breakfast should do a great deal of good. He clenched the hand belonging to the arm stretched under his head to test its muscle. Yes, it felt stronger—no doubt about that. If he kept on eating such breakfasts, the day would come when he would not stand any nonsense from Finch or from any of his brothers, even up to Renny. He supposed he would always let Meg bully him, but then Meg was a woman. A fellow couldn't hit a woman, even though she was his sister.

There came no sound of a footstep to warn him. He simply felt himself helpless in the grasp of two iron hands. He was dazed by a shake, and set roughly on his feet, facing his eldest brother, who was frowning sternly. The two clumber spaniels at Renny's heels jumped on Wakefield, licking his face and almost knocking him down in their joy at discovering him.

Renny, still gripping his shoulder, demanded: "Why are you loafing about here, when you ought to be at Mr. Fennel's? Do you know what time it is? Where are your books?"

Wakefield tried to wriggle away. He ignored the first two questions, feeling instinctively that the third led to less dangerous channels. "Left them at Mr. Fennel's yesterday," he murmured.

"Left them at Fennel's? How the devil did you expect to do your home work?"

Wakefield thought a moment. "I used an old book of Finch's for my Latin. I knew the poetry already. The history lesson was just to be the same thing over again, so's I'd have time to think up my opinion of Cromwell. The Scripture of course I could get out of Meg's Bible at home, and"—he warmed to his subject, his large dark eyes shining—"and I was doing the arithmetic in my head as you came along." He looked earnestly up into his brother's face.

"A likely story." But Renny was somewhat confused by the explanation, as he was meant to be. "Now look here, Wake, I don't want to be hard on you, but you've got to do better. Do you suppose I pay Mr. Fennel to teach you for the fun of it? Just because you're too delicate to go to school isn't any excuse for your being an idle little beast without an idea in your head but play. What have you got in your pockets?"

"Marbles—just a few, Renny."

"Hand them over."

Renny held out his hand while the marbles were reluctantly extracted from the child's pockets and heaped on his own palm. Wakefield did not feel in the least like crying, but his sense of the dramatic prompted him to shed tears as he handed over his treasures. He could always cry when he wanted to. He had only to shut his eyes tightly a moment and repeat to himself, "Oh, how terrible! How terrible!"—and in a moment the tears would come. When he made up his mind not to cry, no amount of abuse would make him. Now, as he dropped the marbles into Renny's hand, he secretly moaned the magic formula, "Oh, how terrible! How terrible!" His chest heaved, the muscles in his throat throbbed, and soon tears trickled down his cheeks like rain.

Renny pocketed the marbles. "No sniveling now." But he did not say it unkindly. "And see that you're not late for dinner." He lounged away, calling his dogs.

Wakefield took out his handkerchief, a clean one, still folded in a little square, put in his pocket by his sister that morning, and wiped his eyes. He watched Renny's tall retreating figure till Renny looked back over his shoulder at him, then he broke into a jog trot toward the rectory. But the freedom of the morning was no longer his. He was full of care, a slender, sallow boy of nine, whose dark brown eyes seemed too large for his pointed face, wearing a greenish tweed jacket and shorts, and green stockings that showed his bare brown knees.

He crossed the field, climbed a sagging rail fence, and began to trot along a path that led beside a muddy, winding road. Soon the blacksmith shop appeared, noisy and friendly, between two majestic elms. An oriole was darting to and fro from elm to elm, and, when the clanging on the anvil ceased for a moment, its sweet liquid song was scattered down in a shower. Wakefield stopped in the doorway to rest.

"Good morning, John," he said to John Chalk, the smith, who was paring the hoof of a huge hairy-legged farm horse.

"Good morning," answered Chalk, glancing up with a smile, for he and Wake were old friends. "It's a fine day."

"A fine day for those that have time to enjoy it. I've got beastly old lessons to do."

"I suppose you don't call what I'm doing work, eh?" returned Chalk.

"Oh, well, it's nice work. Interesting work. Not like history and comp."

"What's 'comp.'?"

"Composition. You write about things you're not interested in. Now, my last subject was 'A Spring Walk.'"

"Well, that ought to be easy. You've just had one."

"Oh, but that's different. When you sit down to write about it, it all seems stupid. You begin, 'I set out one fine spring morning,' and then you can't think of a single thing to write about."

"Why not write about me?"

Wakefield gave a jeering laugh. "Who'd want to read about you! This comp. stuff has got to be *read*, don't you see?"

Conversation was impossible for a space, while the blacksmith hammered the shoe into place. Wakefield sniffed the delicious odor of burnt hoof that hung almost visibly on the air.

Chalk put down the large foot he had been nursing, and remarked:—

"There was a man wrote a piece of poetry about a blacksmith once. 'Under a spreading chestnut tree,' it began. Ever read it? He must have wrote it to be read, eh?"

"Oh, I know that piece. It's awful bunk. And besides, he wasn't your kind of blacksmith. He didn't get drunk and give his wife a black eye and knock his kids around—"

"Look here!" interrupted Chalk with great heat. "Cut out that insultin' kind of talk or I'll shy a hammer at you."

Wakefield backed away, but said, judicially, "There you go. Just proving what I said. You're not the kind of blacksmith to write comp. or even poetry about. You're not beautiful. Mr. Fennel says we should write of beautiful things."

"Well, I know I ain't beautiful," agreed Chalk, reluctantly. "But I ain't as bad as all that."

"All what?" Wakefield successfully assumed Mr. Fennel's air of schoolmasterish probing.

"That I can't be writ about."

"Well, then, Chalk, suppose I was to write down everything I know about you and hand it to Mr. Fennel for comp. Would you be pleased?"

"I say I'll be pleased to fire a hammer at you if you don't clear out!" shouted Chalk, backing the heavy mare toward the door.

Wakefield moved agilely aside as the great dappled flank approached, then he set off down the road—which had suddenly become a straggling street—with much dignity. The load of care that he had been carrying slid from him, leaving him light and airy. As he approached a cottage enclosed by a neat wicket fence, he saw a six-year-old girl swinging on the gate.

"Oo, Wakefield!" she squealed, delightedly. "Come an' swing me. Swing me!"

"Very well, my little friend," agreed Wakefield, cheerily. "You shall be swung, *ad infinitum. Verbum sapienti.*"

He swung the gate to and fro, the child laughing at first, then shrieking, finally uttering hiccoughing sobs as the swinging became wilder, and her foothold less secure, while she clung like a limpet to the palings.

The door of the cottage opened and the mother appeared.

"Leave her be, you naughty boy!" she shouted, running to her daughter's assistance. "You see if I don't tell your brother on you!"

"Which brother?" asked Wakefield, moving away. "I have four, you know."

"Why, the oldest to be sure. Mr. Whiteoak that owns this cottage."

Wakefield spoke confidentially now. "Mrs. Wigle, I wouldn't if I were you. It upsets Renny terribly to have to punish me, on account of my weak heart,—I can't go to school because of it,—and he'd have to punish me if a lady complained of me, of course, though Muriel did ask me to swing her and I'd never have swung her if I hadn't thought she was used to being swung, seeing the way she was swinging as I swung along the street. Besides, Renny mightn't like to think that Muriel was racking the gate to pieces by swinging on it, and he might raise your rent on you. He's a most peculiar man, and he's liable to turn on you when you least expect it."

Mrs. Wigle looked dazed. "Very well," she said, patting the back of Muriel, who still sobbed and hiccoughed against her apron; "but I do wish he'd mend my roof, which leaks into the best room like all possessed every time it rains."

"I'll speak to him about it. I'll see that it's mended at once. Trust me, Mrs. Wigle." He sailed off, erect and dignified.

Already he could see the church, perched on an abrupt, cedar-clad knoll, its square stone tower rising, almost menacing, like a battlement against the sky. His grandfather had built it seventy-five years before. His grandfather, his father, and his mother slept in the churchyard beside it. Beyond the church and hidden by it was the rectory, where he had his lessons.

Now his footsteps lagged. He was before the shop of Mrs. Brawn, who had not only sweets but soft drinks, buns, pies, and sandwiches for sale. The shop was simply the front room of her cottage, fitted with shelves and a counter, and her wares were displayed on a table in the window. He felt weak and faint. His tongue clove to the roof of his mouth with thirst. His stomach felt hollow and slightly sick. Plainly, no one on earth had ever needed refreshment more than he, and no one on earth had less means for the payment for such succor. He examined the contents of his pockets, but, though there was much in them of great value to himself, there was not one cent in hard cash, which was all that Mrs. Brawn really cared about. He could see her crimson face inside the window, and he smiled ingratiatingly, for he owed her thirteen cents and he did not see where he was ever going to get the money to pay it. She came to the door.

"Well, young man, what about that money you owe me?" She was brusque indeed.

"Oh, Mrs. Brawn, I aren't feeling very well this morning. I get these spells. I dare say you've heard about them. I'd like a bottle of lemon soda, please. And about paying—" He passed his hand across his brow and continued hesitatingly: "I don't believe I should have come out in the sun without my cap, do you? What was I saying? Oh, yes, about paying. Well, you see my birthday's coming very soon and I'll be getting money presents from all the family. Eighteen cents will seem no more to me than thirteen then. Even a dollar will be nothing."

"When does your birthday come?" Mrs. Brawn was weakening.

Again he passed his hand across his forehead, then laid it on his stomach, where he believed his heart to be. "I can't ezactly remember, 'cos there are so many birthdays in our family I get mixed up. Between Grandmother's great age and my few years and all those between, it's a little confusing, but I know it's very soon." As he talked, he had entered the shop and stood leaning against the counter. "Lemon soda, please, and *two* straws," he murmured.

Peace possessed him as Mrs. Brawn produced the bottle, uncorked it, and set it before him with the straws.

"How is the old lady?" she inquired.

"Nicely, thank you. We're hoping she'll reach one hundred yet. She's trying awfully hard to. 'Cos she wants to see the celebration we'll have. A party, with a big bonfire and skyrockets. She says she'd be sorry to miss it, though of course we won't have it if she's dead, and she couldn't miss what never really happened, could she, even if it was her own birthday party?"

"You've a wonderful gift of the gab." Mrs. Brawn beamed at him admiringly.

"Yes, I have," he agreed, modestly. "If I hadn't, I'd have no show at all, being the youngest of such a large family. Grandmother and I do a good deal of talking, she at her end of the line and I at mine. You see, we both feel that we may not have many years more to live, so we make the most of everything that comes our way."

"Oh, my goodness, don't talk that way. You'll be all right." She was round-eyed with sympathy. "Don't worry, my dear."

"I'm not worrying, Mrs. Brawn. It's my sister does the worrying. She's had a terrible time raising me, and of course I'm not raised yet." He smiled sadly, and then bent his small dark head over the bottle, sucking ecstatically.

Mrs. Brawn disappeared into the kitchen behind the shop. A fierce heat came from there, and the tantalizing smell of cakes baking, and the sound of women's voices. What a good time women had! Red-faced Mrs. Brawn especially. Baking all the cakes she wanted and selling all those she couldn't eat, and getting paid for them. How he wished he had a cake. Just one little hot cake!

As he drew the lovely drink up through the straws, his eyes, large and bright, roved over the counter. Near him was a little tray of packets of chewing gum. He was not allowed to chew it, but he yearned over it, especially that first moment of chewing, when the thick, sweet, highly flavored juice gushed down the throat, nearly choking him. Before he knew it—well, almost before he knew it—he had taken a packet from the tray, dropped it into his pocket, and gone on sucking, but now with his eyes tightly closed.

Mrs. Brawn returned with two hot little sponge cakes on a plate and set them down before him. "I thought you'd like them just out of the oven. They're a present, mind. They'll not go on your account."

He was almost speechless with gratitude. "Oh, thank you, thank you," was all he could say, at first. Then, "But what a shame! I've gone and drunk up all my soda and now I'll have to eat my cakes dry, unless, of course, I buy another bottle of something." His eyes flew over the shelves. "I believe I'll take ginger ale this time, Mrs. Brawn, thank you. And those same straws will do."

"All right." And Mrs. Brawn opened another bottle and plumped it down before him.

The cakes had a delicious crisp crust and, buried in the heart of each, about six juicy currants. Oh, they were lovely!

As he sauntered from the shop and then climbed the steep steps to the church, he pondered on the subjects assigned for to-day's lessons. Which of his two most usual moods, he wondered, would Mr. Fennel be in? Exacting, alert, or absent-minded and drowsy? Well, whatever the mood, he was now at the mercy of it, little, helpless, alone.

He trotted through the cool shadow of the church, among the gravestones, hesitating a moment beside the iron fence which enclosed his family's plot. His eyes rested on the granite plinth bearing the name "Whiteoak"; then, wistfully, on the small stone marked "Mary Whiteoak, wife of Philip Whiteoak." His mother's grave. His grandfather lay there too; his father; his father's first wife,—the mother of Renny and Meg;—and several infant Whiteoaks. He had always liked this plot of ground. He liked the pretty iron fence and the darling little iron balls that dangled from it. He wished he could stay there this morning and play beside it. He must bring a big bunch of the kingcups that he had seen spilled like gold along the stream yesterday, and lay them on his mother's grave. Perhaps he would give a few to the mother of Renny and Meg also, but none to the men, of course; they wouldn't care about them; nor to the babies, unless to "Gwynneth, aged five months," because he liked her name.

He had noticed that when Meg brought flowers to the graves she always gave the best to her own mother, "Margaret," while to "Mary"—his mother and Eden's and Piers's and Finch's—she gave a smaller, less beautiful bunch. Well, he would do the same. Margaret should have a few, but they should be inferior—not wilted or anything, but not quite so fine and large.

The rectory was a mellow-looking house with a long sloping roof and high pointed gable. The front door stood open. He was not expected to knock, so he entered quietly, first composing his face into an expression of meek receptiveness. The library was empty. There lay his books on the little desk in the corner at which he always sat. Feebly he crossed the worn carpet and sank into his accustomed chair, burying his head in his hands. The tall clock ticked heavily, saying, "Wake-field—Wake-field—Wake—Wake—Wake—Wake—" Then, strangely, "Sleep—sleep—sleep—sleep . . ."

The smell of stuffy furniture and old books oppressed him. He heard the thud of a spade in the garden. Mr. Fennel was planting potatoes. Wakefield dozed a little, his head sinking nearer and nearer the desk. At last he slept peacefully.

He was awakened by Mr. Fennel's coming in, rather earthy, rather dazed, very contrite.

"Oh, my dear boy," he stammered, "I've kept you waiting, I'm afraid. I was just hurrying to get my potatoes in before the full of the moon. Superstitious, I know, but still– Now, let's see; what Latin was it for to-day?"

The clock buzzed, struck twelve.

Mr. Fennel came and bent over the little boy. "How have you got on this morning?" He was peering at the Latin textbook that Wakefield had opened.

"As well as could be expected, by myself, thank you." He spoke with gentle dignity, just touched by reproach.

Mr. Fennel leaned still closer over the page. "Um-m, let's see. *Etsi in his locis–maturae sunt hiemes–*"

"Mr. Fennel," interrupted Wakefield.

"Yes, Wake." He turned his shaggy beard, on which a straw was pendent, toward the boy.

"Renny wondered if you would let me out promptly at twelve to-day. You see, yesterday I was late for dinner, and it upset Grandmother, and at her age–"

"Certainly, certainly. I'll let you off. Ah, that was too bad, upsetting dear Mrs. Whiteoak. It must not happen again. We must be prompt, Wakefield. Both you and I. Run along then, and I'll get back to my potatoes." Hurriedly he assigned the tasks for to-morrow.

"I wonder," said Wakefield, "if Tom" (Mr. Fennel's son), "when he's got the pony and cart out this afternoon, would drop my books at the house for me. You see, I'll need both dictionaries and the atlas. They're pretty heavy, and as I am late already I'll need to run every bit of the way."

He emerged into the noontide brightness, light as air, the transportation of his books arranged for, his brain untired by encounters with Cæsar or Oliver Cromwell, and his body refreshed by two sponge cakes and two bottles of soft drink, ready for fresh pleasurable exertion.

He returned the way he had come, only pausing once to let an importunate sow, deeply dissatisfied with the yard where she was imprisoned, into the road. She trotted beside him for a short distance, pattering along gayly, and when they parted, where an open garden gate attracted her, she did not neglect to throw a glance of roguish gratitude over her shoulder to him.

Glorious, glorious life! When he reached the field where the stream was, the breeze had become a wind that ruffled up his hair and whistled through his teeth as he ran. It was as good a playfellow as he wanted, racing him, blowing the clouds about for his pleasure, shaking out the blossoms of the wild cherry tree like spray.

As he ran, he flung his arms forward alternately like a swimmer; he darted off at sudden tangents, shying like a skittish horse, his face now fierce with rolling eyes, now blank as a gamboling lamb's.

It was an erratic progress, and, as he crept through his accustomed hole in the cedar hedge on to the shaggy lawn, he began to be afraid that he might, after all, be late for dinner. He entered the house quietly and heard the click of dishes and the sound of voices in the dining room.

Dinner was in progress, the older members of the family already assembled, when the youngest (idler, liar, thief, wastrel that he was!) presented himself at the door.

II. THE FAMILY

There seemed a crowd of people about the table, and all were talking vigorously at once. Yet, in talking, they did not neglect their meal, which was a hot, steaming dinner, for dishes were continually being passed, knives and forks clattered energetically, and occasionally a speaker was not quite coherent until he had stopped to wash down the food that impeded his utterance with a gulp of hot tea. No one paid any attention to Wakefield as he slipped into his accustomed place on the right of his half sister Meg. As soon as he had begun to come to table he had been set there, first in a high chair, then, as he grew larger, on a thick volume of *British Poets,* an anthology read by no member of the family and, from the time when it was first placed under him, known as "Wakefield's book." As a matter of fact, he did not need its added inches to be able to handle competently his knife and fork now, but he had got used to it, and for a Whiteoak to get used to anything meant a tenacious and stubborn clinging to it. He liked the feel of its hard boards under him, though occasionally, after painful acquaintance with Renny's shaving strop or Meg's slipper, he could have wished the *Poets* had been padded.

"I want my dinner!" He raised his voice, in a very different tone from the conciliatory one he had used to Mrs. Brawn, Mrs. Wigle, and the rector. "My dinner, please!"

"Hush." Meg took from him the fork with which he was stabbing the air. "Renny, will you please give this child some beef. He won't eat the fat, remember. Just nice lean."

"He ought to be made to eat the fat. It's good for him." Renny hacked off some bits of the meat, adding a rim of fat.

Grandmother spoke, in a voice guttural with food: "Make him eat the fat. Good for him. Children spoiled nowadays. Give him nothing but the fat. I eat fat and I'm nearly a hundred."

Wakefield glared across the table at her resentfully. "Shan't eat the fat. I don't want to be a hundred."

Grandmother laughed throatily, not at all ill pleased. "Never fear, my dear, you won't do it. None of you will do it but me. Ninety-nine, and I never miss a meal. Some of the dish gravy, Renny, on this bit of bread. Dish gravy, please."

She held up her plate, shaking a good deal. Uncle Nicholas, her eldest son, who sat beside her, took it from her and passed it to Renny, who tipped the platter till the ruddy juice collected in a pool at one end. He put two spoonfuls of this over the square of bread. "More, more," ordered Grandmother, and he trickled a third spoonful. "Enough, enough," muttered Nicholas.

Wakefield watched her, enthralled, as she ate. She wore two rows of artificial teeth, probably the most perfect, most efficacious that had ever been made. Whatever was put between them they ground remorselessly into fuel for her endless vitality. To them many of her ninety-and-nine years were due. His own plate, to which appetizing little mounds of mashed potatoes and turnips had been added by Meg, lay untouched before him while he stared at Grandmother.

"Stop staring," whispered Meg, admonishingly, "and eat your dinner."

"Well, take off that bit of fat, then," he whispered back, leaning toward her.

She took it on to her own plate.

The conversation buzzed on in its former channel. What was it all about, Wake wondered vaguely, but he was too much interested in his dinner to care greatly. Phrases flew over his head, words clashed. Probably it was just one of the old discussions provocative of endless talk: what crops should be sown that year; what to make of Finch, who went to school in town; which of Grandmother's three sons had made the worst mess of his life—Nicholas, who sat on her left, and who had squandered his patrimony on fast living in his youth; Ernest, who sat on her right, and who had ruined himself by nebulous speculations and the backing of notes for his brothers and his friends; or Philip, who lay in the churchyard, who had made a second marriage (and that beneath him!) which had produced Eden, Piers, Finch, and Wakefield, unnecessary additions to the family's already too great burdens.

The dining room was a very large room, full of heavy furniture that would have overshadowed and depressed a weaker family. The sideboard, the cabinets, towered toward the ceiling. Heavy cornices glowered ponderously from above. Inside shutters and long curtains of yellow velours, caught back by cable-like cords, with tassels at the ends shaped like the wooden human figures in a Noah's ark, seemed definitely to shut out the rest of the world from the world of the Whiteoaks, where they squabbled, ate, drank, and indulged in their peculiar occupations.

Those spaces on the wall not covered by furniture were covered by family portraits in oil, heavily framed, varied in one instance by the bright Christmas supplement of an English periodical, framed in red velvet by the mother of Renny and Meg, when she was a gay young bride.

Chief among the portraits was that of Captain Philip Whiteoak in his uniform of a British officer. He was Grandfather, who, if he were living, would have been more than a hundred, for he was older than Grandmother. The portrait showed a well-set-up gentleman of fair skin, waving brown hair, bold blue eyes, and sweet, stubborn mouth.

He had been stationed at Jalna, in India, where he had met handsome Adeline Court, who had come out from Ireland to visit a married sister. Miss Court not only had been handsome and of good family,—even better than the Captain's own, as she had never allowed him to forget,—but had had a pleasing little fortune of her very own, left to her by a maiden great-aunt, the daughter of an earl. The pair had fallen deeply in love, she with his sweet, stubborn mouth, and he with her long, graceful form, rendered more graceful by voluminous hooped skirts, her "waterfall" of luxuriant dark red hair, and most of all with her passionate red-brown eyes.

They had been married in Bombay in 1848, a time of great uneasiness and strife almost throughout the world. They felt no unease and anticipated no strife, though enough of that and to spare followed, when much of the sweetness of his mouth was merged into stubbornness, and the tender passion of her eyes was burned out by temper. They were the handsomest, most brilliant couple in the station. A social gathering without them was a tame and disappointing affair. They had wit, elegance, and more money than any others of their youth and military station in Jalna. All went well till a baby girl arrived, a delicate child, unwanted by the pleasure-loving couple, who with its wailing advent brought a train of physical ills to the young mother which, in spite of all that the doctors and a long and dull sojourn in the hills could do, seemed likely to drag her down into invalidism. About the same time Captain Whiteoak had a violent quarrel with his colonel, and he felt that his whole world, both domestic and military, had somehow suddenly become bewitched.

Fate seemed to have a hand in bringing the Whiteoaks to Canada, for just at the moment when the doctor insisted that the wife, if she were to be restored to health, must live for some time in a cool and bracing climate, the husband got notice that an uncle, stationed in Quebec, had died, leaving him a considerable property.

Philip and Adeline had decided simultaneously—the only decision of moment except their marriage that they ever arrived at without storm and stress—that they were utterly sick of India, of military life, of trying to please stupid and choleric superiors, and of entertaining a narrow, gossiping, middle-class set of people. They were made for a freer, more unconventional life. Suddenly their impetuous spirits yearned toward Quebec. Philip had had letters from his uncle, eloquent on the subject of the beauties of Quebec, its desirability as a place of residence, its freedom from the narrow conventionalities of the Old World, combined with a grace of living bequeathed by the French.

Captain Whiteoak had a very poor opinion of the French,—he had been born in the year of Waterloo, and his father had been killed there,—but he liked the descriptions of Quebec, and when he found himself the owner of property there, with a legacy of money attached, he thought he would like nothing better than to go there to live—for a time, at any rate. He visualized a charming picture of himself and his Adeline, clinging to his arm, parading the terrace by the river after Sunday morning service, he no longer in an uncomfortable uniform but in tight, beautifully fitting trousers, double-breasted frock coat, and glittering top hat, all from London, while Adeline seemed literally to float amid fringes, ruches, and gayly tinted veils. He had other visions of himself in company with lovely French girls when Adeline would possibly be occupied with a second accouchement, though, to do him justice, these visions never went beyond the holding of velvety little hands and the tranced gazing into dark-fringed eyes.

He sold his commission, and the two sailed for England with the delicate baby and a native ayah. The few relations they had in England did not proffer them a very warm welcome, so their stay there was short, for they were equally proud and high-spirited. They found time, however, to have their portraits painted by a really first-class artist, he in the uniform he was about to discard, and she in a low-cut yellow evening gown with camellias in her hair.

Armed with the two portraits and a fine collection of inlaid mahogany furniture,—for their position must be upheld in the Colony,—they took passage in a large sailing vessel. Two months of battling with storms and fogs and even icebergs passed like a nightmare before they sighted the battlements of Quebec. On the way out the ayah died and was buried at sea, her dark form settling meekly into the cold Western waters. Then there was no one to care for the baby girl but the young, inexperienced parents. Adeline herself was ill almost to death. Captain Whiteoak would sooner have set out to subdue a rebellious hill tribe than the squalling infant. Cursing and sweating, while the vessel rolled like a thing in torture and his wife made sounds such as he had never dreamed she could utter, he tried to wrap the infant's squirming chafed legs in a flannel barrow coat. Finally he pricked it with a safety pin, and when he saw blood trickling from the tiny wound he could stand it no longer; he carried the child into the common cabin, where he cast it into the lap of a poor Scotchwoman who already had five of her own to look after, commanding her to care for his daughter as best she could. She cared for her very capably, neglecting her own hardy bairns, and the Captain paid her well for it. The weather cleared, and they sailed into Quebec on a beautiful crisp May morning.

But they lived for only a year in that city. The house in the Rue St. Louis was flush with the street—a dim chilly French house, sad with ghosts from the past. The sound of church bells was never out of their ears, and Philip, discovering that Adeline sometimes went secretly to those Roman churches, began to fear that she would under such influence become a papist. But, as they had lingered in London long enough to have their portraits done, so they lingered in Quebec long enough to become the parents of a son. Unlike little Augusta, he was strong and healthy. They named him Nicholas, after the uncle who had left Philip the legacy (now himself "Uncle Nicholas," who sat at his mother's right hand when Wakefield entered the dining room).

With two young children in a cold drafty house; with Adeline's health a source of anxiety; with far too many French about Quebec to be congenial to an English gentleman; with a winter temperature that played coyly about twenty dazzling degrees below zero; the Whiteoaks felt driven to find a more suitable habitation.

Captain Whiteoak had a friend, a retired Anglo-Indian colonel who had already settled on the fertile southern shore of Ontario. "Here," he wrote, "the winters are mild. We have little snow, and in the long, fruitful summer the land yields grain and fruit in abundance. An agreeable little settlement of *respectable* families is being formed. You and your talented lady, my dear Whiteoak, would receive the welcome here that people of your consequence *merit*."

The property in Quebec was disposed of. The mahogany furniture, the portraits, the two infants, and their nurse were somehow or other conveyed to the chosen Province. Colonel Vaughan, the friend, took them into his house for nearly a year while their own was in process of building.

Philip Whiteoak bought from the government a thousand acres of rich land, traversed by a deep ravine through which ran a stream lively with speckled trout. Some of the land was cleared, but the greater part presented the virgin grandeur of the primeval forest. Tall, unbelievably dense pines, hemlocks, spruces, balsams, with a mingling of oak, ironwood, and elm, made a sanctuary for countless song birds, wood pigeons, partridges, and quail. Rabbits, foxes, and hedgehogs abounded. The edge of the ravine was crowned by slender silver birches, its banks by cedars and sumachs, and along the brink of the stream was a wild sweet-smelling tangle that was the home of water rats, minks, raccoons, and blue herons.

Labor was cheap. A small army of men was employed to make the semblance of an English park in the forest, and to build a house that should overshadow all others in the county. When completed, decorated, and furnished, it was the wonder of the countryside. It was a square house of dark red brick, with a wide stone porch, a deep basement where the kitchens and servants' quarters were situated, an immense drawing-room, a library (called so, but more properly a sitting room, since few books lived there), a dining room, and a bedroom on the ground floor; and six large bedrooms on the floor above, topped by a long, low attic divided into two bedrooms. The wainscoting and doors were of walnut. From five fireplaces the smoke ascended through picturesque chimneys that rose among the treetops.

In a burst of romantic feeling, Philip and Adeline named the place Jalna, after the military station where they had first met. Everyone agreed that it was a pretty name, and Jalna became a place for gayety. An atmosphere of impregnable well-being grew up around it. Under their clustering chimneys, in the midst of their unpretentious park with its short, curving drive, with all their thousand acres spread like a green mantle around them, the Whiteoaks were as happy as the sons of man can be. They felt themselves cut off definitely from the mother country, though they sent their children to England to be educated.

Two boys were born to them at Jalna. One was named Ernest, because Adeline, just before his birth, had been entranced by the story of Ernest Maltravers. The other was given the name Philip for his father. Nicholas, the eldest son, married in England, but after a short and stormy life together his wife left him for a young Irish officer, and he returned to Canada, never to see her again. Ernest remained unmarried, devoting himself with almost monastic preoccupation to the study of Shakespeare and the care of himself. He had always been the delicate one. Philip, the youngest, married twice. First, the daughter of a Scotch physician who had settled near Jalna, and who had brought his future son-in-law into the world. She had given him Meg and Renny. His second wife was the pretty young governess of his two children who were early left motherless. The second wife, treated with coldness by all his family, had four sons, and died at the birth of Wakefield. Eden, the eldest of these, was now twenty-three; Piers was twenty; Finch, sixteen; and little Wake, nine.

Young Philip had always been his father's favorite, and when the Captain died it was to Philip that he left Jalna and its acres—no longer, alas, a thousand, for land had had to be sold to meet the extravagances of Nicholas and the foolish credulities of Ernest with his penchant for backing other men's notes. They had had their share, "more than their share, by God," swore Captain Whiteoak.

He had never had any deep affection for his only daughter, Augusta. Perhaps he had never quite forgiven her the bad time she had given him on the passage from England to Canada. But if he had never loved her, at least he had never had any cause to worry over her. She had married young—an insignificant young Englishman, Edwin Buckley, who had surprised them all by inheriting a baronetcy, through the sudden deaths of an uncle and a cousin.

If Augusta's father had never been able to forgive her for the intricacies of her toilet on that memorable voyage, how much more difficult was it for her mother to forgive her for attaining a social position above her own! To be sure, the Courts were a far more important family than the Buckleys; they were above title-seeking; and Sir Edwin was only the fourth baronet; still, it was hard to hear Augusta called "her ladyship." Adeline was unfeignedly pleased when Sir Edwin died and was succeeded by a nephew, and thus Augusta, in a manner, was shelved.

All this had happened years ago. Captain Whiteoak was long dead. Young Philip and both his wives were dead. Renny was master of Jalna, and Renny himself was thirty-eight.

The clock seemed to stand still at Jalna. Renny's uncles, Nicholas and Ernest, thought of him as only a headlong boy. And old Mrs. Whiteoak thought of her two sons as mere boys, and of her dead son, Philip, as a poor dead boy.

She had sat at that same table for nearly seventy years. At that table she had held Nicholas on her knee, giving him little sips out of her cup. Now he slouched beside her, a heavy man of seventy-two. At that table Ernest had cried with fright when first he heard the explosion of a Christmas cracker. Now he sat on her other side, white-haired—which she herself was not. The central chamber of her mind was hazy. Its far recesses were lit by clear candles of memory. She saw them more clearly as little boys than as they now appeared.

Countless suns had shone yellowly through the shutters on Whiteoaks eating heartily as they ate to-day, talking loudly, disagreeing, drinking quantities of strong tea.

The family was arranged in orderly fashion about the table with its heavy plate and vegetable dishes, squat cruets, and large English cutlery. Wakefield had his own little knife and fork, and a battered silver mug which had been handed down from brother to brother and had many a time been hurled across the room in childish tantrums. At one end sat Renny, the head of the house, tall, thin, with a small head covered with dense, dark red hair, a narrow face, with something of foxlike sharpness about it, and quick-tempered red-brown eyes; facing him, Meg, the one sister. She was forty, but looked older because of her solid bulk, which made it appear that, once seated, nothing could budge her. She had a colorless, very round face, full blue eyes, and brown hair with a strand of gray springing from each temple. Her distinguishing feature was her mouth, inherited from Captain Whiteoak. In comparison with the mouth in the portrait, however, hers seemed to show all its sweetness with none of its stubbornness. In her it became a mouth of ineffable feminine sweetness. When she laid her cheek against her hand, her short thick arm resting on the table, she seemed to be musing on that which filled her with bliss. When she raised her head and looked at one of her brothers, her eyes were cool, commanding, but the curve of her mouth was a caress. She ate little at the table, attending always to the wants of others, keeping the younger boys in order, cutting up her grandmother's food for her, sipping endless cups of China tea. Between meals she was always indulging in little lunches, carried to her own room on a tray—thick slices of fresh bread and butter with gooseberry jam, hot muffins with honey, or even French cherries and pound cake. She loved all her brothers, but her love and jealousy for Renny sometimes shook her solidity into a kind of ecstasy.

The half brothers were ranged in a row along one side of the table, facing the window. Wakefield; then Finch (whose place was always vacant at dinner time because he was a day boy at a school in town); next Piers, he too resembling Captain Whiteoak, but with less of the sweetness and more of the stubbornness in his boyish mouth; last Eden, slender, fair, with the appealing gaze of the pretty governess, his mother.

Across the table the grandmother and the two uncles; Ernest with his cat, Sasha, on his shoulder; Nicholas with his Yorkshire terrier, Nip, on his knees. Renny's two clumber spaniels lay on either side of his armchair.

Thus the Whiteoaks at table.

"What is accepted?" shouted Grandmother.

"Poems," explained Uncle Ernest, gently. "Eden's poems. They've been accepted."

"Is that what you're all chattering about?"

"Yes, Mamma."

"Who is she?"

"Who is who?"

"The girl who's accepted them."

"It's not a girl, Mamma. It's a publisher."

Eden broke in: "For God's sake, don't try to explain to her!"

"He shall explain it to me," retorted Grandmother, rapping the table violently with her fork. "Now then, Ernest, speak up! What's this all about?"

Uncle Ernest swallowed a juicy mouthful of rhubarb tart, passed up his cup for more tea, and then said: "You know that Eden has had a number of poems published in the university magazine and—and in other magazines, too. Now an editor—I mean a publisher—is going to bring out a book of them. Do you understand?"

She nodded, the ribbons on her large purple cap shaking. "When's he going to bring it out? When's he coming? If he's coming to tea I want my white cap with the mauve ribbons on. Is he going to bring it out in time for tea?"

"My God!" groaned Eden, under his breath, "listen to her! Why do you try to tell her things? I knew how it would be."

His grandmother glared across at him. She had heard every word. In spite of her great age, she still bore traces of having been a handsome woman. Her fierce eyes still were bright under her shaggy reddish eyebrows. Her nose, defiant of time, looked as though it had been moulded by a sculptor who had taken great pains to make the sweep of the nostrils and arch of the bridge perfect. She was so bent that her eyes stared straight on to the victuals that she loved.

"Don't you dare to curse at me!" She thrust her face toward Eden. "Nicholas, order him to stop cursing at me."

"Stop cursing at her," growled Nicholas, in his rich, deep voice. "More tart, Meggie, please."

Grandmother nodded and grinned, subsiding into her tart, which she ate with a spoon, making little guttural noises of enjoyment.

"Just the same," said Renny, carrying on the conversation, "I don't altogether like it. None of us have ever done anything like that."

"You seemed to think it was all right for me to write poetry when I only had it published in the varsity magazine. Now when I've got a publisher to bring it out—"

Grandmother was aroused. "Bring it out! Will he bring it to-day? If he does, I shall wear my white cap with mauve—"

"Mamma, have some more tart," interrupted Nicholas. "Just a little more tart."

Old Mrs. Whiteoak's attention was easily diverted by an appeal to her palate. She eagerly held out her plate, tilting the juice from it to the cloth, where it formed a pinkish puddle.

Eden, after sulkily waiting for her to be helped to some tart, went on, a frown indenting his forehead: "You simply have no idea, Renny, how difficult it is to get a book of poems published. And by a New York house, too! I wish you could hear my friends talk about it. They'd give a good deal to have accomplished what I have at my age."

"It would have been more to the point," returned Renny, testily, "to have passed your exams. When I think of the money that's been wasted on your education—"

"Wasted! Could I have done this if I hadn't had my education?"

"You've always been scribbling verses. The question is, can you make a living by it?"

"Give me time! Good Lord, my book isn't in the printer's hands yet. I can't tell what it may lead to. If you—any of you—only appreciated what I've really done—"

"I do, dear!" exclaimed his sister. "I think it's wonderfully clever of you, and, as you say, it may lead to—to anywhere."

"It may lead to my being obliged to go to New York to live, if I'm going to go in for writing," said Eden. "One should be near one's publishers."

Piers, the brother next to him, put in: "Well, it's getting late. One must go back to one's spreading of manure. One's job may be lowly—one regrets that one's job is not writing poetry."

Eden pocketed the insult of his tone, but retorted: "You certainly smell of your job."

Wakefield tilted back in his chair, leaning toward Piers. "Oh, I smell him!" he cried. "I think the smell of stable is very appetizing."

"Then I wish," said Eden, "that you'd change places with me. It takes away my appetite."

Wakefield began to scramble down, eager to change, but his sister restrained him. "Stay where you are, Wake. You know how Piers would torment you if you were next him. As for you going to New York, Eden—you know how I should feel about that." Tears filled her eyes.

The family rose from the table and moved in groups toward the three doorways. In the first group Grandmother dragged her feet heavily, supported by a son on either side, Nicholas having his terrier tucked under one arm and Ernest his cat perched on his shoulder. Like some strange menagerie on parade, they slowly traversed the faded medallions of the carpet toward the door that was opposite Grandmother's room. Renny, Piers, and Wakefield went through the door that led into a back passage, the little boy trying to swarm up the back of Piers, who was lighting a cigarette. Meg and Eden disappeared through the double doors that led into the library.

Immediately the manservant, John Wragge, known as "Rags," began to clear the table, piling the dishes precariously on an immense black tray decorated with faded red roses, preparatory to carrying it down the long steep stairs to the basement kitchen. He and his wife inhabited the regions below, she doing the cooking, he carrying, besides innumerable trays up the steep stairs, all the coal and water, cleaning brasses and windows, and waiting on his wife in season and out. Yet she complained that he put the burden of the work on her, while he declared that he did his own and hers too. The basement was the scene of continuous quarrels. Through its subterranean ways they pursued each other with bitter recriminations, and occasionally through its brick-floored passages a boot hurtled or a cabbage flew like a bomb. Jalna was so well built that none of these altercations were audible upstairs. In complete isolation the two lived their stormy life together, usually effecting a reconciliation late at night, with a pot of strong tea on the table between them.

Rags was a drab-faced, voluble little cockney, with a pert nose and a mouth that seemed to have been formed for a cigarette holder. He was at the head of the back stairs as Renny, Piers, and Wakefield came along the passage. Wakefield waited till his brothers had passed, and then leaped on Rags's back, scrambling up him as though he were a tree, and nearly precipitating themselves and the loaded tray down the stairs.

"Ow!" screamed Rags. "'E's done it again! 'E's always at it! This time 'e nearly 'ad me down. There goes the sugar bison! There goes the grivy boat! Tike 'im orf me, for pity's sike, Mr. W'iteoak!"

Piers, who was nearest, dragged Wakefield from Rags's back, laughing hilariously as he did so. But Renny came back frowning. "He ought to be thrashed," he said, sternly. "It's just as Rags says—he's always after him." He peered down the dim stairway at the Whiteoak butler gathering up the débris.

"I'll stand him on his head," said Piers.

"No—don't do that. It's bad for his heart."

But Piers had already done it, and the packet of gum had fallen from Wakefield's pocket.

"Put him on his feet," ordered Renny. "Here, what's this?" And he picked up the pink packet.

Wake hung a bewildered, buzzing head. "It's g-gum," he said faintly. "Mrs. Brawn gave it to me. I didn't like to offend her by saying I wasn't allowed to chew it. I thought it was better not to offend her, seeing that I owe her a little bill. But you'll notice, Renny,"—he raised his large eyes pathetically to his brother's face,—"you'll notice it's never been opened."

"Well, I'll let you off this time." Renny threw the packet down the stairs after Rags. "Here, Rags, throw this out!"

Rags examined it, then his voice came unctuously up the stairway: "Ow, naow, Mr. W'iteoak, I'll give it to the missus. I see it's flivored with vaniller. 'Er fivorite flivor. It'll do 'er a world of good to chew this when one of 'er spells comes on."

Renny turned to Wakefield. "How much do you owe Mrs. Brawn?"

"I think it's eighteen cents, Renny. Unless you think I ought to pay for the gum. In that case it would be twenty-three."

Renny took out a handful of silver and picked out a quarter. "Now take this and pay Mrs. Brawn, and don't run into debt again."

Grandmother had by this time reached the door of her room, but, hearing sounds that seemed to contain the germ of a row, which she loved only second to her meals, she ordered her sons to steer her in the direction of the back stairs. The three bore down, clasped closely together, presenting a solid, overwhelming front, awe-inspiring to Wakefield as a Juggernaut. The sun, beaming through a stained-glass window behind them, splashed bright patches of color over their bodies. Grandmother's taste ran to gaudy hues. It was she who had installed the bright window there to light the dim passage. Now, clad in a red velvet dressing gown, clasping her gold-headed ebony stick, she advanced toward the grandsons, long-beaked, brilliant as a parrot.

"What's this going on?" she demanded. "What's the child been doing, Piers?"

"Climbing up Rags's back, Gran. He nearly threw him downstairs. Renny promised him a licking next time he did it, and now he's letting him off."

Her face turned crimson with excitement. She looked more like a parrot than ever. "Let him off, indeed!" she cried. "There's too much letting off here. That's what's the matter. I say flog him. Do you hear, Renny? Flog him well. I want to see it done. Get a cane and flog him."

With a terrified scream, Wakefield threw his arms about Renny's waist and hid his face against him. "Don't whip me, Renny!" he implored.

"I'll do it myself," she cried. "I've flogged boys before now. I've flogged Nicholas. I've flogged Ernest. I'll flog this spoiled little rascal. Let me have him!" She shuffled toward him, eager with lust of power.

"Come, come, Mamma," interposed Ernest, "this excitement's bad for you. Come and have a nice peppermint pâté or a glass of sherry." Gently he began to wheel her around.

"No, no, no!" she screamed, struggling, and Nip and Sasha began to bark and mew.

Renny settled it by picking up the little boy under his arm and hurrying along the passage to the side entrance. He set him down on the flagged path outside and shut the door behind them with a loud bang. Wakefield stood staring up at him like a ruffled young robin that has just been tossed from its nest by a storm, very much surprised, but tremendously interested in the world in which it finds itself.

"Well," observed Renny, lighting a cigarette, "that's that."

Wakefield, watching him, was filled with a passion of admiration for Renny—his all-powerful brown hands, his red head, his long, sharp-featured face. He loved him. He wanted Renny's love and Renny's pity more than anything else in the world. He must make Renny notice him, be kind to him, before he strode off to the stable after Piers.

Closing his eyes, he repeated the potent words that never failed to bring tears to his eyes. "This is terrible! Oh, it is terrible!" Something warm swelled within him. Something gushed upward, tremulous, through his being. He felt slightly dizzy, then tears welled sweetly into his eyes. He opened them and saw Renny through their iridescent brilliance, staring at him with amused concern.

"What!" he demanded. "Did Gran frighten you?"

"N-no. A little."

"Poor old fellow!" He put his arm around Wakefield and pressed him against his side. "But look here. You mustn't cry so easily. That's twice to-day I've seen you. You won't have the life of a dog when you go to school if you keep on like this."

Wake twisted a button on Renny's coat.

"May I have my marbles—and—ten cents?" he breathed. "You see, it will take the quarter to pay Mrs. Brawn, and I would like just one little drink of lemon sour."

Renny handed over ten cents and the marbles.

Wake threw himself on the grass, flat on his back, staring up at the friendly blue of the sky. A sense of joyous peace possessed him. The afternoon was before him. He had nothing to do but enjoy himself. Lovingly he rattled the marbles in one pocket and the thirty-five cents in the other. Life was rich, full of infinite possibilities.

Presently a hot sweet smell assailed his sensitive nostrils. It was rising from the window of the basement kitchen near him. He rolled over and sniffed again. Surely he smelled cheese cakes. Delicious, crusty, lovely cheese cakes. He crept briskly on his hands and knees to the window and peered down into the kitchen. Mrs. Wragge had just taken a pan of them out of the oven. Rags was washing the dishes and already chewing the gum. Mrs. Wragge's face was crimson with heat. Looking up, she saw Wakefield.

"Have a cake?" she asked, and handed one up to him.

"Oh, thanks. And—and—Mrs. Wragge, please may I have one for my friend?"

"You ain't got no friend with yer," said Rags, vindictively champing the gum.

Wakefield did not deign to answer him. He only held out one thin little brown hand for the other cake. Mrs. Wragge laid it on his palm. "Look out it don't burn ye," she advised.

Blissfully he lay on the shaggy grass of the lawn, munching one cake and gazing quietly at the other recumbent on the grass before him. But when he came to it he really had not room for the second cake. If Finch had been there, he could have given it to him and Finch would have asked no uncomfortable questions. But Finch was at school. Was his whole glorious afternoon to be spoiled by the responsibility of owning a cake too many?

What did dogs do when they had a bone they didn't need at the moment? They buried it.

He walked round and round the perennial border, looking for a nice place. At last, near the root of a healthy-looking bleeding heart he dug a little hole and placed the cake therein. It looked so pretty there he felt like calling Meg out to see it. But no—better not. Quickly he covered it with the moist warm earth and patted it smooth. Perhaps one day he would come and dig it up.

III. ERNEST AND SASHA

Ernest Whiteoak was at this time seventy years old. He had reached the age when after a hearty dinner a man likes repose of body and spirit. Such scenes as the one his mother had just staged inclined to upset his digestion, and it was with as petulant a look as ever shadowed his gentle face that he steered her at last to her padded chair by her own fire and ensconced her there. He stood looking down at her with a singular mixture of disgust and adoration. She was a deplorable old vixen, but he loved her more than anyone else in the world.

"Comfortable, Mamma?" he asked.

"Yes. Bring me a peppermint. A Scotch mint—not a humbug."

He selected one from a little tin box on the dresser and brought it to her in his long pale fingers that seemed almost unnaturally smooth.

"Put it in my mouth, boy." She opened it, pushing forward her lips till she looked like a hungry old bird.

He popped in the peppermint, withdrawing his fingers quickly as though he were afraid she would bite him.

She sucked the sweet noisily, staring into the dancing firelight from under shaggy red brows. On the high back of her chair her brilliantly colored parrot, Boney, perched, vindictively pecking at the ribbons on her cap. She had brought a parrot with her from India, named Boney in derision of Bonaparte. She had had several since the first one, but the time was long past when she was able to differentiate between them. They were all "Boney," and she frequently would tell a visitor of the time she had had fetching this one across the ocean seventy-five years ago. He had been almost as much trouble as the baby, Augusta. Grandmother and her two sons had each a pet, which gave no love to anyone but its owner. The three with their pets kept to their own apartments like superior boarders, seldom emerging except for meals and to pay calls on each other, or to sit in the drawing-room at whist in the evening.

Grandmother's room was thickly carpeted and curtained. It smelled of sandalwood, camphor, and hair oil. The windows were opened only once a week, when Mrs. Wragge "turned it out" and threw the old lady into a temper for the day.

Her bed was an old painted leather one. The head blazed with oriental fruit, clustered about the gorgeous plumage of a parrot and the grinning faces of two monkeys. On this Boney perched all night, only at daylight flapping down to torment his mistress with pecks and Hindu curses which she herself had taught him.

He began to swear now at Sasha, who, standing on her hind legs, was trying to reach his tail with a curving gray paw.

"Kutni! Kutni! Kutni!" he rapped out. "Paji! Paji! Shaitan ka katla!" He rent the air with a metallic scream.

"Pick up your horrid cat, Ernest," ordered his mother. "She's making Boney swear. Poor Boney! Pretty Boney! Peck her eyes out, Boney!"

Ernest lifted Sasha to his shoulder, where she humped furiously, spitting out in her turn curses less coherent but equally vindictive.

"Comfortable now, Mamma?" Ernest repeated, fondling the ribbon on her cap.

"M-m. When's this man coming?"

"What man, Mamma?"

"The man that's going to bring out Eden's book. When's he coming? I want to have on my écru cap with the mauve ribbons."

"I'll let you know in time, Mamma."

"M-m. . . . More wood. Put more wood on the fire. I like to be warm as well as anyone."

Ernest laid a heavy piece of oak log on the fire and stood looking down at it till slender flames began to caress it; then he turned to look at his mother. She was fast asleep, her chin buried in her breast. The Scotch mint had slipped out of her mouth and Boney had snatched it up and carried it to a corner of the room, where he was striking it on the floor to crack it, imagining it was some rare sort of nut. Ernest smiled and retreated, gently closing the door after him.

He slowly mounted the stairs, Sasha swaying on his shoulder, and sought his own room. The door of his brother's room stood open, and as he passed he had a glimpse of Nicholas sprawling in an armchair, his gouty leg supported on a beaded ottoman, his untidy head enveloped in cigar smoke. In his own room he was surprised and pleased to find his nephew, Eden. The young men did not often call on him; they favored Nicholas, who had ribald jokes to tell. Nevertheless, he liked their company, and was always ready to lay aside his work—the annotating of Shakespeare—for the sake of it.

Eden was sitting on the edge of a book-littered table, swinging his leg. He looked self-conscious and flustered.

"I hope I'm not troubling you, Uncle," he said. "Just say the word if you don't want me and I'll clear out."

Ernest sat down in the chair farthest from his desk, to show that he had no thought of study. "I'm glad to have you, Eden. You know that. I'm very pleased about this success of yours—this book, and all the more so because you've read a good many of the poems to me in this very room. I take a great interest in it."

"You're the only one that really understands," answered Eden. "Understands the difference the publishing of this book will make in my life, I mean. Of course Uncle Nick has been very nice about praising my poems—"

"Oh," interrupted Ernest, with a hurt feeling, "you read them to Nicholas in his room, also, eh?"

"Just a few. The ones I thought would interest him. Some of the love poems. I wanted to see how they affected him. After all, he's a man of the world. He's experienced a good deal in his time."

"And how did they affect him?" asked Ernest, polishing the nails of one hand against the palm of the other.

"They amused him, I think. Like yourself, he has difficulty in appreciating the new poetry. Still, he thinks I have good stuff in me."

"I wish you could have gone to Oxford."

"I wish I could. And so I might if Renny could have been brought to see reason. Of course, he feels now that the education he has given me has been wasted, since I refuse to go on with the study of law. But I can't, and that's all there is to it. I'm awfully fond of Renny, but I wish he weren't so frightfully materialistic. The first thing he asked about my book was whether I could make much money out of it. As though one ever made much out of a first book."

"And poetry at that," amended Ernest.

"He doesn't seem to realize that I'm the first one of the family who has done anything to make our name known to the world—" The armor of his egotism was pierced by a hurt glance from Ernest and he hastened to add, "Of course, Uncle, there's your work on Shakespeare. That will get a lot of attention when it comes out. But Renny won't see anything in either achievement to be proud of. I think he's rather ashamed for us. He thinks a Whiteoak should be a gentleman farmer or a soldier. His life's been rather cramped, after all."

"He was through the War," commented Ernest. "That was a great experience."

"And what impressions did he bring back from it?" demanded Eden. "Almost the first questions he asked when he returned were about the price of hay and steers, and he spent most of his first afternoon leaning over a sty, watching a litter of squirming young pigs."

"I sympathize with you very greatly, my dear boy. And so does Meggie. She thinks you're a genius."

"Good old Meg. I wish she could convince the rest of the clan of that. Piers is a young beast."

"You mustn't mind Piers. He gibes at everything connected with learning. After all, he's very young. Now tell me, Eden, what shall you do? Shall you take up literature as a profession?" Eager to be sympathetic, he peered into the boy's face. He wanted very much to hold him, to keep his confidence.

"Oh, I'll look about me. I'll go on writing. I may join an expedition into the North this summer. I've an idea for a cycle of poems about the Northland. Not wild, rugged stuff, but something delicate, austere. One thing is certain—I'm not going to mix up law and poetry. It wouldn't do for me at all. Let's see what sort of reviews I get, Uncle Ernie."

They discussed the hazards of literature as a means of livelihood. Ernest spoke as a man of experience, though in all his seventy years he had never earned a dollar by his pen. Where would he be now, Eden wondered, if it were not for the shelter of Renny's roof. He supposed Gran would have had to come across with enough to support him, though to get money from her was to draw blood from a stone.

When Eden had gone, Ernest remained motionless in his chair by the window, looking out over the green meadows, and thinking also of his mother's fortune. It was the cause of much disturbing thought to him. Not that it was what one could call a great fortune, but a comfortable sum it certainly was. And there it was lying, accumulating for no one knew whom. In moments of the closest intimacy and affection with her, she never could be ever so gently led to disclose in whose favor her will was made. She knew that much of her power lay in keeping that tantalizing secret. He felt sure, by the mirthful gleam he had discovered in her eyes when the subject of money or wills was approached, that in secret she hugged the joy of baffling them all.

Ernest loved his family. He would feel no deep bitterness should any one of them inherit the money. He greatly longed, nevertheless, to be the next heir himself, to be in his turn the holder of power at Jalna, to experience the thrill of independence. And if he had it, he would do such nice things for them all, from brother Nicholas down to little Wake! By means of that power he would guide their lives into the channels that would be best for them. Whereas, if Nicholas inherited it,—it had been divulged by Mrs. Whiteoak that the money was to be left solidly to one person,—well, Ernest could not quite think dispassionately of Nicholas as his mother's heir. He might do something reckless. Nicholas frequently made very reckless jokes about what he would do when he got it,—he seemed to take it for granted that, as the eldest, he would get it,—jokes which Ernest was far too generous to repeat to his mother, but it made him positively tremble to think where the family might end if Nicholas had a fling with it. In himself he was aware of well-knit faculties, cool judgment, a capacity for power. Nicholas was headstrong, arbitrary, ill balanced.

As for Renny, he was a good fellow, but he was letting the place run down. It had deteriorated while he was away at the War, and his return had not stayed the downward progression. The younger nephews could scarcely be looked on as rivals. Still, one never could be certain where the whim of an aged woman was in question.

Ernest sighed and looked toward the bed. He thought he should take a little nap after such a substantial dinner. With a last look at the pretty green meadows, he drew down the blind and laid his slender body along the coverlet. Sasha leaped up after him, snuggling her head close to his on the pillow. They gazed into each other's eyes, his blue and drowsy, hers vivid green in the shadowed room, speculative, mocking.

She stretched out a round paw and laid it on his cheek, then, lest he should rest too secure in her love, she put out her claws just a little way and let him feel their sharpness.

"Sasha, dear, you're hurting me," he breathed.

She withdrew her claws, patted him, and uttered short throaty purrs.

"Pretty puss," sighed Ernest, closing his eyes. "Gentle puss!"

She was sleepy, too, so they slept.

IV. NICHOLAS AND NIP

As nephew Eden had sought out Uncle Ernest that he might discuss his future with him, so that same afternoon nephew Renny sought out Uncle Nicholas that they too might discuss Eden's prospects.

Both rooms, the scenes of these conversations, would appear to an outside observer overfurnished. The two elderly men had collected there all the things which they particularly fancied or to which they thought they had a claim, but while Ernest's taste ran to pale water colors, china figures, and chintz-covered chairs, Nicholas had the walls of his room almost concealed by hunting prints and pictures of pretty women. His furniture was leather-covered. An old square piano, the top of which was littered with pipes, several decanters and a mixer, medicine bottles,—he was always dosing himself for gout,—and music, stood by the window.

Nip, the Yorkshire terrier, had a bone on the hearth-rug when Renny entered. Hearing the step, he darted forward, nipped Renny on the ankle, and darted back to his bone, snarling as he gnawed. Nicholas, his bad leg stretched on the ottoman, looked up from his book with a lazy smile.

"Hullo, Renny! Come for a chat? Can you find a chair? Throw those slippers on to the floor. Place always in a mess—yet if I let Rags in here to tidy up he hides everything I use, and what with my knee—well, it puts me in the devil of a temper for a week."

"I know," agreed Renny. He dropped the slippers to the floor and himself into the comfort of the chair. "Have you got a good book, Uncle Nick? I never seem to have any time for reading."

"I wish I hadn't so much, but when a man's tied to his chair, as I am a great deal of the time, he must do something. This is one Meggie got the last time she was in town. An English authoress. The new books puzzle me, Renny. My God! if everything in this one is true, it's amazing what nice women will do and think these days. The thoughts of this heroine—my goodness, they're appalling. Have a cigar?"

Renny helped himself from a box on the piano. Nip, thinking Renny had designs on his bone, darted forth once more, bit the intruder's ankle, and darted back growling, fancying himself a terrifying beast.

"Little brute!" said Renny. "I really felt his teeth that time. Does he think I'm after his bone?"

Nicholas said: "Catch a spider! Catch a spider, Nip!" Nip flew to his master, tossing his long-haired body round and round him, and yapping loudly.

A loud thumping sounded through the thick walls. Nicholas smiled maliciously. "It always upsets Ernie to hear Nip raise his voice. Yet I'm expected to endure the yowls of that cat of his at any hour of the night." He clapped his palms together at the little dog. "Catch a spider, Nip! Catch a spider!" Hysterically yelping, Nip sped around the room, looking in corners and under chairs for an insect. The thumping on the wall became frantic.

Renny picked up the terrier and smothered his barks under his arm. "Poor Uncle Ernest! You'll have him unnerved for the rest of the day. Shut up, Nip, you little scoundrel."

Nicholas's long face, the deep downward lines of which gave an air of sagacity to his most trivial remarks, was lit by a sardonic smile. "Does him good to be stirred up," he remarked. "He spends too much time at his desk. Came to me the other day jubilant. He had got what he believed to be two hundred and fifty mistakes in the text of Shakespeare's plays. Fancy trying to improve Shakespeare's text at this time. I tell him he has not an adequate knowledge of the handwriting of the day, but he thinks he has. Poor Ernie, he always was a little nutty."

Renny puffed soberly at his cigar. "I hope to God Eden is not going to take after him. Wasting his time over poetry. I feel a bit upset about this book of his. It's gone to his head. I believe the young fool thinks he can make a living from poetry. You don't think so, do you, Uncle Nick?" He regarded Nicholas almost pathetically.

"I don't believe it's ever been done. I like his poetry, though. It's very nice poetry."

"Well, he must understand he's got to work. I'm not going to waste any more money on him. He's quite made up his mind he won't go on with his profession. After all I've spent on him! I only wish I had it back."

Nicholas tugged at his drooping moustache. "Oh, he had to have a university education."

"No, he didn't. Piers hasn't. He didn't want it. Wouldn't have it. Eden could have stopped at home. We could find plenty of work for him on one of the farms."

"Eden farming? My dear Renny! Don't worry. Let him go on with his poetry and wait and see what happens."

"It's such a damned silly life for a man. All very well for the classic poets—"

"They were young fellows once. Disapproved of by their families, too."

"*Is* his poetry good enough?"

"Well, it's good enough to take the fancy of this publisher. For my part, I think it's very adroit. A sort of delicate perfection—a very wistful beauty that's quite remarkable."

Renny stared at his uncle, suspiciously. Was he making fun of Eden? Or was he just pulling the wool over his own eyes to protect Eden? "Adroit, delicate, wistful"—the adjectives made him sick. "One thing's damned certain," he growled; "he'll not get any more money out of me."

Nicholas heaved himself about in his chair, achieving a more comfortable position. "How are things going? Pretty close to the wind?"

"Couldn't be closer," Renny assented.

Nicholas chuckled. "And yet you would like to keep all the boys at Jalna instead of sending them out into the world to shift for themselves. Renny, you have the instincts of the patriarch. To be the head of a swarming tribe. To mete out justice and rewards, and grow a long red beard."

Renny, somewhat nettled, felt like saying that both Nicholas and his brother Ernest had taken advantage of this instinct in him, but he satisfied himself by pulling the little dog's ears. Nip growled.

"Catch a spider, Nip," commanded his master, clapping his hands at him.

Once again Nip hurled himself into a frenzy of pursuit after an imagined insect. The thumping on the wall broke out anew. Renny got up to go. He felt that his troubles were not being taken seriously. Nicholas, looking up from under his shaggy brows, saw the shadow on Renny's face. He said, with sudden warmth: "You're an uncommonly good brother, Renny, *and* nephew. Have a drink?"

Renny said he would, and Nicholas insisted on getting up to mix it for him. "Shouldn't take one myself with this damn knee—" but he did, hobbling about his liquor cabinet in sudden activity.

"Well, Eden can do as he likes this summer," said Renny, cheered by his glass, "but by fall he's got to settle down, either in business or here at Jalna."

"But what would the boy do at Jalna, Renny?"

"Help Piers. Why not? If he would turn in and help, we could take over the land that is rented to old Hare and make twice as much out of it. It's a good life. He could write poetry in his spare time if he wanted to. I'd not say a word against it, so long as I wasn't asked to read it."

"The ploughman poet. It sounds artless enough. But I'm afraid he has very different ideas for his future. Poor young whelp. Heavens! How like his mother he is!"

"Well," mumbled Renny. "He'll not get around me. I've wasted enough on him. To think of him refusing to try his finals! I've never heard of such a thing. Now he talks of going down to New York to see his publisher."

"I expect this particular germ has been working in him secretly for a long time. Perhaps the boy's a genius, Renny."

"Lord! I hope not."

Nicholas made the subterranean noises that were his laughter. "You're a perfect Court, Renny. No wonder Mamma is partial to you."

"Is she? I'd never noticed it. I thought Eden was her pet. He has a way with women of all ages. Well, I'm off. Hobbs, up Mistwell way, is having a sale of Holsteins. I may buy a cow or two."

"I should go with you if it were horses, in spite of my knee, but I can't get worked up over cows. Never liked milk."

Renny had got to the door when Nicholas asked suddenly: "How about Piers? Have you spoken to him of the girl yet?"

"Yes. I've told him he must cut out these meetings with her. He never dreamed they'd been seen. He was staggered."

"He seemed all right at dinner time."

"Oh, we had our little talk two days ago. He's not a bad youngster. He took it very well. There aren't many girls about here—attractive ones—and there's no denying Pheasant is pretty."

Nicholas's brow darkened. "But think what she is. We don't want that breed in the family. Meg would never stand it."

"The girl is all right," said Renny, in his contradictory way. "She didn't choose the manner of her coming into the world. The boys have always played about with her."

"Piers will play about with her once too often."

"That's all right," returned Renny, testily. "He knows I'll stand no nonsense." He went out, shutting the door noisily, as he always did.

Nip was still busy with his bone. Regarding him, Nicholas feared that he would be in for an attack of indigestion if he got any more of the gristle off it. He dragged the treasure from him, and with difficulty straightened himself. Once bent over, it was no joke to rise. What a responsibility a little pet dog was! "No, no, no more gristle. You'll get a tummy-ache."

Nip protested, dancing on his hind legs. Nicholas laid the bone on the piano and wiped his fingers on the tail of his coat. Then the bottle of Scotch and the siphon caught his eye. He took up his glass. "Good Lord, I shouldn't be doing this," he groaned, but he mixed himself another drink. "Positively the last to-day," he murmured, as he hobbled toward his chair, glass in hand.

A deep note was struck on the piano. Nip had leaped to the stool and from there to the keys. Now he had stretched his head to recapture the bone. Nicholas sank with a grunt of mingled pain and amusement into his chair. "I suppose we may as well kill ourselves," he commented, ruefully,

"You in your small corner,
And I in mine."

Nip growled, gnawing his bone on the top of the piano.

Nicholas sipped his whiskey and soda dreamily. The house was beautifully quiet now. He would doze a little, just in his chair, when he had finished his glass and Nip his bone. The rhythmic crunching of Nip's teeth as he excavated for marrow was soothing. A smile flitted over Nicholas's face as he remembered how the little fellow's barking had upset Ernest. Ernest did get upset easily, poor old boy! Well, he was probably resting quietly now beside his beloved Sasha. Cats. Selfish things. Only loved you for what they could get out of you. Now Nip—there *was* devotion.

He stretched out his hand and looked at it critically. Yes, that heavy ring with the square green stone in its antique setting became it. He was glad he had inherited his mother's hands—Court hands. Renny had them, too, but badly cared for. No doubt about it, character, as well as breeding, showed in hands. A vision of the hands of his wife, Millicent, came before him,—clawlike hands with incredibly thin, very white fingers, and large curving nails. . . . She was still living; he knew that. Good God, she would be seventy! He tried to picture her at seventy, then shook his head impatiently—no, he did not want to picture her at either seventy or seventeen. He wanted to forget her. When Mamma should die, as she must soon, poor old dear, and he should inherit the money, he would go to England for a visit. He'd like to see old England once again before he—well, even he would die some day, though he expected to live to be at least ninety-nine like Mamma. He was a Court, and they were famous for their longevity and—what was the other? Oh, yes, their tempers. Well, thank goodness, he hadn't inherited the Court temper. It would die with Mamma, though Renny when he was roused was a fierce fellow.

Nip was whining to be lifted from the piano top. He was tired of his bone, and wanted his afternoon nap. Little devil, to make him get out of his chair again just when he was so comfortable!

With a great grunt he heaved himself on to his feet and limped to the piano. He took up the little dog, now entirely gentle and confiding, and carried him back under his arm. His knee gave him a sharp twinge as he lowered his weight into the chair once more, but his grimace of pain changed to a smile at the shaggy little face that was turned up to his. He had a sudden impulse to say, "Catch a spider, Nip!" and start a fresh skirmish. He even framed the words with his lips, and a sudden tenseness in Nip's body, a gleam in his eye, showed that he was ready; but he must not upset old Ernie again, and he was very drowsy—that second drink had been soothing.

"No, no, Nip," he murmured, "go to sleep. No more racketing, old boy." He stroked the little dog's back with a large, indolent hand.

Nip lay along his body, as he half reclined, gazing into his eyes. Nicholas blew into Nip's face. Nip thumped his tail on Nicholas's stomach.

They slept.

V. PIERS AND HIS LOVE

It was almost dark when Piers crossed the lawn, passed through a low wicket gate in the hedge, and pressed eagerly along a winding path that led across a paddock where three horses were still cropping the new grass. The path wandered then down into the ravine; became, for three strides, a little rustic bridge; became a path again, still narrower, that wound up the opposite steep, curved through a noble wood; and at last, by a stile, was wedded to another path that had been shaped for no other purpose but to meet it on the boundary between Jalna and the land belonging to the Vaughans.

Down in the ravine it was almost night, so darkly the stream glimmered amid the thick undergrowth and so close above him hung the sky, not yet pricked by a star. Climbing up the steep beyond, it was darker still, except for the luminous shine of the silver birches that seemed to be lighted by some secret beam within. A whippoorwill darted among the trees, catching insects, uttering, each time it struck, a little throaty cluck, and showing a gleam of white on its wings. Then suddenly, right over his head, another whippoorwill burst into its loud lilting song.

When he reached the open wood above, Piers could see that there was still a deep red glow in the west, and the young leaves of the oaks had taken a burnished look. The trees were lively with the twittering of birds seeking their nests, their lovemaking over for the day—his just to begin.

His head was hot and he took off his cap to let the cool air fan it. He wished that his love for Pheasant were a calmer love. He would have liked to stroll out with her in the evenings, just pleasantly elated, taking it as a natural thing, as natural as the life of these birds, to love a girl and be loved by her. But it had come upon him suddenly, after knowing her all his life, like a storm that shook and possessed him. As he hurried on through the soft night air, each step drawing him nearer to the stile where Pheasant was to meet him, he tormented himself by picturing his disappointment if she were not there. He saw, in his fancy, the stile, bare as a waiting gallows, mocking the sweet urge that pressed him. He saw himself waiting till dark night and then stumbling back to Jalna filled with despair because he had not held her in his arms. What was it that had overtaken them both that day, when, meeting down in the ravine, she had been startled by a water snake and had caught his sleeve and had pointed down into the stream where it had disappeared? Bending over the water, they had suddenly seen their two faces reflected in a still pool, looking up at them not at all like the faces of Piers and Pheasant who had known each other all their days. The faces reflected had had strange, timid eyes and parted lips. They had turned to look at each other. Their own lips had met.

Remembering that kiss, he began to run across the open field toward the stile.

She was sitting on it, waiting for him, her drooping figure silhouetted against the blur of red in the west. He slackened his pace as soon as he saw her, and greeted her laconically as he came up.

"Hullo, Pheasant!"

"Hullo, Piers! I've been waiting quite a while."

"I couldn't get away. I had to stop and admire a beastly cow Renny bought at Hobbs's sale to-day."

He climbed to the stile and sat down beside her. "It's the first warm evening, isn't it?" he observed, not looking at her. "I got as hot as blazes coming over. I wasn't letting the grass grow under my feet, I can tell you." He took her hand and drew it against his side. "Feel that."

"Your heart is beating rather hard," she said, in a low voice. "Is it because you hurried or because—" She leaned against his shoulder and looked into his face.

It was what Piers had been waiting for, this moment when she should lean toward him. Not without a sign from her would he let the fountain of his love leap forth. Now he put his arms about her and pressed her to him. He found her lips and held them with his own. The warm fragrance of her body made him dizzy. He was no longer strong and practical. He wished in that moment that they two might die thus happily clasped in each other's arms in the tranquil spring night.

"I can't go on like this," he murmured. "We simply must get married."

"Remember what Renny has said. Are you going to defy him? He'd be in a rage if he knew we were together here now."

"Renny be damned! He's got to be taught a lesson. It's time he was taught that he can't lord it over everyone. He's spoiled, that's the trouble with him. I call him the Rajah of Jalna."

"After all, you have the right to say who you will marry, even if the girl is beneath you, haven't you?"

He felt a sob beneath her breast; her sudden tears wet his cheek.

"Oh, Pheasant, you little fool," he exclaimed. "You beneath me? What rot!"

"Well, Renny thinks so. All your family think so. Your family despise me."

"My family may go to the devil. Why, after all, you're a Vaughan. Everybody knows that. You're called by the name."

"Even Maurice looks down on me. He's never let me call him Father."

"He deserves to be shot. If I had ever done what he did, I'd stand by the child. I'd brave the whole thing out, by God!"

"Well, he has—in a way. He's kept me. Given me his name."

"His parents did that. He's never liked you or been really kind to you."

"He thinks I've spoiled his life."

"With Meggie, you mean. Picture Meg and Maurice married!" He laughed and kissed her temple, and, feeling her silky brow touch his cheek, he kissed that, too.

She said: "I can picture that more easily than I can our own marriage. I feel as though we should go on and on, meeting and parting like this forever. In a way I think I'd like it better, too."

"Better than being married to me? Look here, Pheasant, you're just trying to hurt me."

"No, really. It's so beautiful, meeting like this. All day I'm in a kind of dream, waiting for it; then after it comes the night, and you're in the very heart of me all night—"

"What if I were beside you?"

"It couldn't be so lovely. It couldn't. Then in the morning, the moment I waken, I am counting the hours till we meet again. Maurice might not exist. I scarcely see or hear him."

"Dreams don't satisfy me, Pheasant. This way of living is torture to me. Every day as the spring goes on it's a greater torture. I want you—not dreams of you."

"Don't you love our meeting like this?"

"Don't be silly! You know what I mean." He moved away from her on the stile and lighted a cigarette. "Now," he went on, in a hard, businesslike tone, "let us take it for granted that we're going to be married. We are, aren't we? Are we going to be married, eh?"

"Yes . . . You might offer me a cigarette."

He gave her one and lighted it for her.

"Very well. Can you tell me any reason for hanging back? I'm twenty, you're seventeen. Marriageable ages, eh?"

"Too young, they say."

"Rot. They would like us to wait till we're too decrepit to creep to this stile. I'm valuable to Renny. He's paying me decent wages. I know Renny. He's good-natured at bottom, for all his temper. He'd never dream of putting me out. There's lots of room at Jalna. One more would never be noticed."

"Meg doesn't like me. I'm rather afraid of her."

"Afraid of Meggie! Oh, you little coward! She's gentle as a lamb. And Gran always liked you. I'll tell you what, Pheasant, we'll stand in with Gran. She has a lot of influence with the family. If we make ourselves pleasant to her, there's no knowing what she may do for us. She's often said that I am more like my grandfather than any of the others, and she thinks he was the finest man that ever lived."

"What about Renny? She's always talking about his being a perfect Court. Anyhow, I expect her will was made before we were born."

"Yes, but she's always changing it or pretending that she does. Only last week she had her lawyer out for hours, and the whole family was upset. Wake peeked in at the keyhole and he said all she did was feed the old fellow peppermints. Still, you can never tell." He shook his head sagaciously and then heaved a gusty sigh. "One thing is absolutely certain: I can't go on like this. I've either got to get married or go away. It's affecting my nerves. I scarcely knew what I was eating at dinner to-day, and such a hullabaloo there was over this book of Eden's. Good Lord! Poetry! Think of it! And at tea time Finch had come home with a bad report from one of his masters and there was another row. It raged for an hour."

But Pheasant had heard nothing but the calculated cruelty of the words "go away." She turned toward him a frightened, wide-eyed face.

"Go away! How can you say such a thing? You know I'd die in this place without you."

"How pale you've got," he observed, peering into her face. "Why are you turning pale? Surely it wouldn't matter to you if I went away. You could go right on dreaming about me, you know."

Pheasant burst into tears and began to scramble down from the stile. "If you think I'll stop here to be tortured!" she cried, and began to run from him.

"Yet you expect me to stay and be tortured!" he shouted.

She ran into the dusk across the wet meadow, and he sat obstinately staring after her, wondering if her will would hold out till she reached the other side. Already her steps seemed to be slackening. Still her figure became less clear. What if she should run on and on till she reached home, leaving him alone on the stile with all his love turbulent within him? The mere thought of that was enough to make him jump down and begin to run after her, but even as he did so he saw her coming slowly back, and he clambered again to his seat just in time to save his dignity. He was thankful for that.

She stopped within ten paces of him.

"Very well," she said, in a husky voice, "I'll do it."

He was acutely aware of her nearness in every sensitive nerve, but he puffed stolidly at his cigarette a moment before he asked gruffly: "When?"

"Whenever you say." Her head drooped and she gave a childish sob.

"Come here, you little baggage," he ordered peremptorily. But when he had her on the stile again a most delicious tenderness took possession of him and withal a thrilling sense of power. He uttered endearments and commands with his face against her hair.

All the way home he was full of lightness and strength, though he had worked hard that day. Halfway down the steep into the ravine a branch of an oak projected across the path above him. He leaped up and caught it with his hands and so hung aloof from the earth that seemed too prosaic for his light feet. He swung himself gently a moment, looking up at the stars that winked at him through the young leaves. A rabbit ran along the path beneath, quite unaware of him. His mind was no longer disturbed by anxiety, but free and exultant. He felt himself one with the wild things of the wood. It was spring, and he had chosen his mate.

When he crossed the lawn he saw that the drawing-room was lighted. Playing cards as usual, he supposed. He went to one of the French windows and looked in. By the fire he could see a table drawn up, at which sat his grandmother and his uncle Ernest, playing at draughts. She was wrapped in a bright green-and-red plaid shawl, and wearing a much beribboned cap. Evidently she was beating him, for her teeth were showing in a broad grin and a burst of loud laughter made the bridge players at the other table turn in their chairs with looks of annoyance. The long aquiline face of Uncle Ernest drooped wistfully above the board. On the blackened walnut mantelpiece Sasha lay curled beside a china shepherdess, her gaze fixed on her master with a kind of ecstatic contempt.

At the bridge table sat Renny, Meg, Nicholas, and Mr. Fennel, the rector. The faces of all were illumined by firelight, their expressions intensified: Nicholas, sardonic, watchful; Renny, frowning, puzzled; Meg, sweet, complacent; Mr. Fennel, pulling his beard and glowering. Poor creatures all, thought Piers, as he let himself in at the side door and softly ascended the stair, playing their little games, their paltry pastimes, whilst he played the great game of life.

A light showed underneath Eden's door. More poetry, more paltry pastime! Had Eden ever loved? If he had, he'd kept it well to himself. Probably he only loved his Muse. His Muse— ha, ha! He heard Eden groan. So it hurt, did it, loving the pretty Muse? Poetry had its pain, then. He gave a passing thump to the door.

"Want any help in there?"

"You go to hell," rejoined the young poet, "unless you happen to have a rag about you. I've upset the ink."

Piers poked his head in at the door. "My shirt isn't much better than a rag," he said. "I can let you have that."

Eden was mopping the stained baize top of the desk with blotting paper. On a sheet of a writing pad was neatly written what looked like the beginning of a poem.

"I suppose you get fun out of it," remarked Piers.

"More than you get from chasing a girl about the wood at night."

"Look here, you'd better be careful!" Piers raised his voice threateningly, but Eden smiled and sat down at his desk once more.

It was uncanny, Piers thought, as he went on to his room. How ever had Eden guessed? Was it because he was a poet? He had always felt, though he had given the matter but little thought, that a poet would be an uncommonly unpleasant person to have in the house, and now, by God, they had a full-fledged one at Jalna. He didn't like it at all. The first bloom of his happy mood was gone as he opened the door into his bedroom.

He shared it with sixteen-year-old Finch. Finch was now humped over his Euclid, an expression of extreme melancholy lengthening his already long sallow face. He had been the centre of a whirlpool of discussion and criticism all tea time, and the effect was to make his brain, never quite under his control, completely unmanageable. He had gone over the same problem six or seven times and now it meant nothing to him, no more than a senseless nursery rhyme. He had stolen one of Piers's cigarettes to see if it would help him out. He had made the most of it, inhaling slowly, savoring each puff, retaining the stub between his bony fingers till they and even his lips were burned, but it had done no good. When he heard Piers at the door he had dropped the stub, a mere crumb, to the floor and set his foot on it.

Now he glanced sullenly at Piers out of the corners of his long light eyes.

Piers sniffed. "H-m. Smoking, eh? One of my fags, too, I bet. I'll just thank you to leave them alone, young man. Do you think I can supply you with smokes? Besides, you're not allowed."

Finch returned to his Euclid with increased melancholy. If he could not master it when he was alone, certainly he should never learn it with Piers in the room. That robust, domineering presence would crush the last spark of intelligence from his brain. He had always been afraid of Piers. All his life he had been kept in a state of subjection by him. He resented it, but he saw no way out of it. Piers was strong, handsome, a favorite. He was none of these things. And yet he loved all his family, in a secret, sullen way, even Piers who was so rough with him. Now, if Piers had been some brothers one might ask him to give one a helping hand with the Euclid; Piers had been good at the rotten stuff. But it would never do to ask Piers for help. He was too impatient, too intolerant of a fellow who got mixed up for nothing.

"I'd thank you," continued Piers, "to let my fags, likewise my handkerchiefs, socks, and ties alone. If you want to pinch other people's property, pinch Eden's. He's a poet and probably doesn't know what he has." He grinned at his reflection in the glass as he took off his collar and tie.

Finch made no answer. Desperately he sought to clamp his attention to the problem before him. Angles and triangles tangled themselves into strange patterns. He drew a grotesque face on the margin of the book. Then horribly the face he had created began to leer at him. With a shaking hand he tried to rub it out, but he could not. It was not his to erase. It possessed the page. It possessed the book. It was Euclid personified, sneering at him!

Piers had divested himself of all his clothes and had thrown open the window. A chill night wind rushed in. Finch shivered as it embraced him. He wondered how Piers stood it on his bare skin. It fluttered the pages of a French exercise all about the room. There was no use in trying; he could not do the problem.

Piers, in his pyjamas now, jumped into bed. He lay staring at Finch with bright blue eyes, whistling softly. Finch began to gather up his books.

"All finished?" asked Piers, politely. "You got through in a hurry, didn't you?"

"I'm not through," bawled Finch. "Do you imagine I can work with a cold blast like that on my back and you staring at me in front? It just means I'll have to get up early and finish before breakfast."

Piers became sarcastic. "You're very temperamental, aren't you? You'll be writing poetry next. I dare say you've tried it already. Do you know, I think it would be a good thing for you to go down to New York in the Easter holidays and see if you can find a publisher."

"Shut up," growled Finch, "and let me alone."

Piers was very happy. He was too happy for sleep. It would ease his high spirits to bait young Finch. He lay watching him speculatively while he undressed his long, lanky body. Finch might develop into a distinguished-looking man. There was something arresting even now in his face; but he had a hungry, haunted look, and he was uncomfortably aware of his long wrists and legs. He always sat in some ungainly posture and, when spoken to suddenly, would glare up, half defensively, half timidly, as though expecting a blow. Truth to tell, he had had a good many, some quite undeserved.

Piers regarded his thin frame with contemptuous amusement. He offered pungent criticisms of Finch's prominent shoulder blades, ribs, and various other portions of his anatomy. At last the boy, trembling with anger and humiliation, got into his nightshirt, turned out the light, and scrambled over Piers to his place next the wall. He curled himself up with a sigh of relief. It had been a nervous business scrambling over Piers. He had half expected to be grabbed by the ankle and put to some new torture. But he had gained his corner in safety. The day with its miseries was over. He stretched out his long limbs.

They lay still, side by side, in the peaceful dark. At length Piers spoke in a low, accusing tone.

"You didn't say your prayers. What do you mean by getting into bed without saying your prayers?"

Finch was staggered. This was something new. Piers, of all people, after him about prayers! There was something ominous about it.

"I forgot," he returned, heavily.

"Well, you've no right to forget. It's an important thing at your time of life to pray long and earnestly. If you prayed more and sulked less, you'd be healthier and happier."

"Rot. What are you givin' us?"

"I'm in dead earnest. Out you get and say your prayers."

"You don't pray yourself," complained Finch, bitterly. "You haven't said prayers for years."

"That's nothing to you. I've a special compact with the Devil, and he looks after his own. But you, my little lamb, must be separated from the goats."

"Oh, let me alone," growled Finch. "I'm sleepy. Let me alone."

"Get up and say your prayers."

"Oh, Piers, don't be a—"

"Be careful what you call me. Get out."

"Shan't." He clutched the blankets desperately, for he feared what was coming.

"You won't get up, eh? You won't say your prayers, eh? I've got to force you, eh?"

With each question Piers's strong fingers sought a tenderer spot in Finch's anatomy.

"Oh–oh–oh! Piers! Please let me up! Ow-eee-ee!" With a last terrible squeak Finch was out on the floor. He stood rubbing his side cautiously. Then he almost blubbered: "What the hell do you want me to do, anyway?"

"I want you to say your prayers properly. I'm not going to have you start being lax at your age. Down on your knees."

Finch dropped to his knees on the cold floor. Kneeling by the bedside in the pale moonlight, he was a pathetic young figure. But the sight held no pathos for Piers.

"Now, then," he said. "Fire away." Finch pressed his face against his clenched hands.

"Why don't you begin?" asked Piers, rising on his elbow and speaking testily.

"I–I have begun," came in a muffled voice.

"I can't hear you. How do you expect the Almighty to hear you if I can't? Speak up."

"I c-can't. I won't!"

"You *shall*. Or you'll be sorry."

In the stress of the moment, all Finch's prayers left him, as earlier all his Euclid had done. In the dim chaos of his soul only two words of supplication remained. "Oh, God," he muttered, hoarsely, and because he could think of nothing else, and must pray or be abused by that devil Piers, he repeated the words again and again in a hollow, shaking voice.

Piers lay listening blandly. He thought Finch the most ridiculous duffer he had ever known. He was a mystery Piers would never fathom. Suddenly he thought: "I'm fed up with this," and said: "Enough, enough. It's not much of a prayer you've made, but still you've a nice intimate way with the Almighty. You'd make a good Methodist of the Holy Roller variety." He added, not unkindly, "Hop into bed now."

But Finch would not hop. He clutched the counterpane and went on sobbing, "Oh, God!" The room was full of the presence of the Deity to him, now wearing the face of the terrible, austere Old Testament God, now, miraculously, the handsome, sneering face of Piers. Only a rap on the head brought him to his senses. He somehow got his long body back into bed, shivering all over.

Eden threw the door open. "One might as well," he complained in a high voice, "live next door to a circus. You're the most disgusting young–" and he delivered himself of some atrocious language. He interrupted himself to ask, cocking his head, "Is he crying? What's he crying for?"

"Just low-spirited, I expect," replied Piers, in a sleepy voice.

"What are you crying for, Finch?"

"Let me alone, can't you?" screamed Finch, in a sudden fury. "You let me alone!"

"I think he's sniveling over his report. Renny was up in the air about it," said Piers.

"Oh, is that it? Well, study will do more than sniveling to help that." And Eden disappeared as he had come.

The two brothers lay in the moonlight. Finch was quiet save for an occasional gulp. Piers's feelings toward him were magnanimous now. He was such a helpless young fool. Piers thought it rather hard that he had been born between Eden and Finch. Wedged in between a poet and a fool. What a sandwich! Of a certainty, he was the meaty part.

His thoughts turned to Pheasant. She was of never-failing interest to him: her pretty gestures, her reckless way of throwing her heart open to him, her sudden withdrawals, the remoteness of her profile. He could see her face in the moonlight as though she were in the room with him. Soon she would be, instead of snuffling young Finch! He loved her with every inch of his body. He alone of all the people in Jalna knew what real love was. Strange that, being absorbed by love as he was, he should have time to play with young Finch and make him miserable. No denying that there lurked a mischievous devil in him. Then, too, he had suffered so much anxiety lately that to have everything settled, to be certain of having his own way, made him feel like a young horse suddenly turned out into the spring pastures, ready to run and kick and bite his best friend from sheer high spirits.

Poor old Finch! Piers gave the bedclothes a jerk over Finch's protruding shoulder and put an arm around him.

VI. PHEASANT AND MAURICE

Two weeks later Pheasant awakened one morning at sunrise. She could not sleep, because it was her wedding day. She jumped out of bed and ran to the window to see whether the heavens were to smile on her.

The sky was radiant as a golden sea, and just above the sun a cloud shaped like a great red whale floated as in a dream. Below her window, shutting in the lawn, the cherry orchard had burst into a sudden perfection of bloom. The young trees stood in snowy rows like expectant young girls awaiting their first communion. A cowbell was jangling down in the ravine.

Pheasant leaned across the sill, her cropped brown hair all on end, her nightdress falling from one slim shoulder. She was happy because of the gay serenity of the morning, because the cherry trees had come into bloom for her wedding day; yet she was depressed, because it was her wedding day and she had nothing new to wear. Besides, she would have to go to live at Jalna, where nobody wanted her except Piers.

She was to meet him at two o'clock. He had borrowed a car, and they were to drive to Stead to be married. This was outside Mr. Fennel's parish. Then they were to go to the city for the night, but they must be back at Jalna the next day because Piers was anxious about the spring sowing. What sort of reception would the family at Jalna give them? They had been kind always, but would they be kind to her as Piers's wife? Still, Piers would take care of her. She would face the world with him at her side.

She drummed her white fingers on the sill, watching the sun twinkle on her engagement ring which thus far she had only dared to wear at night. She thought of that blissful moment when each had stared into the other's face, watching love flower there like the cherry tree bursting into bloom. She would love him always, let him cuddle his head against her shoulder at night, and go into the fields with him in the morning. She was glad he had chosen the land as his job, instead of one of the professions. She was too ignorant to be the wife of a learned young man. To Piers she could unfold her childish speculations about life without embarrassment.

For the hundredth time she examined the few clothes she had laid in an immense shabby portmanteau for her wedding journey—her patent-leather shoes and her one pair of silk stockings, a pink organdie dress, really too small for her, four handkerchiefs,—well, she had plenty of them, at least, and one never knew when one might shed tears,—a nightdress, and an India shawl that had been her grandmother's. She did not suppose she would need the shawl; she had never worn it except when playing at being grown up, but it helped to make a more impressive trousseau, and it might be necessary to have a wrap at dinner in the hotel, or if they went to the opera. She felt somewhat cheered as she replaced them and fastened the spongy leather straps. After all, they might have been fewer and worse.

She got out her darning things and mended—or rather puckered together—a large hole in the heel of a brown stocking she was to wear on the journey. She mended the torn buttonholes of her brown coat, sprinkled a prodigious amount of cheap perfume over the little brown dress that lay in a drawer ready to put on, and found herself chilled, for she had not yet dressed.

She hastily put on her clothes, washed her face, and combed her hair, staring at herself in the glass. She thought dismally: "Certainly I am no beauty. Nannie has trimmed my hair badly. I'm far too thin, and I haven't at all that sleek look becoming in a bride. No one could imagine a wreath of orange blossoms on my head. A punchinello's cap would be more appropriate. Ah, well, there have been worse-looking girls led to the altar, I dare say."

Maurice Vaughan was already at the table, eating sausages and fried potatoes. He did not say good morning, but he put some of the food on a plate and pushed it toward her. Presently he said:—

"Jim Martin is coming with a man from Brancepeth to-day. Have Nannie put the dinner off till one. We'll be busy."

Pheasant was aghast. She was to meet Piers at two. How could she get away in time? And if she did not turn up for dinner Maurice might make inquiries, get suspicious. Her hands shook as she poured her tea. She could not properly see the breakfast things.

Maurice stared at her coldly. "Did you hear what I said?" he asked. "What's the matter with you this morning?"

"I was busy thinking. Yes, you want dinner at two; I heard."

"I said one o'clock. I'd better give the order myself, if you haven't the wit."

Pheasant was regaining her self-possession.

"How easily you get out of temper," she said, coolly. "Of course I'll remember. I hope Mr. Martin will be soberer than he was the last time he was here. He put a pickle in his tea instead of sugar, and slept all evening, I remember, in his chair."

"I don't."

"I dare say you don't. You were pretty far gone yourself."

Vaughan burst out laughing. The audacities of this only half-acknowledged young daughter of his amused him. Yet, perversely, when she was meek and eager to please, he was often unkind to her, seeming to take pleasure in observing how she had inherited a capacity for suffering equal to his own.

Maurice Vaughan was the grandson and only male descendant of the Colonel Vaughan whose letters had persuaded Philip Whiteoak to remove westward from Quebec. He was an only child, who had come to his parents late in life. He had been too gently reared, and had grown into a heavily built, indolent, arrogant youth, feeling himself intellectually above all his associates, even Renny Whiteoak whom he loved. At twenty he nourished the illusion that he would become a great man in the affairs of his country with no effort on his part. At twenty-one he became engaged to Meg Whiteoak, charmed by that ineffably sweet smile of hers and her drowsy quiescence toward himself. The parents of the two were almost beside themselves with pleasure. They scarcely dared to breathe lest a breath too hot or too cold should damp the ardor of the young pair and the so desirable match be not consummated.

Meggie would not be hurried. A year's engagement was proper, and a year's engagement she would have. Maurice, idle and elegant, attracted the attention of a pretty, sharp-featured village girl, Elvira Gray. She took to picking brambleberries in the woods where Maurice slouched about with his gun—the same woods where Piers and Pheasant now met. Maurice, while he waited impatiently for Meg, was comforted by the love of Elvira.

A month before the marriage was to take place, a tiny bundle containing a baby was laid one summer night on the Vaughans' doorstep. Old Mr. Vaughan, awakened by its faint cry, went downstairs in his slippers, opened the front door, and found the bundle, on which a note was pinned, which read: "Maurice Vaughan is the father of this baby. Please be kind to it. It hasn't harmed no one."

Mr. Vaughan fell in a faint on the steps and was found, lying beside the baby, by a farm laborer who read the note and quickly spread the news. The child was carried into the house and the news of its arrival to Jalna.

As proper in the heroine of such a tragedy, Meg locked herself in her room and refused to see anyone. She refused to eat. Maurice, after a heart-rending morning with his parents, during which he acknowledged everything, went and hid himself in the woods. It was found that Elvira, an orphan, had disappeared.

Meg's father, accompanied by his brothers, Nicholas and Ernest, went to thrash out the matter with Mr. Vaughan. They were quite twenty years younger than he, and they all raged around the poor distracted man at once, in true Whiteoak fashion. Still, in spite of their outraged feelings, they agreed that the engagement was not to be broken, that the marriage must take place at the appointed time. A home could be found for the baby. They drove back to Jalna, after having had some stiff drinks, feeling that, thank God, everything had been patched up, and it would be a lesson to the young fool, though rather rough on Meggie.

Meggie could not be persuaded to leave her room. Trays of food placed outside her door were left untouched. One night, after four days of misery, young Maurice rode over to Jalna on his beautiful chestnut mare. He threw a handful of gravel against Meggie's window and called her name. She made no answer. He repeated it with tragic insistence. Finally Meg appeared in the bright moonlight, framed as a picture by the vine-clad window. She sat with her elbow on the sill and her chin on her palm, listening, while he, standing with the mare's bridle over his arm, poured out his contrition. She listened impassively, with her face raised moonward, till he had done, and then said: "It is all over. I cannot marry you, Maurice. I shall never marry anyone."

Maurice could not and would not believe her. He was unprepared for such relentless stubbornness beneath such a sweet exterior. He explained and implored for two hours. He threw himself on the ground and wept, while the mare cropped the grass beside him.

Renny, whose room was next Meg's, could bear it no longer. He flew downstairs to Maurice's side and joined his supplications to his friend's in rougher language. Nothing could move Meggie. She listened to the impassioned appeals of the two youths with tears raining down her pale cheeks; then, with a final gesture of farewell, she closed the window.

Meggie was interviewed by each of her elders in turn. Her father, her uncles, her young stepmother,—who had hoped so soon to be rid of her,—all exercised their powers of reasoning with her. Grandmother also tried her hand, but the sight of Meggie, suave yet immovable as Gibraltar, was too much for the old lady. She hit her on the head, which caused Philip Whiteoak to intervene, and say that he would not have his little girl forced into any distasteful marriage, and that it was small wonder if Meggie couldn't stomach a bridegroom who had just made a mother of a chapped country wench.

Meggie emerged from her retirement, pale but tranquil. Her life suffered little outward derangement from this betrayal of her affections. However, she cared less for going out with other young people, and spent many hours in her bedroom. It was at this time that she acquired the habit of eating almost nothing at the table, getting ample nourishment from agreeable little lunches carried to her room. She became more and more devoted to her brothers, pouring out on them a devotion with which she sought to drown the image of her lover.

Maurice never again came nearer to Jalna than its stables. The friendship between him and Renny still endured. Together they went through the hardships of the War years later. When Pheasant was three years old, Mr. and Mrs. Vaughan died within the year, and she was left to the care of an unloving young father whom she could already call "Maurice." Misfortune followed close upon bereavement. Mining stocks in which nearly all of the Vaughans' money was invested became worthless and Maurice's income declined from ten thousand a year to less than two. He made something from breeding horses, but as Pheasant grew up she never knew what it was to have two coins to rub together or attractive garments with which to clothe her young body. The thousand acres bought from the government by the first Vaughan had dwindled to three hundred. Of these only fifty lay under cultivation; the rest were in pasture and massive oak woods. The ravine that traversed Jalna narrowly spread into a valley through Vaughanlands, ending in a shallow basin, in the middle of which stood the house, with hanging shutters, sagging porch, and moss-grown roof.

The one servant now kept was an old Scotchwoman, Nannie, who spoke but rarely and then in a voice scarcely above a whisper. Beside Jalna, teeming with loud-voiced, intimate, inquisitive people, Vaughanlands seemed but an echoing shell, the three who dwelt there holding aloof in annihilating self-absorption.

Dinner at one, instead of half-past twelve as usual, threw Pheasant's plans into confusion. She felt suddenly weak, defenseless, insecure. She felt afraid of herself. Afraid that she would suddenly cry out to Maurice: "I'm going to run away to be married at half-past one! Dinner *must* be at the regular time."

What a start that would give him! She pictured his heavy, untidy face startlingly concentrated into dismay.

"What's that?" he would exclaim. "What's that, you little devil?"

Then she would hiss: "It's true. I'm going to be married this very day. And I'm going to marry into the Jalna family who wouldn't have you, my fine fellow."

Instead of this she said meekly: "Oh, Maurice, I'm afraid I'll have to take my dinner at half-past twelve. I've an appointment with the dentist in Stead at two o'clock."

She wondered why she had said that, for she had never been to a dentist in her life. She did not know the name of one.

"What are you making appointments with the dentist for?" he growled. "What's the matter with your teeth?"

"I've been troubled by toothache lately," she said, truthfully, and he remembered an irritating smell of liniment about her at odd times.

They went on with their breakfast in silence, she, a wave of relief sweeping over her at the absence of active opposition, drinking cup after cup of strong tea; he thinking that after all it were better the child should not be at the table with the two men who were coming. Martin had a rough tongue. Not the sort of man a decent fellow would want to introduce to his young daughter, he supposed. But then, what was the use of trying to protect Pheasant? She was her mother's daughter and he had had no respect for her mother; he had very little for himself, her father. Not all the beastly allegations current about the countryside against him since his first mishap were true, but they had damaged his opinion of himself, his dignity. He knew he was considered a rip, and always would be even when the patch of white that was coming above one temple spread over his whole head.

As for Pheasant, she was filled by sudden unaccountable compassion for him. Poor Maurice! To-morrow morning, and all the mornings to come, he would be eating breakfast alone. To be sure, they seldom spoke, but still she was there beside him; she carried his messages to Nannie; she poured his tea; and she had always gone with him to admire the new colts. Well, perhaps when she was not there he would be sorry that he had not been nicer to her.

She was so inexperienced that she thought of going to live at Jalna as of removal to a remote habitation where she would be cut off permanently from all her past life.

When Maurice had swallowed the last mouthful of tea, he rose slowly and went to the bow window, which, being shadowed by a verandah, gave only a greenish half-light into the room. He stood with his back toward her and said: "Come here."

Pheasant started up from her chair, all nerves. What was he going to do to her? She had a mind to run from the room. She gasped: "What do you want?"

"I want you to come here."

She went to his side with an assumed nonchalance.

"You seem to be playing the heavy father this morning," she said.

"I want to see that tooth you're talking about."

"I wasn't talking about it. It's you who are talking about it. I only said I was going to have it filled."

"Please open your mouth," he said, testily, putting his hand under her chin.

She prayed, "Oh, God, let there be a large hole in it," and opened her mouth so wide that she looked like a young robin beseeching food.

"H-m," growled Maurice. "It should have been attended to some time ago." He added, giving her chin a grudging stroke: "You've pretty little teeth. Get the fellow to fix them up properly."

Pheasant stared. He was being almost loving. At this late hour! He had stroked her chin—given it a little dab with his fingers, anyway. She felt suddenly angry with him. The idea of getting demonstratively affectionate with her at this late hour! Making it harder for her to leave him.

"Thanks," she said. "I'll be a beauty if I keep on, shan't I?"

He answered seriously: "You're too skinny for beauty. But you'll fill out. You're nothing but a filly."

"This is the way fillies show their pleasure," she said, and rubbed her head against his shoulder. "I wish I could whinny! But I *can* bite."

"I know you can," he said, gravely. "You bit me when you were five. And I held your head under the tap for it."

She was glad he had reminded her of that episode. It would be easier to leave him after that.

He went into the hall and took his hat from a peg.

"Good-bye," she called after him.

She watched him go along the path toward the stables, filling his pipe, walking with his peculiar, slouching, hangdog gait. She threw open the window and called after him:—

"Oh, hullo, Maurice!"

"Yes?" he answered, half wheeling.

"Oh—good-bye!"

"Well, I'll be—" she heard him mutter, as he went on.

He must think her a regular little fool. But, after all, it was a very serious good-bye. The next time they met, if ever they met again, she would be a different person. She would have an honorable name—a name with which she could face the world. She would be Mrs. Piers Whiteoak.

VII. PIERS AND PHEASANT MARRIED

He had arrived on the very tick of two. She had been there twenty minutes earlier, very hot, but pale from excitement and fatigue; she had jogged—sometimes breaking into a run—for nearly half a mile, lugging the heavy portmanteau. She had been in a state of panic at the approach of every vehicle, thinking she was pursued. Three times she had fled to the shelter of a group of wayside cedars, to hide while a wagon lumbered or a car sped by.

Piers stowed the portmanteau in the back of the car, and she flung herself into the seat beside him. He started the car—a poor old rattletrap, but washed for the occasion—with a jerk. He looked absurdly Sundayish in his rigid best serge suit, and with an expression rather more wooden than exultant.

"They needed this car at home to-day," he said. "I'd a hard time getting away."

"So had I. Maurice was having two guests to dinner, and it had to be later, and he wanted me there to receive them."

"H-m. Who were they?"

"A Mr. Martin and another man. Both horse breeders."

" 'Receive them'! Good Lord! You do say ridiculous things!"

She subsided into her corner, crushed. Was this what it was like to elope? A taciturn, soap-shining lover in a bowler hat, who called one ridiculous just at the moment when he should have been in an ecstasy of daring and protective love!

"I think you're very arrogant," she said.

"Perhaps I am," he agreed, letting the speed out. "I can't help it if I am," he added, not without complaisance. "It's in the blood, I expect."

She took off her hat and let the wind ruffle her hair. Road signs rushed past, black-and-white cattle in fields, cherry orchards in full bloom, and apple orchards just coming into bud.

"Gran said at dinner that I need disciplining. You'll have to do it, Pheasant." He looked around at her, smiling, and seeing her with her hair ruffled, her eyes shining, he added: "You precious darling!"

He snatched a kiss, and Pheasant put her hand on the wheel beside his. They both stared at the hand, thinking how soon the wedding ring must outshine the engagement ring in importance. They experienced a strange mixture of sensations, feeling at the same moment like runaway children (for they had both been kept down by their elders) and tremendous adventurers, not afraid of anything in this shining spring world.

They were married by the rector of Stead, a new man who had barely heard the names of their families, with perhaps a picturesque anecdote attached. Piers was so sunburned and solid that he looked like nothing but an ordinary young countryman, and Pheasant's badly cut dress and cheap shoes transformed her young grace into coltish awkwardness. He hoped they would come regularly to his church, he said, and he gave them some very good advice in the cool vestry. When they had gone and he examined the fee which Piers had given him in an envelope, he was surprised at its size, for Piers was determined to carry everything through as a Whiteoak should.

As they flew along the road which ran like a trimming of white braid on the brown shore that skirted the lake, Piers began to shout and sing in an ecstasy of achievement.

"We're man and wife!" he chanted. "Man and wife! Pheasant and Piers! Man and wife!"

His exuberance and the speed at which they drove the car made people stare. The greenish-blue lake, still stirred by a gale which had blown all night but had now fallen to a gentle breeze, beat on the shore a rhythmic accompaniment, an extravagant wedding march. Cherry orchards flung out the confetti of their petals on the road before them, and the air was unimaginably heavy with the heady incense of spring. Piers stopped the wagon of a fruit vender and bought oranges, of which Pheasant thrust sections into his mouth as he drove, and ate eagerly herself, for excitement made them thirsty. As they neared the suburbs of the city she threw the rinds into the ditch and scrubbed her lips and hands on her handkerchief. She put on her hat and sat upright then, her hands in her lap, feeling that everyone who met them must realize that they were newly married.

Piers had spoken for rooms in the Queen's hotel which the Whiteoaks had frequented for three generations. He had not been there very much himself—a few times to dinner in company with Renny, twice for birthday treats as a small boy with Uncle Nicholas.

Now on his wedding day he had taken one of the best bedrooms with bath adjoining. His blood was all in his head as the clerk gave a surreptitious smile and handed the key to a boy. The boy went lopsidedly before them to the bedroom, carrying the antiquated portmanteau. All the white closed doors along the corridor made Pheasant feel timid. She fancied there were ears against all the panels, eyes to the keyholes. What if Maurice should suddenly pounce out on them? Or Renny? Or terrible Grandmother Whiteoak?

When they were alone in the spacious, heavily furnished hotel bedroom, utterly alone, with only the deep rumble of the traffic below to remind them of the existence of the world, a sudden feeling of frozen dignity, of aloofness from each other, took possession of them.

"Not a bad room, eh? Think you'll be comfortable here?" And he added, almost challengingly: "It's one of the best rooms in the hotel, but if there's anything you'd like different—"

"Oh, no. It's nice. It'll do nicely, thank you."

Could they be the young runaway couple who had raced along the lakeshore road, singing and eating oranges?

"There's your bag," he said, indicating the ponderous portmanteau.

"Yes," she agreed. "I've got the bag all right."

"I wonder what we'd better do first," he added, staring at her. She looked so strange to him in this new setting that he felt as though he were really seeing her for the first time.

"What time is it?"

"Half-past five."

She noticed then that the sun had disappeared behind a building across the street, and that the room lay in a yellowish shadow. Evening was coming.

"Hadn't you better send the telegrams?"

"I expect I had. I'll go down and do that, and see that we've a table reserved; and, look here, shouldn't you like to go to the theatre to-night?"

Pheasant was thrilled at that. "Oh, I'd love the theatre! Is there something good on?"

"I'll find out, and get tickets, and you can be changing. Now about those telegrams. How would it do if I just send one to Renny, something like this: 'Pheasant and I married. Home to-morrow. Tell Maurice.' Would that be all right?"

"No," she said, firmly. "Maurice must have a telegram all to himself, from me. Say: 'Dear Maurice–' "

"Good Lord! You can't begin a telegram, 'Dear Maurice.' It isn't done. Tell me what you want to say and I'll put it in the proper form."

Pheasant spoke in an incensed tone. "See here; is this your telegram or mine? I've never written a letter or sent a telegram to Maurice in my life and I probably never shall again. So it's going to begin: 'Dear Maurice.' "

"All right, my girl. Fire away."

"Say, 'Dear Maurice: Piers and I are married. Tell Nannie. Yours sincerely, Pheasant.' That will do."

Piers could not conceal his mirth at such a telegram, but he promised to send it, and after giving her body a convulsive squeeze and receiving a kiss on the sunburned bridge of his nose he left her.

She was alone. She was married. All the old life was over and the new just beginning. She went to the dressing table and stood before the three-sectioned mirror. It was wonderful to see her own face there, from all sides at once. She felt that she had never really seen herself before–no wonder her reflection looked surprised. She turned this way and that, tilting her head like a pretty bird. She took off her brown dress and stood enthralled by the reflection of her charms in knickers and a little white camisole. She turned on the electric light, and made a tableau with her slender milky arms upraised and her eyes half closed. She wished she could spend a long time playing with these magical reflections, but Piers might come back and find her not dressed.

A bell in some tower struck six.

She saw that her hands needed washing and hoped there would be soap in the bathroom. She gasped when she had pressed the electric button and flooded the room with a hard white light. The fierce splendor of it dazzled her. At home there was a bathroom with a bare uncovered floor on which stood an ancient green tin bath, battered and disreputable. The towels were old and fuzzy, leaving bits of lint all over one's body, and the cake of soap was always like jelly, because Maurice would leave it in the water. Here were glistening tile and marble, nickel polished like new silver, an enormous tub of virgin whiteness, and a row of towels fit only for a bride. "And, by my halidom," she exclaimed,–for she was devoted to Sir Walter Scott,–"I am the bride!"

She locked herself in and took a bath, almost reverently handling the luxurious accessories. Such quantities of steaming water! Such delicate soap! Such satiny towels! As she stepped dripping on to the thick bath mat she felt that never till that moment had she been truly clean.

Her hair was sleekly brushed, and she was doing up her pink-and-white dress when Piers arrived. He had sent off the telegrams–and not neglected the "Dear" for Maurice. He had got orchestra chairs for a Russian vaudeville. He took her to the ladies' drawing-room and set her in a white-and-gold chair where she waited while he scrubbed and beautified himself.

They were at their own table in a corner where they could see the entire dining room: rows and rows of white-clothed tables, glimmering with silver, beneath shaded lights; a red-faced waiter with little dabs of whisker before his ears, who took a fatherly interest in their dinner.

Piers whispered: "What will you have, Mrs. Piers Whiteoak?"—and put everything out of her head but those magic words.

Piers ordered the dinner. Delicious soup. A tiny piece of fish with a strange sauce. Roast chicken. Asparagus. Beautiful but rather frightening French pastries—one hardly knew how to eat them. Strawberries like dissolving jewels. ("But where do they come from, Piers, at this time of year?") Such dark coffee. Little gold-tipped cigarettes, specially bought for her. The scented smoke circled about their heads, accentuating their isolation.

Four men at the table next them did not seem able to keep their eyes off her. They talked earnestly to each other, but their eyes, every now and again, would slide toward her, and sometimes, she was sure, they were talking about her. The odd thing was that the consciousness of their attention did not confuse her. It exhilarated her, gave her a certainty of poise and freedom of gesture which otherwise she would not have had.

She had carried the gold-embroidered India shawl that had been her grandmother's down to dinner, and when she became aware that these four dark men were watching her, speculating about her, some instinct, newly awakened, told her to put the shawl about her shoulders, told her that there was something about the shawl that suited her better than the little pink-and-white dress. She held it closely about her, sitting erect, looking straight into Piers's flushed face, but she was conscious of every glance, every whisper from the four at the next table.

When she and Piers passed the men on their way out, one of them was brushed by the fringe of her shawl. His dark eyes were raised to her face, and he inclined his head toward the shawl as though he sought the light caress from it. He was a man of about forty. Pheasant felt that the shawl was a magic shawl, that she floated in it, that it bewitched all it touched. Her small brown head rose out of its gorgeousness like a sleek flower.

The Russian company was a new and strange experience. It opened the gates of an undreamed-of and exotic world. She heard the "Volga Boat Song" sung in a purple twilight by only dimly discerned foreign seamen. She heard the ragings and pleadings in a barbarous tongue when a savage crew threw their captain's mistress overboard because she had brought them ill luck. The most humorous acts had no smile from her. They were enthralling, but never for a moment funny. The moon-faced showman, with his jargon of languages, had a dreadful fascination for her, but she saw nothing amusing in his patter. To her he was the terrifying magician who had created all this riot of noise and color. He was a sinister man, at whom one gazed breathlessly, gripping Piers's hand beneath the shawl. She had never been in a theatre before. And Piers sat, brown-faced, solid, smiling steadily at the stage, and giving her fingers a steady pressure.

Passing through the foyer, there was a dense crowd that surged without haste toward the outer doors. Pheasant pressed close to Piers, looking with shy curiosity at the faces about her. Then someone just behind took her wrist in his hand, and slid his other hand lightly along her bare arm to beneath the shoulder, where it rested a moment in casual caress, then was withdrawn.

Pheasant trembled all over, but she did not turn her head. She knew without looking that the hand had been the hand of the man whose head she had brushed with her shawl. When she and Piers reached the street she saw the four men together, lighting cigarettes, just ahead.

She felt old in experience.

It was only a short distance to the hotel. They walked among other laughing, talking people, with a great full moon rising at the end of the street, and with the brightness of the electric light giving an air of garish gayety to the scene. Pheasant felt that it must last forever. She could not believe that to-morrow it would be all over, and they would be going back to Jalna, facing the difficulties there.

From their room there was quite an expanse of sky visible. Piers threw the window open and the moon seemed then to stare in at them.

They stood together at the window looking up at it.

"The same old moon that used to shine down on us in the woods," Piers said.

"It seems ages ago."

"Yes. How do you feel? Tired? Sleepy?"

"Not sleepy. But a little tired."

"Poor little girl!"

He put his arms about her and held her close to him. His whole being seemed melting into tenderness toward her. At the same time his blood was singing in his ears the song of possessive love.

VIII. WELCOME TO JALNA

The car moved slowly along the winding driveway toward the house. The driveway was so darkened by closely ranked balsams that it was like a long greenish tunnel, always cool and damp. Black squirrels flung themselves from bough to bough, their curving tails like glossy notes of interrogation. Every now and again a startled rabbit showed its downy brown hump in the long grass. So slowly the car moved, the birds scarcely ceased their jargon of song at its approach.

Piers felt horribly like a schoolboy returning after playing truant. He remembered how he had sneaked along this drive, heavy-footed, knowing he would "catch it," and how he had caught it, at Renny's efficient hands. He slumped in his seat as he thought of it. Pheasant sat stiffly erect, her hands clasped tightly between her knees. As the car stopped before the broad wooden steps that led to the porch, a small figure appeared from the shrubbery. It was Wakefield, carrying in one hand a fishing rod, and in the other a string from which dangled a solitary perch.

"Oh, hullo," he said, coming over the lawn to them. "We got your telegram. Welcome to Jalna!"

He got on to the running board and extended a small fishy hand to Pheasant.

"Don't touch him," said Piers. "He smells beastly."

Wakefield accepted the rebuff cheerfully.

"I like the smell of fish myself," he said pointedly to Pheasant. "And I forgot that some people don't. Now Piers likes the smell of manure better because working with manure is his job. He's used to it. Granny says that one can get used—"

"Shut up," ordered Piers, "and tell me where the family is."

"I really don't know," answered Wakefield, flapping the dead fish against the door of the car, "because it's Saturday, you see, and a free day for me. I got Mrs. Wragge to put me up a little lunch—just a cold chop and a hard-boiled egg, and a lemon tart and a bit of cheese, and—"

"For heaven's sake," said Piers, "stop talking and stop flapping that fish against the car! Run in and see what they're doing. I'd like to see Renny alone."

"Oh, you can't do that, I'm afraid. Renny's over with Maurice this afternoon. I expect they're talking over what they will do to you two. It takes a lot of thought and talk, you see, to arrange suitable punishments. Now the other day Mr. Fennel wanted to punish me and he simply couldn't think of anything to do to me that would make a suitable impression. Already he'd tried—"

Piers interrupted, fixing Wakefield with his eye: "Go and look in the drawing-room windows. I see firelight there. Tell me who is in the room."

"All right. But you'd better hold my fish for me, because someone might look out of the window and see me, and, now I come to think of it, Meggie told me I wasn't to go fishing to-day, and it slipped right out of my head, the way things do with me. I expect it's my weak heart."

"If I don't thrash you," said his brother, "before you're an hour older, my name isn't Piers Whiteoak. Give me the fish." He jerked the string from the little boy's hand.

"Hold it carefully, please," admonished Wakefield over his shoulder, as he lightly mounted the steps. He put his face against the pane, and stood motionless a space.

Pheasant saw that the shadows were lengthening. A cool damp breeze began to stir the shaggy grass of the lawn, and the birds ceased to sing.

Piers said: "I'm going to throw this thing away."

"Oh, no," said Pheasant, "don't throw the little fellow's fish away." A nervous tremor ran through her, more chill than the breeze. She almost sobbed: "Ugh, I'm so nervous!"

"Poor little kid," said Piers, laying his hand over hers. His own jaws were rigid, and his throat felt as though a hand were gripping it. The family had never seemed so formidable to him. He saw them in a fierce phalanx bearing down on him, headed by Grandmother ready to browbeat—abuse him. He threw back his shoulders and drew a deep breath. Well—let them! If they were unkind to Pheasant, he would take her away. But he did not want to go away. He loved every inch of Jalna. He and Renny loved the place as none of the others did. That was the great bond between them. Piers was very proud of this fellowship of love for Jalna between him and Renny.

"Confound the kid!" he said. "What is he doing?"

"He's coming."

Wakefield descended the steps importantly.

"They're having tea in the parlor just as though it were Sunday," he announced. "A fire lighted. It looks like a plate of Sally Lunn on the table. Perhaps it's a kind of wedding feast. I think we'd better go in. I'd better put my fish away first though."

Piers relinquished the perch, and said: "I wish Renny were there."

"So do I," agreed Wakefield. "A row's ever so much better when he's in it. Gran always says he's a perfect Court for a row."

Piers and Pheasant went slowly up the steps and into the house. He drew aside the heavy curtains that hung before the double doors of the drawing-room and led her into the room that seemed very full of people.

There were Grandmother, Uncle Nicholas, Uncle Ernest, Meg, Eden, and young Finch, who was slumped on a beaded ottoman devouring seedcake. He grinned sheepishly as the two entered, then turned to stare at his grandmother, as though expecting her to lead the attack. But it was Uncle Nicholas who spoke first. He lifted his moustache from his teacup, and raised his massive head, looking rather like a sardonic walrus. He rumbled:—

"By George, this is nothing more than I expected! But you pulled the wool over Renny's eyes, you young rascal."

Meg broke in, her soft voice choked with tears:—

"Oh, you deceitful, unfeeling boy! I don't see how you can stand there and face us. And that family—Pheasant—I never spoke to you about it, Piers—I thought you'd *know* how I'd feel about such a marriage."

"Hold your tongues!" shouted Grandmother, who so far had only been able to make inarticulate sounds of rage. "Hold your silly tongues, and let me speak." The muscles in her face were twitching, her terrible brown eyes were burning beneath her shaggy brows. She was sitting directly in front of the fire, and her figure in its brilliant tea gown was illumined with a hellish radiance. Boney, sitting on the back of her chair, glowed like an exotic flower. His beak was sunken on his puffed breast, and he spread his feathers to the warmth in apparent oblivion to the emotion of his mistress.

"Come here!" she shouted. "Come over here in front of me. Don't stand like a pair of ninnies in the doorway."

"Mamma," said Ernest, "don't excite yourself so. It's bad for you. It'll upset your insides, you know."

"My insides are better than yours," retorted his mother. "I know how to look after them."

"Come closer, so she won't have to shout at you," ordered Uncle Nicholas.

"Up to the sacrificial altar," adjured Eden, who lounged near the door. His eyes laughed up at them as they passed toward Mrs. Whiteoak's chair. Pheasant gripped Piers's coat in icy fingers. She cast an imploring look at Nicholas, who had once given her a doll and remained a kind of god in her eyes ever since, but he only stared down his nose, and crumbled the bit of cake on his saucer. If it had not been for the support of Piers's arm, she felt that she must have sunk to her knees, she trembled so.

"Now," snarled Grandmother, when she had got them before her, "aren't you ashamed of yourselves?"

"No," answered Piers, stoutly. "We've only done what lots of people do. Got married on the quiet. We knew the whole family would get on their hind feet if we told them, so we kept it to ourselves, that's all."

"And do you expect—" she struck her stick savagely on the floor—"do you expect that I shall allow you to bring that little bastard here? Do you understand what it means to Meg? Maurice was her fiancé and he got this brat—"

"Mamma!" cried Ernest.

"Easy, old lady," soothed Nicholas.

Finch exploded in sudden, hysterical laughter.

Meg raised her voice. "Don't stop her. It's true."

"Yes, what was I saying? Don't dare to stop me! This brat—this brat—he got her by a slut—"

Piers bent over her, glaring into her fierce old face.

"Stop it!" he shouted. "Stop it, I say!"

Boney was roused into a sudden passion by the hurricane about him. He thrust his beak over Grandmother's shoulder, and riveting his cruel little eyes on Piers's face, he poured forth a stream of Hindu abuse:—

"Shaitan! Shaitan ka bata! Shaitan ka butcha! Piakur! Piakur! Jab kutr!"

This was followed by a cascade of mocking, metallic laughter, while he rocked from side to side on the back of Grandmother's chair.

It was too much for Pheasant. She burst into tears, hiding her face in her hands. But her sobs could not be heard for the cursing of Boney; and Finch, shaking from head to foot, added his hysterical laughter.

Goaded beyond endurance, his sunburned face crimson with rage, Piers caught the screaming bird by the throat and threw him savagely to the floor, where he lay, as gayly colored as painted fruit, uttering strange coughing sounds.

Grandmother was inarticulate. She looked as though she would choke. She tore at her cap and it fell over one ear. Then she grasped her heavy stick. Before anyone could stop her—if indeed they had wished to stop her—she had brought it with a resounding crack on to Piers's head.

"Take that," she shouted, "miserable boy!"

At the instant that the stick struck Piers's head, the door from the hall was opened and Renny came into the room, followed by Wakefield, who, behind the shelter of his brother, peered timidly yet inquisitively at the family. All faces turned toward Renny, as though his red head were a sun and they sun-gazing flowers.

"This is a pretty kettle of fish," he said.

"He's abusing Boney," wailed Grandmother. "Poor dear Boney! Oh, the young brute! Flog him, Renny! Give him a sound flogging!"

"No! No! No! No!" screamed Pheasant.

Nicholas heaved himself about in his chair, and said:–

"He deserved it. He threw the bird on the floor."

"Pick poor Boney up, Wakefield dear," said Ernest. "Pick him up and stroke him."

Except his mistress, Boney would allow no one but Wakefield to touch him. The child picked him up, stroked him, and set him on his grandmother's shoulder. Grandmother, in one of her gusts of affection, caught him to her and pressed a kiss on his mouth. "Little darling," she exclaimed. "Gran's darling! Give him a piece of cake, Meg."

Meg was crying softly behind the teapot. Wakefield went to her, and receiving no notice, took the largest piece of cake and began to devour it.

Renny had crossed to Piers's side and was staring at his head.

"His ear is bleeding," he remarked. "You shouldn't have done that, Granny."

"He was impudent to her," said Ernest.

Eden cut in: "Oh, rot! She was abusing him and the girl horribly."

Grandmother thumped the floor with her stick.

"I wasn't abusing him. I told him I wouldn't have that girl in the house. I told him she was a bastard brat, and so she is. I told him–bring me more tea–more tea–where's Philip? Philip, I want tea!" When greatly excited she often addressed her eldest son by his father's name.

"For God's sake, give her some tea," growled Nicholas. "Make it hot."

Ernest carried a cup of tea to her, and straightened her cap.

"More cake," she demanded. "Stop your sniveling, Meggie."

"Grandmother," said Meg, with melancholy dignity, "I am not sniveling. And it isn't much wonder if I do shed tears, considering the way Piers has acted."

"I've settled him," snorted Grandmother. "Settled him with my stick. Ha!"

Piers said, in a hard voice: "Now, look here, I'm going to get out. Pheasant and I don't have to stop here. We only came to see what sort of reception we'd get. Now we know, and we're going."

"Just listen to him, Renny," said Meg. "He's lost all his affection for us, and it seems only yesterday that he was a little boy like Wake."

"Heaven knows whom Wakefield will take up with," said Nicholas. "The family's running to seed."

"Will you have some tea, Renny?" asked Meg.

"No, thanks. Give the girl some. She's awfully upset."

"I don't want tea!" cried Pheasant, looking wildly at the hostile faces about her. "I want to go away! Piers, please, please, take me away!" She sank into a wide, stuffed chintz chair, drew up her knees, covered her face with her hands, and sobbed loudly.

Meg spoke with cold yet furious chagrin.

"If only he *could* send you home and have done with you! But here you are bound fast to him. You'd never rest till you'd got him bound fast. I know your kind."

Nicholas put in: "They don't wait till they're out of pinafores—that kind."

Eden cried: "Oh, for God's sake!"

But Piers's furious voice drowned him out.

"Not another word about her. I won't stand another word!"

Grandmother screamed: "You'll stand another crack on the head, you young whelp!" Crumbs of cake clung to the hairs on her chin. Wake regarded them, fascinated. Then he blew on them, trying to blow them off. Finch uttered hysterical croaking sounds.

"Wakefield, don't do that," ordered Uncle Ernest, "or you'll get your head slapped. Mamma, wipe your chin."

Meg said: "To think of the years that I've kept aloof from the Vaughans! I've never spoken to Maurice since that terrible time. None of them have set foot in this house. And now his daughter—that child—the cause of all my unhappiness—brought here to live as Piers's wife."

Piers retorted: "Don't worry, Meg. We're not going to stay."

"The disgrace is here forever," she returned bitterly, "if you go to the other end of the earth." Her head rested on her hand, supported by her short plump arm. Her sweetly curved lips were drawn in at the corners, in an expression of stubborn finality. "You've finished things. I was terribly hurt at the very beginning of my life. I've tried to forget. Your bringing this girl here has renewed all the hurt. Shamed me, crushed me—I thought you loved me, Piers—"

"Oh, Lord, can't a man love his sister and another too?" exclaimed Piers, regarding her intently, with scarlet face, cut to the heart, for he loved her.

"No one who loved his sister could love the daughter of the man who had been so faithless to her."

"And besides," put in Nicholas, "you promised Renny you'd give the girl up."

"Oh, oh," cried Pheasant, sitting up in her chair. "Did you promise that, Piers?"

"No, I didn't."

Nicholas roared: "Yes, you did! Renny told me you did."

"I never promised. Be just, now, Renny! I never promised, did I?"

"No," said Renny. "He didn't promise. I told him to cut it out. I said there'd be trouble."

"Trouble—trouble—trouble," moaned Grandmother, "I've had too much trouble. If I didn't keep my appetite, I'd be dead. Give me more cake, someone. No, not that kind—devil's cake. I want devil's cake!" She took the cake that Ernest brought her, bit off a large piece, and snortled through it: "I hit the young whelp a good crack on the head!"

"Yes, Mamma," said Ernest. Then he inquired, patiently, "*Must* you take such large bites?"

"I drew the blood!" she cried, ignoring his question, and taking a still larger bite. "I made the lad smart for his folly."

"You ought to be ashamed, Gran," said Eden, and the family began to argue noisily as to whether she had done well or ill.

Renny stood looking from one excited face to another, feeling irritated by their noise, their ineffectuality, yet, in spite of all, bathed in an immense satisfaction. This was his family. His tribe. He was head of his family. Chieftain of his tribe. He took a very primitive, direct, and simple pleasure in lording it over them, caring for them, being badgered, harried, and importuned by them. They were all of them dependent on him except Gran, and she was dependent, too, for she would have died away from Jalna. And beside the fact that he provided for them, he had the inherent quality of the chieftain. They expected him to lay down the law; they harried him till he did. He turned his lean red face from one to the other of them now, and prepared to lay down the law.

The heat of the room was stifling; the fire was scarcely needed; yet now, with sudden fervor, it leaped and crackled on the hearth. Boney, having recovered from Piers's rough handling, was crying in a head-splitting voice, "Cake! Cake! Devil cake!"

"For God's sake, somebody give him cake," said Renny.

Little Wake snatched up a piece of cake and held it toward Boney, but just as the parrot was at the point of taking it he jerked it away. With flaming temper Boney tried three times, and failed to snatch the morsel. He flapped his wings and uttered a screech that set the blood pounding in the ears of those in the room.

It was too much for Finch. He doubled up on his footstool, laughing hysterically; the footstool slipped,—or did Eden's foot push it?—and he was sent sprawling on the floor.

Grandmother seized her cane and struggled to get to her feet.

"Let me at them!" she screamed.

"Boys! Boys!" cried Meggie, melting into sudden laughter. This was the sort of thing she loved—"rough-house" among the boys, and she sitting solidly, comfortably in her chair, looking on. She laughed; but in an instant she was lachrymose again, and averted her eyes from the figure of Finch stretched on the floor.

Renny was bending over him. He administered three hard thumps on the boy's bony, untidy person, and said:—

"Now, get up and behave yourself."

Finch got up, red in the face, and skulked to a corner. Nicholas turned heavily in his chair, and regarded Piers.

"As for you," he said, "you ought to be flayed alive for what you've done to Meggie."

"Never mind," Piers returned. "I'm getting out."

Meg looked at him scornfully. "You'd have to go a long way to get away from scandal—I mean, to make your absence really a help to me, to all of us."

Piers retorted: "Oh, we'll go far enough to please you. We'll go to the States—perhaps." The "perhaps" was mumbled on a hesitating note. The sound of his own voice announcing that he would go to a foreign country, far from Jalna and the land he had helped to grow things on, the horses, his brothers, had an appalling sound.

"What does he say?" asked Grandmother, roused from one of her sudden dozes. Boney had perched on her shoulder and cuddled his head against her long flat cheek. "What's the boy say?"

Ernest answered: "He says he'll go to the States."

"The States? A Whiteoak go to the States? A Whiteoak a Yankee? No, no, no! It would kill me. He mustn't go. Shame, shame on you, Meggie, to drive the poor boy to the States! You ought to be ashamed of yourself. Oh, those Yankees! First they take Eden's book and now they want Piers himself. Oh, don't let him go!" She burst into loud sobs.

Renny's voice was raised, but without excitement.

"Piers is not going away—anywhere. He's going to stay right here. So is Pheasant. The girl and he are married. I presume they've lived together. There's no reason on earth why she shouldn't make him a good wife—"

Meg interrupted:—

"Maurice has never forgiven me for refusing to marry him. He has made this match between his daughter and Piers to punish me. He's done it. I know he's done it."

Piers turned to her. "Maurice has known nothing about it."

"How can you know what schemes were in his head?" replied Meg. "He's simply been waiting his chance to thrust his brat into Jalna."

Piers exclaimed: "Good God, Meggie! I didn't know you had such a wicked tongue."

"No back chat, please," rejoined his sister.

Renny's voice, with a vibration from the chest which the family knew foreboded an outburst if he were opposed, broke in.

"I have been talking the affair over with Maurice this afternoon. He is as upset about it as we are. As for his planning the marriage to avenge himself on you, Meg, that is ridiculous. Give the man credit for a little decency —a little sense. Why, your affair with him was twenty years ago. Do you think he's been brooding over it ever since? And he was through the War too. He's had a few things to think of besides your cruelty, Meggie!"

He smiled at her. He knew how to take her. And she liked to have her "cruelty" referred to. Her beautifully shaped lips curved a little, and she said, with almost girlish petulance:—

"What's the matter with him, then? Everyone agrees that there's something wrong with him."

"Oh, well, I don't think there is very much wrong with Maurice, but if there is, and you are responsible, you shouldn't be too hard on him, or on this child, either. I told Piers that if he went on meeting her there'd be trouble, and there has been, hasn't there? Lots of it. But I'm not going to drive him away from Jalna. I want him here—and I want my tea, terribly. Will you pour it out, Meggie?"

Silence followed his words, broken only by the snapping of the fire and Grandmother's peaceful, bubbling snores. Nicholas took out his pipe and began to fill it from his pouch. Sasha leaped from the mantelpiece to Ernest's shoulder and began to purr loudly, as though in opposition to Grandmother's snores. Wakefield opened the door of a cabinet filled with curios from India, with which he was not allowed to play, and stuck his head inside.

"Darling, don't," said Meg, gently.

Renny, the chieftain, had spoken. He had said that Piers was not to be cast out from the tribe, and the tribe had listened and accepted his words as wisdom. All the more readily because not one of them wanted to see Piers cast out, even though they must accept with him an unwelcome addition to the family. Not even Meg. In truth, Renny was more often the organ of the family than its head. They knew beforehand what he would say in a crisis, and they excited, harried, and goaded him till he said it with great passion. Then, with apparent good grace, they succumbed to his will.

Renny dropped into a chair with his cup of tea and a piece of bread and butter. His face was redder than usual, but he looked with deep satisfaction at the group about him. He had quelled the family riot. They depended on him, from savage old Gran down to delicate little Wake. They depended on him to lead them. He felt each one of them bound to him by a strong, invisible cord. He could feel the pull of the cords, drawn taut from himself to each individual in the room. To savage old Gran. To beastly young Finch. To that young fool Piers with his handkerchief against his bleeding ear. To Meggie, who pictured Maurice as brooding in black melancholy all these years. Well, there was no doubt about it, Maurice was a queer devil. He had let two women make a very different man of him from what Nature had intended him to be. Renny felt the cords from himself stretching dark and strong to each member of the family. Suddenly he felt a new drawing, a fresh cord. It was between Pheasant and him. She was one of them now. His own. He looked at her, sitting upright in the big chair, her eyes swollen from crying, but eating her tea like a good child. Their eyes met, and she gave a little watery pleading smile. Renny grinned at her encouragingly.

Rags had come in and Meg was ordering a fresh pot of tea.

This was the Whiteoak family as it was when Alayne Archer came into their midst from New York.

IX. EDEN AND ALAYNE

Eden found that his steps made no noise on the thick rug that covered the floor of the reception room of the New York publishing firm of Cory and Parsons, so he could pace up and down as restlessly as he liked without fear of attracting attention. He was horribly nervous. He had a sensation in his stomach that was akin to hunger, yet his throat felt so oddly constricted that to swallow would have been impossible.

A mirror in a carved frame gave him, when he hesitated before it, a greenish reflection of himself that was not reassuring. He wished he had not got such a brazen coat of tan in the North that summer. These New Yorkers would surely look on him as a Canadian backwoodsman. His hands, as he grasped the package containing his new manuscript, were almost black, it seemed to him, and no wonder, for he had been paddling and camping among the Northern lakes for months. He decided to lay the manuscript on a table, picking it up at the last minute before he entered Mr. Cory's private office. It had been Mr. Cory with whom he had corresponded about his poems, who had expressed himself as eager to read the long narrative poem composed that summer. For the book published in midsummer was being well reviewed, American critics finding an agreeable freshness and music in Eden's lyrics. As books of poems went, it had had a fair sale. The young poet would get enough out of it perhaps to buy himself a new winter overcoat. He stood now, tall and slender in his loosely fitting tweeds, very British-looking, feeling that this solemn, luxurious room was the threshold over which he would step into the world of achievement and fame.

The door opened and a young woman entered so quietly that she was almost at Eden's side before he was aware of her presence.

"Oh," he said, starting, "I beg your pardon. I'm waiting to see Mr. Cory."

"You are Mr. Whiteoak, aren't you?" she asked in a tranquil voice.

He flushed red, very boyishly, under his tan.

"Yes. I'm Eden Whiteoak. I'm the–"

Just in time he choked back what he had been about to say: that he was the author of *Under the North Star*. It would have been a horrible way to introduce himself–just as though he had expected the whole world to know about his book of poems.

However, she said, with a little excited catch of the breath:–

"Oh, Mr. Whiteoak, I could not resist coming to speak to you when I heard you were here. I want to tell you how very, very much I have enjoyed your poems. I am a reader for Mr. Cory, and he generally gives me the poetry manuscripts, because—well, I am very much interested in poetry."

"Yes, yes, I see," said Eden, casting about to collect his thoughts.

She went on in her low even voice:—

"I cannot tell you how proud I was when I was able to recommend your poems to him. I have to send in adverse reports on so many. Your name was new to us. I felt that I had discovered you. Oh, dear, this is very unbusiness-like, telling you all this, but your poetry has given me so much pleasure that —I wanted you to know."

Her face flashed suddenly from gravity into smiling. Her head was tilted as she looked into his eyes, for she was below medium height. Eden, looking down at her, thought she was like some delicately tinted yet sturdy spring flower, gazing upward with a sort of gentle defiance.

He held the hand she offered in his own warm, deeply tanned one.

"My name is Alayne Archer," she said. "Mr. Cory will be ready to see you in a few minutes. As a matter of fact, he told me to have a little talk with you about your new poem. It is a narrative poem, is it not? But I did so want to tell you that I was the 'discoverer' of your first."

"Well then, I suppose I may as well hand the manuscript over to you at once."

"No. I should give it to Mr. Cory."

They both looked down at the packet in his hand, then their eyes met and they smiled.

"Do you like it very much yourself?" she asked. "Is it at all like the others?"

"Yes, I like it—naturally," he answered, "and yes, I think it has the same feeling as the others. It was good fun writing it, up there in the North, a thousand miles from anywhere."

"It must have been inspiring," she said. "Mr. Cory is going to visit the North this fall. He suffers from insomnia. He will want to hear a great deal about it from you." She led the way toward two upholstered chairs. "Will you please sit down and tell me more about the new poem? What is it called?"

" 'The Golden Sturgeon.' Really, I can't tell you about it. You'll just have to read it. I'm not used to talking about my poetry. In my family it's rather a disgrace to write poetry."

They had sat down, but she raised herself in her chair and stared at him incredulously. She exclaimed in a rather hushed voice: "Poetry? A disgrace?"

"Well, not so bad as that, perhaps," said Eden, hurriedly. "But a handicap to a fellow—something to be lived down."

"But are they not proud of you?"

"Y-Yes. My sister is. But she doesn't know anything about poetry. And one of my uncles. But he's quite old. Reads nothing this side of Shakespeare."

"And your parents? Your mother?" It seemed to her that he must have a mother to adore him.

"Both dead," he replied, and he added: "My brothers really despise me for it. There is a military tradition in our family."

She asked: "Were you through the War?"

"No. I was only seventeen when peace came."

"Oh, how stupid I am! Of course you were too young."

She began then to talk about his poetry. Eden forgot that he was in a reception room of a publisher's office. He forgot everything except his pleasure in her gracious, self-possessed, yet somehow shy presence. He heard himself talking, reciting bits of his poems,—he had caught something of the Oxford intonation from his uncles,—saying beautiful and mournful things that would have made Renny wince with shame for him, could he have overheard.

A stenographer came to announce that Mr. Cory would see Mr. Whiteoak. They arose, and looking down on her, he thought he had never seen such smooth, shining hair. It was coiled about her head like bands of shimmering satin.

He followed the stenographer to Mr. Cory's private room, and was given a tense handshake and a tenser scrutiny by the publisher.

"Sit down, Mr. Whiteoak," he said, in a dry, precise voice. "I am very glad that you were able to come to New York. I and my assistant, Miss Archer, have been looking forward to meeting you. We think your work is exceedingly interesting."

Yet his pleasure seemed very perfunctory. After a short discussion of the new poem which Mr. Cory took into his charge, he changed the subject abruptly, and began to fire at Eden question after question about the North. How far north had he been? What supplies were needed? Particularly, what underwear and shoes. Was the food very bad? He suffered at times from indigestion. He supposed it was very rough. His physicians had told him that a hunting trip up there would set him up, make a new man of him. He was strong enough but—well, insomnia was a disagreeable disorder. He couldn't afford to lower his efficiency.

Eden was a mine of information. He knew something about everything. As Mr. Cory listened to these details he grew more animated. A faint ashes-of-roses pink crept into his grayish cheeks. He tapped excitedly on his desk with the tips of his polished finger nails.

Eden in his mind was trying to picture Mr. Cory in that environment, but he could not, and his fancy instead followed Miss Archer, with her bands of shimmering hair and her gray-blue eyes, set wide apart beneath a lovely white brow. He followed her shadow, grasping at it as it disappeared, imploring it to save him from Mr. Cory, for he had begun to hate Mr. Cory, since he believed he had found out that he was interesting to the publisher only as a Canadian who knew all about the country to which a physician had ordered him.

Yet at that moment Mr. Cory was asking him almost genially to dinner at his house that night.

"Miss Archer will be there," added Mr. Cory. "She will talk to you about your poetry with much more understanding than I can, but I like it. I like it very well indeed."

And, naturally, Eden suddenly liked Mr. Cory. He suddenly seemed to discover that he was very human, almost boyish, like a very orderly grayish boy who had never been really young. But he liked him, and shook his hand warmly as he thanked him, and said he would be glad to go to dinner.

Eden had no friends in New York, but he spent the afternoon happily wandering about. It was a brilliant day in mid-September. The tower-like skyscrapers and the breezy canyons of the streets fluttering bright flags—he did not know what the occasion was—exhilarated him. Life seemed very full, brimming with movement, adventure, poetry, singing in the blood, crying out to be written.

Sitting in a tearoom, the first lines of a new poem began to take form in his mind. Pushing his plate of cinnamon toast to one side, he jotted them down on the back of an envelope. A quiver of nervous excitement ran through him. He believed they were good. He believed the idea was good. He found that he wanted to discuss the poem with Alayne Archer, to read those singing first lines to her. He wanted to see her face raised to his with that look of mingled penetration and sweet enthusiasm for his genius—well, she herself had used the word once; in fact, one of the reviewers of *Under the North Star* had used the word, so surely he might let it slide through his own mind now and again, like a stimulating draught. Genius. He believed he had a spark of the sacred fire, and it seemed to him that she, by her presence, the support of her admiration, had the power to fan it to a leaping flame.

He tried to sketch her face on the envelope. He did not do so badly with the forehead, the eyes, but he could not remember her nose,—rather a soft feature, he guessed,—and when the mouth was added, instead of the look of a spring flower, gentle but defiant, that he had tried to achieve, he had produced a face of almost Dutch stolidity. Irritably he tore up the sketch and his poem with it. She might not be strictly beautiful, but she was not like that.

That evening, in his hotel, he took a good deal of care with his dressing. His evening clothes were well fitting, and the waistcoat, of the newest English cut, very becoming. If it had not been for that Indian coat of tan, his reflection would have been very satisfying. Still, it made him look manlier. And he had a well-cut mouth. Girls had told him it was fascinating. He smiled and showed a row of gleaming teeth, then snapped his lips together. Good Lord! He was acting like a movie star! Or a dentifrice advertisement. Ogling, just that. If Renny could have seen him ogling himself in the glass, he would have knocked his block off. Perhaps it were better that genius (that word again!) should be encased in a wild-eyed, unkempt person. He scowled, put on his hat and coat, and turned out the light.

Mr. Cory lived on Sixty-first Street, in an unpretentious house, set between two very pretentious ones. Eden found the rest of the guests assembled except one, an English novelist who arrived a few minutes later than himself.

There were Mr. Cory; his wife; his daughter, a large-faced young woman with straight black shingled hair; a Mr. Gutweld, a musician; and a Mr. Groves, a banker, who it was soon evident was to accompany Mr. Cory on his trip to Canada; Alayne Archer; and two very earnest middle-aged ladies.

Eden found himself at dinner between Miss Archer and one of the earnest ladies. Opposite were the English novelist, whose name was Hyde, and Miss Cory. Eden had never seen a table so glittering with exquisite glass and slender, shapely cutlery. His mind flew for an instant to the dinner table at Jalna with its huge platters and cumbersome old English plate. For an instant the faces of those about him were blotted out by the faces of the family at home, affectionate, arrogant, high-tempered—faces that, once seen, were not easily forgotten. And when one had lived with them all one's life—But he put them away from him and turned to the earnest lady. Alayne Archer's shoulder was toward him as she listened to Mr. Groves on her other side.

"Mr. Whiteoak," said the lady, in a richly cultivated voice, "I want to tell you how deeply I appreciate your poetry. You show a delicate sensitiveness that is crystal-like in its implications." She fixed him with her clear gray eyes, and added: "And such an acute realization of the poignant transiency of beauty." Having spoken, she conveyed an exquisite silver spoon filled with exquisite clear soup unflinchingly to her lips.

"Thanks," mumbled Eden. "Thank you very much." He felt overcome with shyness. Oh, God, that Gran were here! He would like to hide his head in her lap while she warded off this terrible woman with her stick. He looked at her, a troubled expression shadowing his blue eyes, but she was apparently satisfied, for she went on talking. Presently Mr. Cory claimed her attention and he turned to Alayne Archer.

"Speak to me. Save me," he whispered. "I've never felt so stupid in my life. I've just been asked what my new poem was about and all I could say was —'a fish'!"

She was looking into his eyes now and he felt an electrical thrill in every nerve at her nearness, and an intangible something he saw in her eyes.

She said: "Mr. Groves has something he wants to ask you about supplies for a hunting trip to Canada."

Mr. Groves leaned nearer. "How about canned goods?" he said. "Could we take all our supplies over from here, or must we buy them in Canada?"

They talked of tinned meats and vegetables, till Mr. Groves turned to examine cautiously, through his glasses, a new dish offered by the servant. Then Miss Archer said softly:—

"So you are feeling shy? I do not wonder. Still, it must be very pleasant to hear such delightful things about your poetry."

Looking down over her face he thought her eyelids were like a Madonna's. "I tried to make a sketch of you to-day, but I tore it up—and some verses with it. You'll scarcely believe it, but I made you look quite Dutch."

"That is not so surprising," she answered. "On my mother's side I am of

Dutch extraction. I think I show it quite plainly. My face is broad and rather flat, and I have high cheek bones."

"You draw an engaging picture of yourself, certainly."

"But it is quite true, is it not?" She was smiling with a rather malicious amusement. "Come, now, I do look a stolid Dutch Fräulein; acknowledge it."

He denied it stoutly, but it was true that the Dutch blood explained something about her. A simplicity, a directness, a tranquil tenacity. But with her lovely rounded shoulders, her delicately flushed cheeks, those Madonna eyelids, and that wreath of little pink and white flowers in her hair, he thought she was a thousand times more charming than any girl he had ever met.

Hyde, the novelist, was saying, in his vibrant tones: "When I come to America, I always feel that I have been starved at home. I eat the most enormous meals here, and such meals! Such fruit! Such cream! I know there are cows in England. I've seen them with my own eyes. I ran against one once with my car. But they don't give cream. Their milk is skimmed—pale blue when it comes. Can anyone explain why? Mr. Whiteoak, tell me, do you have cream in Canada?"

"We only use reindeer's milk there," replied Eden.

After dinner Hyde sauntered up to him.

"You are the lucky dog! The only interesting woman here. Who is she?"

"Miss Alayne Archer. She is an orphan. Her father was an old friend of Mr. Cory's."

"Does she write?"

"No. She reads. She is a reader for the publishing house. It was she who—" But he bit that sentence off just in time. He wasn't going to tell this bulgy-eyed fellow anything more.

Hyde said: "Mr. Whiteoak, had you a relative in the Buffs? A red-haired chap?"

"Yes. A brother—Renny. Did you know him?"

Hyde's eyes bulged a little more.

"Did I know him? Rather. One of the best. Oh, he and I had a hell of a time together. Where is he now? In Canada?"

"Yes. He farms."

Hyde looked Eden over critically. "You're not a bit like him. I can't imagine Whiteoak writing poetry. He told me he had a lot of young brothers. 'The whelps,' he used to call you. I should like to see him. Please remember me to him."

"If you can manage it, you must come to see us."

Hyde began to talk about his adventures with Renny in France. He was wound up. He seemed to forget his surroundings entirely and poured out reminiscences ribald and bloody which Eden scarcely heard. His own eyes followed Alayne Archer wherever she moved. He could scarcely forbear leaving Hyde rudely and following her. He saw the eyes of Mr. Cory and Mr. Groves on him, and he saw gleaming in them endless questions about hunting in the North. It seemed as though walls were closing in on him. He felt horribly young and helpless among these middle-aged and elderly men. In desperation he interrupted the Englishman.

"You said you would like to meet Miss Archer."

Hyde looked blank, then agreed cheerfully: "Yes, yes, I did."

Eden took him over to Alayne, turning his own back firmly on the too eager huntsmen.

"Miss Archer," he said, and saw a swift color tinge her cheeks and pass away, leaving them paler than before. "May I introduce Mr. Hyde?"

The two shook hands.

"I have read your new book in the proof sheets," she said to Hyde, "and I think it is splendid. Only I object very strongly to the way you make your American character talk. I often wish that Englishmen would not put Americans into their books. The dialect they put into their mouths is like nothing spoken on land or sea." She spoke lightly, but there was a shadow of real annoyance in her eyes. She had plenty of character, Eden thought; she was not afraid to speak her mind. He pretended to have noticed the same thing. The Englishman laughed imperturbably.

"Well, it's the way it sounds to us," he said. "Then my man, you remember, is a Southerner. He doesn't speak as you do here."

"Yes, but he is an educated Southerner, who would not prefix every sentence with 'Gee' and call other men 'guys,' and continually say, 'It sure is'—I hope I'm not being rude?"

But Hyde was not annoyed. He was merely amused. No protests could change his conception of American speech. He said to Eden: "Why don't you Canadians write about Americans and see if you have better luck?"

"I shall write a poem about Americans," laughed Eden, and the glance that flashed from his eyes into Alayne's was like a sunbeam that flashes into clear water and is held there.

Would they never be alone together? Yes, the pianist was sitting down before the piano. They melted into a quiet corner. There was no pretending. Each knew the other's desire to escape from the rest. They sat without speaking while the music submerged them like a sea. They were at the bottom of a throbbing sea. They were hidden. They were alone. They could hear the pulsing of the great heart of life. They could feel it in their own heartbeats.

He moved a little nearer to her, staring into the room straight ahead of him, and he could almost feel her head on his shoulder, her body relaxing into his arms. The waves of Chopin thundered on and on. Eden scarcely dared to turn his face toward her. But he did, and a faint perfume came to him from the wreath of little French flowers she wore. What beautiful hands lying in her lap! Surely hands for a poet's love. God, if he could only take them in his and kiss the palms! How tender and delicately scented they would be—

The pianist was playing Debussy. Miss Cory had switched off the lights, all but a pale one by the piano. The sea was all delicate singing wavelets then. He took Alayne's hands and held them to his lips.

As he held them, his being was shaken by a throng of poems rushing up within him, crying out to be born, touched into life by the contact of her hands.

X. ALAYNE AND LIFE

Alayne Archer was twenty-eight years old when she met Eden Whiteoak. Her father and mother had died within a few weeks of each other, during an epidemic of influenza three years before. They had left their daughter a few hundreds in the bank, a few thousands in life insurance, and an artistic stucco bungalow in Brooklyn, overlooking golf links and a glimpse of the ocean. But they had left her an empty heart, from which the love that had been stored increasingly for them during the twenty-five years flowed in an anguished stream after them into the unknown. It had seemed to her at first that she could not live without those two precious beings whose lives had been so closely entwined with hers.

Her father had been professor of English in a New York State college, a pedantic but gentle man, who loved to impart information to his wife and to instruct his daughter, but who, in matters other than scholastic, was led by them as a little child.

Her mother was the daughter of the principal of a small theological college in the state of Massachusetts, who had got into trouble more than once because of his advanced religious views—had, in fact, escaped serious trouble only because of his personal magnetism and charm. These qualities his daughter had inherited from him, and had in her turn transmitted them to her own daughter Alayne.

Though an earnest little family who faced the problems of the day and their trips to Europe anxiously, they were often filled by the spirit of gentle fun. The gray bungalow resounded to professorial gayety and the youthful response from Alayne. Professor and Mrs. Archer had married young, and they often remarked that Alayne was more like an adored young sister to them than a daughter. She had no intimate friends of her own age. Her parents sufficed. For several years before his death Professor Archer had been engaged in writing a history of the American Revolutionary War, and Alayne had thrown herself with enthusiasm into helping him with the work of research. Her admiration had been aroused for those dogged Loyalists who had left their homes and journeyed northward into Canada to suffer cold and privation for the sake of an idea. It was glorious, she thought, and told her father so. They had argued, and after that he had called her, laughingly, his little Britisher; and she had laughed, too, but she did not altogether like it, for she was proud of being an American. Still, one could see the other person's side of a question.

Mr. Cory had been a lifelong friend of her father's. When Professor Archer died, he came forward at once with his assistance. He helped Alayne to dispose of the bungalow by the golf links—those golf links where Alayne and her father had had many a happy game together, with her mother able to keep her eye on them from the upstairs sitting-room window; he had looked into the state of her father's financial affairs for her, and had given her work in reading for the publishing house of Cory and Parsons.

The first blank grief, followed by the agony of realization, had passed, and Alayne's life settled into a sad tranquillity. She had taken a small apartment near her work, and night after night she pored over her father's manuscript, correcting, revising, worrying her young brain into fever over some debatable point. Oh, if he had only been there to settle it for her! To explain, to elucidate his own point of view in his precise and impressive accents! In her solitude she could almost see his long thin scholar's hands turning the pages, and tears swept down her cheeks in a storm, leaving them flushed and hot, so that she would have to go to the window, and press her face to the cool pane, or throw it open and lean out, gazing into the unfriendly street below.

The book was published. It created a good impression, and reviewers were perhaps a little kinder to it because of the recent death of the author. It was praised for its modern liberality. But a few critics pointed out errors and contradictions, and Alayne, holding herself responsible for these, suffered great humiliation. She accused herself of laxness and stupidity. Her dear father's book! She became so white that Mr. Cory was worried about her. At last Mrs. Cory and he persuaded her to share an apartment with a friend of theirs, Rosamund Trent, a commercial artist, a woman of fifty.

Miss Trent was efficient, talkative, and nearly always good-humored. It was when Alayne joined Miss Trent that she settled down into tranquillity. She read countless manuscripts, some of them very badly typed, and the literary editor of Cory and Parsons learned to rely on her judgment, especially in books other than fiction. In fiction her taste, formed by her parents, was perhaps too conventional, too fastidious. Many of the things she read in manuscript seemed horrid to her. And they had a disconcerting way of cropping up in her mind afterward, like strange weeds that, even after they are uprooted and thrown away, appear again in unexpected places.

She would sit listening to Rosamund Trent's good-humored chatter, her chin in her curled palm, her eyes fixed on Miss Trent's face, yet not all of her was present in the room. Another Alayne, crying like a deserted child, was wandering through the little bungalow; wandering about the garden among the rhododendrons and the roses, where the grass was like moist green velvet, and not a dead leaf was allowed by the professor to lie undisturbed; wandering, weeping over the links with the thin gray shadow of her father, turning to wave a hand to the watching mother in the window.

Sometimes the other Alayne was different, not sad and lonely but wild and questioning. Had life nothing richer for her than this? Reading, reading manuscripts, day in, day out, sitting at night with gaze bent on Miss Trent's chattering face, or going to the Corys' or some other house, meeting people who made no impression on her. Was she never going to have a real friend to whom she could confide everything—well, almost everything? Was she never—for the first time in her life she asked herself this question in grim earnest—was she never going to have a lover?

Oh, she had had admirers—not many, for she had not encouraged them. If she went out with them she was sure to miss something delightful that was happening at home. If they came to the house they seldom fitted in with the scheme of things. Sexually she was one of those women who develop slowly; who might, under certain conditions, marry, rear a family, and never have the wellspring of her passions unbound.

There had been one man who might almost have been called a lover, a colleague of her father's, but several years younger. He had come to the house, first as her father's friend, then more and more as hers. He had fitted into their serious discussions, even into their gayeties. Once he had gone to Europe with them. In Sorrento, on a morning when the spring was breaking and they had been walking up a narrow pathway across a hill, filled with the wonder of that ecstatic awakening, he had asked her to marry him. She had begged him to wait for his answer till they returned to America, for she was afraid that her delight was not in him but in Italy.

They had been back in America only a month when her mother was taken ill. The next two months were passed in heart-piercing suspense and agony. Then, at the end, she found herself alone. Again her father's friend, in old-fashioned phrasing, which she loved in books but which did not move her in real life, asked her to marry him. He loved her and he wanted to care for her. She knew that her father had approved of him, but her heart was drained empty, and its aching spaces desired no new occupant.

When the manuscript of young Whiteoak's book was given her to read, Alayne was in a mood of eager receptivity to beauty. The beauty, the simplicity, the splendid abandon of Eden's lyrics filled her with a new joy. When the book appeared, she had an odd feeling of possession toward it. She rather hated seeing Miss Trent's large plump hands caressing it,—"Such a ducky little book, my dear!"—and she hated to hear her read from it, stressing the most striking phrases, sustaining the last word of each line with an upward lilt of her throaty voice—"Sheer beauty, that bit, isn't it, Alayne dear?" She felt ashamed of herself for grudging Miss Trent her pleasure in the book, but she undoubtedly did grudge it.

She rather dreaded meeting Eden for fear he should be disappointing. Suppose he were short and thickset, with beady black eyes and a long upper lip. Suppose he had a hatchet face and wore horn-rimmed spectacles.

Well, however he looked, his mind was beautiful. But she had quaked as she entered the reception room.

When she saw him standing tall and fair, with his crest of golden hair, his sensitive features, his steady but rather wistful smile, she was trembling, almost overcome with relief. He seemed to carry some of the radiance of his poetry about his own person. Those brilliant blue eyes in that tanned face! Oh, she could not have borne it had he not been beautiful!

It seemed as natural to her that they two should seek a quiet corner together, that he should, when the opportunity offered, take her hands in his and press ecstatic kisses upon them, as that two drops of dew should melt into one, or two sweet chords blend.

It seemed equally natural to her to say yes when, two weeks later, he asked her to marry him.

He had not intended to ask her that. He realized in his heart that it was madness to ask her, unless they agreed to a long engagement, but the autumn night was studded with stars and heavy with the teasing scents of burning leaves and salt air. They were gliding slowly along an ocean driveway in Rosamund Trent's car. Rosamund was slouching over the wheel, silent for once, and they two in the back seat alone, in a world apart. He could no more stop himself from asking her to marry him than he could help writing a poem that burned to be expressed.

His love for her was a poem. Their life together would be an exquisite, enchanted poem, a continual inspiration for him. He could not do without her. The thought of holding her intimately in his arms gave him the tender sadness of a love poem to be written. Yet he must not ask her to marry him. He must not and—he did.

"Alayne, my beautiful darling—will you marry me?"

"Eden, Eden—" She could scarcely speak, for the love now filling her heart that had been drained empty of love almost drowned her senses. "Yes—I will marry you if you want me. I want you with all my soul."

XI. BELOVED, IT IS MORN

"I like your young poet immensely," said Rosamund Trent. "He must be a delightful lover. But, Alayne dear,—now you must not mind my saying this; I am so much older,—don't you think it is rather reckless to plunge into matrimony without waiting to see how he gets on in the world? You are both such dears, but you are so inexperienced. Here are you, giving up a good position, and going to a country you know nothing about, arranging to spend some months with a family you have never seen—"

"His sister," said Alayne patiently, "has written me a delightful letter. They have a big old house. She seems to want me. Even the dear grandmother sent me a message of welcome. Then I have a little money of my own; I shall not be quite dependent. And if it were ever necessary, I—"

"Oh, my dear, I am sure it will be all right. But you are so precipitate. If you would only wait a little."

"I have been waiting for Eden all these years!" exclaimed Alayne, flushing. "I realize that now. Neither he nor I feel like wasting any of the precious time we might be together. After we are married I shall visit his people, and Eden will look about. If he cannot get into anything satisfactory that will leave him plenty of time in which to develop his talent, or if I do not like Canada, we shall come back to New York. I know he could have something with Mr. Cory in the publishing business, but—oh, I do not want him to do anything that will hamper him. I want him to live for his art."

Miss Trent made a little gesture of impatience. Then she made a large gesture of great affection, and gathered Alayne to her heart.

"You two darlings!" she said. "I know it will be all right. And why waste time when you are young and beautiful!"

She realized that such were the glamour and wonder of Alayne's feeling toward Eden that it was useless to reason with her. Alayne herself was conscious of such subtleties in her love for him that she felt at times bewildered. He was a young god of the sun, a strong deliverer from her prison of heartbreak; he was a fledgling genius; he was a stammering, sunburned, egotistical young Canadian with not too good an education; he was a blue-eyed, clinging-fingered child; he was a suddenly wooden and undemonstrative young Britisher. An evening with him excited her so that she could not sleep after it. And as she spent every evening with him, she grew drowsy-eyed from lying awake thinking of him. The curves of her mouth became more tender, more yielding from those same thoughts.

Eden had begun the letter to Meg telling her of his engagement in much trepidation. But as he wrote he gained confidence, and told of Alayne's beauty, her endearing qualities, her influential friends who would be able to do so much for him in the publishing world. And she was independent —not an heiress, not the rich American girl of fiction; still, she would be a help, not a handicap to him. Meg was to believe that she was absolutely desirable.

The family at Jalna, always credulous, with imaginations easily stirred, snatched with avidity at the bare suggestion of means. They settled it among themselves that Alayne was a rich girl, and that Eden for some reason wished to depreciate her wealth.

"He's afraid some of us will want to borrow a few bucks," sneered Piers.

"He'd have never been such a fool as to marry if the girl had not had lots of brass," growled Nicholas.

"He was bound to attract some cultivated rich woman with his talents, his looks, and his lovely manners," said Meg, her smile of ineffable calm sweetness curving her lips. "I shall be very nice to her. Who knows, she may do something for the younger boys. American women are noted for their generosity. Wakefield is delicate and he's very attractive. Finch is—"

"Neither delicate nor attractive," put in Renny, grinning, and Finch, who was wrestling in a corner with his Latin, blushed a deep pink, and gave a snort of mingled amusement and embarrassment.

Grandmother shouted: "When is she coming? I must wear my cream-colored cap with the purple ribbons."

Piers said: "Eden always was an impulsive fool. I'll bet he's making a fool marriage." He rather hoped that Eden was, for he found it hard to endure the thought of Eden's making a marriage which would be welcomed by the whole family while he himself was continually forced to feel that he had made a mess of his life.

Meg wrote her letter to Alayne, inviting her to come to Jalna for as long as she liked. She was to consider Jalna her home. All the family were so happy in dear Eden's happiness. Dear Grandmother sent her love. ("Have you got that down, Meggie? That I send my love? Underline it. No mistake.") Alayne was deeply touched by this letter.

What delight she took in showing New York to her lover! Theatres, museums, cathedrals, shops, and queer little tearooms. Down dingy steps they went, she feeling thrilled because he was thrilled, into dim rooms, lighted by candles, where waitresses wore smocks or other distinctive regalia, and the places bore such names as The Pepper Pot, The Samovar, The Mad Hatter, or The Pig and Whistle. Together they stood, as the evening fell, looking down from the twentieth story of a pale, columnlike building into the street below, where the electric signs became a chain of burning jewels, out across the Hudson and the harbor with its glittering ferryboats, or, raising their happy eyes, saw all the dim towers flower into fairy brightness.

She took him up the Hudson to visit her two aunts, the sisters of her father, who lived in a house with a pinkish roof overlooking the river. They were delighted with Alayne's young Canadian. He had such an easy, pleasant voice, he was so charmingly deferential to them. Even while they regretted that Alayne was going away, for a time at least, they were exhilarated, elated by her bliss. They took Eden to their hearts, and, seated in their austerely perfect little living room, they asked him innumerable questions about his family. He, lounging much less than when in Alayne's apartment, looked with curiosity into the clear eyes of those two elderly women, wondering whether they had always been so earnest, so elegantly poised, so essentially well behaved. Yes, he thought so. He pictured them sitting in high-chairs, investigating rubber dolls and rattles with the selfsame expression. They were inclined to stoutness. Their faces were just pleasantly lined. Their graying hair was rolled back from their foreheads with well-groomed precision. Their dresses of soft neutral tints blended perfectly with the delicate self-tones of the wall paper and hangings. Groups of little black framed prints and etchings of the doorways of European cathedrals, old bridges, or quiet landscapes gave distinction to the walls. Yet, in spite of the studied austerity, Eden felt that these two elderly ladies were incurably romantic. He was nervous lest he should say something to shatter the brittle atmosphere in which they had their being. He tried, when questioned, to present the family at Jalna in as neutral tints as possible. But it was difficult. He realized for the first time that they were high-colored and flamboyant.

Miss Harriet was asking:—

"Let me see, there are six of you, aren't there? How very interesting. Just imagine Alayne having brothers and sisters, Helen. She used always to be praying for them when she was little, didn't you, Alayne?"

"There is only one sister," said Eden.

"She wrote Alayne such a kind letter," murmured Miss Helen.

Miss Harriet proceeded: "And your older brother went through all the terrors of the War, did he not?"

"Yes, he was through the War," replied Eden, and he thought of Renny's rich vocabulary.

"And the brother next to you is married, Alayne tells us. I do hope his wife and Alayne will be friends. Is she about Alayne's age? Have you known her long?"

"She is seventeen. I've known her all my life. She's the daughter of a neighbor." His mind flew for an instant to the reception given to Piers and Pheasant when they returned to Jalna after their marriage. He remembered the way poor young Pheasant had howled, and Piers had stood holding his bleeding ear.

"I trust Alayne and she will be congenial. Then there are the two younger brothers. Tell us about them."

"Well, Finch is rather a—oh, he's just at the hobbledehoy period, Miss Archer. We can hardly tell what he'll be. At present he's immersed in his studies. Wake is a pretty little chap. You'd quite like him. He is too delicate to go to school, and has all his lessons with our rector. I'm afraid he's very indolent, but he's an engaging young scamp."

"I am sure Alayne will love him. And she will have uncles, too. I am glad there are no aunts. Yes, Alayne, we were saying only this morning we are glad there are no aunts. We really want no auntly opposition in loving you."

"Then," put in Miss Helen, "there is Eden's remarkable grandmother. Ninety-nine, did you say, Eden? And all her faculties almost unimpaired. It is truly wonderful."

"Yes, a regular old—yes, an amazing old lady, Grandmother is." And he suddenly saw her grinning at him, the graceless ancient, with her cap askew, Boney perched on her shoulder, rapping out obscene Hindu oaths in his raucous voice. He groaned inwardly and wondered what Alayne would think of his family.

He had written asking Renny to be best man for him. Renny had replied: "I have neither the *time*, the *togs*, nor the *tin* for such a bust-up. But I enclose a check for my wedding present to you, which will help to make up for my absence. I am glad Miss Archer has money. Otherwise I should think you insane to tie yourself up at this point in your career, when you seem to be going in several directions at once and arriving nowhere. However, good luck to you and my very best regards to the lady. Your aff. bro. Renny."

The check was sufficient to pay for the honeymoon trip and to take them home to Jalna. Eden, with his head among the stars, thanked God for that.

They were married in the austerely perfect living room of Alayne's aunts' house on the Hudson. Late roses of so misty a pink that they were almost mauve, and asters of so uncertain a mauve that they were almost pink, blended with the pastel shades worn by the tremulously happy aunts. A Presbyterian minister united them, for the Misses Archer were of that denomination. They had felt it keenly when their brother had embraced Unitarian doctrines, though they had never reproached him for his change of faith. Intellectually Alayne was satisfied with Unitarianism, but she had sometimes wished that the faith in which she had been reared were more picturesque even though less intellectual. In truth, religious speculation had played a very small part in her life, and when bereavement came to her she found little consolation in it. With a certain sad whimsicality, she liked at times to picture the spirit of her father meticulously going over the golf course, stopping now and again to wave a ghostly hand to the spirit of her mother peering from an upper window of the stucco bungalow.

She thought of them a good deal on this her wedding day. They would have been so happy in her happiness. They would have loved Eden. He looked so radiant, sunburned, and confident as he smiled down at her that she became radiant and confident too.

The Corys, Rosamund Trent, and the other friends at the wedding repast thought and said that they had never seen a lovelier couple.

As they motored to New York to take their train Eden said:—

"Darling, I have never met so many well-behaved people in my life. Darling, let us be wild and half-mad and delirious with joy! I'm tired of being good."

She hugged him to her. She loved him intensely, and she longed with great fervor to experience life.

XII. WELCOME AGAIN TO JALNA

Wakefield slept late that morning, just when he had intended to be about early. When he opened his eyes he found that Renny's head was not on the pillow next his as usual. He was not even dressing. He was gone, and Wake had the bed and the room to himself. He slept with Renny because he sometimes had a "bad turn" in the night and it was to his eldest brother he clung at such times.

He spread-eagled himself on the bed, taking up all the room he could, and lay luxuriously a few minutes, rejoicing in the fact that he did not have to go to Mr. Fennel's for lessons on this day, because it had been proclaimed a holiday by Grandmother. It was the day on which Eden and his bride were expected to arrive at Jalna. Their train was to reach the city at nine that morning and Piers had already motored to fetch them the twenty-five miles to Jalna, where a great dinner was already in preparation.

The loud wheezing that preceded the striking of the grandfather's clock in the upstairs hall now began. Wake listened. After what seemed a longer wheeze than usual the clock struck nine. The train carrying the bride and groom must at this moment be arriving at the station. Wakefield had seen pictures of wedding parties, and he had a vision of Eden traveling in a top hat and long-tailed coat with a white flower in his buttonhole, seated beside his bride, whose face showed but faintly through a voluminous veil and who carried an immense bouquet of orange blossoms. He did wish that Meg had allowed him to go in the car to meet them. It seemed too bad that such a lovely show should be wasted on Piers, who had not seemed at all keen about meeting them.

Wake thought that he had better give his rabbit hutches a thorough cleaning, for probably one of the first things the bride would wish to inspect would be his rabbits. It would be some time before they arrived, for they were to have breakfast in town. He began to kick the bedclothes from him. He kicked them with all his might till he had nothing over him, then he lay quite still a moment, his small dark face turned impassively toward the ceiling, before he leaped out of bed and ran to the window.

It was a day of thick yellow autumn sunshine. A circular bed of nasturtiums around two old cedar trees burned like a slow fire. The lawn still had a film of heavy dew drawn across it, and a procession of bronze turkeys, led by the red-faced old cock, left a dark trail where their feet had brushed it.

"Gobble, gobble, gobble," came from the cock, and his wattles turned from red to purple. He turned and faced his hens and wheeled before them, dropping his wings with a metallic sound.

Wake shouted from the window: "Gobble, gobble, gobble! Get off the lawn! I say, get off the lawn!"

"Clang, clang, clang," resounded the gobbler's note of anger, and the hens made plaintive piping sounds.

"I suppose you think," retorted Wakefield, "that you're fifteen brides and a groom. Well, you're not. You're turkeys; and you'll be eaten first thing you know. The real bride and groom will eat you, so there!"

"Gobble, gobble, gobble."

The burnished procession passed into the grape arbor. Between purple bunches of grapes, Wake could see the shine of plumage, the flame of tossing wattles.

It was a lovely morning! He tore off his pyjamas and, stark naked, ran round and round the room. He stopped breathless before the washstand, where the brimming basin foaming with shaving lather showed how complete had been Renny's preparations for the bride and groom.

Wakefield took up the shaving soap and the shaving brush, and immersed the brush in the basin. He made a quantity of fine, fluffy, and altogether delightful lather. First he decorated his face, then produced a nice epaulette for each shoulder. Then he made a collar for his round brown neck. Next his two little nipples attracted him. He adorned them as if with the filling from two cream puffs. In order he decorated all the more prominent features of his small person. By twisting about before the mirror he managed to do even his back. It took most of the shaving stick, but the effect when his toilet was completed was worth all the trouble. He stood in rapt admiration before the glass, astonished at what a little ingenuity and a lot of lather could do. He pictured himself receiving the bride and groom in this simple yet effective attire. He was sure that Alayne would think it worth while traveling all the way from New York to see a sight like this.

He was lost in reverie when a smothered scream disturbed him. It was uttered by Mrs. Wragge, who stood in the doorway, one hand clapped to her mouth, the other carrying a slop pail.

"My Gawd!" she cried. "Wot a norrible sight! Ow, wot a turn it give me! My 'eart's doawn in my boots and my stumick's in the top of my 'ead."

She was too funny standing there, red-faced and open-mouthed. Wakefield could not refrain from doing something to her. He danced toward her and, before she realized the import of the brandished shaving brush, she had a snowy meringue of lather fairly between the eyes and down the bridge of the nose. With a scream, this time unsmothered, Mrs. Wragge dropped the pail of slops and pawed blindly at her ornate face. Meg, giving a last satisfied examination to Eden's room, which had been prepared for the bridal pair, hurried toward the sounds of distress from her handmaiden, and, catching the little boy by the ankle just as he was disappearing under the big four-poster, dragged him forth and administered three sharp slaps.

"There," she said, "and there, and *there!* As though I hadn't enough to do!"

When Wakefield descended the stairs half an hour later, his expression was somewhat subdued but he carried himself with dignity, and he was conscious of looking extremely well in his best Norfolk suit and a snowy Eton collar. He had begged for just a little hair cream to make his hair lie flat, but Meg liked it fluffy, and he had not wished to insist on anything on a morning when she was already somewhat harassed.

As he passed the door of his grandmother's room, he could hear her saying in a cajoling tone to Boney: "Say 'Alayne' now, Boney. 'Pretty Alayne.' Say 'Alayne.' Say 'Hail Columbia.'" Then her voice was drowned by the raucous tones of Boney uttering a few choice Hindu curses.

Wakefield smiled and entered the dining room. The table was cleared, but a tray was laid on a small table in a corner. Bread and butter, marmalade, milk. He knew that if he rang the bell Rags would bring him a dish of porridge from the kitchen. It was an old silver bell in the shape of a little fat lady. He loved it, and handled it caressingly a moment before ringing it long and clearly.

He went to the head of the basement stairs and listened. He could hear Rags rattling things on the stove. He heard a saucepan being scraped. Nasty, sticky, dried-up old porridge! He heard Rags's step on the brick floor approaching the stairway. Lightly he glided to the clothes cupboard and hid himself inside the door, just peeping through a narrow crack while Rags mounted the stairs and disappeared into the dining room, a cigarette stuck between his pale lips and the plate of porridge tilted at a precarious angle. Wakefield reflected without bitterness that Rags would not have dared to wait on any other member of the family with such a lack of decorum. But he smiled slyly as he glided down the stairs into the basement, leaving Rags and the porridge in the dining room alone.

The kitchen was an immense room with a great unused fireplace and a coal range that was always in use. The table and dressers were so heavy that they were never moved, and one wall was covered by an oak rack filled with platters from successive Whiteoak dinner sets. Many of these would have given delight to a collector, but the glazing on all was disfigured by innumerable little cracks from being placed in ovens far too hot.

Wakefield gave one longing look into the pantry. How he would have liked to forage for his breakfast among those richly laden shelves! He saw two fat fowls trussed up in a roasting pan ready to put into the oven, and a huge boiled ham, and a brace of plum tarts. But he dared not. Rags would be returning at any moment. On the kitchen table he found a plate of cold toast and a saucer of anchovy paste. Taking a slice of toast and the anchovy paste, he trotted out of the kitchen and along the brick passage into the coal cellar. He heard Rags clattering down the kitchen stairs, muttering as he came. A window in the coal cellar stood open, and mounted on an empty box he found he could easily put his breakfast out on the ground and climb out after it.

He was sorry to see how black his hands and bare knees had become in the operation. He scrubbed them with his clean handkerchief, but the only result was that the handkerchief became black. He did not like to return such a black rag to the pocket of his best suit, so he pushed it carefully out of sight in a crack just under the sill of the cellar window. Some little mouse, he thought, would be glad to find it and make a nice little nest of it.

He carried his toast and anchovy paste to the old carriage house, and sought a favorite retreat of his. This was a ponderous closed carriage that Grandfather Whiteoak had sent to England for when he and Grandmother had first built Jalna. It had a great shell-like body, massive lamps, and a high seat for the coachman. It must have been a splendid sight to see them driving out. It had not been used for many years. Wakefield slumped on the sagging seat, eating his toast and anchovy paste with unhurried enjoyment. The fowls clucking and scratching in the straw made a soothing accompaniment to his thoughts.

"Now, if I had my way I'd meet the brideangroom with this beautiful carriage, drawn by four white horses. I'd have the wheels all done up in wreaths of roses like the pictures of carnivals in California. And a big bunch of roses for her to carry, and a trumpeter sitting on the seat beside the coachman tooting a trumpet. And a pretty little dwarf hanging on behind, with a little silver whistle to blow when the trumpeter stopped tooting. What a happy brideangroom they'd be!"

"Brideangroom. . . . Brideangroom." He liked the pleasant way those words ran together. Still, he must not linger here too long or he would not be on hand to welcome them. He decided that there was no time left for cleaning the rabbit hutches. He would go across the meadow to the road, and wait by the church corner. Then he would have a chance to meet them before the rest of the family. He clambered out of the carriage, a cobweb clinging to his hair and a black smudge across his cheek. He set the saucer containing the remainder of the anchovy on the floor and watched five hens leap simultaneously upon it, a tangle of wings and squawks, while a rooster side-stepped about the scrimmage, watching his wives with a distracted yellow eye.

He trotted across the meadow, climbed the fence, and gained the road. He stopped long enough to pass the time of day with Chalk, the blacksmith, and was almost by the Wigles' cottage when Muriel accosted him from the gate:—

"I've got ten thents."

He hesitated, looking at the little girl over his shoulder. "Have you? Where did you get it?" he asked with polite interest.

"It'th a birthday prethent. I'm thaving up to buy a dolly."

Wake went to her and said kindly: "Look here, Muriel, you're awfully silly if you do that. A doll costs a dollar or more, and if you save ten cents every single birthday it'd be years and years before you'd have enough to buy one. By that time you'd be too old to play with it. Better come to Mrs. Brawn's now and buy yourself a chocolate bar. I'll buy you a bottle of cream soda to drink with it."

"I don't like cream thoda," replied Muriel, petulantly. She opened her small hot palm and examined the coin lying on it.

Wakefield bent over it. "Why, it's a Yankee dime!" he exclaimed. "Goodness, Muriel, you'd better hurry up and spend it, because likely as not it'll be no good by next week."

Mrs. Wigle put her head out of the window of the cottage.

"When's your brother goin' to mend my roof?" she demanded. "It's leakin' like all possessed."

"Oh, he was just speaking about that this morning, Mrs. Wigle. He says that just as soon as he gets this wedding reception off his hands, he's going to attend to your roof."

"Well, I hope he will," she grumbled, and withdrew her head.

"Come along now, Muriel," said Wake. "I haven't much time to spare, but I'll go with you to Mrs. Brawn's so's you won't feel shy."

He took her hand and the little girl trotted beside him with a rather dazed expression. They presented themselves before Mrs. Brawn's counter.

"Well, Master Whiteoak," she said, "I hope you've come to pay your account."

"I'm afraid not this morning," replied Wake. "We're so very busy getting ready for the brideangroom that I forgot. But Muriel here wants a bottle of cream soda and a chocolate bar. It's her birthday, you see."

They sat on the step outside the shop with the refreshments, Wakefield sucking the sickly drink placidly through a straw, Muriel nibbling the chocolate.

"Have a pull, Muriel," he offered.

"Don't like it," she said. "You have a bite of chocolate." She held the bar to his lips, and so they contentedly ate it, bite about.

How happy he was! "Brideangroom. . . . Brideangroom." The pleasant words went singing through his head. A spiral of wood smoke curled upward from a mound of burning leaves in a yard across the street. A hen and her half-grown brood scratched blithely in the middle of the road. Muriel was gazing into his face with slavish admiration.

A car was coming. Their own car. He recognized its peculiar hiccoughing squeaks. Hastily he drained the last drops and pushed the bottle into Muriel's hands.

"You may return the bottle, Muriel," he said. "I must go to meet the brideangroom."

The car was in sight. He espied a clump of Michaelmas daisies growing by the side of the road, and he swiftly ran and plucked a long feathery spray. It was rather dusty, but still very pretty, and he stood clasping it, with an expectant smile on his face, as the car approached. Piers, who was driving, would have gone by and left him standing there, but Eden sharply told him to stop, and Alayne leaned forward full of eager curiosity.

Wakefield mounted the running board and held the Michaelmas daisies out to her.

"Welcome to Jalna," he said.

XIII. INSIDE THE GATES OF JALNA

Eden had not been sorry to see his little brother waiting at the roadside with daisies for Alayne. The meeting with Piers, the breakfast in his company at the Queen's, and the subsequent drive home had not been altogether satisfactory. Alayne had been tired and unusually quiet, Piers actually taciturn. Eden resented this taciturnity because he remembered having been very decent to Piers and Pheasant on the occasion of their humiliating return to Jalna. He had been the first, and the only one except Renny, to stand up for them. He regarded his brother's solid back and strong sunburned neck with growing irritation as the car sped along the lake shore road.

Alayne gazed out over the misty blue expanse of the lake with a feeling approaching sadness. This sea that was not a sea, this land that was not her land, this new brother with the unfriendly blue eyes and the sulky mouth, she must get used to them all. They were to be hers. Ruth—"amid the alien corn."

But she should not feel that they were alien. It was a lovely land. The language was her own. Even this new brother was probably only rather shy. She wished that Eden had told her more about his family. There were so many of them. She went over their names in her mind to prepare herself for the meeting. A tiny shudder of apprehension ran through her nerves. She put her hand on Eden's and gripped his fingers.

"Cheer up, old dear," he said. "We'll soon be there."

They had left the lake shore and were running smoothly over a curving road. A quaint old church, perched on a wooded knoll, rose before them. Then a diminutive shop, two children staring, Eden's voice saying, "There's young Wake, Piers!" And a little boy on the running board, pushing flowers into her hand.

"Welcome to Jalna," he said, in a sweet treble, "and I thought maybe you'd like these Michaelmas daisies. I've been waiting ever so long."

"Hop in," commanded Eden, opening the door.

He hopped in, and squeezed his slender body between theirs on the seat. Piers had not looked round. Now he started the car with a jerk.

Wakefield raised his eyes to Alayne's face and scrutinized her closely. "What eyelashes!" she thought. "What a darling!" His little body pressed against her seemed the most delightful and pathetic thing. Oh, she could love this little brother. And he was delicate, too. Not strong enough to go to school. She would play with him, help to teach him. They smiled at each other. She looked across his head at Eden and formed the words "A darling" with smiling lips.

"How is everyone at home?" asked Eden.

"Nicely, thank you," said Wakefield, cheerfully. "Granny has had a little cough, and Boney imitates her. Uncle Ernest's nose is rather pink from hay fever. Uncle Nick's gout is better. Meggie eats very little, but she is getting fatter. Piers took the first prize with his bull at the Durham show. It wore the blue ribbon all the way home. Finch came out fifty-second in his Greek exam. I can't think of any news about Pheasant and Rags and Mrs. Wragge except that they're there. I hope you like your flowers, Alayne. I should have got more, but I saw your car coming just as I was beginning to gather them."

"They are beautiful," said Alayne, holding them to her face, and Wakefield close to her side. "I am so very glad you came to meet me."

In truth she was very glad. It seemed easier to meet the family with the little boy by her side. Her cheeks flushed a pretty pink, and she craned her neck eagerly to catch a first glimpse of the house as they passed between the stalwart spruces along the drive.

Jalna looked very mellow in the golden sunlight, draped in its mantle of reddening Virginia creeper and surrounded by freshly clipped lawns. One of Wake's rabbits was hopping about, and Renny's two clumber spaniels were stretched on the steps. A pear tree near the house had dropped its fruit on the grass, where it lay richly yellow, giving to the eyes of a town dweller an air of negligent well-being to the scene. Alayne thought that Jalna had something of the appearance of an old manorial farmhouse, set among its lawns and orchards. The spaniels lazily beat their plumed tails on the step, too indolent to rise.

"Renny's dogs," commented Eden, pushing one of them out of the way with his foot that Alayne might pass. "You'll have to get used to animals. You'll find them all over the place."

"That will not be hard. I have always wanted pets." She bent to stroke one of the silken heads.

Eden looked down at her curiously. How would she and his family get on, he wondered. Now that he had brought her home he realized suddenly that she was alien to his family. He had a disconcerting sensation of surprise at finding himself married. After all, he was not so elated as he had expected to be when Rags opened the door and smiled a self-conscious welcome.

Rags was always self-conscious when he wore his livery. It consisted of a shiny black suit with trousers very tight for him and a coat a size too large, a stiff white collar, and a greenish-black bow tie. His ash-blond hair was clipped with convictlike closeness, his pallid face showed a cut he had given himself when shaving. His air had something of the secretive smirk of an undertaker.

"Welcome 'ome, Mr. Eden," he said, sadly. "Welcome 'ome, sir."

"Thanks, Rags. Alayne, this is Wragge, our–" Eden hesitated, trying to decide how Mr. Wragge should be described, and continued, "our factotum."

"Welcome 'ome, Mrs. Whiteoak," said Rags, with his curiously deprecating yet impudent glance. It said to Eden silently but unmistakably: "Ow, you may fool the family, young man, but you can't fool me. You 'aven't married a heiress. And 'ow we're to put up with another young woman 'ere Gawd only knows."

Alayne thanked him, and at the same moment the door of the living room was opened and Meg Whiteoak appeared on the threshold. She threw her arms about Eden's neck and kissed him with passionate tenderness. Then she turned to Alayne, her lips, with their prettily curved corners, parted in a gentle smile.

"So this is Alayne. I hope you will like us all, my dear. We're so happy to have you."

Alayne found herself enfolded in a warm plump embrace. She thought it was no wonder the brothers adored their sister,–Eden had told her they did,–and she felt prepared to make a sister, a confidante, of her. How delightful!

A real sister. She held tightly to Meg's hand as they went into the living room where more of the family had assembled.

It was so warm that even the low flameless fire seemed too much; none of the windows were open. Slanting bars of sunlight penetrating between the slats of the inside shutters converged at one point, the chair where old Mrs. Whiteoak sat. Like fiery fingers they seemed to point her out as the most significant presence in the room. Yet she was indulging in one of her unpremeditated naps. Her head, topped by a large purple cap with pink rosettes, had sunk forward so that the only part of her face visible was her heavy jaw and row of too perfect under teeth. She wore a voluminous tea gown of purple velvet, and her shapely hands clasping the gold top of her ebony stick were heavy with rings worn for the occasion. A steady bubbling snore escaped her. The two elderly men came forward, Nicholas frowning because of the painful effort of rising, but enfolding Alayne's hand in a warm grasp. They greeted her in mellow whispers, Ernest excusing their mamma's momentary oblivion.

"She must have these little naps. They refresh her. Keep her going."

Wakefield, who stood gazing into his grandmother's face, remarked: "Yes. She winds herself up, rather like a clock, you know. You can hear her doing it, can't you? B-z-z-z-z—"

Meg smiled at Alayne. "He thinks of everything," she said. "His mind is never still."

"He ought to be more respectful in speaking of his grandmamma," rebuked Ernest. "Don't you think so, Alayne?"

Nicholas put his arm about the child. "She'd probably be highly amused by the comparison, and talk of nothing else for an hour." He turned with his sardonic smile to Alayne. "She's very bright, you know. She can drown us all out when she—"

"Begins to strike," put in Wake, carrying on the clock simile. Nicholas rumpled the boy's hair.

"We had better sit down," said Meg, "till she wakens and has a little talk with Alayne. Then I'll take you up to your room, my dear. You must be tired after the journey. And hungry, too. Well, we're going to have an early dinner."

"Chicken and plum tart! Chicken and plum tart!" exploded Wakefield, and old Mrs. Whiteoak stirred in her sleep.

Uncle Nicholas covered the child's face with his hand, and the family's gaze was fixed expectantly on the old lady. After a moment's contortion, however, her face resumed the calm of peaceful slumber; everyone sat down, and conversation was carried on in hushed tones.

Alayne felt as though she were in a dream. The room, the furniture, the people were so different from those to which she was accustomed that their strangeness made even Eden seem suddenly remote. She wondered wistfully whether it would take her long to get used to them. Yet in looking at the faces about her she found that each had a distinctive attraction for her. Or perhaps it was fascination. Certainly there was nothing attractive about the grandmother unless it were the bizarre strength of her personality.

"I lived in London a good many years," mumbled Uncle Nicholas, "but I don't know much about New York. I visited it once in the nineties, but I suppose it has changed a lot since then."

"Yes, I think you would find it very changed. It is changing constantly."

Uncle Ernest whispered: "I sailed from there once for England. I just missed seeing a murder."

"Oh, Uncle Ernest, I wish you'd seen it!" exclaimed Wakefield, bouncing up and down on the padded arm of his sister's chair.

"Hush, Wake," said Meg, giving his thigh a little slap. "I'm very glad he didn't see it. It would have upset him terribly. Isn't it a pity you have so many murders there? And lynchings, and all?"

"They don't have lynchings in New York, Meggie," corrected Uncle Ernest.

"Oh, I forgot. It's Chicago, isn't it?"

Eden spoke for almost the first time. "Never met so many orderly people in my life as I met in New York."

"How nice," said Meg. "I do like order, but I find it so hard to keep, with servants' wages high, and so many boys about, and Granny requiring a good deal of waiting on."

The sound of her own name must have penetrated Mrs. Whiteoak's consciousness. She wobbled a moment as though she were about to fall, then righted herself and raised her still handsome, chiseled nose from its horizontal position and looked about. Her eyes, blurred by sleep, did not at once perceive Alayne.

"Dinner," she observed. "I want my dinner."

"Here are Eden and Alayne," said Ernest, bending over her.

"Better come over to her," suggested Nicholas.

"She will be so glad," said Meg.

Eden took Alayne's hand and led her to his grandmother. The old lady peered at them unseeingly for a moment; then her gaze brightened. She clutched Eden to her and gave him a loud, hearty kiss.

"Eden," she said. "Well, well, so you're back. Where's your bride?"

Eden put Alayne forward, and she was enfolded in an embrace of surprising strength. Sharp bristles scratched her cheek, and a kiss was planted on her mouth.

"Pretty thing," said Grandmother, holding her off to look at her. "You're a very pretty thing. I'm glad you've come. Where's Boney, now?" She released Alayne and looked around sharply for the parrot. At the sound of his name he flapped heavily from his ring perch to her shoulder. She stroked his bright plumage with her jeweled hand.

"Say 'Alayne,'" she adjured him. "Say 'Pretty Alayne.' Come, now, there's a darling boy!"

Boney, casting a malevolent look on Alayne with one topaz eye, for the other was tight shut, burst into a string of curses.

"Kutni! Kutni! Kutni!" he screamed. "Shaitan ke khatla! Kambakht!"

Grandmother thumped her stick loudly on the floor. "Silence!" she thundered. "I won't have it. Stop him, Nick. Stop him!"

"He'll bite me," objected Nicholas.

"I don't care if he does. Stop him!"

"Stop him yourself, Mamma."

"Boney, Boney, don't be so naughty. Say 'Pretty Alayne.' Come, now."

Boney rocked himself on her shoulder in a paroxysm of rage. "Paji! Paji! Kuzabusth! Iflatoon! Iflatoon!" He glared into his mistress's face, their two hooked beaks almost touching, his scarlet and green plumage, her purple and pink finery, blazing in the slanting sun rays.

"Please don't trouble," said Alayne, soothingly. "I think he is very beautiful, and he probably does not dislike me as much as he pretends."

"What's she say?" demanded the old lady, looking up at her sons. It was always difficult for her to understand a stranger, though her hearing was excellent, and Alayne's slow and somewhat precise enunciation was less clear to her than Nicholas's rumbling tones or Ernest's soft mumble.

"She says Boney is beautiful," said Nicholas, too indolent to repeat the entire sentence.

Grandmother grinned, very well pleased. "Aye, he's beautiful. A handsome bird, but a bit of a devil. I brought him all the way from India seventy-three years ago. A game old bird, eh? Sailing vessels then, my dear. I nearly died. And the ayah did die. They put her overboard. But I was too sick to care. My baby Augusta nearly died, poor brat, and my dear husband, Captain Philip Whiteoak, had his hands full. You'll see his portrait in the dining room. The handsomest officer in India. I could hold my own for looks, too. Would you think I'd ever been a beauty, eh?"

"I think you are very handsome now," replied Alayne, speaking with great distinctness. "Your nose is really—"

"What's she say?" cried Grandmother.

Ernest murmured: "She says your nose—"

"Ha, ha, my nose is still a beauty, eh? Yes, my dear, it's a good nose. A Court nose. None of your retroussé, surprised-looking noses. Nothing on God's earth could surprise my nose. None of your pinched, sniffing, cold-in-the-head noses, either. A good reliable nose. A Court nose." She rubbed it triumphantly.

"You've a nice-looking nose, yourself," she continued. "You and Eden make a pretty pair. But he's no Court. Nor a Whiteoak. He looks like his poor pretty flibbertigibbet mother."

Alayne, shocked, looked indignantly toward Eden, but he wore only an expression of tolerant boredom, and was putting a cigarette between his faintly smiling lips.

Meg saw Alayne's look and expostulated: "Grandmamma!"

"Renny's the only Court among 'em," pursued Mrs. Whiteoak. "Wait till you see Renny. Where is he? I want Renny." She thumped the floor impatiently with her stick.

"He'll be here very soon, Granny," said Meg. "He rode over to Mr. Probyn's to get a litter of pigs."

"Well, I call that very boorish of him. Boorish. Boorish. Did I say boorish? I mean Boarish. There's a pun, Ernest. You enjoy a pun. Boarish. Ha, ha!"

Ernest stroked his chin and smiled deprecatingly. Nicholas laughed jovially.

The old lady proceeded with a rakish air of enjoyment. "Renny prefers the grunting of a sow to sweet converse with a young bride—"

"Mamma," said Ernest, "shouldn't you like a peppermint?"

Her attention was instantly distracted. "Yes. I want a peppermint. Fetch me my bag."

Ernest brought a little old bead-embroidered bag. His mother began to fumble in it, and Boney, leaning from her shoulder, pecked at it and uttered cries of greed.

"A sweet!" he babbled. "A sweet—Boney wants a sweet—Pretty Alayne—Pretty Alayne—Boney wants a sweet!"

Grandmother cried in triumph: "He's said it! He's said it! I told you he could. Good Boney." She fumbled distractedly in the bag.

"May I help you?" Alayne asked, not without timidity.

The old lady pushed the bag into her hand. "Yes, quickly. I want a peppermint. A Scotch mint. Not a humbug."

"Boney wants a humbug!" screamed the parrot, rocking from side to side. "A humbug—Pretty Alayne—Kutni! Kutni! Shaitan ke khatla."

Grandmother and the parrot leaned forward simultaneously for the sweet when it was found, she with protruding wrinkled lips, he with gaping beak. Alayne hesitated, fearing to offend either by favoring the other. While she hesitated Boney snatched it, and with a whir of wings flew to a far corner of the room. Grandmother, rigid as a statue, remained with protruding mouth till Alayne unearthed another sweet and popped it between her lips, then she sank back with a sigh of satisfaction, closed her eyes, and began to suck noisily.

Alayne longed to wipe her fingers, but she refrained. She looked at the faces about her. They were regarding the scene with the utmost imperturbability, except Eden, who still wore his look of faintly smiling boredom. A cloud of smoke about his head seemed to emphasize his aloofness.

Meg moved closer to him and whispered: "I think I shall take Alayne upstairs. I've had new chintzes put in your room, and fresh curtains, and I've taken the small rug from Renny's room and covered the bare spot on the carpet with it. I think you'll be pleased when you see it, Eden. She's a perfect dear."

Brother and sister looked at Alayne, who was standing with the two uncles at a window. They had opened the shutters and were showing her the view of the oak woods that sloped gradually down to the ravine. A flock of sheep were quietly grazing, tended by an old sheep dog. Two late lambs were vying with each other in plaintive cries.

Meg came to Alayne and put an arm through hers. "I know you would like to go to your room," she said.

The two women ascended the stairway together. When they reached Eden's door Meg impetuously seized Alayne's head between her plump hands and kissed her on the forehead. "I'm sure we can love each other," she explained, with childish enthusiasm, and Alayne returned the embrace, feeling that it would be easy to love this warm-blooded woman with a mouth like a Cupid's bow.

When Eden came up, he found Alayne arranging her toilet articles on the dressing table and humming a happy little song. He closed the door after him and came to her.

"I'm glad you can sing," he said. "I had told you that my family were an unusual set of people, but when I saw you among them I began to fear they'd be too much for you–that you'd get panicky, perhaps, and want to run back to New York."

"Is that why you were so quiet downstairs? You had an odd expression. I could not quite make it out. I thought you looked bored."

"I was. I wanted to have you to myself." He took her in his arms.

Eden was at this moment inexplicably two men. He was the lover, strongly possessive and protective. As opposed to this, he was the captive, restless, nervous, hating the thought of the responsibility of introducing his wife to his family, of translating one to the other in terms of restraint and affection.

She said, stroking his hair, which was like a shining metallic casque over his head: "Your sister–Meg–was delightful to me. She seems quite near already. And she tells me she had this room done over for me–new chintz and curtains. I am so glad it looks out over the park and the sheep. I can scarcely believe I shall have sheep to watch from my window."

"Let me show you my things," cried Eden, gayly, and he led her about the room, pointing out his various belongings from schooldays on, with boyish naïveté. He showed her the ink-stained desk at which he had written many of his poems.

"And to think," she exclaimed, "that I was far away in New York, and you were here, at that desk, writing the poems that were to bring us together!" She stroked the desk as though it were a living thing, and said, "I shall always want to keep it. When we have our own house, may we take it there, Eden?"

"Of course." But he wished she would not talk about having their own house yet. To change the subject he asked, "Did you find Gran rather overpowering? I'm afraid I scarcely prepared you for her. But she can't be explained. She's got to be seen to be credible. The uncles are nice old boys."

"Do you think"–she spoke hesitatingly, yet with determination–"that it is good for her to spoil her so? She absolutely dominated the room."

He smiled down at her quizzically. "My dear, she will be a hundred on her next birthday. She was spoiled before we ever saw her. My grandfather attended to that. Quite possibly she was spoiled before ever he saw her. She probably came into the world spoiled by generations of tyrannical hot-tempered Courts. You will just have to make the best of her."

"But the way she spoke about your mother. I cannot remember the word—flibberty-something. It hurt me, dearest."

Eden ran his hand through his hair in sudden exasperation. "You must not be so sensitive, Alayne. Words like that are a mere caress compared to what Gran can bring out on occasion."

"But about your dear mother," she persisted.

"Aren't women always like that about their daughters-in-law? Wait till you have one of your own and see. Wait till you are ninety-nine. You may be no more sweet-tempered than Gran by then."

Eden laughed gayly, but with an air of dismissing the subject, and drew her to the chintz-covered window seat. "Let's sit down here a bit and enjoy Meggie's new decoration. I think she's done us thundering well, don't you?"

Alayne leaned against him, breathing deeply of the tranquil air of Indian summer that came like a palpable essence through the open window. The earth, after all its passion of bearing, was relaxed in passive and slumbrous contentment. Its desires were fulfilled, its gushing fertility over. In profound languor it seemed to brood neither on the future nor on the past, but on its own infinite relation to the sun and to the stars. The sun had become personal. Red and rayless, he hung above the land as though listening to the slow beating of a great heart.

She became aware that Eden was observing someone in the grounds outside. She heard the sound of a horse's hoofs and, turning, saw a man leaning from his horse to fasten the gate behind him. Her beauty-loving eye was caught first by the satin shimmer of the beast's chestnut coat. Then she perceived that the rider was tall and thin, that he stooped in the saddle with an air of slouching accustomedness, and, as he passed beneath the window, that he had a red, sharp-featured face that looked rather foxlike beneath his peaked tweed cap.

The two clumber spaniels had rushed out to greet him and were bounding about the horse, their long silken ears flapping. Their barking irritated the horse, and, after a nip or two at them, he broke into a canter and disappeared with his rider behind a row of Scotch firs that hid the stables from the house.

"Renny," murmured Eden, "back from his porcine expedition."

"Yes, I thought it must be Renny, though he is not like what I expected him to be. Why did you not call to him?"

"He's rather a shy fellow. I thought it might embarrass both of you to exchange your first greetings from such different altitudes."

Alayne, listening to the muffled sound of hoofs, remarked: "He gives the impression of a strong personality."

"He has. And he's as wiry and strong as the Devil. I've never known him to be ill for a day. He'll probably live to be as old as Gran."

"Gran—Gran," thought Alayne. Every conversation in this family seemed to be punctuated by remarks about that dreadful old woman.

"And he owns all this," she commented. "It does not seem quite fair to all you others."

"It was left that way. He has to educate and provide for the younger family. The uncles had their share years ago. And of course Gran simply hoards hers. No one knows who will get it."

"Gran" again.

A gentle breeze played with a tendril of hair on her forehead. Eden brushed his lips against it. "Darling," he murmured, "do you think you can be happy here for a while?"

"Eden! I am gloriously happy."

"We shall write such wonderful things—together."

They heard steps on the graveled path that led to the back of the house. Alayne, opening her eyes, heavy with a momentary sweet languor, saw Renny enter the kitchen, his dogs at his heels. A moment later a tap sounded on the door.

"Please," said Wake's voice, "will you come down to dinner?"

He could not restrain his curiosity about the bride and groom. It seemed very strange to find this young lady in Eden's room, but it was disappointing that there were no confetti and orange blossoms about.

Alayne put her arm around his shoulders as they descended the stairs, feeling more support from his little body in the ordeal of meeting the rest of the family than the presence of Eden afforded her. There were still Renny and the wife of young Piers.

Their feet made no sound on the thick carpet of the stairs. The noontide light falling through the colored glass window gave the hall an almost church-like solemnity, and the appearance at the far end of old Mrs. Whiteoak emerging from her room, supported on either side by her sons, added a final processional touch. Through the open door of the dining room Alayne could see the figures of Renny, Piers, and a young girl advancing toward the table. Meg already stood at one end of it, surveying its great damask expanse as some high priestess might survey the sacrificial altar. On a huge platter already lay two rotund roasted fowls. Rags stood behind a drawn-back chair, awaiting Mrs. Whiteoak. As the old lady saw Alayne and her escorts approaching the door of the dining room, she made an obviously heroic effort to reach it first, shuffling her feet excitedly, and snuffing the good smell of the roast with the excitement of an old war horse smelling blood.

"Steady, Mamma, steady," begged Ernest, steering her past a heavily carved hall chair.

"I want my dinner," she retorted, breathing heavily. "Chicken. I smell chicken. And cauliflower. I must have the pope's nose, and plenty of bread sauce."

Not until she was seated was Alayne introduced to Renny and Pheasant. He bowed gravely, and murmured some only half-intelligible greeting. She might have heard it more clearly had her mind been less occupied with the scrutiny of him at sudden close quarters. She was observing his narrow, weather-beaten face, the skin like red-brown leather merging in color into the rust-red of his hair, his short thick eyelashes, his abstracted, yet fiery eyes. She observed too his handsome, hard-looking nose, which was far too much like his grandmother's.

Pheasant she saw as a flower-like young girl, a fragile *Narcissus poeticus* in this robust, highly colored garden of Jalna.

Alayne was seated at Renny Whiteoak's left, and at her left Eden, and next him Pheasant and Piers. Wakefield had been moved to the other side of the table, between his sister and Uncle Ernest. Alayne had only glimpses of him around the centrepiece of crimson and bronze dahlias, flowers that in their rigid and uncompromising beauty were well fitted to withstand the overpowering presence of the Whiteoaks. Whenever Alayne's eyes met the little boy's, he smiled. Whenever her eyes met Meg's, Meg's lips curved in their own peculiar smile. But when her eyes met those of Mrs. Whiteoak, the old lady showed every tooth in a kind of ferocious friendliness, immediately returning to her dinner with renewed zeal, as though to make up for lost time.

The master of Jalna set about the business of carving with the speed and precision of one handing out rations to an army. But there was nothing haphazard about his method of apportioning the fowl. With carving knife poised, he shot a quick look at the particular member of the family he was about to serve, then, seeming to know either what they preferred or what was best for them, he slashed it off and handed the plate to Rags, who glided with it to Meg, who served the vegetables.

To one accustomed to a light luncheon, the sight of so much food at this hour was rather disconcerting. Alayne, looking at these enormous dinner plates mounded with chicken, bread sauce, mashed potatoes, cauliflower, and green peas, thought of little salad lunches in New York with mild regret. They seemed very far away. Even the table silver was enormous. The great knife and fork felt like implements in her hands. The salt cellars and pepper pots seemed weighted by memories of all the bygone meals they had savored. The long-necked vinegar bottle reared its head like a tawny giraffe in the massive jungle of the table.

Renny was saying, in his vibrant voice that was without the music of Eden's, "I'm sorry I could not go to your wedding. I could not get away at that time."

"Yes," chimed in Meg, "Renny and I wanted so very much to go, but we could not arrange it. Finch had a touch of tonsillitis just then, and Wakefield's heart was not behaving very well, and of course there is Grandmamma."

Mrs. Whiteoak broke in: "I wanted to go, but I'm too old to travel. I did all my traveling in my youth. I've been all over the world. But I sent my love. Did you get my love? I sent my love in Meggie's letter. Did you get it, eh?"

"Yes, indeed," said Alayne. "We were so very glad to get your message."

"You'd better be. I don't send my love to everyone, helter-skelter." She nodded her cap so vigorously that three green peas bounced from her fork and rolled across the table. Wakefield was convulsed by laughter. He said, "Bang!" as each pea fell, and shot one of his own after them. Renny looked down the table sharply at him, and he subsided.

Grandmother peered at her fork, shrewdly missing the peas.

"My peas are gone," she said. "I want more peas; more cauliflower and potatoes, too."

She was helped to more vegetables, and at once began to mould them with her fork into a solid mass.

"Mamma," objected Ernest mildly, "must you do that?"

Sasha, who was perched on his shoulder, observing that his attention was directed away from his poised fork, stretched out one furry paw and drew it toward her own whiskered lips. Ernest rescued the morsel of chicken just in time. "Naughty, naughty," he said.

As though there had been no interruption, Meg continued:—

"It must have been such a pretty wedding. Eden wrote us all about it."

By this time Renny had attacked the second fowl with his carvers. Alayne had made no appreciable inroads on her dinner, but all the Whiteoaks were ready for more.

"Renny, did you get the pigs?" asked Piers, breaking in on conversation about the wedding with, Alayne thought, ostentatious brusqueness.

"Yes. You never saw a grander litter. Got the nine and the old sow for a hundred dollars. I offered ninety; Probyn wanted a hundred and ten. I met him halfway." The master of Jalna began to talk of the price of pigs with gusto. Everyone talked of the price of pigs; and everyone agreed that Renny had paid too much.

Only the disheveled carcass of the second fowl remained on the platter. Then it was removed, and a steaming blackberry pudding and a large plum tart made their appearance.

"You are eating almost nothing, dear Alayne," said Meg. "I do hope you will like the pudding."

Renny was looking at Alayne steadily from under his thick lashes, the immense pudding spoon expectantly poised.

"Thank you," she answered. "But I really could not. I will take a little of the pie."

"Please don't urge her, Meggie," said Eden. "She is used to luncheon at noon."

"Oh, but the pudding," sighed Meg. "It's such a favorite of ours."

"I like it," said the grandmother with a savage grin; "please give me some."

She got her pudding and Alayne her tart, but when Meg's turn arrived, she breathed: "No, thank you, Renny. Nothing for me." And Renny, knowing of the trays carried to her room, made no remark, but Eden explained in an undertone, "Meggie eats nothing—at least almost nothing at the table. You'll soon get used to that."

Meggie was pouring tea from a heavily chased silver pot. Even little Wake had some; but how Alayne longed for a cup of coffee, for the plum tart, though good, was very rich. It seemed to cry out for coffee.

Would she ever get used to them, Alayne wondered. Would they ever seem near to her—like relatives? As they rose from the table and moved in different directions, she felt a little oppressed, she did not quite know whether by the weight of the dinner or by the family, which was so unexpectedly foreign to her.

Old Mrs. Whiteoak pushed her son Ernest from her, and, extending a heavily ringed hand to Alayne, commanded:—

"You give me your arm, my dear, on this side. You may as well get into the ways of the family at once."

Alayne complied with a feeling of misgiving. She doubted whether she could efficiently take the place of Ernest. The old woman clutched her arm vigorously, dragging with what seemed unnecessary and almost intolerable weight. The two, with Nicholas towering above them, shuffled their way to Mrs. Whiteoak's bedroom and established her there before the fire by painful degrees. Alayne, flushed with the exertion, straightened her back and stared with surprise at the unique magnificence of the painted leather bedstead, the inlaid dresser and tables, the Indian rugs, and flamboyant hangings.

Mrs. Whiteoak pulled at her skirt. "Sit down, my girl, sit down on this footstool. Ha—I'm out o' breath. Winded—" She panted alarmingly.

"Too much dinner, Mamma," said Nicholas, striking a match on the mantelpiece and lighting a cigarette. "If you will overeat, you will wheeze."

"You're a fine one to talk," retorted his mother, suddenly getting her breath. "Look at your own leg, and the way you eat and swill down spirits."

Boney, hearing the voice of his mistress raised in anger, roused himself from his after-dinner doze on the foot of the bed, and screamed: "Shaitan! Shaitan ka bata! Shaitan ka butcha! Kunjus!"

Mrs. Whiteoak leaned over Alayne, where she now sat on the footstool, and stroked her neck and shoulders with a hand not so much caressing as appraising. She raised her heavy red eyebrows to the lace edging of her cap and commented with an arch grin:—

"A bonny body. Well covered, but not too plump. Slender, but not skinny. Meg's too plump. Pheasant's skinny. You're just right for a bride. Eh, my dear, but if I was a young man I'd like to sleep with you."

Alayne, painfully scarlet, turned her face away from Mrs. Whiteoak toward the blaze of the fire. Nicholas was comfortingly expressionless.

"Another thing," chuckled Mrs. Whiteoak, "I'm glad you've lots of brass. I am indeed."

"Easy now," cried Boney. "Easy does it!"

At that moment Grandmother fell into one of her sudden naps. Nicholas smiled down tolerantly at his sleeping parent.

"You mustn't mind what she says. Remember, she's ninety-nine, and she's never had her spirit broken by life—or by the approach of death. You're not offended, are you?"

"N-no. But she says I am—brazen. Why, it almost makes me laugh. I've always been considered rather retiring—even diffident."

Nicholas made subterranean sounds of mirth that had in them a measure of relief, but he offered no explanation. Instead, he took her hand and drew her to her feet.

"Come," he said, "and I'll show you my room. I expect you to visit me often there, and tell me all about New York, and I'll tell you about London in the old days. I'm a regular fossil now, but if you'll believe me, I was a gay fellow once."

He led the way to his room, heaving himself up the stairs by the hand railing. He installed her by the window, where she could enjoy the splendor of the autumn woods and where the light fell over her, bringing out the chestnut tints in her hair and the pearl-like pallor of her skin. It was so long since he had met a young woman of beauty and intelligence that the contact exhilarated him, made the blood quicken in his veins. Before he realized it, he was telling her incidents of his life of which he had not spoken for years. He even unearthed a photograph of his wife in a long-trained evening gown, and showed it to her. His face, massive and heavily lined, looked, as he recalled those bygone days, like a rock from which the sea has long receded, but which bears on its seamed and battered surface irrevocable evidence of the fury of past storms.

He presented her, as a wedding present, with a silver bowl in which he had been accustomed to keep his pipes, first brightening it up with a silk handkerchief.

"You are to keep roses in it now, my dear," he said, and quite casually he put his fingers under her chin, raised her face, and kissed her. Alayne was touched by the gift, a little puzzled by a certain smiling masterfulness in the caress.

A moment later Ernest Whiteoak appeared at the door. Alayne must now inspect his retreat. No, Nicholas was not wanted, just Alayne.

"He intends to bore you with his melancholy annotating of Shakespeare. I warn you," exclaimed Nicholas.

"Nonsense," said Ernest. "I just don't want to feel utterly shelved. Don't be a beast, Nick. Alayne is as much interested in me as she is in you; aren't you, Alayne?"

"She's not interested in you at all," retorted Nicholas, "but she's enthralled by my sweet discourse; aren't you, Alayne?"

They seemed to take pleasure in the mere pronouncing of her name; using it on every occasion.

To Ernest's room she was led then, and because of his brother's gibe he at first would not speak of his hobby, contenting himself with showing her his water colors, the climbing rose whose yellow flowers still spilled their fragrance across his window sill, and the complaisant feline tricks of Sasha. But when Alayne showed an unmistakable interest in the annotation of Shakespeare and an unexpected knowledge of the text, his enthusiasm overflowed like Niagara in springtime. Two hours flew by, in which they established the intimacy of congenial tastes. Ernest's thin cheeks were flushed; his blue eyes had become quite large and bright. He drummed the fingers of one hand incessantly on the table.

So Meg found them when she came to carry Alayne away for an inspection of the house and garden. Eden was off somewhere with Renny, Meg explained, and Alayne had a sudden feeling of anger toward this brother who so arrogantly swept Eden from her side, and who was so casually polite to her himself.

It was warm enough to have tea on the lawn, Meg announced, and when she and Alayne returned from their tour of the mass of overgrown lilacs, syringas, and guelder-rose trees that was called "the shrubbery," and the sleepy kitchen garden where the rows of cabbages and celery and rank bed of parsley were flanked by scarlet sage and heavy-headed dahlias, they found that Rags had arranged the tea things on the wicker table. Some of the family were already disposed about it in deck chairs or on the grass, according to their years.

Alayne's eyes missed no detail of the scene before her: the emerald-green lawn lying in rich shadow, while the upper portions of the surrounding trees were bathed in lambent sunshine which so intensified their varying autumn hues that they had the unreal splendor of colors seen under water. Near the tea table Grandmother dozed in her purple velvet tea gown. Nicholas was stretched, half recumbent, playing idly with the ears of Nip, whose pointed muzzle was twitching expectantly toward the plates of cakes; Ernest stood courteously by his chair; on the grass sprawled bare-kneed Wake with a pair of rabbits, and bony long-limbed Finch, whom she now saw for the first time. Eden, Piers, and Renny did not appear, but before the second pot of tea was emptied young Pheasant slipped into the scene, carrying a branch of scarlet maple leaves, which she laid across the knees of Nicholas.

A mood of gentle hilarity possessed them all. As she ate cucumber sandwiches and cheese cakes, Alayne felt more in harmony with the life that was to be hers among this family. She was relieved by the absence of the three who did not join the party. With Eden away, she could more readily submerge herself in the family, explore the backwater of their relations with each other. In the case of Piers, she felt only relief from a presence that was at least covertly hostile. As for Renny, she could not make him out. She would need time for that. Just now his dominating personality, combined with his air of abstraction, puzzled and rather irritated her.

Eden had told her that Renny did not like his poetry, that he did not like any poetry. She thought of him as counting endless processions of foals, calves, lambs, and young pigs, always with an eye on the market. She would have been surprised, could she have followed him to his bedroom that night, to find how gentle he was toward little Wake, who was tossing about, unable to sleep after the excitement of the day. Renny rubbed his legs and patted his back as a mother might have done. In fact, in his love for his little brother he combined the devotion of both father and mother. Meg was all grown-up sister.

Wake, drowsy at last, curled up against Renny's chest and murmured: "I believe I could go to sleep more quickly if we'd pretend we were somebody else, Renny, please."

"Do you? All right. Who shall we be? Living people or people out of the books? You say."

Wake thought a minute, getting sleepier with each tick of Renny's watch beneath the pillow; then he breathed: "I think we'll be Eden and Alayne."

Renny stifled a laugh. "All right. Which am I?"

Wake considered again, deliciously drowsy, sniffing at the nice odor of tobacco, Windsor soap, and warm flesh that emanated from Renny.

"I think you'd better be Alayne," he whispered.

Renny, too, considered this transfiguration. It seemed difficult, but he said resignedly: "Very well. Fire away."

There was silence for a space; then Wakefield whispered, twisting a button of Renny's pyjamas: "You go first, Renny. Say something."

Renny spoke sweetly: "Do you love me, Eden?"

Wake chuckled, then answered, seriously: "Oh, heaps. I'll buy you anything you want. What would you like?"

"I'd like a limousine, and an electric toaster, and—a feather boa."

"I'll get them all first thing in the morning. Is there anything else you'd like, my girl?"

"M—yes. I'd like to go to sleep."

"Now, see here, you can't," objected the pseudogroom. "Ladies don't pop straight off to sleep like that."

But apparently this lady did. The only response that Wakefield could elicit was a gentle but persistent snore.

For a moment Wake was deeply hurt, but the steady rise and fall of Renny's chest was soothing. He snuggled closer to him, and soon he too was fast asleep.

XIV. FINCH

The coming of Alayne had made a deep and rather overwhelming impression on young Finch. She was unlike anyone he had ever met; she filled his mind with curiosity and tremulous admiration; he could not put the thought of her aside on that first night. Her face was between him and the dry pages over which he pored. He was driven to rise once in the middle of wrestling with a problem in algebra and creep halfway down the stairs, just to watch her for a few minutes through the open door of the drawing-room, where the family sat at bridge and backgammon. Her presence in the house seemed to him a most lovely and disturbing thing, like a sudden strain of music.

He longed to touch her dress, which was of a material he could not remember having seen before, and of a color he could not name. He longed to touch her hands, the flesh of which looked so delicate and yet so firm. As he crouched over his uncongenial tasks in the untidy bedroom, strange thoughts and visions blurred the dog's-eared page before him. A chill breeze coming in at the window carried the sounds and scents of the late autumn countryside: the rustle of leaves that were losing their fresh resilience and becoming sapless and crisp; the scrape of two dead branches, one on the other, as though the oak tree to which they belonged strove to play a dirge for the dead summer; the fantastic tapping of a vine against the pane, dancing a skeleton dance to the eerie music of the oak; the smell of countless acres of land lying heavy and dank, stupefied by the approach of barrenness.

What did it all mean? Why had he been put into this strange confusion of faces, voices, bewildering sounds of night and day? Who was there in the world to love him and care for him as Alayne loved and cared for Eden? No one, he was sure. He belonged to the lonely, fretful sounds which came in at the window rather than to warm human arms and clinging human lips.

His mind dwelt on the thought of kissing the mouth of Eden's wife. He was submerged in an abyss of dreaming, his head sunk on his clenched hands. A second self, white and wraithlike, glided from his breast and floated before him in a pale greenish ether. He watched it with detached exultation in its freedom. It often freed itself from his body at times like these, sometimes disappearing almost instantly, at others floating near him as though beckoning him to follow. Now it moved face downward like one swimming, and another dim shape floated beside it. He pressed his knuckles into his eyes, drawing fiery colors from the lids, trying to see, yet afraid to see, the face of the other figure. But neither of the floating figures had a discernible face. One, he knew, belonged to him because it had emerged from his own body, but the other, fantastically floating, whence came it? Had it risen from the body of the girl in the drawing-room below, torn from her by the distraught questing of his own soul? What was she? What was he? Why were they here, all the warm-blooded hungry people, in this house called Jalna?

What was Jalna? The house, he knew very well, had a soul. He had heard it sighing, moving about in the night. He believed that from the churchyard sometimes the spirits of his father and his father's wives, his grandfather, and even the dead infant Whiteoaks, congregated under this roof to refresh themselves, to drink of the spirit of Jalna, that spirit which was one with the thin and fine rain that now began to fall. They pressed close to him, mocking him—the grandfather in hussar's uniform, the infants in long pale swaddling clothes.

His temples throbbed, his cheeks burned, his hands were clammy and very cold. He rose, letting his books fall to the floor, and went to the window. He knelt there and leaned across the sill, holding his hands out into the rain, in an attitude of prayer, his thin wrists projecting from the frayed edges of his sleeves.

By degrees peace descended on him, but he did not want to look back into the room. He thought of the nights when he had shared the bed with Piers. He had always been longing for the time when he might sleep in peace, free from his brother's tormenting. Now he felt that he would be glad of Piers's wholesome presence to protect him from his own thoughts.

Why did God not protect him? Finch believed desperately and yet gloriously in God. During the Scripture study at school, while other boys were languishing in their seats, his eyes were riveted on the pages that seemed to burn with the grandeur and terror of God. The words of Jesus, the thought of that lonely figure of an inspired young man, were beautiful to him, but it was the Old Testament that shook his soul. When the time came for questions and examinations in Scripture, Finch was so incoherent, so afraid of disclosing his real feelings, that he usually stood at the foot of the class.

"A queer devil, Finch Whiteoak," was the verdict of his schoolfellows, "not in it with his brothers." For Renny's athletic prowess was still remembered; Eden's tennis, his running, his prize-winning in English literature and languages; Piers as captain of the Rugby team. Finch did nothing well. As he traveled back and forth to school in the train, slouching in a corner of the seat, his cap with the school badge pulled over his eyes, he wondered, with a bitterness unusual at his age, what he would do with his life. He seemed fitted for nothing in particular. No business or profession of which he had ever heard awakened any response of inclination in him. He would have liked to stay at home and work with Piers, but he quailed before the thought of a life subject to his brother's tyranny.

Sometimes he dreamed of standing in the pulpit of a vast, dim cathedral, such as he had seen only in pictures, and swaying a multitude by his burning eloquence. He, Finch Whiteoak, in a long white surplice and richly embroidered stole—a bishop—an archbishop, the very head of the Church, next to God Himself. But the dream always ended by the congregation's fleeing from the cathedral, a panic-stricken mob; for he had unwittingly let them have a glimpse of his own frightened, craven soul, howling like a poor hound before the terror of God.

"Wilt thou break a leaf driven to and fro? and wilt thou pursue the dry stubble?"

He was growing quieter now as he hung across the sill, letting the fine mist of rain moisten his hands and head. Below, on the lawn, a bright square of light fell from a window of the drawing-room. Someone came and stood at the window, throwing the shadow of a woman into the bright rectangle. Which of them? Meg, Pheasant, Alayne? Alayne, he felt sure. There was something in the poise. . . . Again he thought of her lips, of kissing them. He drew in his hands, wet with rain, and pressed them against his eyeballs.

"For thou writest bitter things against me, and makest me to possess the iniquities of my youth." Why could he remember these torturing texts, when nothing else would stay in his head? "Make me to hear joy and gladness; that the bones which thou hast broken may rejoice." He pressed his fingers closer, and there began going through his brain things that a Scotch laborer on the farm had told. The man had formerly been a factory hand in Glasgow. Finch remembered an endless jigging song he had sung in a kind of whisper, that had ribald words. He remembered a scene of which he had been an undiscovered witness.

It had been in the pine grove, the last remnant of the primeval forest thereabout. This grove was as dark as a church at twilight, and was hidden in the heart of a great sunny wood of silver birches, maples, and oak, full of bird song and carpeted with glossy wintergreen leaves, which in springtime were starred with windflowers and star-of-Bethlehem and tiny purple orchids. There was little bird song in the pine grove, and no flowers, but the air in there was always charged with the whisperings and the pungent scent of pine needles. The deeply shaded aisles between the trees were slippery with them, and there what little sunshine filtered in was richly yellow.

It was a place of deep seclusion. Finch liked nothing so well as to spend a Saturday morning there by himself, and give himself up to the imaginings that were nearly always free and beautiful among the pines.

He had gone there early on that morning to escape Meg, who had wanted him to do some disagreeable task about the house. He had heard her calling and calling as he had run across the lawn and dived into the shrubbery. He had heard her call to Wake, asking if he had seen him. He had stretched his long legs across the meadow and the pasture, leaped the stream, and disappeared from the sight of all into the birch wood. His pulses had been throbbing and his heart leaping with joy in his freedom. Among the gay, light-foliaged trees he had passed, eager for the depth and solitude of the pines, which with an air of gentle secrecy they seemed to guard. But he had found that he was not alone. In the dimmest recess, where the grove dipped into a little hollow, he had discovered Renny standing with a woman in his arms. He was kissing her with a certain fierce punctiliousness on the mouth, on the neck, while she caressed him with slavish tenderness. While Finch stood staring, they had parted, she smoothing the strands of her long hair as she hurried away, Renny looking after her for a space, waving his hand to her when she looked back over her shoulder and then sauntering with bent head toward home.

Finch had never been able to find out who that woman was, though he had looked eagerly in the faces of all the women he had met for a long time. He had even gone to the pine grove and lain there motionless for hours, hoping, yet fearing, that she and Renny would return, his heart beating expectantly at every sound; but they had never come. He often gazed with envious curiosity into Renny's lean red face, wondering what thoughts were in his head. Piers had observed once to him that women always "fell" for Renny. He could understand why, and he reflected forlornly that they would never fall for him.

He heard Wakefield calling to him plaintively from his bed: "Finch, Finch! Come here, please!"

He went down the hallway, passing Meg's door, which was covered by a heavy chenille curtain that gave an air of cozy seclusion to her sanctum.

"Well?" he asked, putting his head into Renny's room, where Wake sat up in bed, flushed and bright-eyed in the yellow lamplight.

"Oh, Finch, I can't sleep. My legs feel like cotton wool. When do you think Renny'll come?"

"How can I tell?" Finch answered, gruffly. "You go to sleep. That's all nonsense about your legs. They're no more cotton wool than mine are."

"Oh, Finch, please come in. Don't leave me alone! Just come and talk for a little while. Just a minute, *please*."

Finch came in and sat down on the foot of the bed. He took a lone, somewhat disheveled cigarette wrapped in silver paper from his pocket, unwrapped and lighted it.

Wake watched him, the strained look of loneliness passing from his little face.

"Give me a puff or two," he begged, "just a few puffs, please, Finch."

"No," growled Finch, "you'll make yourself sick. You're not allowed."

"Neither are you."

"Yes, I am."

"Well, not many."

"You don't call this many, do you?"

"I've seen you twice, no—three times before to-day."

Finch raised his voice. "You see a darned sight too much."

"Why, I'd never tell on you, Finch." Wake's tone was aggrieved. "I only want one little puff."

With a growl, Finch took the cigarette from his own lips and stuck it between his small brother's. "Now, then," he said, "make the best of your time."

Wake inhaled deeply, luxuriously, his eyes beaming at Finch through the smoke. He exhaled. Again, again. Then he returned the cigarette to its owner, still more battered and very moist. Finch looked at it doubtfully a moment, and then put it back philosophically into his own mouth. He felt happier. He was glad after all that Wake had called him. Poor little devil, he had his own troubles.

The darkness pouring into the room from the strange, dreamlike world outside had a liberating effect on the minds of the two boys. The tiny light of the candle, reflected in the mirror on the dresser, only faintly illuminated their faces, seeming to draw them upward from an immense void.

"Finch," asked Wake, "do you believe in God?"

A tremor ran through Finch's body at the question. He peered at the child, trying to make out whether he had divined any of his imaginings.

"I suppose I do," he answered. Then he asked, almost timidly, "Do you?"

"Yes. But what I'm wondering is—what kind of face has He? Has He a real face, Finch, or—just something flat and white where His face ought to be? That's what I think sometimes." Wake's voice had fallen to a whisper, and he pulled nervously at the coverlet.

Finch clutched his knees, staring at the candle that was now sputtering, almost out.

"His face is always changing," he said. "That's why you can't see it. Don't you ever try to see it, Wake; you're too young. You're not strong enough. You'd go nutty."

"Have you seen it, Finch?" This conversation was like a ghost story to Wake, frightening, yet exhilarating. "Do tell me what you've seen."

"Shut up," shouted Finch, springing up from the bed. "Go to sleep. I'm going." He lunged toward the door, but the candle had gone out and he had to grope his way.

"Finch, Finch, don't leave me," Wake was wailing.

But Finch did not stop till he reached his own bed, and threw himself face downward upon it. There he lay until he heard the others coming up the stairs.

XV. MORE ABOUT FINCH

The next morning a mild, steady wind was blowing, which had appropriated to itself every pungent autumn scent in its journeying across wood and orchard. It blew in at the window and gently stirred the hair on Finch's forehead, and brought to his cheeks a childish pink. He did not hurry to get up, but stretched at ease a while, for it was a Saturday morning. His morbid fancies of the night before were gone, and his mind was now occupied in making a momentous decision. Should he put on some old clothes and steal out of the house with only something snatched from the kitchen for breakfast, thus avoiding a meeting with Eden's wife, for this morning he was shy of her, or should he dress with extra care and make a really good impression on her by appearing both well turned out and at ease?

Those who were early risers would have had their breakfast by now and be about the business of the day, but Eden never showed up till nine, and Finch supposed that a New York girl would naturally keep late hours. He wanted very much to make a good impression on Alayne.

He got up at last, and, after carefully washing his face and hands and scrubbing his neck at the washstand, he took from its hanger his new dark blue flannel suit. When it was on and his best blue-and-white striped shirt, he was faced by the problem of a tie. He had a really handsome one of blue and gray, which Meggie had given him on his last birthday, but he was nervous about wearing it. Meg would be sure to get on her hind feet if she caught him sporting it on a mere Saturday. Even wearing the suit was risky. He thought he had better slip upstairs after breakfast and change into an old one. Perhaps he had better change now. He was a fool to try to please Alayne's fastidious New York eye. He hesitated, admiring his reflection in the looking glass. He longingly fingered the tie. The thought of going to Piers's room and borrowing one of his ties entered his mind, but he put it aside. Now that Piers was married, young Pheasant was always about.

Damn it all! The tie was his, and he would wear it if he wanted to.

He tied it carefully. He cleaned and polished his nails on a worn-out buffer Meggie had thrown away. Meticulously he parted and brushed his rather lank fair hair, plastered it down with a little pomade which he dug out of an empty jar Eden had thrown aside.

A final survey of himself in the glass brought a grin, half pleased, half sheepish, to his face. He sneaked past the closed door of his sister's room and slowly descended the stairs.

It was as he had hoped. Eden and Alayne were the only occupants of the dining room. They sat close together at one side of the table. His place was on Alayne's left. With a muttered "Good morning" he dragged forth his chair and subsided into it, crimson with shyness.

After one annoyed glance at the intruder, Eden vouchsafed him no attention whatever, speaking to Alayne in so low a tone that Finch, with ears strained to catch these gentle morning murmurings of young husband to young wife, could make out no word. He devoted himself to his porridge, humbly taking what pleasure he could draw from the proximity of Alayne. A fresh sweetness seemed to emanate from her. Out of the corner of his eye he watched the movements of her hands. He tried very hard not to make a noise over his porridge and milk, but every mouthful descended his throat with a gurgling sound. His very ears burned with embarrassment.

Alayne thought she had never before seen anyone eat such an immense plate of cereal. She hated cereals. She had said to Eden almost pettishly: "I do not want any cereal, thank you, Eden." And he had almost forced her to take it.

"Porridge is good for you," he had said, heavily sugaring his own.

He did not seem to notice that this breakfast was not at all the sort to which she was used. There was no fruit. Her soul cried out for coffee, and there was the same great pot of tea, this time set before her to pour. Frizzled fat bacon, so much buttered toast, and bitter orange marmalade did not tempt her. Eden partook of everything with hilarity, crunching the toast crusts in his strong white teeth, trying brazenly to put his arm about her waist before the inquisitive eyes of the boy. Something fastidious in her was not pleased with him this morning. Suddenly she found herself wondering whether if she had met him first in his own home she would so quickly have fallen in love. But one look into his mocking yet tender eyes, one glance at his sensitive, full-lipped mouth, reassured her. She would, oh yes, she would!

She addressed a sentence now and again to Finch, but it seemed hopeless to draw him into the conversation. He so plainly suffered when she attempted it that she gave up trying.

As they got up from the table Eden, who was already cherishing a cigarette between his lips, turned to his brother as if struck with an idea.

"Look here, Finch. I wish you'd show Alayne the pine grove. It's wonderful on a morning like this. It's deep and dark as a well in there, Alayne, and all around it grow brambles with the biggest, juiciest berries. Finch will get you some, and he'll likely be able to show you a partridge and her young. I've got something in my head that I want to get out, and I must have solitude. You'll take care of her, won't you, Finch?"

In spite of the lightness of his tone, Alayne discovered the fire of creative desire in it. Her gaze eagerly explored his face. Their eyes met in happy understanding.

"Do go off by yourself and write," she agreed. "I shall be quite content to wander about by myself if Finch has other plans."

She almost hoped he had. The thought of a tête-à-tête with this embarrassed hobbledehoy was not alluring. He drooped over his chair, his bony hands resting on the back, and stared at the disarranged table.

"Well," said Eden, sharply, "what are your plans, brother Finch?"

Finch grinned sheepishly. "I'd like to take her. Yes, thank you," he replied, gripping the back of the chair till his knuckles turned white.

"Good boy," said Eden. He ran upstairs to get a sweater coat for Alayne, and she and Finch waited his return in absolute silence. Her mind was absorbed by the thought that Eden was going to write. He had said one day that he had an idea for a novel. Little tremors of excitement ran through her as she pictured him beginning it that very morning. She stood in the bow window looking out at the dark hemlocks, from which issued a continuous chirping as a flock of swallows gathered for their flight south.

Rags was beginning to clear the table. His cynical light eyes took in every detail of Finch's attire. They said to the boy, as plainly as words: "Ho, ho, my young feller! You've decked yerself all up for the occasion, 'aven't yer? You think you've made an impression on the lidy, don't yer? But if you could only see yerself! *And* just you wait till the family catches you in your Sunday clothes. There won't be nothink doing, ow naow!"

Finch regarded him uncomfortably. Was it possible that these thoughts were in Rags's head, or did he just imagine it? Rags had such a secret sneering way with him.

Eden followed them to the porch. They met Meg in the hall, and the two women kissed, but it was dim there and Finch, clearing his throat, laid one hand on the birthday necktie and concealed it.

It was a day of days. As golden, as mature, as voluptuous as a Roman matron fresh from the bath, the October morning swept with indolent dignity across the land. Alayne said something like this to the boy as they followed a path over the meadows, and, though he made no reply, he smiled in a way that lighted up his plain face with such sudden sweetness that Alayne's heart warmed to him. She talked without waiting for him to reply, till by degrees his shyness melted, and she found herself listening to him. He was telling her how this path that led through the birch wood was an old Indian trail, and how it led to the river six miles away where the traders and Indians had long ago been wont to meet to barter skins of fox and mink for ammunition and blankets. He was telling her of the old fiddler, "Fiddler Jock," who had had his hut in this wood before the Whiteoaks had bought Jalna.

"My grandad let him stay on. He used to play his fiddle at weddings and parties of all sorts. But one night some people gave him such a lot of drink before he started for his hut that he got dazed, and it was a bitterly cold night, and he could not find his way home through the snow. When he got as far as Grandad's barnyard he gave up and he crawled into a straw stack and was frozen to death. Gran found him two days after when she was out for a walk. He was absolutely rigid, his frozen eyes staring out of his frozen face. Gran was a young woman then, but she's never forgotten it. I've often heard her tell of finding him. She had Uncle Nick with her. He was only a little chap, but he's never forgotten the way the old fellow had his fiddle gripped, just as though he'd been playing when he died."

Alayne looked curiously at the boy. His eyes had a hallucinated expression. He was evidently seeing in all its strangeness the scene he had just described.

They had now entered the pine grove. A shadow had fallen over the brightness of the morning like the wing of a great bird. In here there was a cathedral hush, broken only by the distant calling of crows. They sat down on a fallen tree, on the trunk of which grew patches of moss of a peculiarly vivid green, a miniature forest in itself.

"I don't believe I'd mind," said Finch, "going about with a fiddle and playing tunes at the weddings of country people. It seems to me I'd like it." Then he added, with a shade of bitterness in his tone, "I guess I've just the right amount of brains for that."

"I do not see why you should speak of yourself in that way," exclaimed Alayne. "You have a very interesting face." She made the statement with conviction, though she had just discovered the fact.

Finch made a sardonic grimace that was oddly reminiscent of Uncle Nicholas. "I dare say it's interesting, and I shouldn't be surprised if old Fiddler Jock's was interesting, especially when it was frozen stiff."

She felt almost repelled by the boy's expression, but her interest in him was steadily growing.

"Perhaps you are musical? Have you ever had lessons?"

"No. They'd think it a waste of money. And I haven't the time for practising. It takes all my time to keep from the foot of the form."

He seemed determined to present himself in an unprepossessing light to her. And this after all the anxious care over his toilet. Perhaps the truth was that, having seen a gleam of sympathy in her eyes, he was hungry for more of it. But it was difficult to account for the reactions of Finch Whiteoak.

Alayne saw in him a boy treated with clumsy stupidity by his family. She saw herself fiercely taking up cudgels for him. She was determined that he should have music lessons if her influence could bring them about. She drew him on to talk, and he lay on the ground, sifting the pine needles through his fingers and giving his confidence more freely than he had ever given it before. But even while he talked with boyish eagerness, his mind more than once escaped its leash and ran panting after strange visions. Himself, alone with her in this dark mysterious place, embracing her with ecstasy, not with the careless passion of Renny's caressing of the strange woman. After one of these excursions of the mind he would draw himself up sharply and try to look into her eyes with the same expression of friendly candor which she gave him.

As they were returning to the house and Alayne's thoughts were flying back to Eden, they came upon a group in the orchard consisting of Piers and several farm laborers, who, under his supervision, were preparing a number of barrels of apples for shipment. Piers, with a piece of chalk in his sunburned hand, was going about marking the barrels with the number of their grade. He pretended not to notice the approach of his brother and Alayne, but when he could no longer ignore them he muttered a sulky "Good morning," and turned to one of the laborers with some directions about carting the apples to the station.

Finch led Alayne from barrel to barrel with a self-consciously possessive air, knowing that the farm hands were regarding them with furtive curiosity. He explained the system of grading to her, bringing for comparison apples from the different barrels. He asked her to test the flavor of the most perfect specimen he could find, glossy, red, and flawless as a drop of dew.

"Mind that you replace that apple, Finch," said Piers curtly in passing. "You should know better than to disturb apples after they are packed. They'll be absolutely rattling about by the time they reach Montreal." He took a hammer from one of the men and began with deafening blows to "head in" a barrel.

Finch noticed Alayne's discomposure, and his own color rose angrily as he did as he was bid. When they had left the orchard Alayne asked: "Do you think Piers dislikes me?"

"No. It's just his way. He's got a beastly way with him. I don't suppose he dislikes me, but sometimes—" He could not finish what he had been going to say. One couldn't tell Alayne the things Piers did.

Alayne continued reflectively:—

"And his wife—I just noticed her a moment ago disappearing into the shrubbery when she saw us approach. I am afraid she does not approve of me either."

"Look here," cried Finch, "Pheasant's shy. She doesn't know what to say to you." But in his heart he believed that both Piers and Pheasant were jealous of Alayne.

He parted with her at the front door and went himself to the side entrance, for he was afraid of meeting his sister. He entered a little washroom next the kitchen—which served as a sort of downstairs lavatory for the brothers—to wash his hands. The instant he opened the door he discovered Piers already there, but it was not possible to retreat, for Piers had seen him. He was washing before going to the station with the fruit. His healthy face, still red from the towel, took on an unpleasant sneer.

"Well," he observed, "of all the asses I've ever known! The suit—the tie—the hair—good Lord! Has she taken you on as her dancing partner? Or what is your particular capacity? Pheasant and I want to know."

"Let me alone," growled Finch, moving toward the basin and twitching up his cuffs. "Somebody has to be decent to the girl, I guess."

Piers, drying his hands, moved close to him, surveying him jocularly.

"The tie, the hair, 'the skin you love to touch,'" he chuckled. "You are all the toilet advertisements rolled into one, aren't you?"

Finch, breathing heavily, went on lathering his hands.

Piers assumed the peculiarly irritating smile characteristic of Mr. Wragge.

"I do 'ope," he said, unctuously, "that the young lidy appreciates all your hefforts to be doggish, sir."

Goaded beyond bearing, Finch wheeled, and slapped a handful of soapy water full in his brother's face. A moment later Renny, entering the washroom, found young Finch sprawling on the floor, the birthday tie ruined by a trickle of blood from his nose.

"What's this?" demanded the eldest Whiteoak, sternly looking first at the recumbent figure, then at the erect, threatening one.

"He's too damned fresh," returned Piers. "I was chaffing him about dressing up as though he were going to a party when he was escorting Eden's wife to the bush, and he threw some dirty water in my face, so I knocked him down."

Renny took in the boy's costume with a grin, then he gently prodded him with his boot.

"Get up," he ordered, "and change out of that suit before it's mussed up."

When Finch had gone, he turned to Piers and asked: "Where is Eden this morning?"

"Oh, he's writing in the summerhouse, with a few sprays of lilies of the valley on the table beside him. Pheasant peeked in and saw him. I expect it's another masterpiece."

Renny snorted, and the two went out together.

XVI. "IN THE PLACE WHERE THE TREE FALLETH"

Alayne found Eden in the summerhouse, a vine-smothered, spiderish retreat, with a very literary-looking pipe in his mouth, his arms folded across his chest, and a thoughtful frown indenting his brow.

"May I come?" she breathed, fearing to disturb him, yet unable to endure the separation any longer.

He smiled an assent, gripping the pipe between his teeth.

"Have you begun the—you know what?"

"I do *not* know what."

"The n-o-v-e-l," she spelled.

He shook his head. "No; but I've written a corking thing. Come in and hear."

"A poem! I am so glad you are really beginning to write again. It is the first, you know, since we have been married, and I was beginning to be afraid that instead of being an inspiration—"

"Well, listen to this and tell me whether I'm the better or worse for being married."

"Before you begin, Eden, I should just like to remark the way the sunlight coming in through those vines dapples your hair and cheek with gold."

"Yes, darling, and if you had been here all morning you might have remarked how the insect life took to me. They let themselves down from every corner and held a sort of County Fair on me, judging spider stallions, fat ladybugs' race, and earwig baby show. In each case the first, second, third, and consolation prize was a bite of me."

"You poor lamb," said Alayne, settling herself on the bench beside him, her head on his shoulder. "How you suffer for your art!" She searched his face for the mark of a bite, and, really finding one on his temple, she kissed it tenderly.

"Now for the poem," he exclaimed. He read it, and it gained not a little from his mellow voice and expressive, mobile face. Alayne was somewhat disconcerted to find that she had no longer the power to regard his writing judicially. She now saw it colored by the atmosphere of Jalna, tempered by the contacts of their life together. She asked him to read it again, and this time she closed her eyes that she might not see him, but every line of his face and form was before her still, as though her gaze were fixed on him.

"It is splendid," she said, and she took it from him and read it to herself. She was convinced that it was splendid, but her conviction did not have the same austere clarity that it had carried when she was in New York and he an unknown young poet in Canada.

After that Eden spent each morning in the summerhouse, not seeming to mind the increasing dampness and chill as the autumn drew on. The

Whiteoaks seemed to be able to endure an unconscionable amount of either heat or cold. Alayne began to be accustomed to these extremes of temperature, to an evening spent before the blistering heat of the drawing-room fire, and a retiring to a bedroom so chill that her fingers grew numb before she was undressed.

From the summerhouse issued a stream of graceful, carelessly buoyant lyrics like young birds. Indeed, Piers with brutal jocularity remarked to Renny that Eden was like a sparrow, hatching out an egg a day in his lousy nest under the vines.

It became the custom for Eden, Alayne, Ernest, and Nicholas to gather in the latter's room every afternoon to hear what Eden had composed that morning. The four became delightfully intimate in this way, and they frequently—Nicholas making his leg an excuse for this—had Rags bring their tea there. As Grandmother could not climb the stairs, Alayne felt joyously certain of no intrusions from her. The girl found almost past endurance the old lady's way of breaking her cake into her tea and eating it from a spoon with the most aggravating snortlings and gurglings. It was pleasant to pour the tea in Nicholas's room for the three men from an old blue Coalport teapot that wore a heathenish woolly "cozy"; and after tea Nicholas would limp to the piano and play from Mendelssohn, Mozart, or Liszt.

Alayne never forgot those afternoons, the late sunshine touching with a mellow glow the massive head and bent shoulders of Nicholas at the piano, Ernest shadowy in a dim corner with Sasha, Eden beside her, strong in his shapely youth. She grew to know the two elderly men as she knew no other member of Eden's family except poor young Finch. They seemed close to her; she grew to love them.

Piers, when Meg told him of these meetings, was disgusted. They made him sick with their poetry and music. He pictured his two old uncles gloating imaginatively over Alayne's sleek young womanhood. Eden, he thought, was a good-for-nothing idler—a sponger. Meggie herself did not want to join the quartette in Uncle Nick's room. It was not the sort of thing she cared about. But she did rather resent the air of intimacy which was apparent between the uncles and Alayne, an intimacy which she had not achieved with the girl. Not that she had made any great effort to do so. Persistent effort, either mental or physical, was distasteful to Meg, yet she could, when occasion demanded, get her own way by merely exerting her power of passive stubbornness. But passive stubbornness will not win a friend, and as a matter of fact Meg did not greatly desire the love of Alayne. She rather liked her, though she found her hard to talk to,—"terribly different,"—and she told her grandmother that Alayne was a "typical American girl." "I won't have it," Grandmother had growled, getting very red, and Meg had hastened to add, "But she's very agreeable, Gran, and what a blessing it is that she has money!"

To be sure, there was no sign of an excess of wealth. Alayne dressed charmingly, but with extreme simplicity. She had shown no disposition to shower gifts upon the family, yet the family, with the exception of Renny and Piers, were convinced that she was a young woman of fortune. Piers did not believe it, simply because he did not want to believe it; Renny had cornered Eden soon after his return and had wrested from him the unromantic fact that he had married a girl of the slenderest means, and had come home for a visit while he "looked about him." And so strong was the patriarchal instinct in the eldest Whiteoak that Eden and Alayne might have lived on at Jalna for the rest of their lives without his doing more than order Eden to help Piers on the estate.

On one occasion Eden did spend a morning in the orchard grading apples, but Piers, examining the last of the consignment and finding the grading erratic, to say the least of it, had leaped in a fury into his Ford and rushed to the station, where he had spent the rest of the day in a railway car, wrenching the tops from barrels and regrading them. There had been a family row after this, with Renny and Pheasant on the side of Piers, and the rest of the family banded to protect Eden. They had the grace to wait till Alayne went to bed before beginning it. She had gone to her room early that night, feeling something electric in the air, and no sooner had her door closed than the storm burst forth below.

She had been brought up in an atmosphere of a home peaceful as a nest of doves, and this sudden transplanting into the noisy raillery and hawklike dissensions of the Whiteoaks bewildered her. Up in her room she quaked at the thought of her oddness among these people. When Eden came up an hour later he seemed exhilarated rather than depressed by the squall. He sat on the side of the bed, smoking endless cigarettes, and told her what this one had said and how he had squelched that one, and how Gran had thrown her velvet bag in Renny's face; and Alayne listened, languid in the reassurance of his love. He even sat down at his desk before he came to bed and wrote a wild and joyous poem about a gypsy girl, and came back to the bed and read it loudly and splendidly, and Nip, in Uncle Nick's room across the hall, started up a terrific yapping.

One of Eden's cigarette stubs had burned a hole in the quilt.

Lying awake long afterward, while Eden slept peacefully beside her, Alayne wondered if she could be the same girl who had labored over her father's book and paid decorous little visits to her aunts up the Hudson. She wondered, with a feeling of apprehension, when Eden was going to bestir himself to get a position. After the affair of the apples he spent more and more time in the summerhouse, for he had begun another long narrative poem. Proof sheets of his new book had arrived from New York, and they demanded their share of his time.

Alayne, who was supposed to be the inspiration of this fresh wellspring of poetry, found that during the fierce hours of composition the most helpful thing she could do for the young poet was to keep as far away from him as possible. She explored every field and grove of Jalna, followed the stream in all its turnings, and pressed her way through thicket and bramble to the deepest part of the ravine. She came to love the great unwieldy place, of which the only part kept in order was the farm run by Piers. Sometimes Finch or Wakefield accompanied her, but more often she was alone.

On one of the last days of autumn she came upon Pheasant, sitting with a book in the orchard. It was one of those days so still that the very moving of the sphere seemed audible. The sun was a faint blur of red in the hazy heaven, and in the north the smoke of a distant forest fire made a sullen gesture. This conflagration far away seemed to be consuming the very corpse of summer, which, being dead indeed, felt no pain in the final effacement.

Pheasant was sitting with her back against the bole of a gnarled old apple tree, the apples of which had not been gathered but were lying scattered on the grass about her. The ciderish smell of their decay was more noticeable here than the acrid smell of smoke. The young girl had thrown down her book and, with head tilted back and eyes closed, was more than half asleep. Alayne stood beside her, looking down at her, but Pheasant did not stir, exposing her face to the gaze of the almost stranger with the wistful unconcern of those who slumber. It seemed to Alayne that she had never before really seen this child—for she was little more than a child. With her cropped brown head, softly parted lips, and childish hands with their limply upturned palms, she was a different being from the secretive, pale girl always on her guard, whom Alayne met at table and in the drawing-room at cards. Then she seemed quite able to take care of herself, even faintly hostile in her attitude. Now, in this relaxed and passive pose, she seemed to ask for compassion and tenderness.

As Alayne was about to turn away, Pheasant opened her eyes, and, finding Alayne's eyes looking down into them with an expression of friendliness, she smiled as though she could not help herself.

"Hullo," she said, with boyish brevity. "You caught me asleep."

"I hope I did not waken you."

"Oh, I was only cat-napping. This air makes you drowsy."

"May I sit down beside you?" Alayne asked, with a sudden desire to get better acquainted with the young girl.

"Of course." Her tone was indifferent, but not unfriendly. She picked up her hat, which was half full of mushrooms, and displayed them. "I was gathering these," she said, "for Piers's breakfast. He can eat this many all himself."

"But aren't you afraid you will pick poison ones? I should be."

Pheasant smiled scornfully. "I've been gathering mushrooms all my life. These are all alike. The orchard kind. Except this dear little pink one. I shall give it to Wake. It's got a funny smoky taste and he likes it." She twirled the pink mushroom in her slim brown fingers. "In the pine woods I get lots of morels. Piers likes them, too, only not so well. Piers thinks it's wonderful the way I can always find them. He has them for breakfast almost every morning."

Everything was in terms of Piers. Alayne asked:—

"What is your book? Not so interesting as the mushrooms?"

"It's very good. It belongs to Piers. One of Jules Verne's."

Alayne had hoped that they might talk about the book, but she had read nothing of Jules Verne. She asked instead:—

"Have you known Piers many years? I suppose you have, for you were neighbors, weren't you?"

Pheasant stiffened. She did not answer for a moment, but bent forward plucking at the coarse orchard grass. Then she said in a low voice, "I suppose Eden has told you about me."

"Nothing except that you were a neighbor's daughter."

"Come, now. Don't hedge. The others did, then. Meg—Gran—Uncle Nick?"

"No one," answered Alayne firmly, "has told me anything about you."

"Humph. They're a funny lot. I made sure they'd tell you first thing." She mused a moment, biting a blade of grass, and then added: "I suppose they didn't want to tell you anything so shocking. You're so frightfully proper, and all that."

"Am I?" returned Alayne, rather nettled.

"Well, aren't you?"

"I had not thought about it."

"It was one of the first things I noticed about you."

"I hope it hasn't turned you against me," said Alayne, lightly.

Pheasant reflected, and said she did not think so.

"Then what is it?" persisted Alayne, her tone still light, but her face becoming very serious.

Pheasant picked up one of the misshapen apples of the old tree and balanced it on her palm.

"Oh, you're different; that's the principal thing. You don't seem to know anything about real life."

Alayne could have laughed aloud at the answer, that this ignorant little country girl should doubt her experience of life. Yet it was true enough that she did not know life as they in this backwater knew it, where no outside contacts modified the pungent vitality of their relations with each other.

She sat a moment in thought and then she said, gently:—

"You are mistaken if you think that I should be easily upset by anything you would care to tell me. Not that I want to urge your confidence."

"Oh, it's not a matter of confidence," exclaimed Pheasant. "Everybody in the world knows it but you, and of course you'll hear it sooner or later, so I may as well tell you."

She laid the apple on the grass, and, clasping her ankles in her brown hands, sat upright, with the air of a precocious child, and announced: "I'm illegitimate—what Gran in her old-fashioned way calls a bastard. There you are." A bright color dyed her cheeks, but she flung out the words with pathetic bravado.

"I am sorry," murmured Alayne, "but you do not suppose that that will affect my feelings for you, do you?"

"It does most people's." The answer came in a low husky voice, and she went on hurriedly: "My father was the only child of an English colonel. His parents doted on him. He was the delight of their old age. My mother was a common country girl and she left me on their doorstep with a note, exactly the way they do in books. They took me in and kept me, but it broke the old people's hearts. They died not long after. My father—"

"Did you live with him?" Alayne tried to make it easier for her by a tone of unconcern, but her eyes were filled with tears of pity for the child who in such quaint phraseology—"the delight of their old age," indeed—told of the tragedy of her birth.

"Yes, till I was married. He just endured me. But I expect the sight of me was a constant reminder—of what he'd lost, I mean."

"Lost?"

"Yes, Meg Whiteoak. He'd been engaged to her, and she broke it off when I appeared on the scene. That's why she has that glassy stare for me. All the Whiteoaks were against the marriage of course. It was adding insult to injury, you see."

"Oh, my dear."

The significance of looks and chance phrases that had puzzled her became apparent. She was pierced by a vivid pain at the thought of all the unmerited suffering of Pheasant.

"You have had rather a hard time, but surely that is all over. Meg cannot go on blaming you for what is not your fault, and I think the others are fond of you."

"Oh, I don't know."

"I should be if you would let me." Her hand moved across the grass to Pheasant's. Their fingers intertwined.

"All right. But I warn you, I'm not a bit proper."

"Perhaps I am not so proper as you think." Their fingers were still warmly clutched. "By the way, why doesn't Piers like me? I feel that it will not be altogether simple to be your friend when he is so—well, distant."

"He is jealous of you—for my sake, I think. I just think that, mind you; he's never said so. But I think he finds it pretty beastly that you should be thought so much of and me so little, and that you should be made so welcome and me so unwelcome, when after all we're just two girls, except that you're rich and I'm poor, and you're legitimate and I'm up against the bar sinister, and Piers has always taken such an interest in the place and worked on it, and Eden only cares for poetry and having his own way."

Alayne was scarlet. Out of the tangle of words one phrase menaced her. She said, with a little gasp: "Whatever made you think I was rich? My dear child, I am poor—poor. My father was a college professor. You know they are poor enough, in all conscience."

"You may be what you call poor, but you're rich to us," answered Pheasant, sulkily.

"Now listen," continued Alayne, sternly. "My father left me five thousand dollars insurance, and a bungalow which I sold for fourteen thousand, which makes nineteen thousand dollars. That is absolutely all. So you see how rich I am."

"It sounds a lot," said Pheasant, stolidly, and their hands parted and they both industriously plucked at the grass.

The significance of other allusions was now made plain to Alayne. She frowned as she asked: "What put such an idea into your head, Pheasant? Surely the rest of the family are not suffering from that hallucination."

"We all thought you were frightfully well off. I don't know exactly how it came about—someone said—Gran said—no, Meg said it was—" She stopped short, suddenly pulled up by a tardy caution.

"Who said what?" insisted Alayne.

"I think it was Uncle Nick who said—"

"Said what?"

"That it was a good thing that Eden—oh, bother, I can't remember what he said. What does it matter, anyhow?"

Alayne had to subdue a feeling of helpless anger before she answered, quietly: "It does not matter. But I want you not to have the notion that I am rich. It is ridiculous. It puts me in a false position. You knew that I worked for my living before I married Eden. Why did you think I did that?"

"We knew it was publishing books. It didn't seem like work."

"My child, I was not publishing. I only read manuscripts for the publisher. Do you see the difference?"

Pheasant stared at her uncomprehendingly, and Alayne, moved by a sudden impulse, put her arm about her and kissed her. "How silly of me to mind! May we be friends, then?"

Pheasant's body relaxed against her with the abandon of a child's. "It's lovely of you," she breathed, "not to mind about my—"

Alayne stopped her words with a kiss. "As though that were possible! And I hope Piers will feel less unfriendly to me when he knows everything."

Pheasant was watching over Alayne's shoulder two figures that were approaching along the orchard path.

"It's Renny," she said, "and Maurice. I wonder what they're up to. Renny's got an axe."

The men were talking and laughing rather loudly over some joke, and did not see the girls at once. Alayne sat up and stroked her hair.

"I'll bet it is some war joke," whispered Pheasant. "They're always at it when they're together." Pheasant took up an apple and rolled it in their direction. "Hullo, Maurice, why such hilarity?"

The two came up, Maurice removing his tweed cap. Renny, already bareheaded, nodded, the reminiscent grin fading from his face.

"Alayne," he said, "this is Maurice Vaughan, our nearest neighbor."

They shook hands, and Alayne, remembering having heard a reference to the fact that Vaughan drank a good deal, thought he showed it in his heavy eyes and relaxed mouth. He gave Pheasant a grudging smile, and then turned to Renny.

"Is this the tree?" he asked.

"Yes," returned Renny, surveying it critically.

"What are you going to do?" asked Alayne.

"Cut it down. It's very old, and it's rotting. It must make room for a new one."

Alayne was filled with dismay. To her the old apple tree was beautiful, standing strong and yet twisted with age in the golden October sunshine. From it seemed to emanate the spirit of all the seasons the tree had known, with their scents of fragile apple blossoms and April rains, of moist orchard earth and mellowing fruit. A lifetime of experience was recorded on its rugged trunk, the bark of which enfolded it in mossy layers, where a myriad tiny insects had their being.

She asked, trying not to look too upset, for she was never certain when the Whiteoaks would be amused at what they thought soft-heartedness or affectation, "Must it come down? I was just thinking what a grand old tree it is. And it seems to have borne a good many apples."

"It's diseased," returned Renny. "Look at the shape of the apples. This orchard needs going over rather badly."

"But this is only one tree and it is such a beautiful shape."

"You must go over to the old orchard. You will find dozens like this there." He pulled off his coat and began to roll up the sleeves from his lean, muscular arms. Alayne fancied that an added energy was given to his movements by her opposition.

She said nothing more, but with a growing feeling of antagonism watched him pick up the axe and place the first blow against the stalwart trunk. She imagined the consternation among the insect life on the tree at that first shuddering shock, comparable to an earthquake on our own sphere. The tree itself stood with a detached air, only the slightest quiver stirring its glossy leaves. Another and another blow fell, and a wedge-shaped chip, fresh with sap, sprang out on to the grass. Renny swung the axe with ease, it and his arms moving in rhythmic accord. Another chip fell, and another, and the tree sent up a groaning sound, as the blows at last penetrated its vitals.

"Oh, oh! Let me get my things," cried Pheasant, and would have darted forward to rescue her hat and mushrooms had not Vaughan caught her by the wrist and jerked her out of the way.

It seemed that the dignity of the gnarled old tree would never be shaken. At each blow a shiver ran through its far-spreading branches and, one by one, the remaining apples fell, but for a long time the great trunk and massive primal limbs received the onslaughts of the axe with a sort of rugged disdain. At last, with a straining of its farthest roots, it crashed to the ground, creating a gust of air that was like the last fierce outgoing of breath from a dying man.

Renny stood, lean, red-faced, triumphant, his head moist with sweat. He glanced shrewdly at Alayne and then turned to Vaughan.

"A good job well done, eh, Maurice?" he asked. "Can you give me a cigarette?"

Vaughan produced a box, and Pheasant, without waiting to be asked, snatched one for herself and, with it between her lips, held up her face to Vaughan's for a light.

"There's a bold little baggage for you," remarked Renny to Alayne, with an odd look of embarrassment.

Pheasant blinked at Alayne through smoke. "Alayne knows I've been badly brought up."

"I think the result is delightful," said Alayne, but she disapproved of Pheasant at that moment.

Pheasant chuckled. "Do you hear that, Maurice? Aren't you proud?"

"Perhaps Alayne doesn't realize that he is your happy parent," said Renny, taking the bull by the horns.

Vaughan gave Alayne a smile, half sheepish, half defiant, and wholly, she thought, unprepossessing. "I expect Mrs. Whiteoak has heard of all my evil doings," he said.

"I did not connect you two in my mind at all. I only heard to-day—a few minutes ago—that Pheasant had a father living. I had stupidly got the idea that she was an orphan."

"I expect Maurice wishes I were, sometimes," said Pheasant. "I don't mean that he wishes himself dead—"

"Why not?" asked Vaughan.

"Oh, because it's such fun being a man, even an ill-tempered one. I mean that he wishes he had no encumbrance in the shape of me."

"You encumber him no longer," said Renny. "You encumber me; isn't that so?"

"Will somebody please get my hat and book and mushrooms?" pleaded the young girl. "They're under the tree."

Renny began to draw aside the heavy branches, the upper ones of which were raised like arms in prayer. An acrid scent of crushed overripe apples rose from among them. His hands, when he had rescued the treasures, were covered by particles of bark and tiny terrified insects.

Vaughan turned toward home, and Pheasant ran after him, showing, now that they were separated, a demonstrative affection toward him that baffled Renny who was not much given to speculation concerning the feelings of his fellows.

As for Alayne, her mind was puzzled more and more by these new connections who were everything that her parents and her small circle of intimates were not. Even while their conduct placed her past life on a plane of dignity and reticence, their warmth and vigor made that life seem tame and even colorless. The response of her nature to the shock of this change in her environment was a variety of moods to which she had never before been accustomed. She had sudden sensations of depression, tinged with foreboding, followed by unaccountable flights of gayety, when she felt that something passionately beautiful was about to happen to her.

Renny, lighting a cigarette, looked at her gravely. "Do you know," he said, "I had no idea that you were so keen about that tree, or I should have left it as it was. Why didn't you make me understand?"

"I did not want to make too much fuss. I thought you would think I was silly. Anyone who knew me at all well would have known how I felt about it. But then—you do not know me very well. I cannot blame you for that."

His gaze on her face became more intense. "I wish I did understand you. I'm better at understanding horses and dogs than women. I never understand them. Now, in this case, it wasn't till the tree was down and I saw your face that I knew what it meant to you. Upon my word, I wouldn't have taken anything—why, you looked positively tragic. You've no idea what a brute I feel." He gave a rueful cut at the fallen tree to emphasize his words.

"Oh, don't!" she exclaimed. "Don't hurt it again!"

He stood motionless among the broken branches, and she moved to his side. He attracted her. She wondered why she had never noticed before how striking he was. But then, she had never before seen him active among outdoor things. She had seen him rather indifferently riding his roan horse. In the house she had thought of him as rather morose and vigilant, though courteous when he was not irritated or excited by his family; and she had thought he held rather an inflated opinion of his own importance as head of the house. Now, axe in hand, with his narrow red head, his red foxlike face and piercing red-brown eyes, he seemed the very spirit of the woods and streams. Even his ears, she noticed, were pointed, and his hair grew in a point on his forehead.

He, having thrown down the axe at her words of entreaty, stood among the broken branches, motionless as a statue, with apparently a statue's serene detachment under inspection. He scarcely seemed to breathe.

One of those unaccountable soarings of the spirit to which she had of late been subject possessed her at this moment. Her whole being was moved by a strange exhilaration. The orchard, the surrounding fields, the autumn day, seemed but a painted background for the gesture of her own personality. She had moved to Renny's side. Now, from a desire scarcely understood by herself, to prove by the sense of touch that she was really she and he was no one more faunlike than Renny Whiteoak, she laid her hand on his arm. He did not move, but his eyes slid toward her face with an odd, speculative look in them. He was faintly hostile, she believed, because of her supersensitiveness about the tree. She smiled up at him, trying to show that she was not feeling childishly aggrieved, and trying at the same time to hide that haunting and willful expectancy fluttering her nerves.

The next moment she found herself in his arms with his lips against hers, and all her sensations crushed for the moment into helpless surrender. She felt the steady thud of his heart, and against it the wild tapping of her own. At last he released her and said, with a rather whimsical grimace: "Did you mind so much? I'm awfully sorry. I suppose you think me more of a brute than ever now."

"Oh," she exclaimed quiveringly, "how could you do that? How could you think I would be willing–"

"I didn't think at all," he said. "I did it on the spur of the moment. You looked so–so–oh, I can't think of a word to describe how you looked."

"Please tell me. I wish to know," she said icily.

"Well–inviting, then."

"Do you mean consciously inviting?" There was a dangerous note in her voice.

"Don't be absurd! Unconsciously, of course. You simply made me forget myself. I'm sorry."

She was trembling all over.

"Perhaps," she said, courageously, "you were not much more to blame than I."

"My dear child–as though you could help the way you looked."

"Yes, but I went over to you, deliberately, when–oh, I cannot say it!" Yet, perversely she wanted to say it.

"When you knew you were looking especially lovely–is that what you mean?"

"Not at all. It's no use–I cannot say it."

"Why make the effort? I'm willing to take all the blame. After all, a kiss isn't such a terrible thing, and I'm a relation. Men occasionally kiss their sisters-in-law. It will probably never happen again unless, as you say, you brazenly approach me when–what *were* you trying to say, Alayne? Now I come to think of it, I believe I have the right to know. It might save me some stabs of conscience."

"Oh, you make it all seem ridiculous. You make me feel very childish–very stupid."

He had seated himself on the fallen tree. Now he raised his eyes contritely to hers.

"Look here. That's the last thing on earth I want to do. I'm only trying to get you not to take it too seriously, and I want all the blame."

Her earnest eyes now looked full into his, taking a great deal of courage, for his were sparkling, so full of interest in her, and at the same time so mocking.

"I see that I must tell you. It is this: I have had odd feelings lately of unrest, and a kind of anticipation, as though just around the corner some moving, thrilling experience were waiting for me. This sensation makes me reckless. I felt it just before I moved toward you, and, I think–I think–"

"You think I was playing up to you?"

"Not quite that. But I think you felt something unusual about me."

"I did, and I do. You're not like any woman I've ever known. Tell me, have you thought of me as—caring for you, thinking a good deal about you?"

"I thought you rather disliked me. But please let us forget about all this. I never want to think of it again."

"Of course not," he assented gravely.

With a stab of almost physical pain, she remembered that she had half unconsciously kissed him back again. Her face and neck were dyed crimson. With a little gasp she said: "Of the two I am the more to blame."

"Is this the New England conscience that I've heard so much about?" he asked, filled with amazement.

"I suppose so."

He regarded her with the same half-mocking, half-quizzical look in his eyes, but his voice deepened.

"Oh, my dear, you are a sweet thing! And to think that you are Eden's wife, and that I must never kiss you again!"

She could not meet his eyes now. She was afraid of him, and still more afraid of herself. She felt that the strange expectancy of mood that had swayed her during these weeks at Jalna was nothing but the premonition of this moment. She said, trying to take herself in hand:—

"I am going back to the house. I think I heard the stable clock strike. It must be dinner time." She turned away and began to walk quickly over the rough orchard grass.

It was significant of the eldest Whiteoak that he made no attempt to follow her, but sat with his eyes on her retreating form, confident that she would look back at him. As he expected, she turned after a dozen paces and regarded him with dignity but with a certain childlike pleading in her voice.

"Will you promise never to think of me as I have been this morning?" she asked.

"Then I must promise never to think of you at all," he returned with composure.

"Then never think of me. I should prefer that."

"Come, Alayne, you know that's impossible."

"Well, promise to forget this morning."

"It is forgotten already."

But, hurrying away through the orchard, she felt that if he could forget as easily as that it would be more terrible to her than if he had brooded on it in his most secret thoughts.

XVII. PILGRIM'S PROGRESS

Alayne had been accustomed to church, but the systematic upheaval of Sunday mornings at Jalna was a revelation to her. She had been used to the intellectual, somewhat detached worship of the Unitarian church, where, seated between her father and mother, she had followed reverently the minister's meticulous analyzation of the teachings of the man Jesus. She had listened, in a church that rather resembled a splendid auditorium, to the unaccompanied singing of a superb quartette. She had seen collection plates all aflutter with crisp American bank notes, and been scarcely conscious of the large congregation of well-groomed, thoughtful men and women.

When she had lived alone after the death of her parents, she had gone less regularly to church, attending the evening service rather than the morning, and when Rosamund Trent had come to live with her she had gone with still less regularity, for Rosamund was one of those who believe that churchgoing is for those who have nothing better to do.

At Jalna there was an iron rule that every member of the family should attend morning service unless suffering from extreme physical disability. Being only half sick would not do at all. One must be prostrated. Alayne had seen Meg almost stumble into the motor, dazed from headache, a bottle of smelling salts held to her nose, and sit through the entire services with closed eyes. She had seen young Finch dragged off, regardless of a toothache.

She was inclined to rebel at first, but when she found Eden slavishly acquiescent, she too succumbed. After all, she thought, there was something rather fine in such devotion, even though religion seemed to play so small a part in it. For the Whiteoaks were not, according to Alayne's standards, a religious family. In fact, she never heard the subject mentioned among them. She remembered the intelligent discussions on religious subjects in her father's house: Would Science destroy Religion? The quoting of Dean Inge, Professor Bury, Pasteur, and Huxley.

The only mention of the Deity's name at Jalna was when Grandmother mumbled an indistinguishable grace, or when one of the young men called on the Almighty to witness that he would do such and such a thing, or that something else was damned. Yet with what heroism they herded themselves into those hard adjacent pews each Sunday!

Wakefield summed it all up for Alayne in these words:—

"You see, Grandfather built the church, and he never missed a Sunday till he died. Gran never misses a Sunday, and she's almost a hundred. She gets awfully sick if any of the rest of us stop home. And the rector and the farmers and other folk about count us every Sunday, and if one is missing, why, it doesn't seem like Sunday to them at all." The little boy's eyes were shining. He was very much in earnest.

Grandmother had never ridden in a motor car, and never expected to ride in one consciously. But she had given orders for the motor hearse from Stead to bear her body to her grave. "For," she said, "I like to think I'll have one swift ride before I'm laid away."

The old phaeton was brought to the front steps every Sunday morning at half-past ten. The two old bay horses, Ned and Minnie, were freshly groomed, and the stout stableman, Hodge, wore a black broadcloth coat with a velvet collar. With his long whip he flicked the flies off the horses, and every moment cast an anxious look at the door and set his hat at a more Sundayish angle.

At a quarter to eleven old Mrs. Whiteoak emerged, supported by Renny and Piers, for it needed plenty of muscle to negotiate the passage from her room to the phaeton. For church she always wore a black moiré silk dress, a black velvet fur-trimmed cloak, and voluminous widow's weeds of the heaviest crêpe. Alayne thought that the old lady never looked so dignified, so courageous, as she did on these occasions, when, like some unseaworthy but gallant old ship, her widow's veil billowing like a sail, she once again set forth from her harbor. When she was installed in a corner of the seat, with a cushion at her back, the old horses invariably made a forward plunge, for they were instantly aware of her arrival, and Rags as invariably, with a loud adjuration to Hodge to "'old 'ard," leaped to the horses' heads with a great show of preventing a runaway.

Her two sons next appeared: Nicholas, with a trace of his elegance of the old days; Ernest, mildly exhilarated, now that he had passed through the stage of preparation. The old phaeton creaked as their weight was simultaneously added to its burden. Then came Meg, usually flustered over some misdeed of Wake's or Finch's. The little boy made the last of the phaeton party, climbing to the seat beside Hodge, and looking, in comparison with that burly figure, very small and dignified in his snowy Eton collar and kid gloves.

The rest of the family followed in the motor car, excepting Finch, who walked through fields and lanes. He preferred to do this because there was not room for him in either vehicle without squeezing, and it was hard enough for him to know what to do with his long legs and arms on ordinary occasions. He liked this Sunday walk by himself, alone with his own thoughts.

Renny drove the car, and it was his chief concern to overtake and pass the phaeton as soon as possible, for if he did not accomplish this before the narrow sloping Evandale road was reached, it was probable that the rest of the drive would take place behind the slow-trotting horses, for Grandmother would not allow Hodge to move aside so that a motor might pass her on the road. She did not want to end her days in a ditch, she said. And she would sit with the utmost composure while Renny's car, with perhaps half a dozen others behind it, moved at a funeral pace, urging her onward with despairing honkings of their horns.

This morning was one such occasion. The drowsy Indian summer heat still continued, but the air had become heavier. The various odors from the earth and fields did not mingle or move about, but hung like palpable essences above the spot from which they rose. All objects were veiled in a thick yellowish haze, and the road dust stirred by the horses' hoofs descended in an opaque cloud on the motor behind.

It was the morning after the scene in the orchard. Alayne had slept little. All night, as she lay tossing, changing sharply from one position to another as the recollection of Renny's kisses made her cheeks burn and her nerves quiver, she had tried to see her position clearly, to ascertain whether she had been truly culpable or merely the passive object of Renny's calculated passion. But here in Jalna she found that she could not think with the same freedom of initiative as formerly. Fantastic visions floated between her and the situation she was trying to puzzle out. At last, in the pale abnormal earth light before the dawn, a friendly languor enfolded her and she sank into a quiet sleep.

Now, sitting behind Renny, she saw only the side of his face when he turned it momentarily toward Piers. She saw his thin cheek bone, the patch of reddish hair at his temple, and the compressed line of his lip and chin. Had he slept soundly, giving scarcely a second thought to what had so disturbed her? He had not appeared at dinner, tea, or supper, sending a message to the house that he and Maurice Vaughan had gone together to a sale of horses. This morning the determination to pass his grandmother's chariot before it reached the Evandale road seemed to absorb him. Pheasant had kept them waiting, and on her he threw a black look as she scrambled into the car.

The engine balked, then started jarringly. Eden, sitting between the girls, took a hand of each and exclaimed: "Oh, my dears, let us cling together! We will come through this safely if we only cling together. Pheasant, give me your little paw."

But, speed though the eldest Whiteoak did, he could not overtake his grandmother before she reached the Evandale road. There was the phaeton creaking along in leisurely fashion in a cloud of yellow dust, resembling an old bark in a heavy fog, Grandmother's veil streaming like a black pirate flag.

Renny, with half-closed eyes, squinted down the road where it dropped steeply into a dusty ditch, gray with thistles. "I believe I could get by," he muttered to Piers. "I've a mind to try."

The occupants of the phaeton recognized the peculiar squeakings of the family motor. They turned their heads, peering out of the dust fog like mariners sighting a hostile craft. Renny emphatically sounded his horn.

They could hear Grandmother shout to Hodge. At once the two old horses were restrained to a walk.

"By Judas!" exclaimed Renny. "I'd like to give the old lady a bump!"

Again he cast his eyes along the narrow strip of road between the phaeton wheels and the ditch. "I believe I'll risk it," he said. "Just go by like the devil and give them a scare."

Piers protested: "You'll put us headfirst into those thistles if you do. And you might frighten the nags."

"True," said Renny, gloomily, and sounded his horn with passionate repetition. Grandmother's face glared out of the fog.

"No back chat!" she shouted; but it was evident that she was enjoying herself immensely.

Farmer Tompkins and Farmer Gregg drew up their respective cars behind, and sounded their horns simultaneously. The eldest Whiteoak frowned. It was all very well for him to torment his ancient relative, but these yokels should not. He slumped in his seat, resigning himself to the progress of a snail. He took off his hat.

The sight of his narrow head suddenly bared, the pointed ears lying close against the closely cropped red hair, had a remarkable and devastating effect on Alayne. She wanted to reach forward, put a hand on either side of it and hold it tightly. She desired to stroke it, to caress it. She gave a frightened look toward Eden, as though to implore him to cast out these devils that were destroying her. He smiled back encouragingly. "We shall arrive," he said, "in God's good time. Behind us is Tompkins, who is a churchwarden, and he's suffering torture at the thought of being late. I've known him since I was three and he has only been twice late in all that time, and on each occasion it was Gran's fault. Tompkins is much worse off than we are."

Alayne scarcely heard what he said, but she slipped her hand in his and clung to it. She was lost in speculation about what thoughts might be in that head toward which her hands were yearning. Were they of her, or had the scene in the orchard been only one of many careless encounters with women? She believed that last was not so, for he had avoided the house for the rest of the day, and this morning had palpably avoided her. There was a sombre melancholy in his face as she caught a glimpse of his reflection in the little mirror before him. But perhaps that was only because he was baffled by old Mrs. Whiteoak.

What had he done to her that had filled her with such unrest? She had got up in the night and crept to the window and, in the mystery of the moonlight, seen the orchard, and even been able to discern the curving bulk of the tree he had felled. She had felt again the hot passion of his kisses.

One thing of which she was keenly sensible this morning was her new intimacy with Pheasant. Every time their eyes met, the young girl gave her a little smile, ingenuous as a child's. Alayne even fancied that Piers was less surly with her than formerly. She had told Eden of the talk with Pheasant, and he had seemed rather amused at Alayne's desire to make friends with her. "She's a dear quaint kid," he had remarked. "But she'll soon bore you. However, perhaps you're so bored already that even the company of Pheasant—"

"Nonsense," she had interrupted, more shortly than she had ever before spoken to him. "I am not bored at all, but Pheasant attracts me. I think I could become very fond of her. She has unusual possibilities."

Now Eden sat between them, holding a hand of each and smiling tolerantly. He did not care if they never got to church.

The bell was ringing as the car chugged up the steep little hill and passed through the gate behind the church. Heads of people mounting the precipitous steps at the front could be seen bobbing upward, as though ascending from a well. Golden sunshine lay like a caress on the irregular green mounds and mossgrown headstones of the churchyard. There was one new grave, on the fresh sandy top of which a wreath of drooping flowers lay.

Wakefield came and put his hand into Alayne's.

"That's Mrs. Miller's grave," he said. "She had a baby, and they're both in there. Isn't it terrible? It was a nice little girl and they'd named it Ruby Pearl. However, Miller has five girls left, so it might be worse."

"Hush, dear," said Alayne, squeezing his hand. "Are you going to sit with me?"

Wakefield had taken pride in sitting by Alayne and finding, with a great fluttering of leaves, the places in the prayer book for her. Now he looked doubtful.

"I'd like to," he said, "but I think Meggie feels lonely at my leaving her. You see, I've sat beside her ever since I was very little and used to go to sleep with my head on her lap. Look, they're getting Granny out of the phaeton. I think I'd better rush over and see that the sexton's holding the door wide open."

He flew across the grass.

Old Mrs. Whiteoak shuffled, with scarcely perceptible progress, along the slat walk that led to the church door. Renny and Piers supported her, and Nicholas, Ernest, and Meg followed close behind, carrying her various bags, books, and cushions. Under her beetling rust-colored brows her piercing gaze swept the faces of those she passed. From side to side her massive old head moved with royal condescension. Sometimes her face was lighted by a smile, as she recognized an old friend, but this was seldom, for most of her friends were long dead. The smile flashed—the mordant and mischievous grin for which the Courts had been famous—at the Misses Lacey, daughters of a retired British admiral. "How's your father, girls?" she panted.

The "girls," who were sixty-four and sixty-five, exclaimed simultaneously: "Still bedridden, dear Mrs. Whiteoak, but *so* bright!"

"No right to be bedridden. He's only ninety. How's your mother?"

"Ah, dear Mrs. Whiteoak, Mamma has been dead nine years!" cried the sisters in unison.

"God bless me, I forgot! I'm sorry." She shuffled on.

Now the grin was bestowed on a bent laborer nearly as old as herself, who stood, hat in hand, to greet her, the fringe of silvery hair that encircled his pink head mingling with his patriarchal beard. He had driven Nicholas and Ernest about in their pony cart when they were little boys.

"Good morning, Hickson. Ha! These slats are hard to get over. Grip my arm tighter, Renny! Stop staring about like a fool, Piers, and hang on to me."

The old man pressed forward, showing his smooth gums in a smile of infantile complacence.

"Mrs. Whiteoak, ma'am, I just am wantin' to tell ye that I've got my first great-great-grandchild."

"Good for you, Hickson! You're smarter than I am—I haven't got even one great yet. Don't drag at me, Piers. One would think I was a load of hay—

ha! and you a cart horse. Tell Todd to stop clanging that bell. It's deafening me. Ha! Now for the steps."

Eden and Alayne had fallen in behind Pheasant and Meg, who had Wakefield by the hand. Alayne wondered what the Corys and Rosamund Trent would have thought if they could have seen her at that moment, moving in that slow procession, rather like courtiers behind an ancient queen. Already Alayne felt a family pride in the old lady. There was a certain fierce grandeur about her. Her nose was magnificent. She looked as though she should have a long record of intrigues, lovers, and duels behind her, yet she had been buried most of her life in this backwater. Ah, perhaps that was the secret of her strong individualism. The individualism of all the Whiteoaks. They thought, felt, and acted with Victorian intensity. They threw themselves into living, with unstudied sincerity. They did not philosophize about life, but no emotion was too timeworn, too stuffy, to be dragged forth by them and displayed with vigor and abandon.

Now they were in the cool, dim church.

The bell had ceased. They were ranged in two pews, one behind the other. Their heads, blond, brown, and gray, were bent. Grandmother's great veil fell across Wake's thin shoulders. She wheezed pathetically.

Little Miss Pink at the organ broke into the processional hymn. Wakefield could see, between the forms of those grown-ups before him, the white-clad figure of Mr. Fennel. How different he looked on Sunday, with his beard all tidy and his hair parted with moist precision! And there was Renny, surpliced too. How had he got into the vestry and changed so quickly? A Whiteoak always read the Lessons. Grandfather had done it for years. Then Father had had his turn. And Uncle Ernest still read them sometimes when Renny was away—all the time Renny had been at the War. Would Wakefield ever read them himself, he wondered? He pictured himself rolling out the words grandly, not in Renny's curt, inexpressive way.

A burst of melody rose from the Whiteoak pews. Strong voices, full of vitality, that bore down upon little Miss Pink and her organ like boisterous waves and swept them along, gasping and wheezing, while the choir tried vainly to hold back. And even Renny in the chancel was against the choir and with the family. The choir, with the organ so weak and Miss Pink so vacillating, had no chance at all against the Whiteoaks.

"Rend your heart, and not your garments, and turn unto the Lord your God: for he is gracious and merciful, slow to anger, and of great kindness, and repenteth him of the evil."

Mr. Fennel's voice was slow and sonorous. Heavy autumn sunshine lay in translucent planes across the kneeling people. Alayne had come to love this little church, its atmosphere of simplicity, of placid acceptance of all she questioned. She kept her eyes on the prayer book which Eden and she shared. Grandmother, in a husky whisper, directly behind them, was asking Meggie for a peppermint. When it was given to her she dropped it, and it rolled under the seat and was lost. She was given another, and sucked it triumphantly. The odors of the peppermint and of the stuff of her crêpe veil were exuded from her. Wakefield dropped his collection money, and Uncle Nick tweaked his ear. Piers and Pheasant whispered, and Grandmother poked at Piers with her stick. Renny mounted the step behind the brass eagle of the lectern and began to read the First Lesson.

"If the clouds be full of rain, they empty themselves upon the earth: and if the tree fall toward the south, or toward the north, in the place where the tree falleth, there it shall be.

"He that observeth the wind shall not sow; and he that regardeth the clouds shall not reap.

"As thou knowest not what is the way of the spirit, nor how the bones do grow in the womb of her that is with child: even so thou knowest not the works of God who maketh all."

The family stared at their chief as he read.

Old Mrs. Whiteoak thought: "A perfect Court! Look at that head, will you? My nose—my eyes. I wish Philip could see him. Ha, where's my peppermint? Must have swallowed it. How far away the lad looks. He's in his nightshirt—going to bed—time for bed—"

She slept.

Nicholas thought: "Renny's wasted here. Ought to be having a gay time in London. Let's see; he's thirty-eight. When I was that age—God, I was just beginning to hate Millicent! What a life!"

He heaved himself in his seat and eased his gouty knee.

Ernest thought: "Dear boy, how badly he reads! Still, his voice is arresting. I always enjoy old Ecclesiastes. I do hope there will not be plum tart for dinner—I shall be sure to eat it and sure to suffer. Mamma is dropping her peppermint—"

He whispered to her: "Mamma, you are losing your peppermint."

Meg thought: "I wish Renny would not get such a close haircut. How splendid he looks. Really, what strange things the Bible says. But very true, of course. How sweet Wake looks! So interested. He has the loveliest eyelashes. He's getting ready to kick Finch on the ankle—"

She bent over Wakefield, and laid a restraining hand on his leg.

Renny's voice read on:—

"Truly the light is sweet, and a pleasant thing it is for the eyes to behold the sun."

Eden thought: "He was a poet, the old chap who wrote that. 'Truly the light is sweet—and a pleasant thing it is for the eyes to behold—' Strange I never noticed before how lovely Pheasant is. Her profile—"

He shifted his position a little, so that he might the better see it.

Piers thought: "I wonder if that piece of land needs potash. I believe I'll try it. Don't see what the dickens can be wrong with the sick ewe. Walking in a circle, like a fool animal in a roundabout. Perhaps she's got gid or sturdy. Must have the vet to her. Let's see–fourteen and twenty-one is thirty-five, and seven is forty-two–owe Baxter forty-two. Pheasant daren't look at me–little rogue–darling little kid–"

He pressed his knee against hers, and looked at her under his lashes.

Pheasant thought: "How big and brown Piers's hands always look on Sunday! Regular fists. I like them that way, too. I wish Eden wouldn't stare. I know perfectly well he's thinking how dowdy I am beside Alayne. Oh, dear, how hard this seat gets! I shall never get used to churchgoing–I wasn't caught young enough. My whole character was completely formed when I married. Neither Maurice nor I have any religion. How nice it was to see him yesterday in the orchard–quite friendly he was, too. Now religion–take Renny: there he stands in his surplice, reading out of the Bible, and yesterday I heard him swearing like a trooper just because a pig ran under his horse. To be sure, it nearly threw him, but then, what good is religion if it doesn't teach forbearance? I don't think he is a bit better than Piers. I wish Piers wouldn't try to make me smile."

She bit her lip and turned her head away.

Wakefield thought: "I do hope there'll be plum tart for dinner–if there isn't plum tart, I hope there'll be lemon tart. . . . But Mrs. Wragge was in a terrible temper this morning. How glad I am I was in the coal cellar when she and Rags had their row! Why, he called her a–hold on, no, I'd better not think of bad things in church. I might be struck dead–dead as a doornail, the very deadest thing. How pretty the lectern is–how beautifully Renny reads. Some day I shall read the Lessons just like that–only louder–that is, of course, if I live to grow up. By stretching my legs very far under the seat in front, I can kick Finch's ankle. Now– Oh, bother Meggie, bother Meggie, always interfering– Bother her, I say!"

He looked up innocently into his sister's face.

Finch thought: "To-morrow is the algebra exam, and I shall fail–I shall fail. . . . If only my head did not get confused! If only I were more like Renny! Nothing in the world will ever tempt me to stand up behind the lectern and read the Lessons. What a beastly mess I'd make of it–"

He became conscious of the words his brother was reading.

"Rejoice, O young man, in thy youth; and let thy heart cheer thee in the days of thy youth, and walk in the ways of thine heart, and in the sight of thine eyes: but know thou, that for all these things God will bring thee into judgment."

Finch twisted unhappily in his seat. Why these eternal threats? Life seemed compact of commands and threats–and the magic of the words in which these old, old threats were clothed. The dark, heavy foreboding. Magic –that was it: their magic held and terrified him. . . . If he could but escape from the cruel magic of words. If he could only have sat by Alayne, that he might have touched her dress as they knelt!

He closed his eyes, and clenched his bony hands tightly on his thighs.

Alayne thought: "How strange his brogues look under his surplice! I noticed this morning how worn and how polished they are—good-looking brogues. . . . How can I think of brogues when my mind is in torment? Am I growing to love him? What shall I do in that case? Eden and I would have to leave Jalna. No, I do not love him. I will not let myself. He fascinates me—that is all. I do not even like him. Rather, I dislike him. Standing there before that brass thing, in his brogues—his red hair—the Court nose—that foxlike look—he is repellent to me."

She too closed her eyes, and pressed her fingers against them.

"Here endeth the First Lesson."

Then, with Miss Pink and the organ tremulously leading the way and the choir fatuously fancying themselves masters of the situation, the *Te Deum* burst forth from every Whiteoak chest save Grandmother's, and she was gustily blowing in a doze. From the deep baritone of Nicholas to the silver pipe of Wake, they informed the heavens and the earth that they praised the Lord and called Him Holy.

That night, after the nine o'clock supper of cold beef and bread and tea, with oatmeal scones and milk for Grandmother and Ernest (who, alas, had partaken of plum tart at dinner as he feared), Meg said to Alayne: "Is it true, Alayne, that Unitarians do not believe in the divinity of Christ?"

"What's that?" interrupted Grandmother. "What's that?"

"The divinity of Christ, Gran. Mrs. Fennel was telling me yesterday that Unitarians do not believe in the divinity of Christ."

"Nonsense," said Mrs. Whiteoak. "Rubbish. I won't have it. More milk, Meggie."

"I suppose you do not believe in the Virgin Birth, either," continued Meg, pouring out the milk. "In that case, you will not find the Church of England congenial."

"I like the service of your church very much," said Alayne, guardedly. There had been something that savored of an attack in this sudden question.

"Of course she does," said Mrs. Whiteoak, heartily. "She's a good girl. Believes what she ought to believe. And no nonsense. She's not a heathen. She's not a Jew. Not believe in the Virgin Birth? Never heard of such a thing in decent society. It's not respectable."

"Why talk of religion?" said Nicholas. "Tell us a story, Mamma. One of your stories, you know."

His mother cocked an eyebrow at him. Then, looking down her nose, she tried to remember a risqué story. She had had quite a store of these, but one by one they were slipping her memory.

"The one about the curate on his holiday," suggested Nicholas, like a dutiful son.

"Nick!" remonstrated Ernest.

"Yes, yes," said the old lady. "This curate had worked for years and years without a holiday. And—and—oh, dear, what comes next?"

"Another curate," prompted Nicholas, "who was also overworked."

"I think the boys should go to bed," said Meg, nervously.

"She'll never remember it," replied Renny, with calm.

"Oh, Wakefield is playing with the Indian curios!" cried Meg. "Do stop him, Renny!"

Renny took the child forcibly from the cabinet, gave him a gentle cuff, and turned him toward the door. "Now, to bed," he ordered.

"Let him say good-night, first!" shouted Grandmother. "Poor little darling, he wants to kiss his Gran good-night."

Boney, disturbed from slumber, rocked on his perch and screamed in far-away nasal tones:—

"Ka butcha! Ka butcha! Haramzada!"

Wakefield made the rounds, distributing kisses and hugs with a nice gauging of the character of the recipient. They ranged in all varieties, from a bearlike hug and smack to Gran, to a courteous caress to Alayne, a perfunctory offering of his olive cheek to his brothers, except Finch, to whom he administered a punch in the stomach which was returned by a sly but wicked dig in the short rib.

The Whiteoaks had a vocation for kissing. Alayne thought of that as she watched the youngest Whiteoak saluting the family. They kissed upon the slightest provocation. Indeed, the grandmother would frequently, on awakening from a doze, cry out pathetically:—

"Kiss me, somebody, quick!"

Ah, perhaps Renny had regarded the kissing of her in the orchard as a light thing!

A sudden impulse drew her to him where he stood before the cabinet of curios, a little ivory ape in his hand.

"I want to speak to you about Finch," she said, steadily.

The light was dim in that corner. Renny scanned her face furtively.

"Yes?"

"I like him very much. He is an unusual boy. And he is at a difficult age. There is something I should like you to do for him."

He regarded her suspiciously. What was the girl up to?

"Yes?" His tone was mildly questioning.

"I want you to give him music lessons. Music would be splendid for him. He is a very interesting boy, and he needs some outlet besides geometry and things like that. I am sure you will not be sorry if you do it. Finch is worth taking a great deal of trouble for."

He looked genuinely surprised.

"Really? I always thought him rather a dull young whelp. And no good at athletics, either. That would be some excuse for being at the bottom of his form most of the time. None of us think of him as 'interesting.'"

"That is just the trouble. Every one of you thinks the same about Finch, and in consequence he feels himself inferior—the ugly duckling. You are like a flock of sheep, all jumping the one way."

Her enthusiasm for Finch made her forget her usual dignified reticence, and with it her embarrassment. She looked at him squarely and accusingly.

"And you look on me as the bellwether, eh? If you turn my woolly wooden head in another direction, the others will follow. I am to believe that Finch will turn out to be the swan then?"

"I should not be surprised."

"And you think his soul needs scales and finger exercises?"

"Please do not make fun of me."

"I shall have the family in my wool, you know. They'll hate the strumming."

"They will get used to it. Finch *is* important, though none of you may think so."

"What makes you sure he has musical talent?"

"I am not sure. But I know he appreciates music, and I think he is worth the experiment. Did you ever watch his face when your uncle Nicholas is playing?"

"No."

"Well, he is playing now. From here you can see Finch quite clearly. Isn't his expression beautiful, revealing?"

Renny stared across the room at his young brother.

"He looks rather idiotic to me," he said, "with his jaw dropped and his head stuck forward."

"Oh, you are hopeless!" she said, angrily.

"No, I'm not. He's going to have his music and I am going to endure the curses of the family. But for my life and soul I can't see anything of promise in him at this moment. Now Uncle Nick, with the lamplight falling on that gray lion's head of his, looks rather splendid."

"But Finch—don't you see the look in his eyes? If only you could understand him—be a friend to him—" Her eyes were pleading.

"What a troubled little thing you are! I believe you do a lot of worrying. Perhaps you are even worrying about me?" He turned his intense gaze into her eyes.

Deep chords from the piano, Grandmother and Boney making love to each other in Hindu. The yellow lamplight, which left the corners of the room in mysterious shadow, isolated them, giving the low tones of their voices a significance that their words did not express.

A passionate unrest seized upon her. The walls of the room seemed to be pressing in on her; the group of people yonder, stolid, inflexible, full-blooded, arrogant, seemed to be crushing her individuality. She wanted to snatch the ivory ape from Renny's hands and hurl it into their midst, frightening them, making the parrot scream and squawk.

Yet she had just been granted a favor that lay near her heart: music for poor young Finch.

The contradictions of her temperament puzzled and amused the eldest Whiteoak. He discovered that he liked to startle her. Her unworldliness, as he knew the world, her reticence, her honesty, her academic ardors, her priggishness, the palpable passion that lay beneath all these, made her an object of calculated sexual interest to him. At the same time he felt an almost tender solicitude for her. He did not want to see her hurt, and he wondered how long it would be before Eden would most certainly hurt her.

"I have forgotten yesterday, as I promised. Have you forgiven?"

"Yes," she returned, and her heart began to beat heavily.

"But giving Finch those music lessons will never make up for cutting down the tree, I'm afraid. You've made me very tender-hearted."

"Are you sorry for that?"

"Yes. I have especial need of hardness just now."

The parrot screamed: "Chore! Chore! Haramzada! Chore!"

"What are you two talking about?" shouted Grandmother.

"Eastern lore," replied her grandson.

"Did you say the War? I like to hear about the War as well as anyone. Do you know the Buffs, Alayne? That was Renny's regiment. Did your country go to war, Alayne?"

"Yes, Mrs. Whiteoak."

"Yes, *Gran*, please!"

"Yes, Gran."

"Ah, I hadn't heard of it. Renny was in the Buffs. One of the most famous regiments in England. Ever hear of the Buffs, Alayne?"

"Not till I came to Jalna, Gran."

"What's that? What's that? Not heard of the Buffs? The girl must be mad! I won't have it!" Her face grew purple with rage. "Tell her about the Buffs, somebody. I forget the beginning of it. Tell her instantly!"

"I'll tell her," said Renny.

Nicholas put the loud pedal down. Grandmother fell into one of her sudden dozes, by which she always recaptured the strength lost in a rage.

They were boring, Alayne thought. They were maddening. They oppressed her, and yet a strange burden of beauty lay on the high-walled room, emanating from the figures disposed about it: Gran and Boney; Nicholas at the piano; Meg, all feminine curves and heavy sweetness; Piers and Eden playing cribbage; Sasha, curled on the mantelpiece.

"I must not get to care for you," Renny said, in a muffled voice. "Nor you for me. It would make an impossible situation."

"Yes," murmured Alayne, "it would be impossible."

XVIII. IN THE WIND AND RAIN

"Here's a letter from New York to say they've got the proofs all right," observed Eden. "They think the book will be ready by the first of March. Do you think that is a good time?"

"Excellent," said Alayne. "Is the letter from Mr. Cory?"

"Yes. He sends his regards to you. Says he misses you awfully. They all do. And he's sending you a package of new books to read."

Alayne was delighted. "Oh, I am so glad. I am hungry for new books. When I think how I used literally to wallow in them! Now the thought of a package of new ones seems wonderful."

"What a brute I am!" exclaimed Eden. "I never think of anything but my damned poetry. Why didn't you tell me you had nothing to read? I've seen you with books, and I didn't realize that they were probably forty years old. What have you been reading?"

"I've been working with Uncle Ernest a good deal. I like that; and I've been indulging in Ouija for the first time, fancy! And reading *Rob Roy* to Wake. I have not done badly."

"You darling! Why don't you simply jump on me when I'm stupid? Here you are, cooped up at Jalna, with no amusements, while it streams November rain, and I lose myself in my idiotic imaginings."

"I am perfectly happy, only I don't see a great deal of you. You were in town three days last week, for instance, and you went to that football match with Renny and Piers one day."

"I know, I know. It was that filthy job I was looking after in town."

"That did not come to anything, did it?"

"No. The hours were too beastly long. I'd have had no time for my real work at all. What I want is a job that will only take a part of my time. Leave me some leisure. And the pay not too bad. A chap named Evans, a friend of Renny's, who has something to do with the Department of Forestry, is going to do something for me, I'm pretty sure. He was overseas with Renny, and he married a relative of the Prime Minister."

"What is the job?"

Eden was very vague about the job. Alayne had discovered that he was very vague about work of any kind except his writing, upon which he could concentrate with hot intensity.

"I'm just a child," he would exclaim, "about worldly things. There's no use, Alayne, you'll never be able to make me grow up. You'll go on to the end of your days, making over your New York frocks, and getting shabbier and shabbier as to hats and shoes, and more and more resigned to—"

"Don't be so sure of that," she had answered with a little asperity. "I am not resigned by nature. As to being poor—according to Pheasant I am rich. At least, she says your family think I am."

He had been staggered. He could not imagine why the family should think so, except for the reason that they thought of all American girls as rich. As for Pheasant, she was a poisonous little mischief-maker, and he would speak to Piers about her.

Alayne had found that, when Eden was irritating, he annoyed her out of all proportion to his words—made her positively want to hurt him. Now, to save her dignity, she changed the subject.

"Eden, I sometimes wish you had gone on with your profession. You would at least have been sure of it. You would have been your own master—"

"Dear," he interrupted, "wish me an ill that I deserve, trample on me, crush me, be savage, but don't wish I were a member of that stuffy, stultifying, atrophying profession. It was Meggie who put me into it, when I was too young and weak to resist. But when I found out the effect it was having on me, thank God, I had the grit to chuck it. My darling, just imagine your little white rabbit spending his young life nosing into all sorts of mouldy lawsuits, and filthy divorce cases, and actions for damages to the great toe of a grocer by a motor driven by the president of the Society for the Suppression of Vice! Think of it!" He rumpled his fair hair and glared at her. "Honestly, I shouldn't survive the strain a week."

Alayne took his head to her breast and stroked it in her soft, rather sedate fashion.

"Don't, darling. You make me feel a positive ogre. And there's no hurry. I've drawn almost nothing from my account yet."

"I should hope not!" he exclaimed savagely.

She asked after a moment: "Will the books from Mr. Cory come straight here or shall we have to go to town for them?"

"It depends upon whether they are held up in the customs. If they are, we'll go in together for them. It will be a little change for you. God knows, you don't get much change."

They were in their own room. He was at his desk, and she standing beside him. He began searching through a box of stamps for a stamp that was not stuck to another one. He was mixing them up thoroughly, partially separating one from another, then in despair throwing them back into the box, in such disorder that she longed to snatch them from him and set them to rights, if possible, but she had learned that he did not like his things put in order. He had been helping Renny to exercise two new saddle horses, and he smelled of the stables. The smell of horses was always in the house; dogs were always running in and out, barking to get in, scratching at doors to get out; their muddy footprints were always in evidence in November. Alayne was getting accustomed to this, but at first it had been a source of irritation, even disgust. She would never forget the shock she had experienced when, coming into her bedroom one afternoon, she had discovered a shaggy, bobtailed sheep dog curled up on the middle of her bed.

She rather liked dogs, but she did not understand them. At home they had never had a dog. Her mother had kept goldfish and a canary, but Alayne had thought these rather a nuisance. She felt that she would like horses better than either dogs or canaries. She wished she could ride, but nothing had been said about her learning, and she was too reserved, too much afraid of being a trouble, to suggest it. Meg had never ridden since her engagement to Maurice had been broken off, but Pheasant rode like a boy.

Eden had at last detached a stamp. He held it against his tongue and then stuck it upside down on his letter.

Watching him, Alayne had a sudden and dispassionate vision of him as an old man, firmly established at Jalna, immovable, contented, without hope or ambition, just like Nicholas and Ernest. She saw him gray-headed, at a desk, searching for a stamp, licking it, fixing it, fancying himself busy. She felt desperately afraid.

"Eden," she said, still stroking his bright head, "have you been thinking of your novel lately? Have you perhaps made a tiny beginning?"

He turned on her, upsetting the box of stamps and giving the ink-pot such a jar that she was barely able to save it.

"You're not going to start bothering me about that, are you?" Rich color flooded his face. "Just when I'm fairly swamped with other things. I hope you're not going to begin nagging at me, darling, because I can't wangle the right sort of job on the instant. I couldn't bear that."

"Don't be silly," returned Alayne. "I have no intention of nagging. I am only wondering if you are still interested in the novel."

"Of course I am. But, my dear lady, a man can't begin a tremendous piece of work like that without a lot of thought. When I begin it I'll let you know." He took up his fountain pen and vigorously shook it. He tried to write, but it was empty.

"Isn't it appalling," he remarked, "how the entire universe seems after one sometimes? Just before you came in, that shelf over there deliberately hit me on the head as I was getting a book from the bookcase. I dropped the book, and, when I picked it up, the sharp corner of the dresser bashed me on the other side of the head. Now my pen's empty, and there is scarcely any ink!"

"Let me fill it for you," said Alayne. "I think there is enough ink."

She filled it, kissed the bumped head, and left him.

As she descended the stairs, she had a glimpse of Piers and Pheasant in a deep window seat on the landing. They had drawn the shabby mohair curtains before them, but she saw that they were eating a huge red apple, bite about, like children. Outside, the wind was howling and the rain was slashing down the windowpane behind them. They looked very jolly and care-free, as though life were a pleasant game. And yet, she reflected, they had their own troubles.

The front door was standing open, and Renny was in the porch, talking to a man whom Alayne knew to be a horse dealer. He was a heavy-jowled man with a deep, husky voice and little shrewd eyes. A raw blast, smelling of the drenched countryside, rushed in at the open door. The feet of the two men had left muddy tracks in the hall, and one of the clumber spaniels was critically sniffing over them. The other spaniel was humped up in the doorway, biting himself ferociously just above the tail. In the sullen twilight of the late afternoon she could not distinguish Renny's features, but she could see his weather-beaten face close to the dealer's, as they talked together.

After all, she thought, he was little better than a horse dealer himself. He spent more time with his horses than he did with his family. Half the time he did not turn up at meals, and when he did appear, riding through the gate on his bony gray mare, his shoulders drooping and his long back slightly bent, as likely as not some strange and horsey being rode beside him.

And the devastating fascination he had for her! Beside him, Eden upstairs at his desk seemed nothing but a petulant child. Yet Eden had bright and beautiful gifts, which Renny had neither the imagination nor the intellect to appreciate.

Rags's face, screwed up with misery, appeared around a doorway at the back of the hall.

"My word, wot a draft!" she heard him mutter. "It's enough to blow the tea things off the tr'y."

"I will shut the door, Wragge," she said, kindly, but, regarding her own offer with cold criticism as she stepped over the long plumed tail of a spaniel, she came to the conclusion that she had made it for the sole reason that she might stand in the doorway an instant with the gale blowing her, and be seen by Renny. After all, she did not quite escape the plumey tail. The high heel of her shoe pinched it sharply, and the spaniel gave an outraged yelp of pain. Renny peered into the hall with a snarl: someone had hurt one of his dogs. His rough red eyebrows came down over his beak of a nose.

"I was going to close the door," explained Alayne, "and I stepped on Flossie's tail."

"Oh," said Renny, "I thought perhaps Rags had hurt her."

The horse dealer's little gray eyes twinkled at her through the gloom.

She tried to close the door, but the other spaniel humped himself against it. He would not budge. Renny took him by the scruff and dragged him into the porch.

"Stubborn things, ain't they?" remarked the horse dealer.

"Thanks, Renny," said Alayne, and she closed the door, and found herself not alone in the hall, but out in the porch with the men.

Renny turned a questioning look on her. Now why had she done that? The wind was whipping her skirt against her legs, plastering her hair back from her forehead, spattering her face with raindrops. Why had she done such a thing?

Merlin, the spaniel, to show that there was no hard feeling, stood on his hind legs and put his paws against her skirt, licking up toward her face.

"Down, Merlin, down," said his master, and he added, perfunctorily,

"Alayne, this is Mr. Crowdy, the man who bought Firelight's foal. Crowdy, Mrs. Eden Whiteoak."

"Pleased to meet you," said Mr. Crowdy, removing his hat. "It's terrible weather, ain't it? But only what we must expect at this time of year. Rain and sleet and snow from now on, eh? You'll be wishing you was back in the States, Mrs. Whiteoak."

"We have cold weather in New York, too," said Alayne, wondering what the man must think of her. She felt sure that Renny saw through her, saw that he had a pernicious fascination that had drawn her, against her will, to the porch.

"Well," observed the horse dealer, "I must be off. Mrs. Crowdy, she'll have it in for me if I'm late to supper." He and Renny made some arrangement to meet at Mistwell the next day, and he drove off in a noisy Ford car.

They were alone. A gust of wind shook the heavy creeper above the porch and sent a shower of drops that drenched their hair. He fumbled for a cigarette and with difficulty lighted it.

"I felt that I had to have the air," she said. "I have been in all day."

"I suppose it does get on your nerves."

"You must have hated my coming out in the middle of your conversation with that man. I do not think I ever did anything quite so stupid before."

"It didn't matter. Crowdy was just going. But are you sure you won't take cold? Shall I get you a sweater out of the cupboard?"

"No. I am going in." But she stood motionless, looking at the sombre shapes of the hemlocks that were being fast engulfed by the approaching darkness. Thought was suspended, only her senses were alive, and they were the senses of elemental things—the rain, the wind, the engulfing darkness, the quiescent, imploring earth—

Was she in his arms—the rough tweed of his sleeve against her cheek—his lips pressing hers—his kisses torturing her, weakening her? No, he had not moved from where he stood. She was standing alone at the edge of the steps, the rain spattering her face as though with tears. Yet, so far as she was concerned, the embrace had been given, received. She felt the ecstasy, the relaxation of it.

He stood there immobile, silhouetted against the window of the library which had been, at that moment, lighted behind him. Then his voice came as though from a long way off.

"What is it? You are disturbed about something."

"No, no. I am all right."

"Are you? I thought you had come out here to tell me something."

"No, I had nothing to tell you. I came because—I cannot explain—but you and that man made a strange sort of picture out here, and I moved out into it unconsciously." She realized with an aching relief that he had not guessed the trick her senses had played her. He had only seen her standing rigid at the top of the wind-swept steps.

A long-legged figure came bounding along the driveway, leaped on to the steps, and almost ran against her. It was Finch back from school. He was drenched. He threw a startled look at them and moved toward the door.

"Oh, Finch, you *are* wet," said Alayne, touching his sleeve.

"That's nothing," he returned gruffly.

"You're late," remarked Renny.

"I couldn't get the earlier train. A bunch of us were kept in."

The boy hesitated, peering at them as though they were strangers whose features he wished to distinguish and remember.

"H-m," muttered Renny. "Well, you had better change into dry things and do some practising before tea."

His tone, abstracted and curt, was unlike his usual air of indolent authority. Finch knew that he was expected to move instantly, but he could not force his legs to carry him into the house. There was something in the porch, some presence, something between those two, that mesmerized him. His soul seemed to melt within him, to go out through his chest gropingly toward theirs. His body a helpless shell, propped there on two legs, while his soul crept out toward them, fawning about them like one of the spaniels, one of the spaniels on the scent of something strange and beautiful.

"You're so wet, Finch," came distantly in Alayne's voice.

And then in Renny's: "Will you do what I tell you? Get upstairs and change."

Finch peered at them, dazed. Then, slowly, his soul skulked back into his body like a dog into its kennel. Once more his legs had life in them.

"Sorry," he muttered, and half stumbled into the house.

Meg was coming down the stairway, and Rags had just turned on the light in the hall.

"How late you are!" she exclaimed. "Oh, what a muddy floor! Finch, is it possible you brought all that mud in? One would think you were an elephant. Will you please take it up, Wragge, at once, before it gets tramped in? How many times have I told you to wipe your boots on the mat outside, Finch?"

"I dunno."

"Well, really, this rug is getting to be a disgrace. You're late, dear. Are you starving?"

She was at the foot of the stairs now. She kissed him, and he rubbed his cheek, moist with rain, against hers, warm and velvety.

"M-m," they breathed, rocking together. Flossie, the spaniel, was scratching at the already much bescratched front door.

"What does Flossie want?" asked Meg.

"I dunno."

"Why, she wants to get out. Merlin must be out there. Was he there when you came in?"

"I didn't see him."

"Let Flossie out, Rags. She wants Merlin."

"No, don't let her out," bawled Finch. "She'll only bring more mud in. Put her in the kitchen."

"Yes, I believe that would be better. Put her in the kitchen, Rags."

Finch said: "I've got to do some practising."

"No, dear," replied his sister, firmly. "It's tea time. You can't practise now. It's time for tea."

"But, look here," cried Finch. "I shan't get any practising to-night, then. I've a lot of lessons to do."

"You shouldn't be so late coming home. That's one reason I didn't want you to have such an expensive teacher. It's so worrying when there's no opportunity for practising. But, of course, Alayne would have it."

"Darn it all!" bawled Finch. "Why can't I practise in peace?"

"Finch, go upstairs this instant and change into dry things."

The door of Gran's room opened and Uncle Nick put his head out.

"What's this row about?" he asked. "Mamma is sleeping."

"It's Finch. He is being very unruly." Meg turned her round sweet face toward Nicholas.

"You ought to be ashamed of yourself. And all the money which is being spent on your music! Get upstairs with you. You deserve to have your ears cuffed."

Finch, with his ears as red as though they had already had the cuffing, slunk up the stairs. Piers and Pheasant, still on the window seat, had drawn the curtains tightly across, so that they were effectually concealed, except for the outline of their knees, and their feet which projected under the edge. Finch, after a glance at the feet, was reasonably sure of their owners. What a lot of fun everyone had, but himself! Snug and dry before warm fires, or petting in corners.

He found Wakefield in his room, sprawled on the bed, reading *Huckleberry Finn*.

"Hullo," said the little boy politely. "I hope you don't mind me being here. I wanted to lie down a bit as I aren't very well, and yours is the only bed I can tumble up without Meggie minding."

"Why don't you tell her you're not well?" asked Finch, pulling off his soaked jacket.

"Oh, she'd fuss over me, keep me on the sofa where she could watch me. I like a little privacy as well as anyone."

He was eating marshmallows and he offered Finch one.

"Thanks," said Finch, who was ravenous. "You seem always to have marshmallows lately." He looked at him with sudden severity. "Does Meggie know you've always got them?"

Wake calmly bit into another. "Oh, I don't suppose so. Any more than she knows you've always got cigarettes about you." His eyes were on his book; one cheek was distended. He looked innocent, and yet, the little devil, it had sounded like a threat.

"You mind your own affairs," broke out Finch, "or I'll chuck you into the hall."

Wakefield's bright eyes were on him. "Don't be cross, Finch. I was only thinking how yellow your second finger looked when you took that marshmallow. You'd better scrub it with pumice stone before tea or someone may notice. You see, your hands are so large and bony that people notice them, and anyone knows that it takes more than one cigarette to give that orangy color."

"You see too damned much," growled Finch. "When you get to school you'll have some of the smugness knocked out of you."

"I dare say," agreed Wake, sadly. "I hope you won't let the other boys bully me, Finch."

"Why, look here, there are five hundred fellows in the school. Do you suppose I can keep an eye on you? I'll never even see you. You'll have to just shift for yourself."

"Oh, I'll manage somehow," said Wake.

Finch thought that Wake would probably be happier at school than he was. He hoped so, for he was very fond of this dark-skinned debonair little brother, so different from himself. In silence he took off his sodden socks, gave his feet a perfunctory rub with a frayed bath towel and threw it into a corner. His brain was going round like a squirrel in a cage. Finding Renny and Alayne alone in the dark rain-drenched porch had brought something to his mind, reminding him curiously of something. He could not think at first what it was, then he remembered. It was the time he had come upon Renny and the unknown woman in the pine wood.

It was not only finding Renny alone with a woman in a dim and sheltered spot, it was something in his attitude—an air of detached attentiveness, as though he were listening, waiting for something that the woman was to do. Some sort of signal.

Finch could not understand why it had affected him so deeply to discover Renny and Alayne in the porch together, unless it was that it had reminded him of that other time. He had been determined that Meg should not know that they were there. But why? There was nothing wrong in their being there together. It was simply that he himself had the kind of mind that—oh, Lord, he seemed to find possibilities of mystery, of evil, where no one else would see anything of import. He had a disturbed and beastly mind, there was no doubt about it. He deserved all the knocks that came his way. He had a horrible mind, he thought.

He did wish Meggie would let him practise his music lesson. Meggie was antagonistic toward the music lessons. No doubt about that. But if he had been taking from Miss Pink it would have been all right. God, women were strange beings!

He went to the drawer where his underclothes were kept, and fumbled hopelessly for a pair of socks that matched.

XIX. A VARIETY OF SCENES

The books from New York were held at the customhouse in the city. The day when the official card arrived informing Alayne of this, the country was so submerged in cold November rain that a trip into town to get them seemed impossible. Alayne, with the despair of a disappointed child, wandered about the house, looking out of first one window and then another, gazing in helpless nostalgia at dripping hemlocks like funeral plumes, then at the meadows where the sheep huddled, next at the blurred wood that dipped to the wet ravine, and last, from a window in the back hall, on to the old brick oven and the clothes drier and a flock of draggled, rowdy ducks. She thought of New York and her life there, of her little apartment, of the publishing house of Cory and Parsons, the reception room, the offices, the packing rooms. It all seemed like a dream. The streets with their cosmopolitan throngs, faces seen and instantly lost, faces seen more closely and remembered for a few hours, the splendid and terrible onward sweep of it. The image of every face here was bitten into her memory, even the faces of the farm laborers, of Rags, of the grocer's boy, and the fishmonger.

How quiet Jalna could be! It lay under a spell of silence, sometimes for hours. Now, in the hall, the only sound was the steady licking of a sore paw by the old sheep dog, and the far-away rattle of coals in the basement below. What did the Wragges do down there in the dim half light? Quarrel, recriminate, make it up? Alayne had seen Wragge, a moment ago, glide through the hall and up the stairs with a tray to Meg's room. Oh, that endless procession of little lunches! Why could not the woman eat a decent meal at the table? Why this air of stale mystery? Why this turgid storing up behind all these closed doors? Grandmother: Boney–India–crinolines–scandal–Captain Whiteoak. Nicholas: Nip–London–whiskey–Millicent–gout. Ernest: Sasha–Shakespeare–old days at Oxford–debts. Meggie: broken hearts–bastards–little lunches–cozy plumpness.

And all the rest of them, getting their rooms ready for their old age–stuffy nests where they would sit and sit under the leaky roof of Jalna till at last it would crash in on them and obliterate them.

She must get Eden away from here before the sinister spell of the house caught them and held them forever. She would buy a house with her own money and still have enough left to keep them for a year or two, until he could make a living from his pen. She would not have him tortured by uncongenial work. Above all, she must not be in the house with Renny Whiteoak. She no longer concealed from herself the fact that she loved him. She loved him as she had never loved Eden–as she had not known that she was capable of loving anyone. A glimpse of him on his bony gray mare would make her forget whatever she was doing. His presence in the dining room or drawing-room was so disturbing to her that she began to think of her feelings as dangerously unmanageable.

The clock struck two. The day was only half gone, and already it seemed as long as any day should be. The rain was now descending tumultuously. How such a rain would bounce again from the pavement in New York! Here it drove in unbroken shining strands like the quivering strings of an instrument. A stableman with a rubber cape thrown over his head came running across the yard, frightening the ducks, and clattered down the steps into the basement. A moment later Mrs. Wragge laboriously climbed the stairs from her domain and appeared in the hall.

"Please, Mrs. Whiteoak," she said, "Mr. Renny 'as sent word from the stables as 'e's goin' into town by motor this afternoon and if you'll send the card from the customs back by Wright, he says, he'll get them books from the States. Or was it boots? Bless me, I've gone and forgot. And there's nothink throws 'im into a stew like a herror in a message."

"It was books," said Alayne. "I will run up to my room and find the notice. Just come to the foot of the stairs and I'll throw it down to you."

The thought of having the books that evening exhilarated her. She flew up the stairs.

Eden was not writing as she expected but emptying the books out of the secretary and piling them on the bed.

"Hullo!" he exclaimed. "See what a mess I'm in. I'm turning out all these old books. There are dozens and dozens I never look at. Taking up room. Old novels. Old *Arabian Nights*. Even old schoolbooks. And *Boys' Own*. Wake may have those."

What a state the bed was in!

"Eden, are you sure they are not dusty?"

"Dusty! I'll bet they haven't been dusted for five years. Look at my hands."

"Oh, dear! Well, never mind. Renny's motoring into town and he will get the books from the customs. Oh, wherever *is* that card? I know I left it on the desk, and you have heaped books all over it. Really, Eden, you are the most untidy being I have ever known."

They argued, searching for the card, which was at last unearthed in the waste-paper basket. In the meantime the car had arrived at the door, and Mrs. Wragge was panting up the stairs with another message.

"'E says 'e's late already, 'm, and will you please send the card. He says it's not half bad out, if you'd like a ride to town. But indeed, 'm, I shouldn't go if I was you, for Mr. Renny, he drives like all possessed, and the 'ighway will be like treacle."

"Great idea," cried Eden. "We'll both go. Eh, Alayne? It'll do us good. I've been working like the devil. I can stir up Evans about the job, and you can do a little shopping. We'll have tea at The George and be home in time for supper. Will you do it, Alayne?"

Alayne would. Anything to be free for a few hours from the cramped and stubborn air of Jalna. Mrs. Wragge panted downstairs with the message.

Alayne had never in her life before gone away leaving her room in such disorder. Impossible to keep even a semblance of order in the place where Eden worked. When they were in their own house, oh, the little cool mauve-and-yellow room she would have for her own!

If Renny were disappointed at the appearance of Eden he did not show it. Husband and wife clambered, rain-coated, into the back seats under the dripping curtains. The wet boughs of the hemlocks swept the windows as they slid along the drive.

It was true that the master of Jalna drove "like all possessed." The highway was almost deserted. Like a taut wet ribbon it stretched before them, to their left alternate sodden woods, fields, and blurred outlines of villages; to their right, the gray expanse of the inland sea, and already, on a sandy point, a lighthouse sending its solitary beam into the mist.

Alayne was set down before a shop. "Are you sure you've plenty of money, dear?" and a half-suppressed grin from Renny. Eden was taken to the customhouse, and then the elder Whiteoak went about his own strange business among legginged, swearing hostlers, and moist smelling straw, and beautiful, satin-coated creatures who bit their mangers and stamped in excess of boredom.

Alayne bought a bright French scarf to send to Rosamund Trent, "just to show her that we have some pretty things up here—" two new shirts for Eden,—a surprise,—a box of sweets for Gran, another, richer, larger one for the family, a brilliant smock that she could not resist for Pheasant, and some stout woollen stockings for herself.

She found Eden and Renny waiting for her in the lobby of an upstairs tearoom. They chose a table near the crackling fire. In a corner on the floor Eden heaped Alayne's purchases on top of the package of books. There were quite eight books in the packet, he informed her, and he had had the devil's own time getting them out of the customs. They had been mislaid and it had taken six clerks to find them. Alayne's eyes gloated over them as they lay there. While they waited for their order, she told what she had bought and for whom—except the shirts, which were to be a surprise.

"And nothing for me?" pleaded Eden, trying to take her foot between his thick-soled boots.

"Wait and see." She sent a warm bright look toward him, trying to avoid Renny's dark gaze.

"Nor me?" he asked.

"Ha," said Eden, "there's nothing for you." And he pressed Alayne's foot.

"My God," he continued, as the waitress appeared with the tray. "The man has ordered poached eggs! Why didn't I?"

He looked enviously for a moment on the two harvest moons that lay on buttered toast before his brother, and then attacked his Sally Lunn and raspberry jam.

"What is that you have?" asked Renny, looking down his nose at Alayne's cake and ice cream.

"You seem to forget," she replied, "that I am an American, and that I haven't tasted our national sweet for months."

"I wish you would let me order an egg for you," he returned, seriously. "It would be much more staying."

Eden interrupted: "Do you know, brother Renny, you smell most horribly horsey?"

"No wonder. I've been embracing the sweetest filly you ever saw. She's going to be mine, too. What a neck! What flanks! And a hide like brown satin." He stopped dipping a strip of toast into the yolk of an egg to gaze ecstatically into space.

Alayne gave way. She stared at him, drank in the sight of the firelight on his carved, weather-beaten face, lost herself in the depths of his unseeing eyes.

"Always horses, never girls," Eden was saying rather thickly, through jam. "I believe you dream o' nights of a wild mane whipping your face, and a pair of dainty hoofs pawing your chest. What a bedfellow, eh, brother Renny?" His tone was affectionate and yet touched by the patronage of the intellectual toward the man who is interested only in active pursuits.

"I can think of worse," said Renny, grinning.

Safe from the wind and rain, the three talked, laughed, and poured amber cups of tea from fat green pots. Golden beads of butter oozed through the pores of toasted Sally Lunns and dimpled on little green plates. Plump currants tumbled from slices of fruit cake; and Alayne gave her share of icing to Eden. A pleasant hum of careless chatter buzzed around them.

"By the way," said Eden, "Evans wants me to stop in town all night. There is a man named Brown he wants me to meet."

"Anything doing yet?" asked Renny.

Eden shook his head. "Everything here is dead in a business way. The offices positively smell mouldy. But Evans says there's bound to be a tremendous improvement in the spring."

"Why?" asked Alayne.

"I really don't know. Evans didn't say. But these fellows have ways of telling."

"Oh, yes," agreed Renny, solemnly. "They know."

"Little boys," thought Alayne, "that's what they are, nothing but little boys where business—city business—is concerned. Believing just what they're told. No initiative. I know five times as much about business as they."

"So," went on Eden, "if you don't mind trusting yourself to Renny, old lady, I'll stop the night here and see this man. You'll just have to chuck those books back into the bookcase, and I'll look after them to-morrow. Too bad I left them all over the place."

"Oh, I'll manage." But she thought: "He doesn't care. He knows I shall have to handle a hundred dusty books, that the bed is all upset, they are even on the chairs and dresser, and he'll never give it a second thought. He's selfish. He's as self-centred as a cat. Like a lithe, golden, tortoise-shell cat;

and Renny's like a fox; and their grandmother is an old parrot; and Meggie is another cat, the soft purry kind that is especially wicked and playful with a bird; and Ernest and Nicholas are two old owls; and Finch a clumsy half-grown lamb—what a menagerie at Jalna!"

As Eden was putting her into the car he whispered: "Our first night apart. I wonder if we'll be able to sleep."

"It will seem strange," she returned.

He pushed his head and shoulders into the dimness inside and kissed her. The rain was slashing against the car. Her parcels were heaped on the seat beside her.

"Keep the rug about you. Are you warm? Now your little paw." He cuddled it against his cheek. "Perhaps you would sooner have sat in the front seat with Renny." She shook her head and he slammed the door, just as the car moved away.

They were off, through the blurred streaming streets, nosing their way through the heavily fumbling traffic. Cars that were like wet black beetles lurching homeward. Every moment Renny's hand, holding a cloth, slid across the glass. No modern improvements on the Jalna car. Then out of the town. Along the shore, where a black cavern indicated the lake and one felt suddenly small and lonely. Why did he not speak to her? Say something ordinary and comforting?

They were running into a lane, so narrow that there was barely room for the motor to push through. Renny turned toward her.

"I have to see a man in here. I shan't be more than five minutes. Do you mind?"

"Of course not." But she thought: "He asks me if I mind, after we are here. If that isn't like the Whiteoaks! Of course I mind. I shall perfectly hate sitting here in the chill dark, alone in this lashing rain. But he does not care. He cares nothing about me. Possibly forgets—everything—just as he promised he would—and I cannot forget—and I suffer."

He had plunged into the darkness and was swallowed as completely as a stone dropped into a pool. There was no sound of retreating footsteps. The stamp of a horse could scarcely have been heard above the wind and rain. At one moment she saw him bent in the doorway of the car; at the next he was apparently extinguished. But after a little she heard a dog bark and then the slam of a door.

She snuggled her chin into the fur about her neck and drew the rug closer. Then she discovered that he had left the door of the motor open. He did not care whether she was wet and chilled to the bone. She could have whimpered—indeed, she did make a little whimpering sound, as she leaned over the seat and clutched at the door. She could not get it shut. She sank back and again pulled the rug closer. It was as though she were in a tiny house in the woods alone, shut in by the echoing walls of rain. Supposing that she lived in a tiny house in the woods alone—with Renny, waiting for him now to come home to her—Oh, God, why could she not keep him out of her thoughts? Her mind was becoming like a hound, always running, panting, on the scent of Renny—Renny, Reynard the Fox!

She and Eden must leave Jalna, have a place of their own, before she became a different being from the one he had married. Even now she scarcely recognized herself. A desperate, gypsy, rowdy something was growing in her —the sedate daughter of Professor Knowlton C. Archer.

She clutched the cord with which the books were tied as though to save herself by it. She would try to guess the titles of the books, knowing what she did of the latest Cory publications. It would be interesting to see how many she could guess correctly. What should she say to him when he came back? Just be cool and distant, or say something that would stir him to realization of her mood, her cruelly tormented mood? Rather be silent and let him speak first.

He was getting into the car. From the black earthy-smelling void into which he had dropped, he as suddenly reappeared, dropping heavily on to the seat and banging the door after him.

"Was I long?" he asked in a muffled tone. "I'm afraid I was more than five minutes."

"It seemed long." Her voice sounded faint and far away.

"I think I'll have a cigarette before we start." He fumbled for his case, then offered it to her.

She took one and he struck a light. As her face was illumined, he looked into it thoughtfully.

"I was thinking, as I came down the lane, that if you weren't the wife of Eden, I should ask you if you would like to be my mistress."

The match was out, and again they were in darkness.

"A man might cut in on another man that way," he went on, "but not one's brother—one's half brother."

"Don't you recognize sin?" she asked, out of the faint smoke cloud that veiled her head.

"No, I don't think I do. At least, I've never been sorry for anything I've done. But there are certain decencies of living. You don't really love him, do you?"

"No. I just thought I did."

"And you do love me?"

"Yes."

"It's rotten hard luck. I've been fighting against it, but I've gone under." He continued on a note of ingenuous wonder. "And to think that you are Eden's wife! What hopelessly rotten luck!"

She was thinking: "If he really lets himself go and asks me that, I shall say yes. That nothing matters but our love. Better throw decency to the winds than have this tumult inside one. I cannot bear it. I shall say yes."

Life in a dark full tide was flowing all about them. Up the lane it swept, as between the banks of a river. They were afloat on it, two leaves that had come together and were caught. They were submerged in it, as the quivering reflections of two stars. They talked in low, broken voices. When had he first begun to love her? When had she first realized that all those exultant, expectant moods of hers were flaring signals from the fresh fire that was now consuming her? But he did not again put into words his desire for her. He, who had all his life ridden desire as a galloping horse, now took for granted that in this deepest love he had known he must keep the whip hand of desire. She, who had lived a life of self-control, was now ready to be swept away in amorous quiescence, caring for nothing but his love.

At last, mechanically he moved under the wheel and let in the clutch. The car moved slowly backward down the sodden lane, lumbered with elephantine obstinacy through the long grass of the ditch, and slid then, hummingly, along the highway.

They scarcely spoke until they reached Jalna, except when he said over his shoulder: "Should you care to ride? This new mare is just the thing for you. She's very young, but beautifully broken, and as kind as a June day. You'd soon learn."

"But didn't you buy her as a speculation?"

"Well—I'm going to breed from her."

"If you think I can learn—"

"I should say that you would ride very well. You have the look of it—a good body."

The family were at supper. Meg ordered a fresh pot of tea for the late comers.

"Could we have coffee instead?" asked Renny. "Alayne is tired of your everlasting tea, Meggie."

Nicholas asked: "What books did they send? I shouldn't mind reading a new novel. I'll have a cup of that coffee when it comes. Where did you get rid of Eden? Aren't you cold, child?"

His deep eyes were on them with a veiled expression, as though behind them he were engaged in some complicated thinking.

"Evans wanted him to stay in town," answered Renny, covering his cold beef with mustard.

"Do you think he will get Eden something?" asked his sister.

"Oh, I don't know. There's no hurry."

Ernest said peevishly: "As I was remarking just before you two came in, something must be done about the young cockerels. They crow, and they crow. I did not get a wink of sleep after gray daylight for them. I was told a month ago that they would soon be killed, and here they are still crowing."

"Ah, say," interrupted Finch, "don't kill all the pretty little Leghorn cockerels. They're so—"

"It doesn't matter to you, Finch," said Ernest, getting angry. "You sleep like a log. But this morning they were dreadful. The big Wyandottes experimented with every variety of crow, from a defiant clarion shout to a hoarse and broken 'cock-a-doodle-do,' and then the little Leghorns with their plaintive reiterations in a minor key, 'Cock-a-doo-doo'! It's maddening."

"You do it very badly," said his brother. "It's more like this." And in stentorian tones he essayed the crow, flapping his arms as wings. Piers and Finch also crowed.

"Then a hen," pursued Ernest, "thought she would lay an egg. Fully twenty times she announced that she thought she had better lay an egg. Then she laid the egg, squawking repeatedly, that the world might know what an agonizing and important task it was. Then her screams of triumph when it was accomplished! Worst of all, every cock and cockerel in the barnyard immediately crowed in unison."

"Each imagining, poor fool," said Nicholas, "that he was the father of the egg."

"I didn't hear them at all," said Meggie.

Ernest raised a long white hand. "If I had the whole gallinaceous tribe," he said, "between the forefinger and thumb of this hand, to-morrow's sun should rise upon a cockless and henless world."

A heavy thumping sounded on the floor of grandmother's room.

"Piers, go and see what she wants," said Meg. "I tucked her up quite an hour ago, and she dropped off instantly."

Piers went, and returned, announcing: "She wants to know who brought the rooster into the house. Says she won't have it. She wants Renny and Alayne to go and kiss her."

"Oh, I think she just wants Renny. I don't think she would trouble Alayne."

"She said she wanted them both to come and kiss her."

"Come along, Alayne," said Renny, throwing down his table napkin. They left the room together.

Just as they reached the bedroom door, a long sigh was drawn within. They hesitated, looking at each other. That quivering intake of breath went to their hearts. She was lying alone in there, the old, old woman with her own thoughts. Her fears perhaps. Of what was she thinking, stretched under her quilt, the old lungs dilating, contracting. They went in and bent over her, one on each side of the bed. She drew them down to her in turn and kissed them with sleepy, bewildered, yet passionate affection, her mouth all soft and sunken with the two sets of teeth removed.

As they tucked the bedclothes about her neck, she lay peering up at them, her eyes queerly bright under the night light, infinitely pathetic.

"Anything more, Gran?" asked Renny.

"No, darling."

"Quite comfy, Gran?" asked Alayne.

She did not answer, for she was again asleep.

Outside, they exchanged tender, whimsical smiles. They wished they did not have to return to the dining room. They loved each other all the more because of their pity for the old woman.

As Nicholas and Ernest separated for the night, Nicholas said in his growling undertone: "Did you notice anything about those two?"

Ernest had been blinking, but now he was alert at once.

"No, I didn't. And yet, now I come to think of it— What d'ye mean, Nick?"

"They're gone on each other. No doubt about that. I'll just go in with you a minute and tell you what I noticed."

The two stepped softly into Ernest's room, closing the door after them.

Renny, in his room, was sitting in a shabby leather armchair, with a freshly filled pipe in his hand. This particular pipe and this chair were sacred to his last smoke before going to bed. He did not light up now, however, but sat with the comfort of the smooth bowl in the curve of his hand, brooding with the bitterness of hopeless love on the soft desirability of the loved one. This girl. This wife of Eden's. The infernal cruelty of it! It was not as though he loved her only carnally, as he had other women. He loved her protectingly, tenderly. He wanted to keep her from hurt. His passion, which in other affairs had burst forth like a flamboyant red flower without foliage, now reared its head almost timidly through tender leaves of protectiveness and pure affection.

There she lay in the next room, alone. And not only alone, but loving him. He wondered if she had already surrendered herself to him in imagination. No subtle vein of femininity ran through the stout fabric of his nature that might have made it possible for him to imagine her feelings. To him she was a closed book in a foreign language. He believed that there were men who understood women because of a certain curious prying in their contacts with them. To him it was scarcely decent. He took what women gave him, and asked no questions.

There she lay in the next room, alone. He had heard her moving about in her preparation for bed. She had seemed to be moving things about, and he had remembered Eden's saying something about emptying out the bookcase. The blasted fool! Leaving her to handle a lot of heavy books. He had thought of going in to do it for her, but he had decided against that. God knows what might have come of it—alone together in there—the rain on the roof, the old mossgrown roof of Jalna pressing above them, all the passions that had blazed and died beneath it dripping down on them, pressing them together.

There she lay in the next room, alone. He pictured her in a fine embroidered shift, curled softly beneath the silk eiderdown like a kitten, her hair in two long honey-colored braids on the pillow. He got up and moved restlessly to the door, opened it, and looked out into the hall. A gulf of darkness there. And a silence broken only by the low rumble of Uncle Nick's snore and the rasping tick of the old clock. God! Why had Eden chosen to stay away to-night?

Wakefield stirred on the bed, and Renny closed the door and came over to him. He opened his eyes and smiled sleepily up at him.

"Renny—a drink."

He filled a glass from a carafe on the washstand, and held it to the child's mouth. Wake raised himself on his elbow and drank contentedly, his upper lip magnified to thickness in the water. He emptied the glass and threw himself back on the pillow, wet-mouthed and soft-eyed.

"Coming to bed, Renny?"

"Yes."

"Had your smoke?"

"Yes."

"M-m. I don't smell it."

"I believe I've forgotten it."

"Funny. I say, Renny, when you get into bed, will you play we're somebody else? I'm nervous."

"Rot. You go to sleep."

"Honestly. I'm as nervous as anything. Feel my heart."

Renny felt it. "It feels perfectly good to me." He pulled the clothes about the boy's shoulders and patted his back. "One would think you were a hundred. You're more trouble than Gran."

"May I go to the Horse Show with you?"

"I guess so."

"Hurrah. Did you buy the filly?"

"Yes."

"When will she be here?"

"To-morrow."

"If I aren't well, may I stay home from lessons?"

"Yes." Renny had no backbone to-night, Wake saw that. He could do what he liked with him.

"May I tell Meggie you said so?"

"I suppose."

"Who shall we be when you come to bed?"

"Well—no pirates or harpooners or birds of that sort. You be thinking up a nice quiet sociable pair while I have my smoke."

A muffled tread sounded in the hall, and a low knock on the door. Renny opened it on Rags, sleep-rumpled but important.

"Sorry to disturb you, sir, but Wright is downstairs. 'E's just come in from the stible and 'e says Cora's colt 'as took a turn for the worse, sir, and would you please 'ave a look at it."

Rags spoke with the bright eagerness of hired help who have bad news to tell.

This was bad indeed, for Cora was a new and expensive purchase.

"Oh, curse the luck," growled Renny, as he and Wright, with coat collars turned up, hurried through the rain, now only a chill drizzle, toward the stable.

"Yes indeed, sir," said Wright. "It's pretty hard luck. I was just going to put the light out and go to bed,"—he and two other men slept above the garage,—"when I saw she was took bad. She'd just been nursed too, and we'd give her a raw egg, but she sort of collapsed and waved her head about, and I thought I'd better fetch you. She'd seemed a bit stronger to-day, too."

Down in the stable it was warm and dry. The electric light burned clearly, —lamps in the house, electricity in the stables at Jalna,—and there was a pleasant smell of new hay. The foal lay on a bed of clean straw in a loose box. Its dam, in the adjoining stall, threw yearning and troubled glances at it over the partition. Why was not its tender nose pressing and snuffling against her? Why, when it suckled, did it pull so feebly, with none of those delicious buntings and furious pullings which, instinct told her, were normal and seemly?

Renny pulled off his coat, threw it across the partition, and knelt beside the foal. It seemed to know him, for its great liquid eyes sought his face with a pleading question in them. Why was it thus? Why had it been dropped from warm indolent darkness into this soul-piercing light? What was it? And along what dark echoing alley would it soon have to make its timid way alone?

Its head, large and carved, was raised above its soft furry body; its stiff foal's legs looked all pitiful angles.

"Poor little baby," murmured Renny, passing his hands over it, "poor little sick baby."

Wright and Dobson stood by, reiterating the things they had done for it. Cora plaintively whinnied and gnawed the edge of her manger.

"Give me the liniment the vet left," said Renny. "Its legs are cold."

He filled his palm with the liquid and began to rub the foal's legs. If only warmth and strength could pass from him into it! "By Judas," he thought, "perhaps there's some fiery virtue in my red head!"

He sent the two men to their beds, for he wanted to look after the foal himself, and they must have their sleep.

He rubbed it till his arms refused to move, murmuring encouragements to it, foolish baby talk: "Little colty—poor little young 'un—does she feel 'ittle bit better then?" and "Cora's baby girl!"

Comforting noises came from other stalls, soft blowings through wide velvety nostrils, deep contented sighs, now and again a happy munching as a wisp of left-over supper was consumed, the deep sucking-in of a drink. He took a turn through the passages between the stalls, sleepy whinnies of recognition welcoming him. In the hay-scented dusk he caught the shine of great liquid eyes, a white blaze on a forehead, a white star on a breast, or the flash of a suddenly tossed mane. God, how he loved them, these swift and ardent creatures! "Shall I ever see the foal standing tall and proud in her box like one of these?"

He went back to her.

Cora had lain down, a dark hump in the shadow of her stall. In her anxiety she had kicked her bedding into the passage, and lay on the bare floor.

The foal's eyes were half closed, but when Renny put his hand on its tawny flank, they flew wide open, and a shiver slid beneath his palm. He felt its legs. Warmer. He was going to save it. He was going to save it! It wanted to rise. He put his arms about it. "There—up she comes now!" It was on its feet, its eyes blazing with courage, its neck ridiculously arched, its legs stiffly braced. Clattering her hoofs, Cora rose, whinnying, and looked over the partition at her offspring. It answered her with a little grunt, took two wavering steps, then, as if borne down by the weight of its heavy head, collapsed again on the straw. "Hungry. Hungry. Poor old baby's hungry. She's coming, Cora. Hold on, pet." He carried the colt to its dam and supported it beneath her.

Oh, her ecstasy! She quivered from head to foot. She nuzzled it, slobbering, almost knocking it over. She nuzzled Renny, wetting his hair. She bit him gently on the shoulder. "Steady on. Steady on, old thing. Ah, the baby's got it. Now for a meal!"

Eagerly it began to suck, but had scarcely well begun when its heart failed it. The foal turned its head petulantly away. Cora looked at Renny in piteous questioning. It hung heavy in his arms. He carried it back, and began the rubbing again. It dozed. He dozed, his face glistening with sweat under the electric light.

But another light was penetrating the stable. Daylight, pale and stealthy as a cat, creeping through the straw, gliding along the cobweb-hung beams, penetrating delicately into the blackest corners. Impatient whinnies were flung from stall to stall. Low, luscious moos answered from the byre. The orchestra of cocks delivered its brazen salute to the dawn. The stallion's blue-black eyes burned in fiery morning rage, but the little foal's eyes were dim.

Renny bent over it, felt its legs, looked into its eyes. "Oh, that long, long, lonely gallop ahead of me," its eyes said. "To what strange pasture am I going?"

Wright came clattering down the stairs, his broad face anxious.

"How's the wee foal, sir?"

"It's dying, Wright."

"Ah, I was afraid we couldn't save her. Lord, Mr. Whiteoak, you shouldn't have stopped up all night! When I saw the light burning I was sure you had, and I came straight over."

Cora uttered a loud terrified whinny.

The two men bent over the foal.

"It's gone, Wright."

"Yes, sir. Cora knows."

"Go in and quiet her. Have it taken away. God! It came suddenly at the last."

The rain was over. A mild breeze had blown a clear space in the sky. It was of palest blue, and the blown-back clouds, pearl and amethyst, were piled up, one on another, like tumbled towers. Behind the wet boles of the pines a red spark of sunrise burned like a torch.

Renny pictured the soul of the foal, strong-legged, set free, galloping with glad squeals toward some celestial meadow, its eyes like stars, its tail a flaming meteor, its flying hoofs striking bright sparks from rocky planets. "What a blithering ass I am—worse than Eden. Writing poetry next. . . . All her foals—and theirs—generations of them—lost."

He went in at the kitchen door, and found young Pheasant, a sweater over her nightdress. She was sitting on the table eating a thick slice of bread and butter.

"Oh, Renny, how is the little colt? I wakened before daylight, and I couldn't go to sleep again for thinking of it, and I got so hungry, and I came down as soon as it was light enough, to get something to eat, and I saw the light under your door and I was sure it was worse. Wake called to me and he said Wright had come for you."

"Yes, Wright came."

He went to the range and held his hands over it. He was chilled through. She studied him out of the sides of her eyes. He looked aloof, unapproachable, but after a moment he said, gently:—

"Make me a cup of tea, like a good kid. I'm starved with the cold in that damned stable. The kettle's singing."

She slid from the table and got the kitchen teapot, fat, brown, shiny, with a nicked spout. She dared not ask him about the colt. She cut some fresh bread and spread it, thinking how strange it was to be in the kitchen at this hour with Renny, just like Rags and Mrs. Wragge. The immense, low-ceiled room, with its beamed ceiling and now unused stone fireplace, was heavy with memories of the past, long-gone Christmas dinners, christening feasts, endless roasts and boilings. The weariness, the bickerings, the laughter, the love-making of generations of servant maids and men. All the gossip that had been carried down with the trays, concerning the carryings on of those who occupied the regions above, had settled in this basement, soaked into every recess. Here lay the very soul of Jalna.

Renny sat down by the table. His thin, highly colored face looked worn. Straws clung to his coat. His hands, which he had washed at a basin in the scullery, looked red and chapped. To Pheasant, suddenly, he was not imposing, but pathetic. She bent over him, putting her arm around his shoulders.

"Is it dead?" she whispered.

He nodded, scowling. Then she saw that there were tears in his eyes. She clasped him to her, and they cried together.

XX. MERRY GENTLEMEN

Early in December, Augusta, Lady Buckley, came from England to visit her family. It would probably, unless her mother proposed to live forever, be the last Christmas the ancient lady would be on earth. At any rate, Augusta said in her letter, it would be the last visit to them in her own lifetime, for she felt herself too old to face the vagaries of ocean travel.

"She has said that on each of her last three visits," observed Nicholas. "She makes as many farewells as Patti. I'll wager she lives to be as old as Mamma."

"Never," interrupted his mother, angrily, "never. I won't have it. She'll never live to see ninety."

"Augusta is a handsome woman," said Ernest. "She has a dignity that is never seen now. I remember her as a dignified little thing when we were in shoulder knots."

"She always has an offended air," returned Nicholas. "She looks as though something had offended her very deeply in early infancy and she had never got over it."

Mrs. Whiteoak cackled. "That's true, Nick. It was on the voyage from India, when I was so sick. Your papa had to change her underthings, and he stuck her with a safety pin, poor brat!"

The brothers laughed callously, and each squeezed an arm of the old lady. She was such an entertaining old dear. They wondered what they should ever do without her. Life would never be the same when she was gone. They would realize then that they were old, but they would never quite realize it while she lived.

They were taking her for her last walk of the season. This always occurred on a mild day in December. After that she kept to the house till the first warm spring day. Peering out between the crimson curtains of her window, she would see something in the air that marked the day as the one for her last walk. "Now," she would exclaim, "here goes for my last walk till spring!" A thrill always ran through the house at this announcement. "Gran's going for her last walk. Hullo, there, what do you suppose? Gran's off for her last toddle, poor old dear."

She invariably went as far as the wicket gate in the hedge beside the drive, a distance of perhaps fifty yards. They had arrived at the gate now, and she had put out her hands and laid them on the warm and friendly surface of it. They shook a good deal from the exertion, so that a tremor ran through her into the gate and was returned like a flash of secret recognition. Those three had stood together at that gate nearly seventy years before, when she was a lovely-shouldered young woman with auburn ringlets, and they two tiny boys in green velvet suits with embroidered cambric vests, and cockscombs of hair atop their heads.

They stood leaning against the gate without speaking, filled for the moment with quaint recollections, enjoying the mild warmth of the sun on their backs. Then Ernest:—

"Shall we turn back, Mamma?"

Her head was cocked. "No. I hear horses' hoofs."

"She does, by gad," said Nicholas. "You've better ears than your sons, Mamma."

Renny and Alayne were returning from a ride. Like soft thunder the sound of their galloping swept along the drive. Then horses and riders appeared, the tall bony gray mare and the bright chestnut; the long, drooping, gray-coated figure of the man, and the lightly poised, black-habited girl.

"Splendid!" cried Nicholas. "Isn't she doing well, Ernie?"

"One would think she had ridden all her life."

"She's got a good mount," observed Renny, drawing in his horse, and throwing a look of pride over the chestnut and his rider.

Alayne's eyes were bright with exhilaration. In riding she had found something which all her life she had lacked, the perfect outdoor exercise. She had never been good at games, had never indeed cared for them, but she had taken to riding as a water fowl to the pond. She had gained strength physically and mentally. She had learned to love a gallop over frozen roads, against a bitter wind, as well as a canter in the temperate sun.

Renny was a severe master. Nothing but a good seat and a seemly use of the good hands nature had given her satisfied him. But when at last she rode well, dashing along before him, bright wisps of hair blown from under her hat, her body light as a bird's against the wind, he was filled with a voluptuous hilarity of merely living. He could have galloped on and on behind her, swift and arrogant, to the end of the world.

They rarely talked when they rode together. It was enough to be flying in unison along the lonely roads, with the lake gulls screaming and sweeping overhead. When they did speak it was usually about the horses. He kept a sharp eye on her mount, and when he tightened a girth for her, or adjusted a stirrup, a look into her eyes said more than any words.

Sometimes Eden and Pheasant and Piers rode with them, and once they were joined by Maurice Vaughan, to Pheasant's childlike delight. It was on this occasion that Eden's horse slipped on the edge of a cliff above the lake, and would have taken him to the bottom had not Renny caught the bridle and dragged horse and rider to safety. He had pushed Piers and Maurice aside to do this, as though with a fierce determination to save Eden himself. Did he covet the satisfaction, Alayne wondered afterward, of risking his life to save Eden's, to make up to him for winning the love of his wife, or was it only the arrogant, protective gesture of the head of the family?

Now at any time the bitterness of winter would descend on them. The rides would be few.

"Watch me," cried Grandmother. "I'm going back to the house now. This is my last walk till spring. Ha—my old legs feel wobbly. Hold me up, Nick. You're no more support than a feather bolster."

The three figures shuffled along the walk, scarcely seeming to move. The horses dropped their heads and began to crop the dank grass of December.

"You've no idea," said Renny, "how much the old lady and the two old boys mean to me."

His grandmother had reached the steps. He waved his riding crop and shouted: "Well done! Bravo, Gran! Now you're safe till spring, eh?"

"Tell them," wheezed Gran to Nicholas, "that when they've put their nags away they're to come and kiss me."

"What does she say?" shouted Renny.

Nicholas rumbled: "She wants to be kissed."

When they had installed their mother in her favorite chair, he said in a heavy undertone to Ernest:—

"Those two are getting in deeper every day. Where's it going to end? Where are Eden's eyes?"

"Oh, my dear Nick, you imagine it. You always were on the lookout for that sort of thing. I've seen nothing. Still, it's true that there is a feeling. Something in the air. But what can we do? I'd hate to interfere with an affair of Renny's. Besides, Alayne is not that sort of girl—"

"They're all that sort. Show me the woman who wouldn't enjoy a love affair with a man like Renny, especially if she were snatched up from a big city and hidden away in a sequestered hole like Jalna. I'd be tempted to have one myself if I could find a damsel decrepit enough to fancy me."

Ernest regarded his brother with a tolerant smile.

"Well, Nick, you have had affairs enough in your day. You and Millicent might be—"

"For God's sake, don't say that," interrupted Nicholas. "I'd rather be dead than have that woman about me."

"Ah, well—" Ernest subsided, but he murmured something about "a dashed sight too many affairs."

"Well, they're all over, aren't they?" Nicholas asked testily. "Ashes without a spark. I can't even remember their names. Did I ever kiss anyone in passion? I can't recall the sensation. What I am interested in is this case of Renny and Alayne; it's serious."

"He scarcely seems to notice her in the house."

"Notice her! Oh, my dear man—" Nicholas bit off the top of a cigar, and scornfully spat it out.

"Well, for an instance, when the young Fennels were in the other night, and the gramophone was playing, Alayne danced oftener with them and Eden, and even young Finch, than with Renny. I only saw her dance with him once."

Nicholas said, pityingly: "My poor blind old brother! They only danced together once because once was all they could stand of it. I saw them dancing in the hall. It was dim there. Her face had gone white, and her eyes—well, I don't believe they saw anything. He moved like a man in a dream. He'd a stiff smile on his face, as though he'd put it on for convenience: a mask. It's serious with him this time, and I don't like it."

"There will be a pretty row if Eden gets on to it."

"Eden won't notice. He's too damned well wrapped up in himself. But I wonder Meggie hasn't."

Ernest took up a newspaper and glanced at the date. "The seventeenth. Just fancy. Augusta will arrive in Montreal to-morrow. I expect the poor thing has had a terrible passage. She always chooses such bad months for crossing." He wanted to change the subject. It upset his digestion to talk about the affairs of Renny and Alayne. Besides, he thought that Nicholas exaggerated the seriousness of it. They might be rather too interested in each other, but they were both too sensible to let the interest go to dangerous lengths. He looked forward to seeing Augusta; he and she had always been congenial.

She arrived two days later. She had made the passage without undue discomfort, never indeed missing a meal, though most of the passengers had been very ill. She had become such a hardened traveler in her infancy that it lay almost beyond the power of the elements now to disarrange her.

Lady Buckley was like a table set for an elaborate banquet at which the guests would never arrive. Her costume was intricate, elegant, with the elegance of a bygone day, unapproachable. No one would ever dare to rumple her with a healthy hug. Even old Mrs. Whiteoak held her in some awe, though behind her back she made ribald and derisive remarks about her. She resented Augusta's title, pretended that she could not recall it, and had always spoken to her acquaintances of "my daughter, Lady Buntley—or Bunting—or Bantling."

Augusta wore her hair in the dignified curled fringe of Queen Alexandra. It was scarcely gray, though whether through the kindness of nature or art was not known. She wore high collars fastened by handsome brooches. She had a long tapering waist and shapely hands and feet, the latter just showing beneath the hem of her rather full skirt. That air of having never recovered from some deep offense, of which Nicholas had spoken, was perhaps suggested by the poise of her head, which always seemed to be drawn back as though in recoil. She had strongly arched eyebrows, dark eyes, become somewhat glassy from age, the Court nose in a modified form, and a mouth that nothing could startle from its lines of complacent composure. She was an extremely well preserved woman, who, though she was older than Nicholas or Ernest, looked many years younger. Since it was her fate to have been born in a colony, she was glad it had been India and not Canada. She thought of herself as absolutely English, refuting as an unhappy accident her mother's Irish birth.

She was most favorably impressed by Alayne. She was pleased by a certain delicate sobriety of speech and bearing that Alayne had acquired from much association with her parents.

"She is neither hoydenish nor pert, as so many modern girls are," she observed to her mother, in her deep, well-modulated voice.

"Got a good leg on her, too," returned the old lady, grinning.

Lady Buckley and Alayne had long conversations together. The girl found beneath the remote exterior a kind and sympathetic nature. Lady Buckley was fond of all her nephews, but especially of the young boys. She would tell old-fashioned stories, some of them unexpectedly blood-curdling, to Wakefield by the hour. She would sit very upright beside Finch while he practised his music lesson, composedly praising and criticizing, and the boy seemed to like her presence in the room. She endeared herself to Alayne by being kind to Pheasant. "Let us ignore her mother's birth," she said, blandly. "Her father is of a fine old English military family, and, if her parents were not married—well, many of the nobility sprang from illegitimate stock. I quite like the child."

It was soon evident that Meg resented her aunt's attitude toward Piers's marriage, her admiration for Alayne, and her influence over Finch and Wakefield. She first showed her resentment by eating even less than formerly at the table. It would have been a marvel how she kept so sleek and plump had one not known of those tempting secret trays carried to her by Rags, who, if he were loyal and devoted to anyone on earth, was loyal and devoted to Miss Whiteoak.

She then took to sitting a great deal with her grandmother with the door shut against the rest of the family, and a blazing fire on the hearth. The old lady thrived on the scorching air and gossip. There was nothing she enjoyed more than "hauling Augusta over the coals" behind her back. To her face she gave her a grudging respect. Since Augusta approved of Finch's music lessons, it was inevitable that his practising should prove a torture to the old lady.

"Gran simply cannot stand those terrible scales and chromatics," Meg said to Renny. "Just at the hour in the day when she usually feels her brightest, her nerves are set on edge. At her age it's positively dangerous."

"If the boy were taking lessons from Miss Pink," retorted Renny, bitterly, "the practising wouldn't disturb Gran in the least."

"Why, Renny, Gran never objected to his taking from Mr. Rogers! It doesn't matter to her whom he takes from, though certainly Miss Pink would never have taught him to hammer as he insists on doing."

"No, she would have taught him to tinkle out little tunes with no more pep than a toy music box. If the youngster is musical, he's going to be properly taught. Alayne says he's very talented."

The words were scarcely out before he knew he had made a fatal mistake in quoting Alayne's opinion. He saw Meg's face harden; he saw her lips curl in a cruel little smile. He floundered.

"Oh, well, anyone can see that he's got talent. I saw it long ago; that is why I chose Mr. Rogers."

She made no reply for a moment, but still smiled, her soft blue eyes searching his. Then she said:—

"I don't think you realize, Renny, how strange your attitude toward Alayne is becoming. You have almost a possessive air. Sometimes I think it would be better if Eden had never brought her here. I've tried to like her, but—"

"Oh, my God!" said Renny, wheeling, and beginning to stride away. "You women make me sick. There's no peace with you. Imagine the entire family by the ears because of a kid's music lessons!" He gave a savage laugh.

Meg, watching him flounder, was aware of depths she had only half suspected. She said:—

"It's not that. It's not that. It's the feeling that there's something wrong

—some sinister influence at work. From the day Eden brought the girl here I was afraid."

"Afraid of what?"

"Afraid of something in her. Something fatal and dangerous. First she wormed her way—"

" 'Wormed her way'! Oh, Meggie, for heaven's sake!"

"Yes, she did! She literally wormed her way into the confidence of the uncles. Then she captivated poor Finch. Just because she told him he was musical, he is willing to practise till he's worn out and Grannie is ill. Then she turned Wake against me. He won't mind a thing I say. And now you, Renny! But this is dangerous. Different. Oh, I've seen it coming."

He had recovered himself.

"Meggie," he said, stifling her in a rough tweed hug, "if you would ever eat a decent meal,—you know you literally starve yourself,—and ever go out anywhere for a change, you wouldn't get such ideas into your head. They're not like you. You are so sane, so well balanced. None of us has as sound a head as you. I depend on you in every way. You know that."

She collapsed, weeping on his shoulder, overwhelmed by this primitive masculine appeal. But she was not convinced. Her sluggish nature was roused to activity against the machinations of Alayne and Lady Buckley.

That evening when Finch went to the drawing-room to practise he found the piano locked. He sought Renny in the harness room of the stable.

"Look here," Finch burst out, almost crying, "what do you suppose? They've gone and locked me out. I can't practise my lesson. They've been after me for a week about it, and now I'm locked out."

Renny, pipe in mouth, continued to gaze in whole-souled admiration at a new russet saddle.

"Renny," bawled Finch, "don't you hear? They've locked me out of the drawing-room, and I met Rags in the hall and he gave one of his beastly grins and said, 'Ow, Miss W'iteoak 'as locked up that pianer. She's not goin' to 'ave any pianer playin' in the 'ouse till the old lidy's recovered. She's in a pretty bad w'y, she is, with all your rattlety-bangin'.' I'd like to know what I'm to do. I may as well throw the whole thing up if I'm not allowed to practise."

Renny made sympathetic noises against the stem of his pipe and continued to gaze at the saddle.

Finch drove his hands into his pockets and slumped against the door jamb. He felt calmer now. Renny would do something, he was sure, but he dreaded a row with himself the centre of it.

At last the elder Whiteoak spoke. "I'll tell you what I'll do, Finch. I'll ask Vaughan if you may practise on his piano. I'm sure he wouldn't mind. The housekeeper's deaf, so her nerves won't be upset. I'll have the piano tuned. It used to be a good one. Then you'll be quite independent."

Soon young Finch might be seen plunging through the ravine on the dark December afternoons to the shabby, unused drawing-room at Vaughanlands.

He brought new life to the old piano, and it, like land that had lain fallow for many years, responded joyfully to his labor, and sent up a stormy harvest of sound that shook the prismed chandelier. Often he was late for the evening meal, and would take what he could get in the kitchen from Mrs. Wragge. Several times Maurice Vaughan asked him to have his supper with him, and Finch felt very much a man, sitting opposite Maurice with a glass of beer beside him, and no question about his smoking.

Maurice always managed to bring the conversation around to Meggie. It was difficult for Finch to find anything pleasant to tell about her in these days, but he discovered that Maurice was even more interested to hear of her cantankerousness than her sweetness. It seemed to give him a certain glum satisfaction to know that things were at sixes and sevens with her.

Finch had not been so happy since he was a very little fellow. He had perhaps never been so happy. He discovered in himself a yearning for perfection in the interpretation of his simple musical exercises, which he had never had in his Latin translations or his Math. He discovered that he had a voice. All the way home through the black ravine he would sing, sometimes at the top of his lungs, sometimes in a tender, melancholy undertone.

But how his school work suffered! His report at the end of the term was appalling. As Eden said, he out-Finched himself. In the storm that followed, his one consolation was that a large share of the blame was hurled at Renny. However, that did him little good in the end, for Renny turned on him, cursing him for a young shirker and threatening to stop the lessons altogether. Aunt Augusta and Alayne stood by him, but with caution. Augusta did not want her visit to become too unpleasant, and Alayne had come to regard her position in the house as a voyageur making his difficult progress among treacherous rocks and raging rapids. She could endure it till the New Year—when Eden was to take a position in town which Mr. Evans had got for him—and no longer.

At this moment, when Finch, a naked wretch at the cart's tail, with fingers of scorn pointing at him from all directions, alternately contemplated running away and suicide, he suddenly ceased to be an object of more than passing scorn, and little Wakefield took the centre of the stage. Piers had for some time been missing cartridges. Wake had for an equal length of time seemed to have an unlimited supply of marshmallows. And a sneaking stableboy had "split," and it was discovered that Wake was emptying the cartridges, making neat little packets of the gunpowder, and selling it to the village boys for their own peculiar violences.

When cornered, Wake had denied all knowledge of gunpowder, whether in cartridges or bulk. But Meg and Piers, searching his little desk, had come upon the neat little packets, all ready to sell, with a box full of coppers, and even a carefully written account of sales and payments. It was serious. Meg said he must be whipped. The young Whiteoaks had set no high standard of morality for a little brother to live up to, but still this was too bad.

"Flog him well," said Gran. "The Courts stole, but they never lied about it."

"The Whiteoaks," said Nicholas, "often lied, but they never stole."

Ernest murmured: "Wakefield seems to combine the vices of both sides."

"He's a little rotter," said Piers, "and it's got to be taken out of him."

Alayne was aghast at the thought of the airy and gentle Wake being subjected to the indignity of physical punishment. "Oh, couldn't he please get off this time?" she begged. "I'm sure he'll never do such a thing again."

Piers gave a short scornful laugh. "The trouble with that kid is he's been utterly ruined. If you'll let me attend to him, I'll wager he doesn't pinch anything more."

"I strongly disapprove of a delicate child like Wakefield being made to suffer," said Lady Buckley.

The culprit, listening in the hall, put his head between the curtains at this and showed his little white, tear-stained face.

"Go away, sir," said Nicholas. "We're discussing you."

"Please, please–"

Renny, who had been captured for the conclave and who stood gloomily, cap in hand, with snow-crusted leggings, turned to go. "Well, I'm off."

"Renny!" cried his sister, peremptorily. "Why are you going? You have got to whip Wake." The opposition of Alayne and Augusta had turned her sisterly anxiety to correct the child into relentless obstinacy.

Renny stood with bent head, looking sulkily into his cap. "The last time I licked him, he shivered and cried half the night. I'll not do it again." And he turned into the hall, pushing Wakefield aside and slamming the front door behind him.

"Well, of all the damned sloppiness!" broke out Piers.

"Don't worry," said Meg, rising. "Wakefield shall be punished." Her immobile sweet face was a shade paler than usual.

"This isn't a woman's job," declared Piers. "I'll do it."

"No. You'll be too hard on him."

"Let me flog the boy," cried Grandmother. "I've flogged boys before now. I've flogged Augusta. Haven't I, Augusta? Get me my stick!" Her face purpled with excitement.

"Mamma, Mamma," implored Ernest, "this is very bad for you."

"Fan her," said Nicholas. "She's a terrible color."

Meg led Wakefield up the stairs. Piers, following her to the foot, entreated: "Now, for heaven's sake don't get chicken-hearted. If you're going to do it, do it thoroughly."

"Oh, don't you wish it were you?" exclaimed Pheasant, tugging at his arm.

"Which?" he laughed. "Giving or getting one?"

"Getting, of course. It would do you good."

Nicholas and Ernest also came into the hall, and after them shuffled Grandmother, so exhilarated that she walked alone, thumping her stick on the floor and muttering: "I've flogged boys before now."

Finch draped himself against the newel post and thought of thrashings of his own. Augusta and Alayne shut themselves in the living room.

Eden came out of his room above to discover the cause of the disturbance, but Meg would not speak. With set face she pushed Wakefield before her into her room and closed the door. However, Piers, in vehement tones, sketched the recent criminal career of the youngest Whiteoak.

Eden perched on the handrail, gazing down at the faces of his brothers, uncles, and grandmother with delight. He said, dangling a leg:—

"You're priceless. It's worth being interrupted in the very heart of a tropic poem to see your faces down there. You're like paintings by the great masters: Old Woman with Stick. The Cronies (that's Uncle Nick and Uncle Ernest). Young Man with Red Face (you, Piers). Village Idiot (you, Finch). As a matter of fact, I was at my wit's end for a rhyme. Perhaps brother Wake, in his anguish, will supply me with one."

"What's he saying?" asked Gran. "I won't have any of his back chat."

Ernest replied mildly: "He is just saying that we look as pretty as pictures, Mamma."

"She's beginning at last," announced Piers, grinning.

A sound of sharp blows cascaded from Meg's room, blows that carried the tingling impact of bare skin. Staccato feminine blows, that ceased as suddenly as they had begun.

"He's not crying, poor little beggar," said Eden.

"That's because he's not hurt," stormed Piers. "What does the woman think she's doing? Giving love taps to a kitten? Good Lord! She'd hardly begun till she'd stopped. Hi, Meggie, what's the matter? Aren't you going to lick the kid?"

Meg appeared at the door of her room. "I have whipped him. What do you want me to do?"

"You don't mean to say that you call that a licking? Better not touch him at all. It's a joke."

"Yes," agreed Nicholas, "if you're going to tan a boy, do it thoroughly."

Grandmother said, her foot on the bottom step: "I'd do it thoroughly. Let me at him!"

"Steady on, Mamma," said Nicholas. "You can't climb up there."

"For God's sake, Meggie," exclaimed Piers, "go back and give him something he'll remember for more than five minutes!"

"Yes, yes, Meggie," said Ernest, "a little swishing like that is worse than nothing."

"Give him a real one! Give him a real one!" bawled Finch, suddenly stirred to ferocity. He had suffered, by God! Let that pampered little Wake suffer for a change.

Boney screamed: "Jab kutr! Nimak haram! Chore!"

Meg swept to the top of the stairs. "You are like a pack of wolves," she said at white heat, "howling for the blood of one poor little lamb. Wake is not going to get one more stroke, so you may as well go back to your lairs."

Eden threw his arms about her, and laid his head on her comfortable shoulder.

"How I love my family!" he exclaimed. "To think that after the New Year I shall be out of it all. Miss such lovely scenes as this."

Meg did not try to understand Eden. She knew that he was pleased with her because he hugged her, and that was enough.

"Do you blame me for telling just how heartless I thought they were?"

"You were perfectly right, old girl."

"Eden, I hope you won't mind what I'm going to say, but I do wish Alayne would not interfere between me and the children. She has *such* ideas."

"Oh, she has the habit of wanting to set everything right. She's the same with me. Always telling me how unmethodical I am, and how untidy with my things. She means well enough. It's just her little professorial ways."

"Poor lamb!" said Meggie, stroking the shining casque of his hair.

Wake's voice came, broken by sobs: "Meggie!"

Meg disengaged herself from Eden's arms. "There, now, I must go to him, and tell him he's forgiven."

The party downstairs had retreated after Meggie's attack, leaving a trail of wrangling behind them. Piers reached for his cap, and, stopping at the door of his grandmother's room, said, loud enough for Alayne to hear: "They're spoiling the two kids among them, anyway. As for Eden, he's no better than another woman!"

"He's like his poor flibbertigibbet mother," said Gran.

The cloud under which Wakefield awoke next morning was no more than a light mist, soon dispelled by the sun of returning favor. Before the day was over he was his own dignified, airy, and graceless self again, a little subdued perhaps, a little more anxious to please, a shade more subtle in the game of his life.

The game of life went on at Jalna. A stubborn heavy game, requiring not so much agility of mind as staying power and a thick skin. The old red house, behind the shelter of spruce and balsam, drew into itself as the winter settled in. It became the centre of whirling snow flurries. Later on, its roof, its gables, and all its lesser projections became bearers of a weight of slumberous, unspotted snow. It was guarded by snow trees. It was walled by a snow hedge. It was decked, festooned, titivated by snow wreaths, garlands, and downy flakes. The sky leaned down toward it. The frozen earth pressed under it. Its habitants were cut off from the rest of the world. Except for occasional tracks in the snow, there was little sign of their existence. Only at night dim lights showed through the windows, not illuminating the rooms, but indicating by their mysterious glow that human beings were living, loving, suffering, desiring, beneath that roof.

Christmas came.

Books for Alayne from New York, with a chastely engraved card enclosed from Mr. Cory. More books, and a little framed etching from the aunts up the Hudson. An overblouse, in which she would have frozen at Jalna, from Rosamund Trent. Alayne carried them about, showing them, and then laid them away. They seemed unreal.

There were no holly wreaths at Jalna. No great red satin bows. But the banister was twined with evergreens, and a sprig of mistletoe was suspended from the hanging lamp in the hall. In the drawing-room a great Christmas tree towered toward the ceiling, bristling with the strange fruit of presents for the family, from Grandmother down to little Wake.

A rich hilarity drew them all together that day. They loved the sound of each other's voices; they laughed on the least provocation; by evening, the young men showed a tendency toward horseplay. There was a late dinner, dominated by the largest turkey Alayne had ever seen. There was a black and succulent plum pudding with brandy sauce. There were native sherry and port. The Fennels were there; the two daughters of the retired admiral; and lonely little Miss Pink, the organist. Mr. Fennel proposed Grandmother's health, in a toast so glowing with metaphor and prickling with wit that she suggested that if he were three sheets in the wind on Sunday he would preach a sermon worth hearing. The admiral's daughters and Miss Pink were flushed and steadily smiling in the tranced gayety induced by wine. Meg was soft and dimpled as a young girl.

A great platter of raisins smothered in flaming brandy was carried in by Rags, wearing the exalted air of an acolyte.

Seeing Rags's hard face in that strange light carried Renny as in a dream to another very different scene. He saw Rags bent over a saucepan in a dugout in France, wearing a filthy uniform, and, oddly enough, that same expression. But why, he could not remember. He had picked Rags up in France. Renny looked up into his eyes with a smile, and a queer worshiping grin spread over Rags's grim hard-bitten face.

The raisins were placed on the table in the midst of the company. Tortured blue flames leaped above them, quivering, writhing, and at last dying into quick-running ripples. Hands, burnished like brass, stretched out to snatch the raisins. Wake's, with its round child's wrist; Finch's, bony and predatory; Piers's, thick, muscular; Grandmother's, dark, its hook-like fingers glittering with jewels—all the grasping, eager hands and the watchful faces behind them illuminated by the flare; Gran's eyes like coals beneath her beetling red brows.

Pheasant's hands fluttered like little brown birds. She was afraid of getting burned. Again and again the blue flames licked them and they darted back.

"You are a little silly," said Renny. "Make a dash for them, or they'll be gone."

She set her teeth and plunged her hand into the flames. "Oh—oh, I'm going to be burned!"

"You've only captured two," laughed Eden, on her other side, and laid a glossy cluster on her plate.

Renny saw Eden's hand slide under the table and cover hers in her lap. His eyes sought Eden's and held them a moment. They gazed with narrowed lids, each seeing something in the other that startled him. Scarcely was this unrecognized something seen when it was gone, as a film of vapor that changes for a moment the clarity of the well known landscape and shows a scene obscure, even sinister– The shadow passed, and they smiled, and Eden withdrew his hand.

Under the mistletoe Mr. Fennel, Grandmother having been carefully steered that way by two grandsons, caught and kissed her, his beard rough, her cap askew.

Uncle Ernest, a merry gentleman that night, caught and kissed Miss Pink, who most violently became Miss Scarlet.

Tom Fennel caught and kissed Pheasant. "Here now, Tom, you fathead, cut that out!" from Piers.

Finch, seeing everything double after two glasses of wine, caught and kissed two white-shouldered Alaynes. It was the first time she had worn an evening dress since her marriage.

Nicholas growled to Ernest: "Did you ever see a hungry wolf? Look at Renny glowering in that corner. Isn't Alayne lovely to-night?"

"Everything's lovely," said Ernest, rocking on his toes. "Such a nice Christmas!"

They played charades and dumb crambo.

To see Grandmother (inadvertently shouting out the name of the syllable she was acting) as Queen Victoria, and Mr. Fennel as Gladstone!

To see Meg as Mary, Queen of Scots, with Renny as executioner, all but cutting off her head with the knife with which he had carved the turkey!

To see Alayne as the Statue of Liberty, holding a bedroom lamp on high ("Look out, Alayne, don't tilt it so; you'll have the house on fire!"), and Finch as a hungry immigrant!

You saw the family of Jalna at their happiest in exuberant play.

Even when the guests were gone and the Whiteoaks getting ready for bed, they could not settle down. Ernest, in shirt and trousers, prowled through the dim hallway, a pillow from his bed in one hand. He stopped at Renny's door. It was ajar. He could see Renny winding his watch, Wake sitting up in bed, chattering excitedly. Ernest hurled the pillow at Renny's head. He staggered, bewildered by the unexpected blow, and dropped his watch.

"By Judas," he said, "if I get you!" With his pillow he started in pursuit.

"A pillow fight! A pillow fight!" cried Wake, and scrambled out of bed.

Ernest had got as far as his brother's room. "Nick," he shouted, in great fear, "save me!"

Nicholas, his gray mane on end, was up and into it. Piers, like a bullet, sped down the hall. Finch, dragged from slumber, had barely reached the scene of conflict when a back-handed blow from Eden's pillow laid him prostrate.

Nicholas's room was a wreck. Up and down the passage the combatants surged. The young men forgot their loves, their fears, their jealousies, the two elderly men their years, in the ecstasy of physical, half-naked conflict.

"Boys, boys!" cried Meg, drawing aside her chenille curtain.

"Steady on, old lady!" and a flying pillow drove her into retreat.

Pheasant appeared at her door, her short hair all on end. "May I play, too?" she cried, hopping up and down.

"Back to your hole, little hedgehog!" said Renny, giving her a feathery thump as he passed.

He was after Nicholas, who had suddenly become cognizant of his gout and could scarcely hobble. Piers and Finch were after him. They cornered him, and Nicholas, from being the well-nigh exhausted quarry, became the aggressor, and helped to belabor him.

Eden stood at the top of the stairs, laughingly holding off little Wake, who was manfully wielding a long old-fashioned bolster. Ernest, with one last hilarious fling in him, stole forth from his room, and hurled a solid sofa cushion at the pair. It struck Eden on the chest. He backed. He missed his footing. He fell. Down the stairs he went, crashing with a noise that aroused Grandmother, who began to rap the floor with her stick.

"What's up? What have you done?" asked Renny.

"My God, I've knocked the lad downstairs. What if I've killed him!"

The brothers streamed helter-skelter down the stairs.

"Oh, those bloody stairs," groaned Eden. "I've twisted my leg. I can't get up."

"Don't move, old fellow." They began to feel him all over. The women emerged from their rooms.

"I have been expecting an accident," said Augusta, looking more offended than usual.

"Oh, whatever is the matter?" cried Alayne.

Ernest answered, wringing his hands: "Can you ever forgive me, Alayne? Piers says I've broken Eden's leg."

XXI. EDEN AND PHEASANT

Six weeks had passed, and Eden was still unable to leave his room. As well as a broken leg, he had got a badly wrenched back. However, after the first suffering was over, he had not had such a bad time. It was almost with regret that he heard the hearty red-faced doctor say that morning that he would soon be as fit as ever. It had been rather jolly lying there, being taken care of, listening to the complaints of others about the severity of the weather, the depth of the snowdrifts, and the impossibility of getting anywhere with the car. The inactivity of body had seemed to generate a corresponding activity of mind. Never had he composed with less effort. Poetry flowed through him in an exuberant crystal stream. Alayne had sat by his couch and written the first poems out for him in her beautifully legible hand, but now he was able to sit up with a pad on his knee and scrawl them in his own way—decorating the margins with fanciful sketches in illustration.

Alayne had been a dear through it all. She had nursed him herself, fetching and carrying from the basement kitchen to their room without complaint, though he knew he had been hard to wait on in those first weeks. She looked abominably tired. Those brick basement stairs were no joke. Her face seemed to have grown broader, flatter, with a kind of Teutonic patience in it that made him remember her mother had been of Dutch extraction, several generations ago; it was there—the look of solidity and patience. A benevolent, tolerant face it might become in later life, but plainer, certainly.

She must have been disappointed, too, at his inability to take the position got for him by Mr. Evans at the New Year. Though she had not said much about it, he knew that she was eager to leave Jalna and have a house of their own. He had refused to let her put her money into the buying of one, but he had agreed that, he paying the rent from his salary, she might buy the furniture. She had talked a good deal about just how she would furnish it. When his leg was paining and he could not sleep, it was one of her favorite ways of soothing him, to stroke his head and furnish each of the rooms in turn. She had chosen the furniture for his workroom with great care, and also that for his bedroom and hers. He had been slightly aggrieved that she spoke of separate rooms, though upon reflection he had decided that it would be rather pleasant to be able to scatter his belongings all over his room without the feeling that he was seriously disturbing her. She was too serious: that was a fact. She had a way of making him feel like a naughty boy. That had been charming at first, but often now it irritated him.

There was something strange about her of late. Remote, inward-gazing. He hoped and prayed she wasn't going to be mopey. A mopey wife would be disastrous to him, weigh on his spirits most dreadfully. She had slept on the couch in their room during the first weeks after the accident, when he had needed a good deal of waiting on at night. Later, she had taken all her things and moved to a big low-ceiled room in the attic. She spent hours of her time there now. Of course, all he had to do was to ring the little silver bell at his side, and she came flying down the stairs to him, but he could not help wondering what she did up there all alone. Not that he wanted her with him continually, but he could not forgive her for seeking solitude. He was really very happy. He was well except for a not unpleasant feeling of lassitude. He had also a feeling of exquisite irresponsibility and irrelevance. This interval in his life he accepted as a gift from the gods. It was a time of inner development, of freedom of spirit, of ease from the shackles of life.

He had scarcely felt the chafing of those shackles yet, and he did not want to feel them. He should have been a lone unicorn, stamping in inconsequent gayety over sultry Southern plains, leaving bonds to tamer spirits.

He was just thinking this, and smiling at the thought when Pheasant came into the room. She was carrying a plate of little red apples, and she wore the vivid smock bought for her by Alayne.

"Meggie sent you those," she said, setting the plate beside him. "As a matter of fact, I think you eat too much. You're not as slim as you were."

"Well, it's a wonder I'm not thin," he returned with some heat. "God knows I've suffered!" He bit into an apple, and continued: "You've never had any real sympathy for me, Pheasant."

She looked at him, astonished.

"Why, I thought I'd been lovely to you! I've sat with you, and listened to your old poetry, and told you what a wonder you are. What more do you want?"

He reclined, drumming his fingers on the afghan that lay over him, a faint smile shadowing, rather than lighting, his face.

She examined his features and then said darkly: "You're too clever, that's what's the matter with you."

"My dear little Pheasant, don't call me by such a horrid word. I'm not clever. I'm only natural. You're natural. That is why we get on so famously."

"We don't get on," she returned, indignantly. "Uncle Ernest was saying only the other day what a pity it is you and I quarrel so much."

"He's an old ninny."

"You ought to be ashamed to say that. He has done everything in his power to make up to you for hurting you. He has read to you by the hour. I don't think he'll ever get over the shock of seeing you hurtle downstairs with his pillow on top of you."

"I agree with you. It was the most exhilarating thing that has happened to him in years. He looks ten years younger. To have knocked an athletic young fellow downstairs and broken his leg! Just when he began to feel the feebleness of old age creeping on! Why, he's like a young cockerel that's saluted the dawn with its first crow."

"I think you're sardonic."

"And I think you're delicious. I especially admire your wisdom, and that little tuft of hair that stands up on your crown. But I do wish you'd put it down. It excites me."

She passed her hand over it.

"Do you know," he said, "that you pass your hand over your head exactly as I do. We have several identical gestures. I believe our gesture toward life is the same."

"I think your greatest gift," she said, stiffly, "is flattery. You know just how to make a woman pleased with herself."

She was such a ridiculous little child, playing at being grown up, that he could scarcely keep from laughing at her. Neither could he keep the tormenting image of her from his mind when she was away from him. He lay back on the pillow and closed his eyes.

Outside, the snow-covered lawns and fields, unmarked by the track of a human being, stretched in burnished, rosy whiteness toward the sunset. The pines and hemlocks, clothed in the sombre grandeur of their winter foliage, threw shadows of an intense, translucent blueness. And in the hard bright intensity of that northern ether, every smallest twig was bitten against its background as though with acid. An atmosphere hateful to those who see it in alien loneliness, but of the essence and goodness of life to the native born.

When Eden opened his eyes and turned toward her, she was looking out on this scene. He thought there was a frightened look in her eyes. A faint sound of music came from Uncle Nick's room. He was playing his piano as he often did at this hour.

"Pheasant."

"Yes?"

"You look odd. Rather frightened."

"I'm not a bit frightened."

"Not of me, of course. But of yourself?"

"Yes, I am rather frightened of myself, and I don't even know why. I believe it's that wild-looking sky. In a minute it will be dark and so cold. You'll need a fire here."

"I am on fire, Pheasant."

He found her hand and held it. He asked: "Do you think Alayne loves me any more?"

"No, I don't think she does. And you don't deserve it—her love, I mean."

"I don't believe I ever had it. It was my poetry she loved, not me. Do you think she loves—Renny?"

She stared at him, startled. "I'd never thought of that. Perhaps she does."

"A nice mix-up."

"Well, I should not blame Alayne. Here she is pitch-forked into this weird family, with a husband who is absolutely devoted to himself, and a most remarkable-looking and affectionate brother-in-law."

" 'Remarkable-looking and affectionate'! Heavens, what a description!"

"I think it's a very good description."

"Well, I suppose Renny is remarkable—but 'affectionate'! That scarcely describes making love to another man's wife. I don't believe Alayne would fall for him unless he did make love to her. But 'affectionate'—I can't get over that."

"How would you describe your holding my hand? That's affectionate, isn't it?"

He took her other hand and laid both hands on his breast. "I shan't mind about anything," he said, "if you will only care for me." He drew her closer, his face stained by the afterglow that transformed the matter-of-fact room into a strange and passionate retreat.

Pheasant began to cry.

"Don't," she implored. "Don't do that! It's what I've been afraid of."

"You care for me," he whispered. "Oh, my darling little Pheasant! Say that you do—just once. Kiss me, then—you know you want to. It's what you've been dreading, but—desiring, too, my dearest. There's nothing to be afraid of in life; nothing to be ashamed of. Just be your precious self."

She flung herself against him, sobbing.

She did not know whether or not she loved him, but she knew that that room had a sultry fascination for her, that the couch where Eden lay was the centre of all her waking thoughts, that his eyes, blazing in the afterglow, compelled her to do as he willed. She hated Piers for being absorbed in his cattle, seeing nothing of her temptation, not saving her from herself, as he should have done. He knew that she was not like other young girls of his class. She had bad, loose blood. He should have watched her, been hard with her, as Maurice had been. His idea was to make a "pal" of his wife. But she was not that sort of wife. He should have known, oh, he should have known, saved her from herself—from Eden!

As she wept against Eden's shoulder, her tears became no longer the warm tears of surrender, but the tears of black anger against Piers, who had not saved her.

XXII. WAKEFIELD'S BIRTHDAY

Wakefield awoke each morning now with a feeling of gay excitement. The reason for this was that Finch had given him his Boy Scout bugle. Finch had got over being a Boy Scout very quickly. The only thing about it that had suited him was the fact of his being a bugler. However, he soon tired of that, and, coming to the conclusion that he was not the stuff of which good Boy Scouts are made, he gave it up entirely. To perform his little duties with bright alertness, to be ready, to be helpful, to do a kind act every day, seemed beyond him. So he had skulked out of the organization, and locked his bugle in the under part of the secretary in his room, where Wake might not meddle with it.

Now he had given it to Wake for his birthday. Having once decided to do this, he did not hold it till the day itself. The little boy had been in possession of it for a fortnight. And every morning he wakened with his nerves tingling with delicious excitement, for there, at the head of the bed, was the bugle, and he must not get up until he had sounded the reveille. It was thrilling to sit up in bed and send forth from swelling chest and distended cheeks those glorious brazen notes. Feeble, croaking they might sound to the listener, but to Wake they were round with a noble roundness and stirring to the soul.

Luckily, he was usually the last of the family to awake. But this morning was his birthday and he had been the very first. All, all had been roused by that sleep-shattering reveille. Renny, stretched on his back, his arms flung above his head, had been dreaming of galloping on a great wild horse along a steep precipice. Suddenly, with a neigh that shook the universe, the horse had leaped over the precipice, and plunged with him into the sunlit sea.

With a convulsive twitch of the body, Renny awoke into the sunlight of the early morning, his face so comic in its astonishment that Wakefield laughed aloud, lost his wind, and sputtered helplessly into the instrument. Then Renny laughed too, for the sight of his young brother sitting up in bed, so alert, so important, with hair on end and one dark eye cocked roguishly at him above one bulging cheek, was so ridiculous. He was ridiculous, and he was pathetic, too. "Poor little beggar," thought Renny, "a human being like myself, who will have a man's feelings, a man's queer thoughts one day."

"It's my birthday," quoth Wakefield, wiping his chin.

"Many happy returns," said Renny, trying not to look as though he had a delightful present for him.

"I shall probably not live to be as old as Gran. But I may reach ninety if I have good care."

"Oh, you'll get good care, all right. Cuddle down here a bit. It's early yet."

Wake laid the bugle on the table at the head of the bed and flung himself down into the bedclothes. He burrowed against Renny, putting his arms about his neck.

"Oh! I'm so happy," he breathed. "A picnic to-day if you please. The first of the season. It's June. The first of June! My birthday!" His eyes were two narrow slits. "Renny, have you a—you know what?"

Renny yawned prodigiously, showing two rows of strong teeth. "Well, I guess I'll get up."

"Renny, Renny!" He bumped and struggled against his elder's chest. "Oh, Renny, I could kill you!"

"Why?"

"'Cos you won't tell me."

"Tell you what?" Renny held him as in a vise.

"You know what."

"How can I know if you won't tell me?"

"Oh, you beast, Renny! It's you who won't tell me!"

"Tell you what?"

"Whether you have a—you know what—for me."

Renny closed his eyes. "You sound half-witted this morning," he said, coldly. "It seems a pity, when you've reached such an age."

Wakefield examined his brother's hard, weather-bitten visage with its relentless-looking nose. Certainly it was a forbidding face. A face that belonged to a man who was his adored brother and who had no birthday present for him.

He, too, closed his eyes, murmuring to himself: "Oh, this is terrible!" A tear trickled down his cheek and fell on Renny's wrist.

The elder Whiteoak gave the younger a little shake. "Cut that out," he said. They looked into each other's eyes.

"It nearly broke me."

"What did, Renny?"

"Why, the present."

"The *present?*"

"Rather. The birthday present."

"Oh, Renny, for God's sake–"

"Stop your swearing."

"But *what* is it?"

"It's," he plunged the word into Wake's ear, "a pony–a beautiful Welsh pony."

After the first ecstatic questions, Wake lay silent, floating in a golden haze of happiness. He did not want to miss the savor of one lovely moment of this day of days. First a pony, then a picnic, and in between, an orgy of other presents. A birthday cake with ten tall candles. At last he whispered: "Is it a he or a she?"

"A little mare."

A mare! He could hardly believe it. There would be colts–tiny, shaggy colts. His very own. It was almost too much. He wriggled against Renny. Adoring him.

"When will she–oh, I say, Renny, what's her name?"

"She has no name. You may name her."

No name. A nameless gift from the gods. Oh, responsibility overpowering, to name her!

"When will she come?"

"She is here, in the stable."

With a squeal of joy Wake leaped up in the bed; then, espying the bugle, he had an inspiration.

"Renny, wouldn't it be splendid, if I'd sound the reveille and then we'd both instantly get up? I'd like terribly to sound the reveille for you, Renny."

"Fire away, then."

Solemnly the boy placed the bugle against his lips and took a prodigious breath. Renny lay looking at him, amused and compassionate. Poor little devil–a man some day, like himself.

Loudly, triumphantly, the notes of the reveille were sounded. Simultaneously they sprang out on to the floor. June sunshine blazed into the room.

Downstairs, Wakefield said to Finch: "What do you suppose? Renny has given me a pony. We've just been out to the stable to see her. A little pony mare, mind you, Finch. There'll be colts one day. And thanks again for the bugle. Renny and I both got up by it this morning. And there's to be a picnic on the shore, and an absolutely 'normous birthday cake."

"Humph," grunted Finch. "I never remember such a fuss on any of my birthdays."

"You have always had a cake, dear," said Meggie, reproachfully. "And don't forget that nice little engine thing, and your bicycle, and your wrist watch."

"You don't expect the family to rejoice because you were born, do you?" asked Piers, grinning.

"No, I don't expect anything," bawled Finch, "but to be badgered."

"Poor little boy, he's jealous." Piers passed a sunburned hand over Finch's head, stroking downward over his long nose, and ending with a playful jolt under the chin.

Finch's nerves were raw that morning. He was in the midst of the end-of-the-term examinations, and his increasing preoccupation with music seemed to render him less than ever able to cope with mathematics. He knew with dreadful certainty that he was not going to pass into the next form. The fact that his music teacher was not only pleased with him but deeply interested in him, would not make up for that. Combined with a skulking sense of helpless inferiority, he felt the exalted arrogance of one whose spirit moves on occasion in the free and boundless spaces of art.

With a kind of bellow, he turned on Piers and struck him in the chest. Piers caught his wrists and held them, smiling lazily into his wild, distorted face.

"See here, Eden," he called. "This little lamb is baaing because we celebrate Wake's birthday with more pep than we do his. Isn't it a crime?"

Eden lounged over, his lips drawn in a faint smile from his teeth which held a cigarette, and joined in the baiting.

All morning Finch's heart raged within him. At dinner Meggie and her grandmother both chose to correct him, to nag at him. He slouched, they said. He stuck his elbows out. He bolted his food so that he might be ready for the last helping of cherry tart before poor dear Gran. Furious, he muttered something to himself to the effect that she might have it for all he cared, and that if it choked her—

She heard.

"Renny! Renny!" she shouted, turning purple. "He says he hopes it chokes me—chokes me—at my age! Flog him, Renny; I won't stand it. I'll choke. I know I will."

She glared wildly at the head of the house, her eyes blazing under her shaggy red brows.

"Mamma, Mamma," said Ernest.

"It's true," growled Nicholas. "I heard him say it." Renny had been talking to Alayne, trying not to notice the disturbance. Now, in sudden anger, he got up and in a stride stood over Finch.

"Apologize to Gran," he ordered.

"Sorry," muttered Finch, turning white.

"No mumbling! Properly."

"I'm very sorry, Grandmother."

The sight of his hunched shoulders and unprepossessing, sheepish face suddenly threw his elder into one of his quick passions. He gave him a sound and ringing cuff. Perhaps it was because Finch was not properly balanced that day. In any case it always seemed easy to send him sprawling. The next second he was in a sobbing heap on the floor, and his heavy chair had fallen with a crash.

Alayne smothered a cry, and stared at her plate. Her heart was thudding, but she thought: "I must hang on to myself. I must. He didn't mean to do it. He will be sorry. They drove him to it."

Renny sat down. He avoided looking at her. He was humiliated at having been drawn into violence before her. However, if she thought him a brute, so much the better.

Finch gathered up himself and his chair, and resumed his place at the table with a look of utter dejection.

"Now will you give back chat?" asked Grandmother, and she added after another mouthful of tart: "Somebody kiss me."

She kept asking what time the picnic was to be, for she was even more excited about it than Wake. She had her bonnet and cape on long before the hour when the phaeton was to convey her to the shore. She had the picnic hampers ranged beside her chair, and passed the period of waiting by a prolonged and bitter discussion with Boney as to whether or not he should forage among the edibles.

The picnic party was separated into the same parts as the church party, with the difference that Finch rode his bicycle instead of walking, and Piers arrived late on horseback, for it was a busy season with him.

As he tethered his mare to an iron stake which had been driven into that field before any of them could remember, he glanced toward the picnickers to see where Pheasant was. He had not had so much of her company of late as he would have liked. To the regular spring work of his men and himself had been added the setting out of a new cherry orchard and the clearing of a piece of woodland for cultivation. Piers was as strong and wholesome as a vigorous young tree. He was ambitious and he was not afraid of work, but it did seem rather hard that he had so little time to spare in these lovely days of early summer for happy and indolent hours with Pheasant. She seldom came out into the fields or orchards with him now, as she used to do. She looked pale too, and was often petulant, even depressed. He wondered if she were possibly going to have a child. He must take good care of her, give her a little change of some kind. Perhaps he could arrange a motor trip over the week-end. The poor girl was probably envious of Alayne, who had Eden always at her side.

He saw Pheasant standing on a bluff, her slender figure outlined against the sky. Her short green dress was fluttering about her knees. She looked like a flower poised there above the breezy blueness of the lake.

The phaeton had been drawn down the narrow stony road that led to the water's edge between two bluffs. Hodge had loosed the horses, and had led them out into the lake to drink. A fire had been lighted on the beach, and around it the family, with the exception of Pheasant and old Mrs. Whiteoak, were enjoying themselves in their own fashions. Wake, with upturned knickers, was paddling along the water's rim. Renny was throwing sticks for his spaniels. Nicholas and Ernest were skipping stones. Meg, in a disreputable old sweater, was bent over the fire, cherishing the teakettle. Alayne was carrying driftwood. Lady Buckley, very upright on a rug spread on the beach, was knitting at something of a bright red color.

Before Piers joined the others on the beach, he went to speak to his grandmother, who sat regarding the scene from the safety of her seat in the phaeton.

"Well, Gran, are you having a good time?"

"Put your head in so I can kiss you. Ah, there's the boy! Yes, I'm having a very good time. I used to bring the children to picnics here more than sixty years ago. I remember sitting on this very spot and watching your grandfather teach the boys to swim. Nick was a little water dog, but Ernest was always screaming that he was going down. Oh, we had the times! This was a grand country then."

"I suppose so, Gran."

"Yes, the wood pigeons were so thick they'd fly in clouds that would throw a great shadow. The farm boys would trap them. Pretty, pretty things, with eyes like jewels. They'd put the pretty eyes out of one, the brutes! And they'd throw it in a field; and when the flock saw it fluttering they thought it was feeding and they'd alight in a cloud, and the boys and men would shoot them by hundreds."

"No such shooting now, Gran."

"Go and see when tea will be ready. I want my tea. And, Philip—I mean Piers—keep your eye on Pheasant; she's young, aye, she's young, and her mother was bad, and her father a rip. She's worth watching."

"Look here, Gran, I don't like your saying such things about Pheasant. She's all right."

"I dare say she is—but she's worth watching. All women are, if they've any looks. I want my tea."

Piers was smiling at the old lady's advice as he strode along the beach. He was tolerantly amused by her, and yet he thought, "There's a grain of truth in what she says. Girls are worth watching. Still, there's no one about but Tom Fennel that she could—Eden, there's Eden; he has nothing to do—might amuse himself—poets—immoral fellows. I'll spend more time with her. I might take her to the Falls for the week-end. There's that new inn there. She'd like that, poor little young 'un."

The lake was the color of lapis lazuli. Some gulls, disturbed by the barking of the dogs, wheeled, petulantly crying, above its brightness. Beyond them a coaling schooner, with blackened sails, moved imperceptibly, and a steamer bound for Niagara trailed its faint streamer of smoke. Little sailboats were languishing in some yacht-club race.

Piers went up to Renny, whose eyes were fixed on Flossie swimming after a stick, while Merlin, having retrieved his, barked himself off his feet in agonized demand for another opportunity to exhibit his powers. As Piers approached, the spaniel shook himself vigorously, sending a drenching shower over the brothers' legs.

"She has got it," said Renny, his eyes still on Floss, and he called out to her, "Good girl!"

"Damn Merlin!" said Piers. "He's soaked my trouser legs."

"All in white, eh?" observed Renny, looking him over.

"You didn't expect me to come in overalls, did you? Have we time for a swim before tea?"

Renny bent and put his hand in the water. "It's not very cold. Suppose we do. Tea can wait."

"Where is Eden?" asked Piers, casting his eyes over the party.

"He was up on the bluff with Pheasant a bit ago." Looking up, they saw his fair head rising just above the grass where he lay stretched at Pheasant's feet.

"I won't have him hanging about her," burst out Piers.

"Tell him so, then," said Renny, curtly.

"By the Lord, I will! I'll tell him so he'll not forget." His mind suddenly was a seething sea of suspicions. "Why, even Gran thinks there's something wrong. She was warning me just now."

"No need to get in a stew," said Renny, throwing the stick for Merlin, who leaped to the water with a bark of joy, while his place was immediately taken by a dripping, importunate Flossie. "Eden and Alayne will be leaving before the first of July. Evans has a job for him then."

"What a loafer he is!"

"You didn't expect him to work with a broken leg, did you? Don't grouse about anything now: this is Wake's birthday party. Come on and have our swim." He shouted to Wakefield: "Wake, should you like to go in for a swim?"

Wakefield came galloping through the wavelets.

"Should I? Oh, splendid! What if I had the pony here? She'd swim out with me, I'll bet."

"Eden!" called Renny. "We're going in swimming. Better come."

They stared up at him as he scrambled to his feet and began to descend the steep path down the side of the bluff. He still limped from the effects of his fall.

"Won't it be pretty cold?" he asked.

"We might have Meggie boil a kettle of water to warm a spot for you," said Piers.

"Where's Finch?" asked Renny. "Finch will want to come."

Wakefield answered: "He's in the little cove already, lying on the sand." The four made toward the cove.

"Don't let Uncle Ernest come," said Eden. "He's sure to hurt me."

"Uncle Ernest!" shouted Renny. "Eden says you're not to come. You're too rough."

"Eden, Eden," cried Ernest, but with a certain pride, "I wish you would let me forget that."

Grandmother's voice came from the phaeton, sharp with the anguish of hunger: "When are we going to have tea? I told Piers to fetch me tea!"

"I am bringing you a molasses scone to stay you, Mamma," said Augusta. She was carefully making her way across the shingle, the buttered scone in her hand.

When the four brothers reached the little willow-fringed cove, they found Finch lying face downward, his head propped on his arms. "Still sulking?" asked Piers. "Did you know, Renny, that the poor youth is obsessed by the idea that we make more of Wake's birthday than his? Isn't it heart-rending, Wake?"

Wakefield, smiling and self-conscious, stared down at Finch's prostrate form.

"If I get this leg chilled," observed Eden, "I might have rheumatism."

"You won't get chilled if I am with you," said Piers, pulling off his coat.

When the others had plunged into the lake, and Wake was already screaming with delight and terror at Piers's hands, Renny returned to Finch and said with a fatherly air: "Better come in, Finch; it'll do you good. You've been studying too much."

"No. I d' want to," mumbled the boy against his arm.

"Don't be a duffer," said Renny, poking him with his bare foot. "The more Piers sees he can rattle you the more he'll do it."

" 'Tisn't only that."

"Well, look here. It was too bad I gave you that cuff before the others. But you were too damned cheeky. Come along and forget it."

Finch rolled over, disclosing a distorted red face.

"Is there no place I can be let alone?" he bawled. "Have I got to go to the end of the world to be let alone? All I ask is to be let alone, in peace here, and you all come prodding me up!"

"Stay alone, then, you little idiot!" Renny tossed away the cigarette he was smoking and strode to the water's edge.

All very well, Finch thought, for a lordly being like Renny, safe, always sure of himself, unmenaced by dreadful thoughts and bewitchment, of whom even Piers stood in some awe. With his head propped on his hand, he watched his brothers swimming, splashing, diving, the sunshine glistening on their white shoulders. As a creature apart, he watched them, with the idea in his mind that there was a conspiracy against him, that each member of the family played a different part against him, talking him over among themselves, sneering and laughing at him; but, in spite of himself, a slow smile of pleasure in their glistening grace, their agility, crept over his features. Their robust shouts were not unmusical. And the shine of their sleek heads, blond and russet and black, pleased his eyes. He saw that Piers was rough with Eden, and he was glad. He wished they would fight, half kill each other, while he reclined on the sand looking on.

Eden came limping out of the water.

"Are there any towels?" he asked. "Run and ask Meg for towels, like a good fellow, Finch."

Oh, yes! He was a good fellow when there was an errand to be run. But he hurried across the shingle to his sister.

"Towels? Yes, here they are. This big red-and-white one for Renny, mind! And the two smaller ones for Eden and Piers. And send Wake to me. I must give him a good rubbing so he shan't take a chill."

A sudden mood of savage playfulness came over Finch. Snatching the towels, he went, with a wild fling of his body, back toward the cove. There he hurled the twisted bundle at his brothers.

"There are your old towels!" he yelled; and as he crashed among the brushwood beyond the willows, he called back, "You're to go to Meggie, young Wake, and get walloped!"

Alayne had joined Pheasant on the bluff, and presently Renny too mounted the path, his damp russet head appearing first above the brink, like the ruffled crest of some bird of prey. He threw himself on the short thick clover that carpeted the bluff, and lighted his pipe.

"It seems rather hard," said Pheasant in her childish voice, "that Alayne and I could not have bathed. By the noise you made we could imagine the fun you were having."

"It was too cold for girls."

"It is a scientific fact," she said, sententiously, "that our sex can endure more cold than yours."

"We had no bathing suits."

"We should have all brought bathing suits and made a proper party of it. You have no idea how stupid it is to sit twiddling one's thumbs while you males are enjoying yourselves. 'Men must work, and women must weep'—that is the Whiteoak motto. Only you translate it into: 'Men must play, and women—' Do help me out with something really biting, Alayne."

Alayne answered only with a shrug. Renny continued to stare out across the moving brilliance of the water, puffing at his pipe. With a sort of taciturn tyranny he overrode the younger girl's desire for chatter and chaff. She too fell silent, plucking at the grass, and then, after a sidelong glance at the other two, she rose and began slowly to descend the path.

"Why are you going, Pheasant?" called Alayne sharply.

"I think someone should help Meggie to lay the cloth."

"Very well. If I can be of use, please call me."

Now a shudder of excitement ran through her. It was the first time in weeks that she had been alone with Renny. She almost wished that she had followed Pheasant.

For some time he had avoided her. Their rides, which had been interrupted by the heavy snowfalls of January and the illness of Eden, had not been resumed. Although they lived in the house together, they were separated by a wall, a relentless wall of ice, through which each was visible to the other, though distorted by its glacial diffusions. Now on the cliff, in the sunshine, the wall seemed likely to melt, and with it the barrier of her intellectual self-control. If she could only know what he was feeling! His very silence was to her a tentative embrace.

Like incense, the sweetness of the wood smoke rose from the beach. Wake's little naked figure was darting here and there like a sandpiper.

She studied Renny's profile, the carved nose, the lips gripping the pipe, the damp hair plastered against the temples. It was so immobile that a heavy depression began to drown her mood of passionate excitement. Looking at him, remembering Eden, she began to feel that she had had enough of Whiteoaks. She had bruised her soul against their wanton egotism. This Renny whom she loved was as remote, as self-sufficient, as that rock out yonder. His look of passionate immobility might be the mask of nothing more than a brooding desire to acquire some mettlesome piece of horseflesh for his stalls. Yet how could that be, and she have that feeling that his very silence was an embrace! Two shadowy arms seemed to spring from his shoulders toward her, crushing her to him, kissing her with the passion of his kisses in the orchard with, added to them, all the hunger of these months of self-restraint.

His fleshly arms had not moved. One lay across his thigh, the other slanted toward his pipe, the bowl of which lay in his palm.

He took his pipe from his lips, and spoke in a low, husky voice. His words overwhelmed her. She was like a mariner who, fearing certain shoals, watching with both dread and desire for the light that warned of their nearness, is suddenly blinded by that light full in the eyes. Excitement, resentment, depression, all left her. She was conscious only of his love.

"I love you," he said, "and I am in hell because I love you. And there is no way out."

The magical experience of sitting on the cliff with Renny, hearing these words from his mouth, in his restrained voice, filled Alayne with a sense of reckless surrender rather than tragic renunciation. Like a crop from virgin soil, this first profound love gushed upward from her being to embrace the hot sun of his passion.

With Renny it was very different. A man who had loved women both casually and licentiously, who could not speak their language, who had thought to have and craved to have no other sort of feelings toward them, he felt himself betrayed by this new and subtle passion that went deeper than mere possession, that could not be gratified and forgotten. In his eyes was something of the bewilderment of the animal that finds itself wounded, unable to exercise the faculties which had been its chief delight. Love, which had hitherto been to him as a drink of fresh water, now tasted of the bitter salt of renunciation.

He muttered again: "There is no way out."

She said, almost in a whisper: "No, I suppose there is nothing to be done."

It was as though a traveler, pointing to the rising moon, had said to another: "There is no moon."

He caught that strange denial of her words in her tone. Looking into her face, he perceived the warmth and pathos there. He exclaimed, with a groan: "I would cut everything—take you away, if only—he were not my brother!"

In an odd, choking voice that seemed to come from a long way off, she reminded him: "Your half brother."

"I never think of that," he said, coldly. His attachment to his brothers was so tenacious that it always had annoyed him to hear them spoken of as half brothers.

After a moment of silence that seemed made manifest by a veil of wood smoke that rose and hung over them for a space, she said, with a tremor in her voice: "I will do whatever you tell me to."

"I believe you would," he answered. With sudden realization, he knew that her life was to her as important as his to himself, and yet she was putting it into his hands with heroic selflessness.

They became aware that those on the beach were calling to them and, looking down, they saw that they were beckoning. The cloth was laid; already Nicholas, with the help of Piers, was letting himself down heavily into the unaccustomed posture of sitting on the ground.

"Tea is ready. Come down! Come!" echoed the voices.

The two rose mechanically, like two untroubled puppets, under the blue immensity of heaven, and turned toward the path.

"Your heels are too high for such a rough place," he said. "Let me take your hand."

She placed her hand in his, and he held it in his thin, muscular grasp till they reached the shingle.

XXIII. JUNE NIGHT AT JALNA

Two members of the picnic party did not return with the others to Jalna. Piers went through the ravine to Vaughanlands, and with Maurice Vaughan drove to Stead to a meeting of fruit growers. Finch too went to Vaughanlands, but he cycled along the country road and entered by the front road into the house. He knew Maurice was going out with Piers, and since the housekeeper was almost totally deaf, he might make music with all the wild fervor that he chose, with no one but himself to hear.

All day Finch had been straining toward the hour. Yet he knew that he should at this moment be in his room at home "swatting" for the physics exam to-morrow. He should not have gone to the picnic at all, though he had compromised by taking a textbook with him to study at odd moments. In reality, he had not read one word of it. The book had been nothing more than a mask, behind which he had hidden for a while his angry, sullen face.

When he had fastened it in its strap to the handlebar of his bicycle, he had muttered something about going to study with George Fennel. He had lied, and he did not care. This evening he must be free. His soul must stretch its wings in the spaces of the night. Music would set him free.

This new freedom, which music had the power to cast over him like a bright armor, was most of all freedom from his own menacing thoughts and, better still, freedom from God. God no longer frightened him, no longer pursued him in his loneliness, following him even to his bed with face that changed from thunderous darkness to fiery whiteness, from old to young. On evenings when music had made him brave and free he marched home through the ravine, singing as he marched, and no more afraid of God than of the whippoorwills that called to their loves among the trees, or of the quivering stars.

Sometimes the thought of being loved by God rather than pursued by Him, filled him with ecstasy, blinded him with tears. Often, and more often as the months flew on, he did not believe in God at all. God was nothing but a dragon of childhood, Fear personified, of which a Scotch nurse in tiny boyhood had sown the seed. Yet he did not want to lose this fear of God entirely, for it had in it the power of submerging the more terrible fear of himself. Once, in a strange flash of inwardness, he had thought that perhaps God and he were both afraid, each afraid of his own reflection as seen in the other's eyes. Perhaps, even, God and he were one—

In the forsaken house he sat very upright on the piano stool, only his hands moving firmly and with spirit over the keys. The piece he played was no more pretentious than that which any boy of talent might execute after an equal number of lessons. Nevertheless, there was something special in Finch's playing, in the way his sheepish air gave place to confidence when he sat before the piano, in the firm dexterity of his beautiful hands,—such a contrast to his unprepossessing face,—which kept him in his teacher's mind long after the lesson was over. More than once the teacher had said to a colleague: "I have one pupil, a boy named Whiteoak, who isn't like any of the others. He has genius of some kind, I am sure, but whether music is its natural expression, or whether it is just a temporary outlet for something else, I can't yet make out. He's a queer, shy boy."

Finch sat playing now, neither shy nor queer. The room was dark except for the moonlight that serenely fell across his hands on the keys. Through the open window the rich sweet scents of this June night poured in a changeful stream, now the odor of the cool fresh earth, now the heavy scent of certain yellow lilies that grew beneath the window, now the mixed aroma of wild flowers, last year's leaves, and rich mould, that poured up from the ravine. The breeze blew in, now warm and gentle as love's first kiss, now with a chill borne from some sequestered place not yet warmed by the summer sun.

All these scents and warmths and coolnesses Finch wove into his music. He had a strange sensation that night that many years had fled by with averted faces since the hour of the picnic. That all those he knew, indeed all the people of the world, were dead. That he alone lived, and was creating by his will, his music, the June night of a new world.

He felt the wondrous elation of creating, and at the same time a great sadness, for he knew that the world he was creating could not last; that it was no more than the shadow of a shadow; that the dancing streams, the flying petals, the swift winds that were born beneath his fingers would dry and wither and fall as the music sank to silence.

A clock on the chimneypiece struck ten in a thin faraway tone. Finch remembered to-morrow's examination. He must go home and study for a couple of hours, try to get something into that brain of his besides music. But, at any rate, his brain felt clearer for the music. He felt wonderfully clear-headed to-night. All sights and sounds seemed to him magnified, intensified. With luck he might in the next two hours absorb the very problems upon which the questions of the examination would be based. The worst was that, as he had told Meggie he was going to study with George Fennel, he must go a long piece out of his way in order that he might arrive from the direction of the rectory. The night was so mild that some of the family were almost certain to be about, and if he appeared out of the ravine, it would at once be suspected that he had been at Vaughanlands.

Just one piece more! He could not tear himself away yet. He played on, losing himself in the delight of that growing sympathy between his hands and the keyboard. Then he gently closed the piano and went out on to the verandah, shutting the door behind him.

A puff of warm air met him, as though it had been deliberately blown on him to entice him into the woods, to keep him there till he forgot all the things he had so painfully learned at school, and knew only the mathematics of the seasons, and the language of the trees. He mounted his wheel and rode across the lawn.

The basin where the house stood was flooded by moonlight, like a shallow bowl with golden wine. The air was full of whisperings and stirrings. The very grass across which he glided seemed a magic carpet.

He flew along the road, faster and faster, through the little hamlet, past the rectory (there was a light up in George's attic room, and poor George swatting away!). What if he went in and spent the night with George? He could telephone to Jalna.

No, he wanted to be by himself. George was too solid, too prosaic for him to-night. He could see his slow smile, hear his "Whatever puts such fool ideas into your head, Finch?"

Down the lane into the old woods of Jalna. The black pine trees blacker than the blackest night. How did they manage it? No darkness could obliterate them. How lovely the little birch wood must look in the moonlight! All the silver birches in their own fair communion in the midst of the black pines! If he left his wheel here, he might go to the birch wood and see it in this first silvery night of June; take a picture of it back to his room in his mind's eye.

His "mind's eye." What a singular phrase! He thought of his mind's eye—round, glowing, rapturous and frightened by turns.

The mind has a thousand eyes,
And the heart but one;
Yet the light of a whole life dies
When love is done.

It must have been the eye of his heart which he had been imagining—that flaming, rapturous, terrified eye. "When love is done—" Love had not begun for him. He thought it never would. Not that kind of love. He was not at all sure that he wanted it.

He was running lightly along the woodland path that wound among the pines. There were before him five slender young birches, sprung from the trunk of a fallen and decayed pine, like five fabled virgins from the torso of a slain giant. Beyond them the birch wood lay in the mystery of moonlight, the delicate, drooping boughs seemed to float above the immaculate boles.

This was the spot where one morning he had seen Renny standing with a strange woman in his arms. The place had ever since been haunted by that vision. He was therefore scarcely surprised when he heard low voices as he reached the outer fringe of trees. Was Renny up to his love games again? He halted among the young ferns and listened. He peered through the strange misty radiance that seemed to be distilled from the trunks and foliage of the birches themselves rather than to fall from above, and tried to see who were the two who had sought this hidden spot. Every nerve in his body was quivering, taut as the strings of a musical instrument.

At first he could make out nothing but the dew-wet mistiness of light and shade, the strange lustre that hung above a patch of greensward. All about him the air was full of mysterious rustlings and sighings, as though every leaf and blade and fern frond were sentient. Then the murmur of voices, the sound of long, passionate kisses drew his gaze toward a particular spot, sheltered by some hazel bushes. Scarcely breathing, he crept closer. He heard a low laugh, and then the voice that laughed said, "Pheasant, Pheasant, Pheasant," over and over again.

It was Eden's voice.

Then rushing breathless words from Pheasant, and then a deep sigh, and again the sound of kisses.

Oh, they were wicked! He could have rushed in on them in his rage, and slain them. It would have been right and just. They had betrayed Piers, his beloved brother, his hero! In imagination he crashed in on them through the hazel bushes, trampling the ferns, and struck them again and again till they screamed for pity; but he had no pity; he beat them down as they clung about his knees till their blood soaked the greensward and the glade reverberated with their cries–

He was dazed. He drew his hand across his eyes. Then he moved closer toward them through the hazels, not seeing where he was going, dizzy. Her voice gasped: "What was that?"

He stopped.

There was silence, except that the beating of his heart filled the universe.

"What was that?"

"Nothing but a rabbit or a squirrel."

Finch dropped to his knees. With great caution he turned and began to creep away from them. He crept till he reached the path into the pine wood, then he got to his feet and began to run. He sped along the needle-strewn path with great strides like a hunted deer. His mouth was open, his breath coming in sobbing gasps.

When he reached the place where he had left his wheel, he did not stop. Nothing mechanical could move with the speed of his swift, avenging feet. He ran down the lane, waving his arms; he flew across the pasture, past a group of sleeping cattle; missing the bridge, he waded across the stream through the thick, clinging water cress; slipped, and sprawled on the bank into a great golden splash of kingcups; and pressed on toward the stables.

Piers had just driven into the yard when he arrived. Finch ran up in front of the car, his wild white face and disheveled hair startling in the glare of the lamps. His hand was on his side, where a pain like a knife was stabbing him.

"What's the matter?" cried Piers, springing out of the car.

Finch pointed in the direction whence he had come.

"They're there," he said, thickly. "Back there–in the woods!"

"What the devil is the matter with you?" asked Piers, coming around to him. "Have you had a fright?"

Finch caught his brother by the arm and repeated: "In the wood–making love–both of them–kissing–making love–"

"Who? Tell me whom you mean. I don't know what you're talking about." Piers was impatient, yet, in spite of himself, he was excited by the boy's wild words.

"Eden, the traitor!" cried Finch, his voice breaking into a scream. "He's got Pheasant in the wood there–Pheasant. They're wicked, I tell you–false as hell!"

Piers's hand was as a vise on his arm.

"What did you see?"

"Nothing–nothing–but behind the hazel bushes I heard them whispering –kissing–oh, I know. I wasn't born yesterday. Why did they go so far away? She wouldn't have let him kiss her like that unless–"

Piers gave him a shake. "Shut up. No more of that. Now listen to me. You are to go straight to your room, Finch. You are to say nothing of this to anyone. I am going to find them." His full, healthy face was ghastly, his eyes blazed. "I'll kill them both—if what you say is so, Finch. Now go to the house."

He asked then, in a tone almost matter-of-fact, just where Finch had seen them, why he had gone there himself. Finch incoherently repeated everything. Something of their excitement must have been transmitted to the animals, for the dogs began to bark and a loud whinny came from the stables. The moon was sinking, and a deathlike pallor lay across the scene. Piers turned away, cursing as he stumbled over the tongue of a cart. A mist was rising above the paddock, and he ran into this obscurity, disappearing from Finch's eyes, as though swallowed up by some sinister force of nature.

Finch stared after him till he was lost to view, then stumbled toward the house. He felt suddenly tired and weak, and yet he could not go to the house as he had been bid. He saw a light in Alayne's room. Poor Alayne! He shuddered as he thought of what Piers would do to Eden, and yet he had done right to tell this terrible thing. He could not have hidden such evildoing in his heart, connived at their further sin. Still it was possible that his own evil imagination had magnified their act into heinousness. Perhaps even they were no worse than others. He had heard something about the loose morals of the younger generation. Well, Pheasant was only eighteen, Eden twenty-four; they were young, and perhaps no worse than others. What about Alayne herself? Was she good? Those long rides with Renny, her moving into a room by herself, away from Eden—Finch had heard a whispered reference to that between Meg and Aunt Augusta. Would he ever know right from wrong? Would he ever know peace? All he knew was that he was alone—very lonely, afraid—afraid now for Eden and Pheasant, while a few minutes ago he had thought only of crushing them in the midst of their wickedness.

He crossed the lawn and followed the path into the ravine. The stream, narrower here than where he had waded through it crossing the meadows, ran swiftly, still brimming from heavy spring rains. Luxuriant bushes, covered by starry white flowers, filled the night with their fragrance.

Renny was sitting on the strong wooden handrail of the little bridge, smoking and staring dreamily down into the water. Finch would have turned away, but Renny had heard his step on the bridge.

"That you, Piers?" he asked.

"No, it's me—Finch."

"Have you just come back from the rectory?"

"No, Renny, I've been—practising."

He expected a rebuke, but none came. Renny scarcely seemed to hear him, seemed hardly aware of his presence. Finch moved closer, with a dim idea of absorbing some of his strength by mere proximity. In the shadow of that unique magnificence he did not feel quite so frightened. He wished that he might touch Renny, hold on to his fingers, even his tweed sleeve, as he had when he was a little fellow.

Renny pointed down into the water. "Look there," he said.

Looking, Finch saw a glossy wet back gliding across the silver shimmer of the stream. It was a large water rat out on some nocturnal business of its own. They watched it till it reached the opposite bank, where, instead of climbing out as they had expected, it nosed among the sedges for a moment and then moved into the stream again, slowly passing under the bridge. Renny went to the other side and peered after it.

"Here he comes," he murmured.

"Wonder what he's after," said Finch, but he did not move. Down there in the dark brightness of the water he saw a picture—Eden lying dead, with Alayne wringing her hands above his body; and as the wavelets obliterated it, another took its place—Piers, purple-faced, struggling, kicking on a gallows— Icy sweat poured down Finch's face. He put out a hand gropingly, and staggered from the bridge and up the path. On the ridge above the ravine he hesitated. Should he go back and pour out the whole terrible tale to Renny? Perhaps it was not too late, if they ran all the way, to prevent a disaster.

He stood, gnawing at his knuckle distractedly, the clinging wetness of his trouser legs making him shiver from head to foot. He seemed incapable of movement or even thought now; but suddenly he was stirred to both by the sound of Eden's laugh, near at hand, on the lawn. Then Pheasant's voice came, speaking in a natural, unhurried tone. Piers had somehow missed them, and while he was crashing through the woods in pursuit, they were strolling about the lawn, as though they had been there all the while.

Finch moved out from the darkness and stood before them. Eden had just struck a match and was holding it to a cigarette. The flame danced in his eyes, which looked very large and bright, and gave an ironical twist to the faint smile that so often hovered about his lips.

Pheasant uttered an exclamation that was almost a cry.

"Don't go in the house," said Finch, heavily. "I mean—go away. I've told Piers about you. I heard you in the birch wood, and I ran back, and told Piers—"

Eden held the still flaring match near Finch's face, as though it were some supernatural ray by which he could look into his very soul.

"Yes?" he said, steadily. "Go on."

"He's after you. He—he looked terrible. You'd better go away."

Pheasant made a little moaning sound like a rabbit caught in a trap. Eden dropped the match.

"What a worm you are, brother Finch!" he said. "I don't know where we Whiteoaks ever got you." He turned to Pheasant. "Don't be frightened, darling. I will take care of you."

"Oh, oh!" she cried. "What shall we do?"

"Hush."

Finch said: "He'll be back any minute," and turned away.

He could not go into that house with its peacefully shining lights, where the others were still talking perhaps of the picnic, all unwitting of the thunderbolt that hung over them. He skulked around the house, through the kitchen garden, through the orchard, and out on the road that led to the churchyard.

The church steeple, rising from among the tapering cedars, pointed more sharply than they toward the sky. The church had gathered to itself the darkest shadows of tree and tomb, and drawn them like a cloak about its walls. The dead, lying beneath the dewy young grass, seemed to Finch to be watching him, as he climbed the steep steps from the road, out of hollow eye sockets in which no longer was boldness, or terror, or lust, but only resigned decay. They no longer were afraid of God. All was over. They had nothing to do but lie there till their bones were light as the pollen of a flower.

Ah, but he was afraid of God! Fear was his flesh, his marrow, his very essence. Why had the moon sunk and left him in this blackness alone? What had he done? He had ruined the lives of Piers and Eden and Pheasant and Alayne. Were Eden and Pheasant sinful? "Sin?" What a mad word! Could there be sin? All the mouldering bones under this grass—their sins were no more than the odors of spring growth, warm earth, sticky leaf-bud, blessed rain—sweetness. But there was that saying: "To the third and fourth generation." Perhaps he was suffering to-night for the heady sin of some far-off Whiteoak. Perhaps that baby sister, over whose grave he stood, had given up her little ghost because of some shadowy bygone sin. He pictured her lying there, not horrible, not decayed, but fair and tender as the bud of an April flower, with little hands held out to him.

Hands held out to him— Oh, beautiful thought! That was what his lonely spirit yearned for—the comfort of outstretched hands. A sob of self-pity shook him; tears rushed to his eyes and poured down his cheeks. He cast himself on the ground among the graves, and lay there, his face against the grass. All the accumulated experience of the dead beneath him, passing into his body, became one with him. He lay there inert, exhausted, drinking in at every pore the bitter sweetness of the past. Hands stretched out to him, the hands of soldiers, gardeners, young mothers, infants, and One far different from the others. Hands from which emanated a strange white glow, not open-palmed, but holding something toward him—"the living Bread"—Christ's hands.

He knelt among the mounds and held up his own hands, curved like petals, to receive. His thin boy's body was torn by sobs as a sapling in a hailstorm. He put his hands to his mouth—he had received the Bread—he felt the sacred fire of it burn through his veins—scorch his soul—Christ in him.

Overcome, he sank beside his mother's grave and threw his arm about it. Little white daisies shone out of the dark grass like tender, beaming eyes. He pressed closer, closer, drawing up his knees, curling his body like a little child's, thrusting his breast against the grave, and cried: "Mother, oh mother—speak to me! I am Finch, your boy."

XXIV. THE FLIGHT OF PHEASANT

Maurice Vaughan was sitting alone in his dining room. When he and Piers had returned from Stead, he had brought the young fellow into the house for a drink and some cold viands which he had got himself from the pantry. If he had had his way, Piers would still be there, smoking, drinking, and talking with ever less clarity about fertilizers and spraying and the breeding of horses. But Piers had refused to stay for long. He had to rise early, and for some reason he could not get Pheasant out of his head. His thoughts kept flying back to her, to her little white face, her brown cropped hair. Her thin eager hands seemed to tug at his sleeve, drawing him home. He had been abstracted all the evening.

However, Maurice had scarcely noticed this. All he craved was company, the warmth of a human presence to pierce the chill loneliness of the house. When Piers was gone, he sat on and on, slowly, heavily drinking without enjoyment, slowly, heavily thinking in the same numbing circle which his mind, like the glassy-eyed steed of a roundabout, had traversed for twenty years.

He thought of Meg, tender and sedate, a noble young girl, as she was when they had become engaged. He thought of his old parents, their fond joy in him, their ambition, with which he was in accord, that he should become one of the most brilliant and influential men in the country. He pictured his marriage with Meggie, their life together, their family of lovely girls and boys. There were six of these children of his fancy. He had named them all—the boys with family names, the girls with romantic names from the poets he had once admired. From the eldest to the youngest, he knew every line of the six young faces and had a right to know them, for he had shaped them out of the shadows to satisfy the hunger of his heart. For them he had a love he had never given to Pheasant.

He thought of that affair with her mother, of their meetings in the twilight, of her clutching his knees and begging him to marry her when she found she was with child, of his tearing himself away. Then the basket with the baby, the note,—here a feeling approaching nausea made him shift in his chair,—the family consternation, the family conclaves, Meg's throwing him over, his parents' death, financial distresses, the end of ambition. And so on through the whole gloomy business of his life, in which the brightest spot was the War, where he had been able for a time to forget the past and ignore the future.

As he completed the circle, the room reeled a little with him; his chin sank on his breast, and the electric light brought out the increasing whiteness of the patches on his temples. He did not sleep, but consciousness was suspended. The sound of someone softly entering the room did not rouse him. With his heavy underlip dropped, his eyes staring into space, he sat motionless as a sullen rock buried in the heaviness of the sea.

Pheasant felt a pang of pity as she saw him sitting alone in the cold, unshaded, electric light. "He looks frightfully blue," she thought, "and he's getting round-shouldered." Then her mind flew back to her own tragic situation, and she went to him and touched him on the arm.

"Maurice."

He started, and then, seeing who it was, he said in a surly tone: "Well, what do you want?"

"Oh, Maurice," she breathed, "be kind to me! Don't let Piers into the house. I'm afraid he'll kill me."

He stared stupidly at her, and then growled: "Well, it's what you deserve, isn't it?"

"Yes, yes, I deserve it! But how did you know? Have you seen anyone?"

He considered a moment, staring at the decanter on the table.

"Yes, Piers was here."

"Piers here? Oh, he was searching for me!" She wrung her hands frantically. "Oh, Maurice, please, please don't let him in again! I've been wandering about in the dark for hours, and at last I thought I'd come to you, for after all I am your child. You've a right to protect me, no matter what I've done."

He roused himself to say, "What have you done?"

"Didn't Piers tell you anything?"

"No."

"But he was searching for me?"

"No, he wasn't."

"Then how did you know something was wrong?"

"I didn't."

"But you said I deserve to be killed."

"Well, don't you?" he demanded, with drunken raillery.

"Maurice, you're drunk. Oh, whatever shall I do?" She threw herself on his knees, clasping his neck. "Try to understand! Say that you'll not let Piers kill me." She broke into pitiful wails. "Oh, Maurice, I've had to run away from Piers, and I love him so!"

"He was here a bit ago," said Vaughan, staring around as though he expected to find him in a corner. Then, noticing her head against his shoulder, he laid his hand on it in a rough caress, as a man might stroke a dog.

"Don't cry, youngster. I'll take care of you. Glad to have you back. Damned lonely."

She caught his hand and pressed a dozen wild kisses on it.

"Oh, Maurice, how good you are! How good to me! And how good Piers was to me—and I didn't deserve it. Hanging is too good for me!" And she added, melodramatically: " 'Twere better I had never been born!"

She rose then and wiped her eyes. She was a pitiful little figure. Her clothes were torn from running distractedly through a blackberry plantation.

Her hands and even her pale face were bleeding from scratches. She had lost a shoe, and the stockinged foot was wet with mud.

"Yes, 'twere," he repeated, agreeably.

With a certain pathetic dignity, she turned toward the door.

"Will it be all the same to you, Maurice, if I go to my room?"

"Same to me—wherever you go—absolutely."

How different this hall, she thought, as she dragged herself up the bare stairs, from the luxurious hall at Jalna, with its thickly carpeted stairs, its dark red rugs, its stained-glass window. The great moose head which had been her especial terror in childhood now glared down its long hard nose at her, with nostrils distended, as though it longed to toss her on its cruel horns.

She felt dazed. She scarcely suffered, except for the aching in her legs, as she threw herself across her old bed. With half-shut eyes she lay staring at the two pictures on the wall opposite, "Wide Awake," and "Fast Asleep," which had once hung in Maurice's nursery. Darling little baby pictures; how she had always loved them— She wished she had the strength of mind to kill herself. Tear the sheets into strips and wind them tighter and tighter around her throat, or, better still, hang herself from one of the rafters in that back room in the attic. She saw herself dangling there, purple-faced—saw horrified Maurice discovering her—saw herself buried at the crossroad with a stake in her inside. She did not know whether that was still done, but it was possible that the custom would be revived for her—

She fell into a kind of nightmare doze, in which the bed rocked beneath her like a cradle. It rocked faster and faster, rolling her from side to side. She was not a real, a wholesome infant, but a grotesque changeling, leering up at the distraught mother who now peered in at her, shrieking, tearing her hair. Again the scream rent the silence, and Pheasant, with sweat starting on her face, sprang up in bed.

She was alone. The electric light shone brightly. Again came the loud peal—not a scream, but the ringing of the doorbell.

She leaped to the floor. The lock of the door had been broken many years. She began to drag at the washstand to barricade it.

Downstairs the sound had also penetrated Vaughan's stupor. He lurched to the door, which Pheasant had locked behind her, and threw it open. Renny and Piers Whiteoak stood there, their faces like two pale discs against the blackness. Renny at once stepped inside, but Piers remained in the porch.

"Is Pheasant here?" asked Renny.

"Yes." He eyed them with solemnity.

Renny turned to his brother. "Come in, Piers."

Vaughan led the way toward the dining room, but Piers stopped at the foot of the stairs.

"Is she upstairs?" he asked in a thick voice, placing one hand on the newel post as though to steady himself.

Vaughan, somewhat sobered by the strangeness of the brothers' aspect, remembered something.

"Yes, but you're not going up to her. You'll let her alone."

"He won't hurt her," said Renny.

"He's not to go up. I promised her."

He took the youth's arm, but Piers wrenched himself away.

"I order you!" shouted Vaughan. "Whose house is this? Whose daughter is she? She's left you. Very well—let her stay. I want her."

"She is my wife. I'm going to her."

"What the hell's the matter, anyway? I don't know what it's all about. She comes here—done up—frightened out of her wits—I remember now. Then you come like a pair of murderers."

"I must see her."

"You shall not see her." Again he clutched Piers's arm. The two struggled beneath the sinister head of the great moose, under the massive antlers of which their manhood seemed weak and futile.

In a moment Piers had freed himself and was springing up the stairs.

"Come into the dining room, Maurice," said Renny, "and I'll tell you what is wrong. Did she tell you nothing?"

Maurice followed him, growling: "A strange way to act in a man's house at this hour."

"Did she tell you nothing?" asked Renny, when they were in the dining room.

"I don't remember what she said." He picked up the decanter. "Have a drink."

"No, nor you either." He took the decanter from his friend and put it in the sideboard, decisively locking the door.

Vaughan regarded the action with dismal whimsicality.

"What a to-do," he said, "because the kids have had a row!"

Renny turned on him savagely. "Good God, Maurice, you don't call this a row, do you?"

"Well, what's the trouble, anyway?"

"The trouble is this: that brat of yours has wrecked poor young Piers's life."

"The hell she has! Who is the man?"

"His own brother—Eden."

Vaughan groaned. "Where is he?"

"He made off in the car."

"Why didn't she go with him? Why did she come to me?"

"How can I tell? He probably didn't ask her. Oh, the whole rotten business harks back to me! It's my fault. I'd no right to let Eden loaf about all winter, writing poetry. It's made a scoundrel of him!"

A wry smile flitted across Vaughan's face at the unconscious humor of the remark.

"I shouldn't blame myself too much if I were you. If writing poetry has made Eden into a scoundrel, he was probably well on the way beforehand. Possibly that's why he turned to it."

There was a deep understanding between these two. They had confided in each other as they had in no one else. Renny, stirred by the disclosures of the night, burst out: "Maurice, in thought I am no better than Eden! I love his wife. She's never out of my mind."

Vaughan looked into the tormented eyes of his friend with commiseration.

"Do you, Renny? I had never thought of such a thing. She doesn't seem to me your sort of girl at all."

"That is the trouble. She isn't. If she were, it would be easier to put the thought of her aside. She's intellectual, she's—"

"I should say she is cold."

"You're wrong. It is I, all my life, who have had a sort of cold sensuality—no tenderness went with my love for a woman. I don't think I had any compassion. No, I'm sure I hadn't." He knit his brows as though recalling past affairs. "But I'm full of compassion for Alayne."

"Does she love you?"

"Yes."

"What about Eden?"

"She had a romantic devotion to him, but it's over."

"Does she know about this?" Maurice lifted his head in the direction of the room above.

"Yes. I only had a glimpse of her in the hall—the house was in an uproar. She had a strange, exalted look as though nothing mattered now."

"I see. What is Piers going to do?"

"Piers is a splendid fellow—tough as an oak. He said to me, 'She's mine; nothing can change that. I'm going to fetch her home.' But I should pity Eden if he got his hands on him."

"They are coming down. Heavens, they were quiet enough! Must I speak to them?"

"No, let the poor young beggars alone."

The two came slowly down the stairs. Like people leaving the scene of a catastrophe, they carried in their eyes the terror of what they had beheld. Their faces were rigid. Piers's mouth was drawn to one side in an expression of disgust. It was like a mask of tragedy. They stood in the wide doorway of the dining room as in a picture framed. Maurice and Renny smiled at them awkwardly, trying to put a decent face on the affair.

"Going, eh?" Maurice said. "Have something first, Piers." He made a movement toward the sideboard.

"Thanks," returned Piers in a lifeless voice. He entered the dining room. "Where's that key, Renny?"

Renny produced the key; a tantalus was brought forth, and a drink poured for Piers. Maurice, with Renny's eye on him, did not take one himself.

Piers gulped down the spirits, the glass rattling grotesquely against his teeth. Under the ashen tan of his face, color crept back. No one spoke, but the three men stared with gloomy intensity at Pheasant, still framed in the doorway. The magnetic currents between the members of the group seemed palpably to vibrate across the atmosphere of the room. Then Pheasant, putting up her hands, as though to push their peering faces back from her, exclaimed: "Don't stand staring at me like that! One would think you'd never seen me before."

"You look awfully done," said Maurice. "I think you ought to have a mouthful of something to brace you. A little Scotch and water, eh?"

"I might if I were asked," she returned, with a pathetic attempt at bravado. She took the glass in a steady little hand, and drank.

"I shall come along later," said Renny to Piers. "I'm going to stop a while with Maurice." But he continued to stare at Pheasant.

"I know I'm a scarlet woman, but I think you're very cruel. Your eyes are like a brand, Renny Whiteoak."

"Pheasant, I was not even thinking of you. My—my mind was quite somewhere else."

Piers turned on Maurice in a sudden rage. "It's all your fault!" he broke out, vehemently. "You never gave the poor child a chance. She was as ignorant as any little immigrant when I married her."

"She doesn't seem to have learned any good from you," retorted Vaughan.

"She has learned all of decency that she knows. Was she ever sent to school?"

"She had two governesses."

"Yes. They both left inside of six months, because they couldn't live in the house with you."

"Oh, I suppose it is my fault that she inherits her mother's instinct," returned Maurice, bitterly. "And Renny has just been telling me that it is his fault that Eden is a scoundrel. We've taken on a lot of responsibility."

"You are talking like fools," said Renny.

"Please do not quarrel about me," put in Pheasant. "I think I'm going to faint or something."

"Better take her out in the air," said Renny. "The liquor was too strong for her."

"Come along," said Piers, and took her arm.

The touch of his hand had an instant effect on Pheasant. A deep blush suffused her face and neck; she swayed toward him, raising her eyes to his with a look of tragic humility.

Outside, the coolness of the dawn refreshed her. He released her arm, and preceded her through the grove and down into the ravine. They walked in silence, she seeming no more than his shadow, following him through every divergence of the path, hesitating when he hesitated. Centuries before, two such figures might have been seen traversing this same ravine, a young Indian and his squaw, moving as his silent shadow in the first light of morning, primitive figures so much akin to the forest life about them that the awakening birds did not cease twittering as they passed. On the bridge above the stream he stopped. Below lay the pool where they had first seen their love reflected as an opening flower. They looked down into it now, no longer able to share the feelings its mirrored loveliness excited in them. A primrose light suffused the sky and in a deeper tone lay cupped in the pool, around the brink of which things tender and green strove with gentle urgency to catch the sun's first rays.

An English pheasant, one of some imported by Renny, moved sedately among the young rushes, its plumage shining like a coat of mail. Careless, irresponsible bird, Piers thought, and for one wild instant he wished that she were one with the bird—that no man might recognize a woman in her but himself; that he might keep her hidden and love her secretly, untortured by the fear and loathing he now felt.

Pheasant saw, drowned in that pool, all the careless irresponsibility of the past, the weakness, the indolence, that had made her a victim of Eden's dalliance. If Piers loathed her, how much more she loathed the image of Eden's face which faintly smiled at her from the changeful mirror of the pool! Just to live, to make up to Piers by her devotion for what he had suffered—to win from his eyes love again instead of that look of fear which he had turned on her when he entered the bedroom! She had expected rage —fury. And he had looked at her in an agony of fear. But he had taken her back! They were going home to Jalna. She longed for the thick walls of the house as a broken-winged bird for its nest.

"Come," he said, as though awakening from a dream, and moved on up the path that led from the ravine to the lawn.

The turkeys were crossing the lawn, led by the cock, whose blazing wattles swung arrogantly in the first sun rays. His wives, with burnished breasts and beaming eyes, followed close behind, craning their necks, alternately lifting and dragging their slender feet, echoing his bold gobble with plaintive pipings. The hens paused to look with curiosity at the boy and girl who emerged from the ravine, but the cock, absorbed by his own ego, circled before them, swelling himself rigidly, dropping his wings, urging into his wattles a still more burning red.

Down the wet roof Finch's pigeons were strutting, sliding, rooketty-cooing, peering over the eaves at the two who slowly mounted the steps.

Inside, the house lay in silence except for the heavy snoring of Grandmother in her bedroom off the lower hall. It was as if some strange beast had a lair beneath the stairs, and was growling a challenge to the sun.

They passed the closed doors of the hall above and went into their own room. Pheasant dropped into a chair by the window, but Piers, with a businesslike air, began collecting various articles—his brushes, his shaving things, the clothes which he wore about the farm. She watched his movements with the unquestioning submissiveness of a child. One thought sustained her: "How glad I am that I am here with Piers, and not flying with Eden as he wanted me to!"

When he had got together what he wanted, he took the key from the door and inserted it on the outside. He said, without looking at her:—

"Here you stay, till I can stand the sight of your face again."

He went out, locking the door behind him. He climbed the long stairs to the attic, and, throwing his things on the bed in Finch's room, began to change his clothes for the day's work. In the passage he had met Alayne, looking like a ghost. They had passed without speaking.

XXV. FIDDLER'S HUT

Three weeks later Mr. Wragge was an object of great interest one morning to a group of Jersey calves, as he crossed their pasture. They ceased gamboling, butting, and licking each other, to regard him with steadfast scrutiny out of liquid dark eyes. He was in his shirt sleeves, his coat being thrown over one arm, for the day was hot; his hat was tilted over his eyes, and he carried, balanced on one hand, a tray covered with a white cloth. He was smoking, as usual, and his expression was one of deep concern.

When he reached a stile at the far end of the paddock, he set the tray on the top, climbed over, then, balancing the tray at a still more dangerous angle, proceeded on his way. It now lay through an old uncared-for apple orchard, the great trees of which were green with moss, half smothered in wild grapevines and Virginia creeper, and their boughs, like heavy wings, swept to the long coarse grass. Following a winding path, he passed a spring, where long ago a primitive well had been made by the simple process of sinking a wooden box. The lid of this was now gone, the wood decayed, and it was used by birds as a drinking fountain and bath. The liquid gurgle of the spring as it entered the well made a pleasant undertone to the song of birds with which the air was merry.

Embowered in vines, almost hidden by flowering dogwood, stood the hut where Fiddler Jock, by the consent of Captain Philip Whiteoak, had lived in solitude, the story of whose death young Finch had told Alayne on their first walk together.

Here Meg Whiteoak had been living for three weeks.

Before approaching the threshold, Mr. Wragge again set down the tray, put on his coat, straightened his hat, threw away his cigarette, and intensified his expression of concern.

"Miss W'iteoak, it's me, ma'am," he said loudly, as though to reassure her, immediately after knocking.

The door opened and Meg Whiteoak appeared, with an expression as sweetly calm, but a face paler than formerly. "Thank you, Rags," she said, taking the tray. "Thank you very much."

"I'd be gratified, ma'am," he said anxiously, "if you was to lift the napkin and tike a look at wot I've brought you. I'd be better pleased if I knew you found it temptin'."

Miss Whiteoak accordingly peered under the napkin and discovered a plate of fresh scones, a bowl of ripe strawberries, and a jug of thick clotted cream such as she liked with them. A sweet smile curved her lips. She took the tray and set it on the table in the middle of the low, scantily furnished room.

"It looks very tempting, Rags. These are the first strawberries I've seen."

"They are the very first," he announced, eagerly. "I picked them myself, ma'am. There's going to be a wonderful crop, they s'y, but it don't seem to matter, the w'y things are goin' on with us these days."

"That's very true," she said, sighing. "How is my grandmother to-day, Rags?"

"Flourishing amazing, ma'am. My wife says she talked of nothink but 'er birthd'y the 'ole time she was doin' up 'er room. She 'ad a queer little spell on Thursday, but Mr. Ernest, 'e thought it was just that she'd eat too much of the goose grivy. She looked remarkable well yesterd'y, and went to church the sime as usual."

"That is good." She bit her full underlip, and then asked, with an attempt at nonchalance: "Have you heard anything about Mrs. Eden's leaving?"

"I believe she's to go as soon as the birthd'y celebrations are over. The old lidy wouldn't 'ear of it before. Ow, Miss W'iteoak, she's only a shadder of 'er former self, Mrs. Eden is; and Mr. Piers is not much better. Of all the people in the 'ouse those two show the wear and tear of wot we're goin' through the most. Of course, I've never seen Mrs. Piers. She ain't never shown up in the family circle yet, but my wife saw 'er lookin' out of the winder, and she says she looks just the sime. Dear me, some people can stand anythink! As for me, I'm not the man I was at all. My nerves 'ave all gone back on me. It's almost like another attack of shell shock, you might s'y."

"I'm very sorry, Rags. You do look pale."

He took out a clean folded handkerchief and wiped his brow. "It isn't as though my own family relations was wot they were, ma'am. Mrs. Wragge and me, we 'ad our little altercations, as you know, but, tike it as a 'ole, our life together was amiable; but now," he dolefully shook his head, "it's nothing more nor less than terrific. Me being on your side and she all for Mr. Renny, there's never a moment's peace. W'y, yesterd'y—Sunday and all as it was—she up and shied the stove lifter at my 'ead. I escaped to the coal cellar, where she pursued me, and as for 'er language! Well, Mr. Renny 'e 'eard the goings on and 'e came rattling down the basement stairs in a fine rage, and said if 'e 'eard any more of it we should go. The worst was, 'e seemed to blime me for the 'ole affair. I never thought I'd live to see the d'y 'e'd glare at me the w'y 'e did."

"That's because you are on my side, Rags," she said sadly.

"I know, and that makes it all the worse. It's a 'ouse divided against itself.

I've seen deadlocks in my time, but I've never seen a deadlock like this. Well, I'll be takin' aw'y wot little appitite you 'ave with my talk. I must be off. I've a thousand things to do, and of course Mrs. Wragge puts all the 'ard work on to me as usual. And if you'll believe me, ma'am, she's so evilly disposed that I 'ad to steal those little scones I brought you."

He turned away, and when he had gone a few yards he put on his hat, removed his coat, and lighted a cigarette. Just as he reached the stile he met Renny Whiteoak crossing it.

Renny said sarcastically: "I see you have a path worn to the hut, Rags. Been carrying trays to Miss Whiteoak, I suppose."

Rags straightened himself with an air of self-righteous humility.

"And if I didn't carry trays to 'er, wot do you suppose would 'appen, sir? W'y, she'd starve; that's wot she'd do. It would look rather bad, sir, for a lidy to die of starvation on 'er brother's estite, and 'im livin' in the lap of luxury."

This remark was thrown after the retreating figure of his master, who had strode angrily away. Rags stared after him till he disappeared among the trees, muttering bitterly: "This is all the gratitood I get for the w'y I've slaved for you in war and in peace! Curses yesterd'y, and a sneer and a dirty look to-d'y. You ill-tempered, domineerin' red-'eaded slave driver! But you've met your match in Miss W'iteoak, let me tell you—and serves you right."

With this he climbed over the stile, and returned meditatively to the basement kitchen.

When Renny reached the hut, he found the door open, and inside he could see his sister sitting by the table, pouring herself a cup of tea. She looked up as she heard his step, and then, with an expression of remote calm, dropped her eyes to the stream of amber liquid issuing from the spout of the teapot. She sat with one rounded elbow on the table, her head supported on her hand. She looked so familiar and yet so strange, sitting in these poverty-stricken surroundings, that he scarcely knew what to say to her. However, he went in, and stood looking down at the tray.

"What particular meal is this?" he asked.

"I have no idea," she answered, buttering a scone. "I keep no count of meals now."

He looked about him, at the low, rain-stained ceiling, the rusty stove, the uneven, worm-eaten floor, the inner room with its narrow cot bed.

"This is an awful hole you've chosen to sulk in," he commented.

She did not answer, but ate her scone with composure, and after it two strawberries smothered in cream.

"You'll make a charming old lady after you've spent ten years or so here," he gibed.

He saw a sparkle of temper in her eyes then.

"You will have the satisfaction of knowing that you drove me to it."

"That is utter nonsense. I did everything I could to prevent you."

"You did not send that girl away. You allowed Piers to bring her into the house with me, after her behavior."

"Meggie, can't you see anyone's side of this question but your own? Can't you see that poor young Piers was doing a rather heroic thing in bringing her home?"

"I will not live under the same roof with that girl. I told you that three weeks ago, and you still try to force me."

"But I can't allow you to go on like this!" he cried. "We shall be the talk of the countryside."

She regarded him steadfastly. "Have you ever cared what the countryside thought of you?"

"No; but I can't have people saying that my sister is living in a tumble-down hut."

"You can turn me out, of course."

He ignored this, and continued: "People will simply say that you have become demented."

"It will not surprise me if I do."

He stared at her, positively frightened. "Meggie, how can you say such things? By God, I have enough to bear without your turning against me!"

She said, with calculated cruelty: "You have Alayne. Why should you need me?"

"I have not got Alayne," he retorted furiously. "She is going away the day after Gran's birthday."

"I do not think she will go away."

"What do you mean?" he asked, suspiciously.

"Oh, I think you have a pretty little game of progressive marriage going on at Jalna. No, Alayne will not go away."

His highly colored face took on a deeper hue. Its lines became harsh.

"You'll drive me to do something desperate," he said, and flung to the door.

She pushed the tray from her and rose to her feet.

"Will you please go? You are mistaken if you think you can abuse me into putting up with loose women in my house. As to being the talk of the countryside, there must be strange stories about the married couples of our family already."

"Rot! It's all within the family."

"All within the family? Just think those words over. They've got a sinister sound, like the goings on in families in the Middle Ages. We should have been born two hundred years ago at the very least. No woman who respects herself could stay at Jalna."

He broke into a tirade against her, and all hard, narrow-minded women. She followed him to the door, laying her hand on the latch.

"You can never argue, Renny, without using such dreadful language. I can't stand any more of it."

He had stepped outside, and his spaniels, having traced him to the hut, ran to meet him with joyous barks, jumping up to paw him and lick his hands. For an instant Meg almost relented, seeing him there with his dogs, looking so entirely her beloved Renny. But the instant passed; she closed the door firmly and returned to her chair, where she sat plunged in thought, not bitterly reviewing the past as Maurice did, nor creating an imaginary and happy present, but with all her mind concentrated on those two hated alien women in her house.

Renny, returning to his stables, found Maurice there, waiting to talk over some proposed exchange. He was in the stall with Wakefield's pony, feeding her sugar from his pocket. He turned as Renny entered.

"Well," he said, "how are things going now?"

"Like the devil," he returned, slapping the pony sharply, for she had bitten at him, not liking the interruption of her feast. "Piers still keeps Pheasant locked in her room, and goes about with an expression like the wrath of God. Uncle Nicholas and Aunt Augusta quarrel all day long. He's trying to worry her out of the house and back to England, and she won't go. He and Uncle Ernest aren't speaking at all. Alayne is looking ill, and Grandmother talks ceaselessly about her birthday. She's so afraid that something will happen to her before she achieves it that she refuses to leave the room."

"When is it?"

"A week from to-day. Alayne is staying here till it's over; then she goes back to New York, to her old position with a publisher's firm."

"Look here; why doesn't she divorce Eden? Then you and she could marry."

"The proceedings would be too beastly unsavory. No, there's no hope there."

Something vicious in him prompted him to tease the pony. He cuffed her till she drew back her lips, showed all her teeth, bit at him, neighed, and finally reared and struck at him with her sharp hoofs. Maurice moved out of the way.

"Stop it, Renny," he said, half angry and half laughing at the display of temper by the pair. "You'll make her an ugly little brute for Wake to handle."

"That's true." He desisted at once, red-faced from temper, rather ashamed of himself.

"It's a pity Alayne could not have seen that."

"Yes, isn't it?" He began to stroke the pony. "Here, give me a lump of sugar, Maurice."

"No, I'll give it to her myself. She and I are friends. We have no quarrel to patch up. Have we, pet?"

He offered her sugar, but, too upset to take it, she wrinkled her lips and cast baleful glances at them both. As they left the loose box, Maurice asked. "How is Meg, Renny?"

"I've just been to see her. She's still stuck in that awful hut, sulking. Nothing will budge her. It looks as though she would spend the rest of her days there. I don't know what I'm to do. If you could only see her! It would be pathetic if it weren't ridiculous. She has a few sticks of furniture she took from the attic. The floor is bare. They say that all she eats is the little that Rags carries over to her. I met him with a tray. The fellow is nothing but a spy and a talebearer. He keeps her thoroughly posted as to all that goes on in the house. Aunt Augusta was for starving her out, forbidding Rags to take food to her; but I couldn't do that. She shut the door in my face just now."

"It's appalling."

They walked in silence for a space, along the passage between stalls, among the sounds and smells they both loved—deep, quiet drinking, peaceful crunching, soft whinnying, clean straw, harness oil, liniment.

Vaughan said: "I've been wondering—in fact, I lay awake half the night wondering—if there is a chance that Meg might take me now. Pheasant's being gone, and Jalna in such an upset, and things having reached a sort of deadlock, it would be a way of solving the problem for her. Do you think I'd have a show?"

Renny looked at his friend with amazement.

"Maurice, do you really mean it? Are you still in love with her?"

"You know perfectly well I've never cared for any other woman," he answered, with some irritation. "It's not easy for you Whiteoaks to understand that."

"I quite understand, only—twenty years is a long time between proposals."

"If things had not turned out as they have, I should never have asked her again."

"I hope to God she'll have you!" And then, fearing that his tone had been too fervent, he added: "I hate to see you living such a lonely life, old man."

Meg had come out of the cottage, and was bending over a spray of sweetbriar that had thrust its thorny way up through a mass of dogwood. She loved its wild sweetness, and yet it made her sadder than before. Maurice noticed, as she raised a startled face to his, that her white cheeks were dappled by tears. One of them fell, and hung, like a bright dewdrop, on the briar.

"I'm sorry if I frightened you."

His voice, unheard for so many years, came to her with the sombre cadence of a bell sounding through the dark. She had forgotten what a deep voice he had. As a youth, it had seemed too deep for his slenderness, but now, from this heavy frame, she found it strangely, thrillingly moving.

"I had no right to intrude on you," he went on, and stopped, his eyes resting on the spray of briar; for he would not embarrass her by looking into her tear-stained face. Why did she not wipe her cheeks? He reflected, with a shade of annoyance, that it was just like Meggie to leave those glittering evidences of her anguish in full view. It gave her a strange advantage, set her on a plane of suffering above those around her.

Unable to speak, he rolled a cigarette deftly—in one hand, for the other had been crippled in the War. He could not have found a more poignant way of pleading his case. She had passed him often on the road and seen that he was going gray. She had heard that one of his hands was useless, but it was not until she saw the wrist in its leather bandage, above the helpless hand, that she realized how alone he was, how pathetic, how he needed to be taken care of. Renny was hard, careless, unhurt; he was arrogant, immovable. Eden was gone. Piers clung to his wretched young wife. Finch was unsatisfactory, moody. Wake was a self-sufficient little rogue. But here was Maurice, her unhappy lover, seeking her out with a strange, hungry expression in his eyes.

The droop of his mouth stirred something in her that she had forgotten, something buried for years and years. It did not stir weakly, feebly, like a half-dead thing, but boundingly, richly, like the sap that thrilled the growing things in this June day. She swayed beneath the sudden rush of its coming and put out a hand to steady herself. Color flooded her face and neck.

He dropped the cigarette and caught her hand.

"Meggie, Meggie," he burst out. "Have me—marry me! Meggie, oh, my darling girl!"

She did not answer in words, but put her arms about his neck and raised her lips to his. All the stubbornness was gone from their pretty curves, and only the sweetness was left.

XXVI. GRANDMOTHER'S BIRTHDAY

The darkness had just fallen on Grandmother's birthday. It had descended slowly, seeming reluctant to draw the curtain on that day of days. But now the sky was a royal purple, and quite a hundred stars twinkled with all the mystic glamour of birthday candles.

Grandmother had not slept a wink since dawn. Not for worlds would she have missed the savor of one moment of this day, toward which she had been straining for many years. She could sleep all she wanted to after the celebration was over. There would be little else to do. Nothing to look forward to.

With her breakfast had come all the household to congratulate her, wish her joy, and other birthdays to follow. She had put her strong old arms about each body that, in succession, had leaned over her bed, and after a hearty kiss had mumbled: "Thank you. Thank you, my dear." Wakefield, on behalf of the tribe, had presented her with a huge bouquet of red, yellow, and white roses, an even hundred of them, tied with red streamers.

The day had been a succession of heart-touching surprises. Her old eyes had become red-rimmed from tears of joy. The farmers and villagers of the neighborhood, to whom she had been a generous friend in her day, besieged her with calls and gifts of fruit and flowers. Mr. Fennel had had the church bell ring one hundred merry peals for her, the clamor of which, sounding through the valley, had transported her to her childhood in Ireland; she did not know just why, but there it was; she was in County Meath again!

Mrs. Wragge had baked a three-tiered birthday cake, which had been decorated in the city. On the top, surrounded by waves of icing, was a white-and-silver model of a sailing vessel such as she had crossed the ocean in, from India. On the side, in silver comfits, the date of her birth, 1825. This stood on a rosewood table in the middle of the drawing-room, beside a silver-framed photograph of Captain Philip Whiteoak. How Grandmother wished he could have seen the cake! She imagined herself, strong and springy of step, leading him up to the table to view it. She pictured his start of surprise, his blue eyes bulging with amazement, and his, "Ha, Adeline, *there's* a cake worth living a hundred years for!"

Oh, the feel of his firm, muscular arm in her hand! A dozen times that day she had kissed the photograph. At last Ernest had been moved to say: "Mamma, *must* you kiss it so often? You are moistening off all the gloss."

Now night had fallen and the guests were arriving for the evening party. The Fennels, the admiral's daughters, Miss Pink, and even old friends from a long distance. Her chair had been moved to the terrace, where she could see the bonfire all ready to be lighted. It had taken her an unconscionably long time to make the journey there, for she was weak from excitement and lack of sleep. In the summerhouse two violins and a flute discoursed the insouciant, trilling airs of sixty years ago, filling the air with memories and the darkness with plaintive ghosts. Grandmother's sons and eldest grandson had spared no trouble or expense to make the party a memorable one.

On her right hand sat Ernest and Nicholas, and on her left Augusta and Alayne. Augusta remarked to Alayne: "What a blessing that Meg is off on her honeymoon, and not sulking in Fiddler's hut! It would have spoiled the party completely if she had been there, and even more so if she had come."

"She wasted no time when she finally made up her mind, did she?"

"No, indeed. I think she was simply shamed into it. She might have gone on living there forever. Renny would never have given in." Lady Buckley regarded with complacency her nephew's tall figure, silhouetted against the flare of the musician's torches.

"I am afraid," said Alayne, "that Meg hated me very much after our quarrel about Pheasant. I know that she thought my attitude toward her positively indecent."

"My dear, Meg is a narrow-minded Victorian. So are my brothers, though Ernest's gentleness gives him the appearance of broad-mindedness. You and I are moderns—you by birth, and I by the progression of an open mind. I shall be very sorry to see you go to-morrow. I have grown very fond of you."

"Thank you; and I have of you—of most of you. There are so many things I shall miss."

"I know, I know, my dear. You must come back to visit us. I shall not leave Jalna while Mamma lives, though Nicholas would certainly like to see me depart. Yes, you must visit us."

"I'm afraid not. You must come to see me in New York. My aunts would be delighted to meet you."

Augusta whispered: "What do they know about Eden and you?"

"Only that we have separated, and that I am going back to my old work."

"Sensible—very. The less one's relatives know of one's life the better. I had no peace in my married life till the ocean rolled between me and my people. Dear me, Renny's lighting the bonfire. I hope it's quite safe. I wonder if you would mind, Alayne, going down and asking him to be very careful. A spark from it smouldering on the roof, and we might be burned in our beds to-night."

As Alayne moved slowly down the lawn, the first sparkle curled about the base of the pyramid of hardwood sticks that had as their foundation a great chunk of resinous pine. A column of smoke arose, steady and dense, and then was dispersed by the sudden and furious blossoming of flowers of flame. In an instant the entire scene was changed. The ravine lay, a cavernous gulf of blackness, while the branches of the near-by trees were flung out in fierce, metallic grandeur. The torches in the summerhouse became mere flickering sparks: the stars were blown out like birthday candles. The figures of the young men moving about the bonfire became heroic; their monstrous shadows strove together upon the rich tapestry of the evergreens. The air was full of music, of voices, of the crackling of flames.

Out of the shadow thrown by a chestnut tree in bloom, Pheasant ran across the grass to Alayne's side. She seemed to have grown during those weeks of her imprisonment. Her dress looked too short for her. Her movements had the wistful energy of those of a growing child. Her hair, uncut for some time, curved in a quaint little tail at her nape.

"This freedom is wonderful," she breathed. "And all that pretty firelight, and the fiddles! Try as I will, Alayne, I can't help feeling happy to-night."

"Why should you try not to be happy? You must be as happy as a bird, Pheasant. I'm so glad we had that hour together this morning."

"You've been beautiful to me, Alayne. No one in the world has ever been so good to me. Those little notes you slipped under my door!"

Alayne took her hand. "Come, I am to go and tell Renny to be careful. Aunt Augusta is afraid we shall be burned in our beds."

The three youngest of the Whiteoaks were in a group together. As the girls approached, Finch turned his back on them and skulked into the shadow, but Wakefield ran to meet them and put an arm about the waist of each.

"Come, my girls," he said, airily, "join the merry circle. Let's take hands and dance around the bonfire. If only we could get Granny to dance, too! Please, let's dance!" He tugged at their hands. "Piers, take Pheasant's other hand. Renny, take Alayne's hand. We're going to dance."

Alayne felt her hand being taken into Renny's. Wakefield's exuberance was not transmittable, but he ran hither and thither, exhorting the guests to dance, till at last he did get a circle together on the lawn for Sir Roger de

Coverley. But it was the elders who were moved to disport themselves, after a glass or two of punch from the silver bowl on the porch. The younger ones hung back in the shelter of the blazing pile, entangled in the web of emotions which they had woven about themselves.

Eden was not among them, but the vision of his fair face, with its smiling lips, mocked each in turn. To Renny it said: "I have shown you a girl at last whom you can continue to love without possessing, with no hope of possessing, who will haunt you all your days." To Alayne: "I have made you experience, in a few months, love, passion, despair, shame, enough for a lifetime. Now go back to your sterile work and see if you can forget." To Piers: "You sneered at me for a poet. Do you acknowledge that I am a better lover than you?" To Pheasant: "I have poisoned your life." To Finch, hiding in the darkness: "I have flung you, headfirst, into the horrors of awakening."

Renny and Alayne, their fingers still locked, stood looking upward at the flame-colored smoke that rose toward the sky in billows endlessly pursuing each other, while, after the crashing of a log, a shower of sparks sprang upward like a swarm of fireflies. In the glare their faces were transfigured to a strange beauty, yet this beauty was lost, not registered on any consciousness, for they dared not look at each other.

"I have been watching two of those sparks," she said, "sparks that flew up, and then together, and then apart again, till out of sight—like us."

"I won't have it so. Not till out of sight, extinguished—if you mean that. No, I am not hopeless. There's something for us besides separation. You couldn't believe that we'll never meet again, could you?"

"Oh, we may meet again—that is, if you ever come to New York. By that time your feelings may have changed."

"Changed! Alayne, why should you want to spoil our last moments together by suggesting that?"

"I suppose, being a woman, I just wanted to hear you deny it. You've no idea what it is to be a woman. I used to think in my old life that we were equal: men and women. Since I've lived at Jalna, it seems to me that women are only slaves."

Someone had thrown an armful of brushwood on the fire. For a space it died down to a subdued but threatening crackle. In the dimness they turned to each other.

"Slaves?" he repeated. "Not to us."

"Well—to the life you create, to the passions you arouse in us. Oh, you don't know what it is to be a woman! I tell you it's nothing less than horrible. Look at Meg, and Pheasant, and me!"

She caught the glint of a smile. He said: "Look at Maurice, and Piers, and me!"

"It's not the same. It's not the same. You have your land, your horses, your interests that absorb almost all your waking hours."

"What about our dreams?"

"Dreams are nothing. It's reality that tortures women. Think of Meg, hiding in that awful cabin. Pheasant, locked in her room. Me, grinding away in an office."

"I can't," he answered, hesitatingly. "I can't put myself in your place. I suppose it's awful. But never think we don't know a hell more torturing."

"You do, you do! But when you are tired of being tortured you leave your hell—go out and shut the door behind you, while we only heap on more fuel."

"My darling!" His arms were about her. "Don't talk like that." He kissed her quickly, hotly. "There, I said I wouldn't kiss you again, but I have—just for good-bye."

She felt that she was sinking, fainting in his arms. A swirl of smoke, perfumed by pine boughs, enveloped them. A rushing, panting sound came from the heart of the fire. The violins sang together.

"Again," she breathed, clinging to him. "Again."

"No," he said, through his teeth. "Not again." He put her from him and went to the other side of the bonfire, which now blazed forth once more. He stood among his brothers, taller than they, his hair red in the firelight, his carved face set and pale. Recovering herself, she looked across at him, thinking that she would like to remember him so.

In a pool of serene radiance, Grandmother sat. A black velvet cloak, lined with crimson silk, had been thrown about her shoulders; her hands, glittering with rings, rested on the top of her gold-headed ebony stick. Boney, chained to his perch, had been brought out to the terrace at her command, that he might bask in the light of the birthday conflagration. But his head was under his wing. He slept, and paid no heed to lights or music.

She was very tired. The figures moving about the lawn looked like gyrating, gesticulating puppets. The jigging of the fiddles, the moaning of the flute, beat down upon her, dazed her. She was sinking lower and lower in her chair. Nobody looked at her. One hundred years old! She was frightened suddenly by the stupendousness of her achievement. The plumes of the bonfire were drooping. The sky loomed black above. Beneath her the solid earth, which had borne her up so long, swayed with her, as though it would like to throw her off into space. She blinked. She fumbled for something, she knew not what. She was frightened.

She made a gurgling sound. She heard Ernest's voice say: "Mamma, must you do that?"

She gathered her wits about her. "Somebody," she said, thickly, "somebody kiss me—quick!"

They looked at her kindly, hesitated to determine which should deliver the required caress; then from their midst Pheasant darted forth, flung herself before the old lady, and lifted up her child's face.

Grandmother peered, grinning, to see which of them it was, then, recognizing Pheasant, she clasped the girl to her breast. From that hug she gathered new vitality. Her arms grew strong. She pressed Pheasant's young body to her and planted warm kisses on her face. "Ha," she murmured, "that's good!" And again—"Ha!"

DIEPPE

Lionel Shapiro

It was as though the light breeze weaving in off the Channel had been whispering ominously. The atmosphere on the docks was heavy with foreboding.

Medical officers, nursing sisters, and orderlies stood about in small silent groups in the warming sun outside the three huge tents of the casualty clearing station which had been set up during the night. Senior officers, some with red tabs on their lapels and wearing handsome Glengarries, peered out to sea from the edge of the landing stage. The townsfolk were lined along the sea wall, their faces scrubbed and solemn as on a churchgoing day. Even children frolicking in the streets behind the sea wall seemed to understand they must not laugh or shout.

Brad moved restlessly about the docks. It was five hours past 0430 zero and there was no news, at least they were giving out none.

At a signals unit, which had established itself in a shed, a rosy-cheeked lieutenant simply shook his head. "Nobody really knows anything," he said. "The wireless net is all balled up."

A Canadian brigadier, tall and slim and crisply handsome, shaded his eyes as he looked out to sea. "The battle is still engaged," he said curtly, "heavily engaged." He walked a piece down the landing stage in a clear maneuver to avoid further inquiry.

Toward eleven o'clock a new convoy of ambulances rumbled down the gap into the town and parked behind the ambulances which had come in during the night. Everyone turned to watch the drivers slide their vehicles into disciplined rows facing the casualty clearing station. Two jeep-loads of war correspondents and photographers roared in, looked about, and roared away, but not before they had left a rumor in their wake that the first news would soon break on the wireless. By the time it came almost everyone in the dock area had converged on the signals shed.

"The Prime Minister has just informed the House of Commons," an immaculate BBC voice announced, "that shortly before dawn this morning a strong Canadian force joined by small elements of British troops and escorted by ships of the Royal Navy drove onto the French coast in the vicinity of Dieppe. Beyond specifying that no permanent beachhead is being attempted, Mr. Churchill provided no details of the action, but a dispatch just received from Ross Munro of the Canadian Press indicates that some tanks have managed to get ashore and very fierce fighting has developed in the beach area near the Dieppe casino . . ."

Brad went up into the town and searched out the post office. It was a small, well-ordered room staffed by an elderly woman who was brewing tea on an electric burner behind her wicket.

He said, "Can I get through to London?"

"It depends, sir. All the trunks are reserved by the signals people. I can put you through to them. If it's official business I should think they'd have a line open."

He said, "It's not official business."

The woman poured boiling water into a pot and dropped a cosy over it. "I'm ever so sorry, sir."

He didn't have to wonder what Valerie might be thinking. It knifed at his brain. "Are you sure I can't get through? A very short call?"

The woman said, "Oh yes, sir, quite sure. I couldn't possibly."

Making his way back to the docks he remembered about the fierce fighting on the beach and he thought of Timmer. It came as a discovery that, in the crisis, he liked the man enough to worry about him. He moved around the silent, waiting groups of Canadians and sat on an ironhead and smoked. The Channel was sparkling calm; wisps of white cloud made the sky interesting. It was a perfect summer's day and indescribably sad.

The first wounded came in a few minutes after the clock in the town struck noon.

A flight of Spitfires roared low over the docks, banked steeply, and screamed back out to sea as if to herald an approach of importance, and a little later two ships appeared on the horizon. Gradually they became identifiable. One was a tank landing craft, low and stubby, and on its port side a sleek corvette moved slowly in escort.

As the ships passed under the breakwater cannon, a murmur rose from the folk along the sea wall. The LCT was holed and scarred above the waterline and a portion of its bridge had been blown away. A blood-red flare, discharged from the corvette, hung in the air a brief moment. On the landing stage a space had been cleared for medical officers and a host of orderlies hugging stretchers.

The moment the craft was tied up, the orderlies scrambled aboard and carried off the wounded. When all the stretcher cases had been brought into the tents, the walking wounded hobbled off, slowly and with a certain dignity, but their rough stubbled faces were yellowish pale and tense and they spoke not a word until they disappeared inside a reception tent. The last were the dead, eight stretchers bearing bodies snugly rolled in khaki blankets with only their scuffed boots protruding. These were carried to a great empty warehouse at the back of the docks.

The small ships came in all during the afternoon. They arrived in groups of three and sometimes four under escort of a warship and canopied by a flight of fighters. No one asked how the battle had gone. There was no need when an LCI came in under tow, its steel sides twisted and holed, its decks almost awash, its passengers lying in grotesque positions, lying dead; or when battle-shocked soldiers, their faces darkened by terror, were led faltering like whipped children into the reception tent. The crisply handsome brigadier paced a section of the dock, his swagger stick flicking nervously against his thigh.

In the CCS orderly room, a businesslike sergeant allowed Brad to consult the lengthening list of dead and wounded. There were names from Edmonton and Windsor and many towns in the province of Quebec. His eyes lingered on one from Bridgeport, Connecticut, a lieutenant belonging to the 1st U. S. Ranger battalion. There was a French-Canadian name from Ste. Agathe, Quebec. He had often passed through that pretty town on his way to the skiing hills, and he thought how little the man must have dreamed he would wind up wrapped in a khaki blanket on a dock in the south of England.

After a time he wandered to the back of the surgical tent. A medical officer, his rubber apron flecked with blood, sat smoking on a stool.

"Bad?"

The medical officer said, "Bad. Mostly amputations."

"Any idea how the casualties run?"

"Rough guess would be fifty per cent. Maybe more. A lot never got off the beach. We won't know about them until the Germans tell us."

A nurse appeared at the flap of the tent.

"The patient is ready, Major."

The surgeon tossed away his cigarette, looked distastefully at the mess on his rubber apron, blinked up at the sun, and went in.

Brad found himself at the warehouse where the dead lay on stretchers. A three-ton truck covered by a tarpaulin had backed up to the entrance and the dead were being loaded. The boots protruding from each wrapped blanket held him in terrible fascination. As each stretcher was lifted into the truck, the boots jiggled.

He counted the dead being placed in the truck. Eighteen bodies exactly covered the empty space and then the tarpaulin was fastened down and the truck moved off. Another truck backed into position. He was unable to keep his eyes from the operation, yet he was strangely unaffected by it. Death in khaki was a most simple event, final, factual, and trivial as a penny transaction. He studied the boots jiggling as each body was lifted and he remembered the men on the decks of the ships peering inshore. Before the war ended he too might be lifted into a truck, his boots jiggling, and he found he could consider even this possibility without high emotion. But he was too honest not to realize he was safely on England's south coast and that the nearest enemy was fifty miles across the water. He watched the loading and after a time he thought of Timmer and he felt a sudden, terrible urge, like a barbarous cry rising from deep inside him, to run off, anywhere, away from this place.

By late afternoon he began to doubt that Timmer had survived. More than forty ships had put into the harbor, most of them carrying a complement of dead and wounded, but there were a few that arrived unscathed, the troops aboard fresh and cheerful. These belonged to a floating reserve that had not been committed to battle because the situation on the beaches had become hopelessly beyond repair.

The docks surged with troops, some tattered and glassy-eyed, some defiantly happy as if they had proved to their own satisfaction that they were sufficiently tough and unafraid. Most chattered excitedly to anyone within range. Non-coms, seeking to form up the remnants of their units, added to the din, and over everything a loud-speaker crackled out countermanding orders to all ambulance dirvers to take their loads to No. 6 General "and not—repeat not—to No. 5." A bedeviled Red Cross girl found it difficult to get anyone to accept the gum and cigarettes she carried about in a cardboard box and seemed grateful when a war correspondent in a spanking new uniform took a handful.

On the strength of his alien uniform, Brad managed to gain the attention of a full colonel who had just come off a destroyer in company with a lot of important-looking naval officers.

The colonel, panting and harried, said, "If he went in on the flanks, at Berneval or Pourville, he may be all right. If he went in at Dieppe, chances are he's been hit or a prisoner. Sorry, old man," he said and hurried off.

At six o'clock Brad shouldered his way off the docks in search of Arkinson. He found the driver perched on the running board of the car polishing a long-barreled pistol.

"What do you think, Lieutenant?" Arkinson called out, displaying his acquisition. "German Luger for twenty bucks. Bet I can get fifty for it in London. Any sign of the colonel yet?"

Brad said, "We'll give it another half an hour. If he doesn't show we'll have to figure he landed at another port."

"Or he's a dead pigeon," Arkinson volunteered, still admiring his Luger.

They watched a flight of Spitfires circle over the Channel and soon a lone destroyer appeared on the horizon. Brad hurried back to the docks. The clamor had subsided and everyone strained toward the water's edge as the warship steamed slowly toward port. Both of its forward turrets were heaps of blackened, distorted metal. Its deck railings hung like ribbons over the sides. A multitude of uniforms, soldiers and sailors, jammed the afterdeck.

A tug was required to push the ship's stern toward the dock and then the debarkation proceeded in the regular order—the wounded, the walking wounded, the unscathed, and last, the dead. Timmer was not among them, at least not among the living.

There was no point in waiting any longer. It was nearly seven. Brad walked among the milling, excited survivors on the landing stage and tried to convince himself that Timmer had been brought to another port. He couldn't imagine him dead or captured. The man was too strong, too ambitious, too calculating, and though a fragment of shrapnel was neutral in its flight, he wouldn't believe Timmer had fallen when so many lesser men had succeeded in getting away. Whatever else Timmer might be, in the business of being a soldier he was more professional than the genuine article.

He made a last check in the CCS orderly room. The sergeant on duty, weary of the repeated inquiries, shook his head in advance. "No luck, sir. All we got in the line of Americans is a couple of Rangers, a lieutenant, and a W/O. One dead, one wounded. No colonels."

Then, on his last look around before quitting the docks, he caught a glimpse of Timmer.

For a moment he wasn't quite sure. He had spotted him in a break between two platoons of Canadians marching toward a column of trucks. The man sat on a packing case, his body bent forward and his hands circling his eyes like blinkers. He wore no recognizable uniform; a faded khaki shirt open across the chest, and blue, grease-smeared trousers, and white sneakers. But there was hardly any mistaking the rugged shoulders, the shiny black hair, and the square, stubbled jaw.

Brad scrambled across the line of march.

"Colonel!" he called out. "Colonel Timmer!"

The rugged man brought his hands down wearily from his face. He looked about frowning, his mouth agape, and when he caught sight of Brad, his frown deepened.

"I'm glad to see you, Colonel. For a minute I——"

"What are you doing here?" The gruff monotone had taken on a new, almost plaintive quality.

Brad was mystified by the query. The man's face clearly bore the pallor of exhaustion but he appeared in full possession of himself. His arms were crossed on his hairy chest and he was looking away distastefully.

"I asked you what you're doing here."

Brad said, "I don't know what you mean, sir."

"What time is it?"

"About seven, Colonel."

Timmer was still looking away. "What were my orders?"

"You said to wait till six but I decided to stick around awhile longer——"

Timmer growled sharply, "What were my orders?"

"Six o'clock, sir."

"God damn it, why don't you follow orders?"

Brad said, "The way this thing was going, I was frankly worried——"

"To hell with it." Timmer got to his feet. "Let's get to the car."

His sneakers lacked laces and were too big for him. They flopped on the pavement as the two men made their way between trucks and ambulances and columns of marching soldiers to where the car was parked.

Timmer didn't return Arkinson's smart salute, nor did he seem to hear the driver's cheerful, "Oh boy, Colonel, am I glad to see you!" He half stumbled as he entered the car and sat heavily in a corner of the back seat.

Brad said, "Would you like to stretch out, Colonel? I'll sit in front."

"Stop fussing, God damn it!" Timmer growled. "Come on in here." His mouth worked angrily. "After this be goddamn sure you follow orders."

As the car moved slowly forward and merged with the stream of military traffic chugging up the gap, Brad studied his chief. The man's jaw was tense, his teeth tightly clenched, his eyes fixed straight ahead as if trying to spear Arkinson's back. There were signs of traumatic shock but not to be compared with some of the helplessly wailing men who had been led off the ships.

He couldn't credit the first explanation that entered his mind for Timmer's strange attitude of resentment. It was hardly possible that the man had wanted him to return to London alone and report him missing, in order to create as profound an impression as possible on the high command. Thinking back on the sequence of events, he decided it *was* possible. There had been, after all, only one purpose in Timmer's mind.

Progress was slow. The highway was jammed with trucks, troop carriers, ambulances, and huge tank transporters. The latter, most of them vacant, covered almost the whole of the road. Arkinson weaved the light car in and out among the slower vehicles but there was always another lumbering convoy around the next bend.

Timmer remained silent, his small bloodshot eyes open but introverted. After almost an hour he muttered, "I didn't get ashore."

Brad said carefully, "From what I hear, Colonel, perhaps it's just as well."

Timmer didn't seem to hear him. He said, "Our LCI took a direct hit a hundred yards out. Holy Christ, the mess!"

"You were lucky."

For the first time some animation came into Timmer's face. His forehead creased over quizzically and he said, "A lot of guys weren't."

He lapsed into another silence and his tired eyes concerned themselves with Arkinson's driving. The truck convoys were thinning out and the staff car gathered speed as it leaped ahead into the dusk.

Night came swiftly. Timmer sat motionless in his corner. He might have dozed off. Then suddenly, from behind the shield of darkness, he began to speak.

"Twice," he said, picking up a train of thought as if there had been no interval. "I was exploded into the goddamn water twice." His voice retained only a portion of the gruffness he had always affected. Now it was shot through with a nervous, tremulous intensity.

He said, "First time a torpedo boat fished me out and it swung inshore to pick up a couple other guys and then *that* boat caught it smack on the button. Christ! Those German gunners! Had the beach and the approaches taped with enfilading fire. Artillery was deadly—deadly. Second time I hit the water I was naked as a baby. No Mae West. Nothing. I flopped around a hell of a time. They were machine-gunning me out there. Then this sub-chaser picked me up. Christ!"

Brad remembered seeing a sub-chaser tie up a piece down the docks. It hadn't shot a red flare, there seemed to be no troops on its deck, and he hadn't checked it.

Timmer wasn't finished. "Know what I was thinking out there? Get Timmer! That's what I was thinking. Get Timmer! Like the Jerry gunners had an order. The way they were gunning for me that's what I was thinking. Christ!"

That was all. The car rumbled through the darkness. Now Brad understood the man's resentment. He understood it clearly. The key was Timmer's vanity. The man who knew he was better than the professional had discovered he wasn't.

Brad leaned back against the seat and closed his eyes and listened to the wheels singing on the pavement. He laughed to himself. They weren't singing Valerie but he imagined he could hear it. Just a year ago, he remembered, he had been nominated Malton's "young man of the year." His picture had been in the paper, stern and scrubbed, the epitome of civic responsibility. He wondered how it had come about that he needed her so much. He wasn't that young, nor that unhappy, nor that lonesome. Yet he needed her. The very fact that the wheels were spinning toward her brought into play emotions he neither understood nor had ever experienced. For the first time he couldn't analyze a problem involving himself. The trustworthy look fore and aft over the years was failing him. He was living on a level of excitement and Valerie was part of the excitement and he wouldn't know until the excitement was spent what was her real place in the fabric of his life. Meanwhile the wheels were spinning and they were singing Valerie.

He heard Timmer's voice cry, "Pull up here!"

They were passing through a city. The night was black, but there were tiny flashlights weaving on both sides of the street, as though a great many people were strolling, and subdued signs marking the entrances to places of business.

"Pull up! Pull up, Arkinson!"

The car came to a halt and the sudden silence was dominated by Timmer's quick, heavy breathing. He said, "Got any money, Brad? Couple of pounds?" Brad handed him two pounds and he thrust the money at Arkinson. "We just passed a pub. Run back and see if they'll sell you a bottle."

The driver said, "What kind, Colonel?"

"Anything."

"You mean liquor, sir?"

"God damn it, I said anything!"

When Arkinson had gone, Timmer muttered, "They gave me a swallow of rum on the sub-chaser. Water was freezing."

Brad said, "I can understand, Colonel. That and the shock."

"What shock?" the other demanded. "I don't know what the hell you're talking about. Stop fussing! God damn it, stop this fussing!"

Arkinson came back with a bottle. "It's Irish whisky, Colonel. That's all they'd sell me. Came to twenty-six and six."

Timmer held out both hands for the bottle and the change. "All right, let's get going." He pressed the change into Brad's hand. "Swig?"

Brad said, "Not now, Colonel. I'm not up to it."

There was a grunt in reply. Timmer thumbed off the cap and, leaning back to steady himself, took a long drink, gasped, and took another. During the next half hour he took frequent swigs. Between swigs he rested the bottle on the seat between his thighs and stared out the window into the darkness.

He said, "They got guts, those Canadians. Jeez, they got guts. All kinds of guts." The monotone was gruff and virile now as Brad first knew it. "I don't mean only the troops going in. Hell, the poor bastards *had* to have guts. What else have you got?—going in with the Germans sitting behind their emplacements pretty as you please and mowing 'em down like dry hay. Christ, you never saw anything like it."

He chuckled inexplicably and took a long, gurgling drink.

"It's the boyo in command I'm thinking of. The battalion commander. *He* had guts. I tell you, Brad, you got to have it to take your battalion in there when it's pure murder. Going in there and getting shot up—that's all right, but the guy who's got to give the command when there's hardly a hope in hell, *that* takes guts, and whoever it was I take off my hat to him."

He chuckled again. "I know 'cause I was there, right in it. I couldn't believe it when our LCI's began moving into the beach. I knew we'd never make it. I kissed myself good-by a dozen times. Every reason, Brad. I guess there's no more'n half that battalion alive right now. No more'n half, prob'ly less. Takes guts to give orders like that. You got to have it. In the military business you just got to have it. Here's to the baby who gave the order——"

He drank again, but this time only a sip, for the bottle dropped from his hand and fell to the floor boards. Brad grabbed it and handed it back. Not much liquor spilled. There wasn't much left to spill.

The car slowed down and moved in a stream of traffic through a narrow street.

"What's this, Ark'son?" Timmer asked. His voice had become furry.

"Not sure, Colonel. I think it's Croydon."

Timmer said, "Say, boy, that's nice going. We're almost in. Almost in," he repeated. He turned to Brad. "Well, I guess Mister Ed Cantrell didn't win his gamble after all. This crazy coot Timmer went to France and got back in one piece. Whadd'ya think of that? Whadd'ya think of that, eh, Brad? Crazy coot goes to France and gets back. In one piece too. That'll shake Mister Honor Cadet. Eh?"

He took a swig out of the bottle and handed it to Brad.

"Here, take it. Lousy whisky. Plain lousy."

Brad took the bottle, which was nearly empty. Timmer's hand dropped to the seat between them and the big, handsome, stubbled face twitched and rolled from side to side until the car reached Brook Street where he lived.

THE PRINCESS AND THE WILD ONES

W. O. Mitchell

When Miss Henchbaw got up and stood there with her hands folded across her stomach, she had her mouth sort of turned up at the corners, like when she's got something to tell us and it's good. I was looking clear across the room at Lazarus Lefthand. He's in the Grade Ones. We only got four of them. Lazarus' hair is very black and it puts you in mind of those chrysanthemums. He is the only Indian kid we got in Rabbit Hill School.

Miss Henchbaw she looked down at us; her grey hair, that's piled up like those round loaves of bread, was under the writing on the board:

THE GIRL PLAYS WITH THE DOG.
IT IS FUN TO PLAY.

"Children!" Her voice all the time goes up at the end. "There will be a half holiday. Mr. MacTaggart has spoken to the school board and we've decided—they think it would be nice if the girls could wear white dresses with red and blue sashes. The school board are supplying the flags. They'd like the Grade Five choir to open with O Canada." She stared at Stevie Kisiw twirling his ruler on his compass. "Steve!"

Steve's ruler clattered on the desk.

"Now—just the first verse. And Mr. MacTaggart says that whether or not the Princess Elizabeth gets off the train—if she only steps out onto the—"

"Caboose," Stevie said.

"Observation car—he would like a presentation of flowers by one of the school children."

The kids didn't make much noise; you could just hear them sort of draw in their breath. Mariel Abercrombie stuck up her hand. She has chops. "Mother still has dahlias and asters and marigolds and golden glow, Miss Henchbaw."

"That's nice, Mariel . . ."

"They're the last but they're nice still and there's enough of them for a bouquet and nobody else in town have their flowers last as long as ours—or come out so soon."

"Then we can depend on Mariel's mother for flowers to hand to the Princess . . ."

"Who's going to hand them up to her?" That was LaPrelle MacLeod.

"Oh—Mother—if they were our flowers I think Mother would expect *me* to hand them to the Princess . . ." faltered Mariel.

"It's quite an honor to have your flowers *given*, Mariel. I think for the next few weeks we'll keep a close record—attendance—standing in arithmetic and writing and reading. The one who has the highest average—I think as a reward that child would be the proper one to hand the bouquet to the Princess Elizabeth on the station platform."

When I got home after four, Jake was pumping water into the stock trough. Jake's our hired man that helps Ma and me farm our farm. Moses Lefthand was with him. That's Lazarus' father. Moses is Blackfoot but he doesn't live on a reserve. He quit being an Indian and he took out his citizenship papers so he could vote and go in the beer parlor if he felt like it. He can read and write like a white man.

First thing he said, he asked me how Lazarus was doing in school and I said fine.

"First day he didn't do good." Moses doesn't wear braids; his hair is cut short so it's kind of spiky.

"First day none of the Grade Ones do so good, Mr. Lefthand."

"Yeah," Moses said. "But they don't climb under the desk and stay there."

"Well—a lot of 'em bawl," I said. "Lazarus didn't bawl."

"Damn rights he didn't," Moses said. I was wondering if all Indians are built long and lean like Moses. He has a real deep voice. It is so deep it kind of buzzes against your chest. "All these kids gonna be at the depot for the royal train?"

I said they were and Jake let go the pump handle. Jake is built kind of like an Indian too when you think of it. He says that's from back-breaking work all his life from the time he kicked off the dew till the bedsprings twanged at night. "Sure gonna be some reception," he said. "Crocus folks ain't had a hell of a lot to do with royalty, but they're sure goin' after her in high gear."

Moses had hold of a twig and he was sort of drawing in the ground with the end of it. Without looking up he said a funny thing. He said, "My folks —they was kings."

"Well, now," Jake said.

"Chiefs—same thing. Signed the Blackfoot Crossin' Treaty. My uncle—him an' the Queen. She was Queen Victoria."

"That's nice," Jake said. "You oughta be down there when the royal train rolls through."

"They asked us. Reception committee. Wanted us to wear feathers—Mrs. Lefthand to carry Lazarus in a *yo-kay-bo.*"

"Did they?"

"We ain't."

"Ain't what?" Jake said.

"We'll dress proper—like Canadian citizens. Kid's too big to go in a *yo-kay-bo* on his Ma's back anyways. I'm not paintin' myself. I'm not a spectacle.

We don't wear moccasins no more. So they better get some Indians for that kinda stuff. Beads. Feathers. Porcupine quills. Green paint. That kinda stuff."

"M-hhmmm," Jake said.

"The Lefthands are Canadians just like other people. One hundred percent altogether Canadian. We quit. They better get real Indians."

When Moses had left and Jake was sitting on a stool stripping Mary, in the barn, I asked him whether he figured the Prince and Princess would be going CP or CN. He said both.

"I wonder what their train will be like, Jake?"

"They ain't goin' day coach, Kid."

"Bring it over on the boat with 'em?"

"Oh no. Probably take the Superintendent the railroad's special coach—right now they probably got her in the shops—paintin' her purple . . ." he quit.

"What, Jake?"

Jake looked up at me with his head against Mary's flank. "Royal color. Purple. Superintendent the railroad—his coach'd already be purple likely. They'll line her with red velvet—gold-plate the hot- an' cold-water taps."

"Paint a coat of arms on the caboose."

"Yeah." The milk started singing in the pail again. "They'll be eatin' oysters an' lobster an' Winnipeg gold-eye. Her an' alla their ladies-in-waitin'."

"Gee, Jake—I can hardly wait!"

I guess everybody was excited. In town it was all folks talked about—in the post office waiting for their mail—over at Malleable Brown's—MacTaggart's Trading Company—Repeat Golightly's Barber Shop. When Jake and me dropped in at Repeat's and Jake was stretched out in the chair, Repeat said: "Talk—hearin' lots of talk about the royal visit." He left off stropping the razor. "Ought to do somethin' about those blackheads there, Jake."

"Blow dirt—just blow dirt, Repeat."

"Enlarges the pores. Raises aitch with the pores. Lot of talk about this visit." He kind of lowered his voice the way he does and leaned over Jake. "Some folks not showin' the proper spirit."

"No!" Jake started to sit up.

"Hold still there. Can't shave a movin' object." Repeat pushed him back. "Not our own, mind you—not Crocus folks. Foreign element. Conception. Conception district. Few been in the shop."

"But what did they . . ."

"Not making a single preparation. Wonderful thing—royalty. I say royalty's a wond—"

"Yeh."

"Generation to generation." Repeat pulled up the skin under Jake's ear. "Aristocracy."

"Uh-huh."

"Figurehead the shipa state. Empire. Shade to the left. I like to look at the Empire like a crown. Struck me that way, crown. An' Crocus has her place there. Every single part the Empire's a jool."

"Yeah."

"Saskatchewan's one the jools." Repeat wiped off a fluff of lather onto the paper on Jake's chest. "You could say she was one the jools."

"Gettin' her down real fine when you come to towns like Crocus an' Conception, aren't you, Repeat?"

"Facet. One the facets one the jools."

"Huh?"

"Way a jool is cut. Facets. Faces, thousands faces. Facets." Repeat pumped Jake up straight. "Crocus is one of the facets in one the jools—set in the crown the Empire. Fifty cents. That'll be fifty cents, Jake."

Jake and me dropped in at Malleable Brown's and the bellows going *hawgh—hawgh*. Malleable said he was all set for the royal visit. He said he thought it was real nice and gracious and charming of the royal couple to save their visit till after harvest was over. While we walked over to MacTaggart's Trading Company we passed the Credit Union hall and heard the Crocus Band practicin' Rule Britannia under Mr. Tucker. I said to Jake it sounded fine and he said it sounded more like guerrilla warfare. When we got into MacTaggart's store, Mayor MacTaggart said:

"Wheels are rollin'. Set the machin'ry in motion. IODE has been alerted. Women's Auxiliaries all the churches. Rot'ry—Activarians—Junior C. of C. Real burden the reception's being carried by the Crocus Disaster and Emergency Relief Committee."

"Disaster an' . . ."

"Just the official title," Mr. MacTaggart explained to Jake. "Already set up. For the occasion we've changed the purpose. Hig Wheeler's group has switched from Shelter and First Aid to Decoration. Erecting an arch over at the depot covered with wheat and oats and flax and barley bundles. Sign in colored lights—Not like some communities."

"You mean Conception," Jake said.

"Aren't lifting a finger. No civic pride. We live up to our responsibilities. Homer Toovey—MacDougall Implement—supplying DDT."

"What the aitch for!"

"Stockyards and loading platforms. C'rrals—swamping them out—spraying them so's there won't be flies ner smells."

"That's nice," Jake said.

"Got a couple mounties from Brokenshell," Mr. MacTaggart said, "that can ride. Dress uniform. United Church choir's rolling. Flags—bunting—"

"Looks like one the facets one the jools is gonna twinkle."

"Huh?"

"Manner of speakin', Mac. What time of day does this royal train roll through?"

"Thursday afternoon."

"Yeh—I know—what time?"

"Why–say–come to think of it–I'm in the dark about that, Jake. Jus' went along thinking of the regular trains–this one's special. We'll slip over to the depot. Way-freight Brown'll know."

Over at the depot when Mr. Brown came to the wicket, Mr. MacTaggart asked him what time the royal train was stopping in Crocus.

"They are flyin' high over the grey Atlantic," Mr. Brown started off the way he talks like those CPR travel folders. "In a luxuriously appointed strato-cruiser–high above the storms an' tempests–"

"Yeh–I know," Mr. MacTaggart cut in, "but what we were interested in–"

"Down the broad St. Lawrence, past quaint habitant Quebec to the hist'ried city of Montreal–"

"Way-freight," Jake said.

"Through the garden the Dominion–Niagara peninsula–North shore mighty Superior where green-clad pines stand their sentinel watch . . ."

"How–long–are–they–stopping–off–here?" Mr. MacTaggart said each word clear and slow.

Way-freight Brown looked kind of startled. "They aren't."

"Whaaat!"

"Take the Saskatchewan prairies faster'n a greased gopher through a thirty-six-inch thrashin' machine. Eager to catch their first glimpse of the soft swellin' beauty the Alberta foothills."

"They aren't even stoppin'!"

"Regina–Moose Jaw–not here," said Mr. Brown. "Orders."

"Then all this preparation, all this work–it's been useless."

Jake said, "Couldn't you–uh–drop a line to the Superintendent the railroad, Way-freight?"

"Jake," Mr. Brown sighed, "the Superintendent this railroad doesn't even know I'm breathing in Crocus. When they tell me that train's takin' on water down the line at Conception–"

"Whaaat!"

"Huh!"

"Seven minutes–at Conception–got to take on water."

"You'll have to get it changed," Mr. MacTaggart said.

"Mac–nothing's going to get changed. Nobody tampers with this railroad."

"But they could change–"

"If you're looking for your true royalty in North America," Mr. Brown said, "you look at the railroad. There is aristocracy. If you wanta see a royal edict." He waved a sheaf of paper at Jake and Mr. MacTaggart. "Just you take a look at a railway time schedule."

Mr. MacTaggart took it pretty hard. Me and Jake went right along with him whilst he called the town council together. He explained to them how the royal train wasn't even stopping at Crocus–how she was stopping seven minutes to take on water at Conception that hadn't even lifted a finger to a royal welcome. All aitch broke loose and Mr. MacTaggart rapped the table with his gavel. Mr. Tucker that leads the band said they'd have to bring pressure to bear; he said it wasn't any use getting up a pedition—have to write our pressure groups. Malleable Brown asked what were pressure groups.

"When you want something, Malleable," Mr. MacTaggart said, "you work on pressure groups."

"How do you start it rollin' then?" Malleable asked. "We got any pressure groups here in Crocus?"

Mr. MacTaggart said they weren't pressure groups exactly but they'd do: Rotary, Activarians, South Crocus Homemakers, IODE. Whole meeting kind of blew up with councilors shouting where to send letters to—asking for the royal train to take on water at Crocus instead of Conception: provincial and federal members—Minister Education—Minister Agriculture—Minister Lands and Mines.

"Don't stop at Ottawa!" Mr. Tucker yelled. "Send 'em to England!"

"Wouldn't even hurt to send one to Prime Minister England," Malleable shouted.

"Sure," Merton Abercrombie jumped up. "To the Queen—let the IODE do that one. Tell 'em to remind her about that quilt!"

"What quilt?" said Malleable Brown.

Over Mr. MacTaggart's gavel banging, Mr. Abercrombie shouted, "One she sold to the IODE!"

"She didn't sell any quilt to the IODE."

"Sure she did!"

"It was a rug she hooked. Couple million dollars!"

"All right—remind her that rug when they write!"

When Jake and me were riding back to the farm, I asked Jake if he thought she'd work or not. Jake said he didn't know, but they'd sure have to pay attention to those letters to railroad officials, cabinet ministers, Prime Minister. Couldn't ignore the South Crocus Homemakers, Activarians, Young CCF Club, Crocus Caledonian Society of Knock-Out Curlers. Jake he figured they might have a fifty-fifty chance.

But Mr. MacTaggart wasn't the only one having trouble. Out at Rabbit Hill School Mariel Abercrombie and Cora Swengle tied for being the kid that would hand the flowers to the Princess. Miss Henchbaw said all right then we'll have a vote to see who it'll be. Cora Swengle won. Mariel bust out crying. She said her mother wouldn't come across with the flowers. Miss Henchbaw said she thought she would and Mariel cried worse so Miss Henchbaw got mad and she said she didn't like Mariel's attitude and Mariel said she didn't care and she ran out into the cloakroom. I told Jake and Moses Lefthand about it when I got home.

"Don't matter aitch of a lot now," Jake said. "Don't even know if the train's stoppin'."

"Why didn't they pick my kid Lazarus?" Moses said.

"S'posed to be the one with the high av'rage," I told him. "Grade Ones weren't in on it."

"Why not?" Moses said.

"Too little."

"My kid ain't little. He could hand flowers to somebody. He could do it."

"I guess she figgered it should be a older kid, Moses," Jake said.

"My kid's a Canadian kid," Moses said kind of stubborn. "My kid's a good size for his age."

"For his age . . . yeah . . . but . . ."

"She think he's little?" Moses turned to me.

"Search me, Moses. She wants one of the older kids."

"What's the difference?" Jake said. "The whole thing's all tangled up in the britchin' now."

"All the same," Moses said stubborn, "I'm gonna see this teacher. I got to find out about them Grade Ones where Lazarus is." He hitched up his Boss Of the Range pants. "Just in case."

It was a week later and folks still didn't know whether the Princess would even stop at Crocus, that Moses came to Rabbit Hill School. It was after four and I was cleaning off the blackboards.

He walked right up to her desk. She said hello and Moses said:

"He doin' what you say?"

"Oh–yes–Mr. Lefthand. Lazarus is doing very well."

"Like the other kids?"

"He was a little shy at first . . ."

"Now–about these flowers."

"Flowers? I don't . . ."

"These Princess flowers. What you gonna do for the Grade Ones without flowers?"

"Oh–that. We had a little misunderstanding and . . ."

"I'd like my kid to do this."

"Oh," Miss Henchbaw said. "Oh."

"You forgot all about the Grade Ones when you picked your kid," Moses said and he stared down at her. "And my kid."

"Well, no. We have to be fair about it. All the children would love to do it. Their parents would . . ."

"He ain't small."

"I beg your pardon."

"Six years old. He's the right size for that. You better use a Grade One kid. It would be nice if you used Lazarus."

"Oh." Miss Henchbaw cleared her throat. "We–we can't change our plans now, Mr. Lefthand. It wouldn't be–uh–fair. Just–we try to run the classrooms in a democratic way."

"You do this democratic?"

"I think I did."

"Those Grade Ones–did they vote?"

"Why–well–they're so small . . ."

"Miss Henchbaw–I'm sorry you forgot all about those little Grade Ones."

"I suppose I–"

"Poor little Grade One," Moses said.

"There are only four of them."

"You know what that is?" Moses leaned over her desk. "They got no rights your little Grade Ones. Minors. Just little minor group in your school, huh?" Miss Henchbaw didn't say anything. "Poor little Grade Ones," Moses said sad. "Can't give flowers. Can't take a crack at it. Poor little minor Grade Ones group."

"There are no minority groups in my school, Mr. Lefthand!" She just cracked it out.

"Yes."

"I–may have seemed–to overlook–what would you suggest, Mr. Lefthand?"

"This way. Give 'em each a nickel. Then they flip this nickel. Odd Grade One he gives the flowers."

"And what about the twos and threes and fours and the rest of the school?"

"Oh–I didn't think of that."

"Then your oversight"–Miss Henchbaw got up–"is much worse than mine, isn't it?"

"Yeah," Moses said. "Yeah."

I didn't hear what else they said because Miss Henchbaw noticed me and she said I better be going home.

"Sure a mess," Jake said. "Wranglin' about who's gonna give her flowers when they don't even know she's gonna stop off long enough to take 'em."

"Wonder how the council made out with those letters, Jake?"

"We'll find out, Kid. Cream can's full. You an' me'll see Mac when we go into town this afternoon."

Mr. MacTaggart didn't look so cheerful. "Just going over to Way-freight's now," he told us. "See if there's any developments."

Jake and me went with him. Way-freight Brown looked up when we came in. He had that green eyeshade on whilst he sat at the telegraph key.

"We just took a dangle over," Mr. MacTaggart said. "See if there was any–"

Way-freight cleared his throat. He looked kind of dazed. "First time in forty-two years' experience with this railroad–gentlemen–seen everything."

"That royal train," Mr. MacTaggart began.

"Just before you stepped through that door." Mr. Brown kind of brushed at his forehead, like he had a cobweb tickling it or something. "Came through. Been a change."

"Yeah?"

"Yeah!"

"Orders–slight change in orders."

"Concernin' takin' on water at Conception," Mr. MacTaggart prodded him.

"The royal train," Way-freight's voice took a kind of a skip and a jump, "trailin' her snowy plume of steam an' smoke across the wavin' fields of golden grain—takes on her water—uh—at Crocus." He quit and you could hear the telegraph key going to beat anything. "For this she will require—not the usual seven minutes—but eleven."

Everything got rolling; the band started practicing again in the Credit Union Hall; they finished up the arch at the depot. The day the royal visit folks came streaming into town from all over Crocus district—from Brokenshell and Macoun and Ogema and Tiger Lily and Wrist Hills. We drove into town with Baldy and Queen and the democrat and the Lefthands rode with us. Folks came in their cars and wagons, jamming the whole downtown.

Mrs. Lefthand and Lazarus they just sat in the democrat not saying anything. "We got to get near the front," Moses said and he looked down at the newspaper-wrapped parcel Lazarus had on his knee.

"Sure," Jake said.

And he did. We were right down there next the platform. I could see Mayor MacTaggart's hand trembling so the paper speech in his hand was shaking as he walked up and down, his lips moving. Then somebody at the east end of the crowd let out a yell. We heard her whistle.

She wasn't purple like Jake said. She stood there hissing and tinging whilst she took on water. Mr. Tucker and the band started up Rule Britannia. Then I noticed Lazarus Lefthand had taken the paper off his bundle.

They weren't big floppy asters or golden glow or dahlias that won in the flower show. They were buffalo beans he'd picked off of the prairie and Indian paintbrush and brown-eyed Susans. He had them tight in his fist. They were wildflowers.

"All right," Moses said real husky. "Me an' Miss Henchbaw flipped. She lost. You go up there and give her them, Lazarus. When Miss Henchbaw says. Just walk up and hand 'em. You're citizen too. Hers. One hunderd percent. You got kings in you." He sort of gave Lazarus a push. "If you got to do your nose," he warned him, "don't snuff it loud. Use the sleeve. When nobody's lookin'."

Little Lazarus he didn't curtsey like Cora Swengle when she gave her flowers. When the Princess took Lazarus' she smiled at him. She smiled at him and smelled his flowers and she said something to the Prince beside her. She didn't smell Cora's but she smelled Lazarus' bouquet. The wild ones.

RESURRECTION

Thomas H. Raddall

I like Montreal. It has a warmth and flavor even in winter that you find nowhere else in North America. The people smile, they chatter, they have an air about them as if they are all going to a party the moment the shops and offices close. The girls move with a sort of lilt, and without that anxious set of mouth which is the mark of women in Toronto or New York. Even policemen and taxi-drivers regard you with a look of fellowship. You have an impression that Montreal has discovered a joke on the world at large and that if you stay long enough you will find out what it is; and because the hotels are comfortable and the food is marvellous you do not mind how long it takes.

I did not like Montreal so much when I flew up there from the east coast in the frigid January of '44. It was wartime, of course. Other times, other views. I was sitting down to dine in the Mount Royal when I saw a man I knew. He was eating alone at a small table against the far wall, and I made my way over there through the chatter and tinkle and the smell of expensive furs. I did not know Sam Cutliffe very well. He had been an air-pilot barnstorming about the Maritime Provinces when I met him before the war, and someone had told me since that he was flying for Ferry Command. I recalled a brisk pink-faced man of twenty-eight or thirty, very enthusiastic about the air but looking more like an ambitious detective-sergeant on a city police force.

He did not look like that now. His cheeks were sunken and the skin had the faintly moist pallor that comes of a long time indoors. His blue eyes seemed to have drawn back into his head. He stumbled a little when he got up to greet me and I noticed a stout walking-stick hooked over the back of his chair. He wore a suit of grey tweeds that did not fit him very well.

"Hello," I said. "It's been a long time."

"Yes," he said. "Sit down, won't you? I find it awkward standing up without my stick though I'll have to get used to it. You see, I've lost most of my toes and I have a silly tendency to pitch forward on my face. You don't know how useful toes are till you have to get along without 'em."

I sat down. "A crack-up?"

"Yes."

"A nasty one, I should say."

"It wasn't much fun. It's not what you might think, though. I mean we got down all right. The trouble was afterwards. Frostbite."

"Oh? I'm surprised. The last I heard of you, you were down by the equator somewhere, ferrying planes to Africa."

"That's right," he said diffidently. "And after that I was ferrying planes to India. But five or six months ago I was shifted right back where I started, on the North Atlantic run."

"You fellows get around."

"Yes."

"Go on with your meal. I'll order as soon as I can catch a waiter's eye. I take it you've had a rough time. What do you think of all this?"

I jerked my head towards the crowd in the big room, the well-tailored men, not many in uniform, the elaborately made-up women with fur coats draped over their shoulders as if they were cold in that atmosphere of food and wine and cigarette smoke and scent all heated to seventy-five degrees, the hubbub of satisfied voices, English and French, drowning out the soft dinner music of the orchestra.

"I'm afraid you're in the wrong mood," Sam Cutliffe grinned. "You have that look of the Bluenose regarding the ill-gotten wealth of the central provinces and ready to quote Joe Howe at the drop of a balance sheet. Codfish versus caviar. Or is it, to be highly original, just that there's a war on, and you know it and they don't?"

"Put it that way," I said. "You mentioned frostbite. We see a lot of that nowadays where I live. Torpedoed crews making the shore in open boats after days and nights in this kind of weather. The nearest hospital is thirty miles away. So we've rigged up an emergency ward in the school, with beds and bedding and all that kind of thing borrowed from the homes, with our own women for nurses and the local doctor for medical staff. They get some pretty grim cases. When I think of all that and look at all this—but I daresay your first guess was close enough. Codfish versus caviar. I can't help thinking of the kids in the fishing villages who haven't seen candy in four years, while up here the shops are stuffed with it. And the women down there in cotton stockings and pre-war mail-catalogue coats, when every she-leg in this room is covered with nylon and every back with mink. It's the contrast. There's too strong a smell of money here. I confess it never bothered me before. Now it does."

"Ah!" Sam stirred his coffee while the waiter bent over me at last. When the man went away he said, "So money stinks. What an original discovery. O God, O Montreal."

I laughed. "Never mind. Let's talk about something else. Tell me about yourself. What happened, exactly? Or is that on the taboo list? We have to be very careful about the questions we ask down on the coast."

"Oh it's not secret. I doubt if it's even worth talking about. All kinds of things happen to fliers nowadays, 'specially the fighting boys, and there wasn't anything glamorous about what happened to me and my crew. You could call it a battle I suppose but it was just a fight to stay alive and the position was ridiculous. I mean we fought it lying on the ground, huddled together under a few yards of thin waterproof fabric, like the babes in the wood. You just can't be heroic in a state like that."

"Well, go on."

"You don't mean you really want to hear it? The whole story? You're not just being polite? Look here, I'm just finishing a good dinner. I started with cocktails, I had a bottle of claret with the meat, and now I'm having a dram of good brandy with the coffee. And I've been cooped up in the Royal Vic for months, watching my toes go one by one like the ten little niggers in the jingle, only I just lost eight. I might talk your ear off."

"I'll tell you when it hurts," I said. "Go on."

"Okay." He took a sip of brandy. "Remember, you asked for it. Where shall I begin—Ferry Command? I went into that soon after the R.A.F. people organized the hop, taking new bombers over the pond to Britain. At first the crews were all kinds, R.A.F. and civilian, fellows all the way from Texas to Aberdeen. You were always flying with strangers. But after a time I settled down as pilot with a chap named Addison for navigator and a radio operator named Pearce, a Nova Scotian like yourself. We three hit it off well together, we had absolute confidence in each other, and when you had that they usually let you stick together as a team.

"After a time we got shifted to the South Atlantic run, Brazil to West Africa, and then over the jungle and scrub to Khartoum and down the Nile valley to Montgomery's army. After that the India run. It was funny whenever I thought of my pre-war days, that little shoe-string air line that went bust, and then barnstorming about the Maritimes in a rickety Moth, taking the local yokels up for three dollars a flip. After a year or two in Ferry Command you got the notion that time and space didn't mean anything any more. Well, we found out about that. The law of gravity brings you down to earth in a lot of ways that Newton never bothered his head about.

"Last October we flew to Scotland from Algiers, a special job, and then after loafing about Prestwick for some days we were told to fly an old Hampden bomber over to Canada, to be used for training or some such thing. We took off with the kite on the tenth of the month, and made the hop to Iceland all right. The weather held us up three days at Reykjavik but on the morning of the fourteenth we took off for Montreal. It was a fine clear day. After three hours we sighted the white peaks of Greenland, a hundred and fifty miles away. Time and space, you see—nothing, just nothing. Then the port engine coughed and died. Like that. No warning. I suppose the poor old thing was just tired out with all its service and couldn't face another mile.

"You can't keep a Hampden up very long on one motor, so I told Pearce over the intercom to send out a distress signal. We were about an hour's ordinary flying time from the Greenland coast and losing altitude at about a hundred feet a minute. Addison worked out our position quickly. Pearce had to send it out by the emergency battery because the main radio generator worked off the port engine and of course was dead. The distress call wasn't heard anywhere but we didn't know that till long afterwards. We lightened the ship, shoving out of the hatches everything that would move—machine guns, ammo, bomb-sight, our own baggage—everything. But of course we went on losing height. And flying on one engine like that, the kite had a growing tendency to flip over on its back. Finally it did. And again. And again—falling in a tight spin with her nose straight down towards the sea. If you've ever watched one of those double-winged maple seeds drop off the tree and go spinning down to the ground you get the idea. And try to picture three insects trapped inside and pinned to their seats by the centrifugal force of the spin.

"I throttled down the starboard motor and gave the ship full right rudder and a lot of forward stick, hoping to coax her out of it before we hit the drink. We fell three thousand feet, spinning in that dizzy way. All I could think was, *This is it, Sammy, this is it*. But then, just about a thousand feet above the sea, the kite came out of her spin just as if she'd changed her mind. The port engine was still dead of course but I eased back the stick and pointed her nose for Greenland. She lost height all the time but she staggered on and I managed to keep her right side up. About fifteen miles from the coast we were down to five hundred feet and I knew we couldn't clear the cliffs. That country's built on end, a high table mostly covered with ice, and a jumble of alps sticking up through the table top. I don't know what joker called it Greenland. All I've ever seen of it was black rock and blue ice and white snow.

"There was a lot of ice on the sea, too, a mixed pack of bergs and floes, just to make everything nice and hopeless. But suddenly I spotted a long patch of open water right in the middle of the pack, and that patch said to me as plain as print: *Here's your chance, Sam, come on down*. I told the boys I was going to ditch the kite and I called Addison back out of the nose, because his plexiglass was sure to cave in when we hit the water. I figured that with a bit of luck we'd sit the kite down without plowing right under and we'd have maybe two or three minutes to scramble out before she sank.

"Our low port wing bothered me, so I cut the starboard motor and turned away from it as I dived, to bring the ship to an even keel. At about forty feet above the water I leveled out. I didn't lower the landing flaps of course—the kite would stop quick enough when we hit the drink. I lifted the nose once or twice to slow her up as much as I could, and a few feet from the water I pulled it up again, just enough to stall her. That way the tail would touch the sea first and give us a chance forward. And so it did, though it was just a chance, no more. We were going seventy-five knots, at a guess. The tail slapped the sea, and the drag of it pulled the ship down on her belly with a whack that ripped off the bomb bays and stove in the plexiglass at the nose. Water flew everywhere, inside and outside the ship. Solid spouts of it rushing in through the nose and up through the bomb bays. And the hull cracking up. You can't imagine the racket. Terrific. Addison was flung against a fitting and got a nasty gash on his shin, and we all got a thundering shake-up. But we lived and we could move. We couldn't ask more than that just then.

"We had to move fast. In the first rush of water when the ship struck I thought she'd gone right under. Then I saw blue sky through the upper gun-hatch. Addison grabbed the emergency kit and out we went. I yanked my phone-cord clear. Addison's was free already but Pearce forgot his and the cord pulled his helmet off when he scrambled through the hatch. We could feel the ship going down under us. In nothing flat we were on top of her, looking for the dinghy. It was a raft really, a small thing of waterproof fabric, shaped like a six-foot rubber tire with a fabric floor in the central space. It was stowed deflated in the rear of the port engine nacelle, and a carbon-dioxide cartridge blew it up automatically when the ship struck water. And there it was, bobbing at the end of its mooring as nice as could be.

"The port wing was already three inches awash when we walked out on it. We just had time to get into the dinghy, cut the line and paddle clear when the poor old Hampden gave a quarter roll to the right and sank. That was a little more than a minute after she hit the sea and about eleven o'clock in the morning, Greenland time. Nothing was left of that busted kite but a patch of oil and four slim pieces of board. We salvaged the boards and lit cigarettes while we considered the situation.

"Our chief sensation at the moment was relief. After that terrific spin, I mean, and then the nasty choice of smacking into the cliffs or cracking up on the sea ice, and then that one miraculous space of open water just big enough to set her down in. Now here we were, safely down and afloat in the dinghy, with the emergency kit still clutched in Addison's arms. There wasn't much wind, so the ice floes weren't jammed together, in fact there were thin channels of open water wandering through the whole thing. Greenland stood up high to the west of us, looking much closer than it really was, so we took up our little metal-and-canvas paddles and headed for it, threading our way amongst the floes as cheerful as could be. It took us some time to get the hang of paddling the dinghy. The thing was circular and if you paddled too hard on one side or the other it simply spun. Also it was tipsy and we had to sit or lie just so and be careful how we moved.

"For the rest of that day we paddled slowly through the ice. The channels between the floes were sometimes wide, sometimes so narrow that you could hardly get the dinghy through, and they took us all over the place—like a little round bug trying to make its way through a jigsaw puzzle. A lot of the ice seemed to be freshly broken. The edges were sharp and we had to fend off with our hands, because of course one slit in the dinghy's fabric would have finished us. You don't get many hours of daylight in that latitude in October. When the night came down, the air turned cracking cold. Our boots and gloves and flying suits had got soaked when we ditched the ship and wet things aren't much good to you in an atmosphere like that. Pearce and I sat almost opposite each other in the dinghy, so we opened the zippers of our flying suits, laid our legs together, and then zipped up the suits again as far as they would go. And Pearce took Addison's feet inside his jacket to get some warmth from his chest. Symbolic, though we didn't think of it then. One spirit and one flesh. We learned more about that in the days and nights to come.

"The moon was nearly full and there were thousands of stars, so we had something to steer by and very good light for hunting the right channels in the ice. But it was a weird experience. Some of those bergs looked as big as cathedrals in the moonlight and—this is the queer part—they were moving slowly up and down in a perfectly calm sea. Later we knew why, but it was very mysterious and disturbing to us crouching on that flimsy dinghy in the night. Soon we noticed by the stars that the whole pack was drifting southwest. Fortunately that meant it was following the general trend of the coast. But this drift and that strange slow dance of the bergs set up from time to time a series of collisions all through the pack. We had to watch out, because often the floes would come together and squeal with the terrific pressure. And the small bergs groaned and the big ones boomed.

"Some of the big bergs seemed unsteady, too, and now and then one rolled over and set up a surge amongst the floes. And frequently in the distance where the coast loomed there'd be a crack like a fifteen-inch gun and then a splash you could hear for miles. We learned to give the big bergs a wide berth. All this clash and movement would fill the night with a racket like nothing else on this earth. Then sometimes for half an hour there'd be silence. Everything as still as death except for a queer little rustling and tinkling in the channels. The skin of the sea was freezing lightly where it was exposed to the air, and the ice crystals whispered together. God, it was cold.

"For twenty hours altogether we pushed and paddled and pulled that silly beach-toy through the ice. Often we came near being crushed when a tipsy berg set up a rumpus amongst the floes, but somehow we always managed to find a nook where we could harbor until the whole thing settled down. A nightmare? You could call it that, I guess. But I found long ago that a man can only get bothered about anything up to a certain point—the point where he's written off his chances. After that you don't care. You're quite helpless amongst all these terrific forces, there's nothing you can do about it, and after a time you get sort of interested in the whole thing, you wonder what the deuce will happen next.

"When daylight came we found ourselves in fairly open water and close in to the coast. When we got our first good look at the shore it gave us a bit of a shock. We'd been steering as best we could into a bay with a fringe of dark cliffs or what looked like cliffs in the moonlight. Now, in the cold light of day, we saw that the 'cliffs' were in fact the blue face of a glacier, a tremendous thing, and as we watched we saw a big chunk break off and topple into the sea. We'd seen the Greenland glaciers from the air of course, lots of times, but from a great height; we had no idea how big they were on the ground or how fast they moved. Some of those things have a front of several miles and they move into the sea at a rate of fifty to a hundred feet a day. Now all of a sudden we understood a lot of things, including the 'gunfire' we'd heard in the night, and the bobbing of the bergs, and their tipsiness, and the fractures that caused some of them to fall apart in the pack. We sat there staring, nobody saying a word. Finally Pearce broke the silence and he put it very well. 'Cripes,' he said, 'we've come to where they make the stuff.'

"And now we found ourselves in the coastal current where an overfall of the water set the dinghy bouncing. Every time it rose and fell we could feel the thing wobble under us, ready to flop over at the first wrong move. The sooner we got ashore the better. We didn't care for the glacier so we paddled towards a huge rock standing out of the sea like a tooth on the southwest side of the bay. When we got in close we could see it was a solid mass of stone, speckled with patches of ice and snow, that went up a thousand or maybe fifteen hundred feet.

"When we reached it we were tired and stiff, as you can guess, after all that time on that floating doughnut in the ice. Pearce stepped ashore first. His hands were numb—all our fingertips were frost-bitten—and he lost his hold on the rock and nearly fell into the sea. When he got a firm grip we tossed him the line and he pulled the dinghy in. I scrambled out with Addison. The sea had quite a surge and at that moment the line parted and we nearly lost the dinghy and the emergency kit. We jumped into the water and grabbed it just in time. I'd thought my legs were as numb as they could get, but when that cold sea rose about my thighs I felt as if I'd got caught in a bear-trap.

"The first thing was to find a ledge wide enough to hold the three of us and the boat, and high enough to be clear of spray. So we started up the face of the rock, clawing for a hold in every cranny and dragging the dinghy with us. About a hundred feet up was a ledge just big enough for the boat. We left it there for the time being and climbed up to another that was wider. There we peeled off our wet flying suits, wrung them out and spread them in the sun to dry. To dry! What a hope! At that time of year up there the sun moves in a low arc in the southern sky and in the middle of the day you get a little warmth, just enough to melt the snow a bit where the rock faces the sunshine, enough perhaps to dry a handkerchief, but never enough to dry a soggy flying suit or a pair of heavy gloves.

"We took stock of what we had. I was wearing woollen underwear and socks, a shirt, flying boots with a pair of leather shoes inside, a suit of R.A.F. battle-dress, an American infantry winter hat with a cloth crown and fur side-pieces. The others had pretty much the same except that Addison had his flying helmet and Pearce's head was bare. Our shoes inside the flying boots were wet and stiff so we took them off and tossed 'em aside. It was better just to wear the boots. Our gloves and flying suits were sodden as I've said, so we used them and the salvaged bits of board to make a thin couch under us. It was better than lying on the bare rock but that's all you could say for it. Pearce ripped the fur collar off his flying suit and made himself a cap.

"The emergency kit contained a Very pistol and twenty or thirty flares, a small flag on a metal shaft, a helio-signal mirror, twelve dozen malted milk tablets each about three-quarters of an inch square, a dozen small tablets of barley sugar, some pint tins of water, some benzedrine pills, a box of matches, a compass and a first-aid kit. And we had in our pockets a few smashed chocolate bars that we'd bought in a Reykjavik canteen. After checking over all this we went down and hauled the dinghy up to the second ledge.

"Just as we got back we heard aircraft motors. I grabbed the Very pistol and Pearce the flag. Two planes passed right overhead, a Fortress and a Liberator, going towards Iceland at about ten thousand feet. I fired six flares. Pearce waved the flag. And the planes went right on. However we figured they must be looking for us. We figured that our S.O.S. had been picked up and we knew Ferry Command would order a five-day search. We clung to that delusion but another bit of cold truth now sank in. Aircraft coming over Greenland fly very high to keep well clear of the peaks, and they start to pick up height for the crossing while they're still far out to sea. On this rock at the foot of that high coastal shelf we had no more chance of being seen from the air than three dolls in the Colorado canyon. Later that afternoon another Lib went over, about ten miles south of us and high. We shot flares and waved the flag with the same result—nothing.

"I didn't know much about the east coast of Greenland and all I knew was bad. The flow of ice out of the Polar Basin pours down that side all the way to Cape Farewell, and the glaciers bring the ice-cap right down to the coast. The result is a permanent Arctic climate. The floating ice blocks all navigation except for a few sealers and whalers in the summer, and nobody lives there except some Eskimos in a fiord a long way from our rock. The Danes and most of the Eskimos have their settlements about the southern tip of Greenland and up the west coast, where the ice-cap doesn't come right down to the sea. Some of our fliers had cracked up in Greenland and lived to tell the tale, but they'd landed on the cap itself, with dry clothes, and the plane cabin for shelter, and the wreck itself making a good mark for searching aircraft. They'd been supplied from the air with food, fuel, Arctic clothing, sleeping bags and all the rest of it, and finally they'd been taken off. We had nothing but the clothes we stood in and no food but the tablets in the little box. We had no shelter and no fuel. We were stuck on that windy rock between the glacier and a sea covered with floating ice—no place for a plane to sit down and pick us up, even if by some miracle we were seen. And a ship was out of the question up there in October with winter beginning to shut down.

"All this was pretty grim. It was better not to think about it. Addison climbed some distance up the rock and planted our flag in a crack. We hunted for a cave and found nothing. Our four bits of board were too wet to burn. We thought of bird-nests for fuel. There were none. There was no vegetation except a few lichens. In fact the rock had just one thing, fresh water lying in the cracks where the sun melted a little snow each clear noon. We decided on a ration from the tin box. Three bits of chocolate while it lasted and three milk tablets or three bits of barley sugar per man per day. We had twenty-three cigarettes in our pockets and we rationed those too. Three smokes a day, lighting each one carefully and passing it back and forth. They were a help. Surprising what comfort you can get from the small glow that you can see and feel, and the whiff of hot smoke for a moment in your lungs.

"We came to a decision about the dinghy, too. There was no hope of getting anywhere in that. It had taken us twenty hours to make fifteen miles through the ice and we'd nearly perished in a dozen ways. Besides—and this was the urgent thing—we had to have some sort of cover in case of storm. So we deflated it. Once that was done we were committed to the rock, there was no way of inflating it again, and although we knew it had to be done it was a sickening feeling, watching the thing expire and settle into a heap of flabby folds. At dark we spread the limp stuff over our flying suits to make a dry bed under us, and there we lay, huddled together for warmth and trying to sleep. But you couldn't sleep. It was too cold. And towards midnight a gale sprang up whipping snow and sleet at us. We crawled under the fabric then, tucking its ends under our heads and feet and lying on the sides to hold it down. The storm tore at us all that night, all the next day and all the following night.

"By that time all our problems had come down to one and that was grim and simple. It was just to keep alive. You see what it meant. Except when the sun was out we must lie close under that thin fabric, keeping the ends and sides tucked in, not only to keep out the cold but to save the heat of our bodies; and we must stay that way, wrapped in that yellow shroud, breathing the foul air over and over again, day and night, until the end came, whatever the end was to be. And so, as I said, there was nothing romantic about our fight with the North. Fight's the wrong word anyway. In a fight you can feel magnificent. There wasn't anything magnificent about our queer little struggle except the setting. That was grand enough.

"I saw its full scale on the third day, after the storm. The sun shone in a bright but empty sort of way, the rays slanting low from the south. We tried to scrape the snow from our ledge because at noon those rays were just enough to melt the stuff a bit, and that kept the flying suits wet under us. Well, on that day we determined to plant our flag on the summit of the rock. It would take a great effort but it was our only chance of being seen and we decided it must be done. Addison's game leg ruled him out. Pearce and I swallowed benzedrine tablets and started for the top. Those energy pills are fine when you're still comparatively strong. The sensation is marvellous. It took three hours of hard climbing, desperate in places, but at last we stood on the peak and stuck our flag firmly in a cranny.

"The view there was wonderful. All to the east was floating ice. To the west of us, across the channel between our rock and the mainland, rose a sheer cliff as high as our own, and beyond that we could see the wild peaks of the mountains. Just to the north of this cliff the coast turned in to form the bay we'd first seen, and there was the glacier like an enormous cold monster creeping down between the mountains to the sea. We didn't stay long to admire all this, though. After the climb we were sweating and the wind up there went through to the bones. It was just as tough getting down as it was getting up. When we got back to Addison we were played out. But we could see the little flag snapping in the wind up there on the peak. It looked good. Nobody could fail to see it. What a dream! By the next day that bit of bunting had flapped to shreds and gone.

"That night the cold was sharp and we lay with our arms about each other, shivering all the time. We were tired but we weren't hungry any more. That traditional stuff about hunger is quite true. During the first two or three days you have pangs in the belly and you dream about food all the time. Pearce and I fancied thick juicy steaks. Addison went in for cups of scalding coffee and heaps of hot buttered toast. But after that your tummy doesn't trouble you. It was the same thing with our feet. The feeling simply went out of them. We tried to bring it back. Each one took turns at rubbing another's feet and tucking them inside his jacket for a bit of body warmth. It was no good. As the days went by our toes turned a queer greyish color and felt more and more like bits of old rubber. Our clothes were never dry—never. We had those wet flying suits under us and our breath condensed on the inner surface of the dinghy fabric and dripped on us. What a state to be in! If there's a Hell it can't be hot and flaming as they show it in old books. It must be half-dry, half-wet and always cold, or it doesn't serve the purpose.

"We drank water from cracks in the ledge and when that froze we ate snow. We ate a lot of snow. We could claw that under the sides of the fabric without going outside and losing precious heat. We kept our wrist-watches wound. In daylight we could see the time and every minute seemed an hour, but in those long nights you couldn't see a thing and that was worse. Every night was a year. We talked now and then, mostly about our families and friends, and the things we'd do and the places we'd go if we could just wish ourselves out of that. On the fourth morning we were too cramped to lie any longer without a stretch and we turned out just before daylight. The northern lights were putting on a fine show, glittering over the cliffs. The day broke clear. Good flying weather. We still had that false dream of a search for us. But about noon a scud came over the sky with a wind from the south-east and we had to crouch under the fabric. By night it was blowing very hard. The waves breaking on the foot of the rock threw spray clean up to our ledge, a hundred and fifty feet. We stuck it for a time but soon we were lying in a pool of salt water. We had to get out.

"On our climb to the summit Pearce and I had noticed a good wide ledge another hundred feet up. We decided to make for it, there in the dark, in the gale. That really was a nightmare. As soon as we stood up the wind caught at the loose fabric in our hands and nearly dragged all three of us off the ledge. We hung on somehow, and somehow we clawed our way up that rock. Our fingertips had been frost-bitten that first night in the ice, there was no feeling in them now and the fingers were stiff and awkward. You can guess what our feet were like. The fabric flogged in our grip. It seemed to conspire with the wind to catch us in awkward places. In the pitch dark we had to fumble about for every hand-hold and foot-hold. I don't know how we made it but we did, we got to that upper ledge and crawled under the fabric again, holding the edges down. We'd abandoned the flying suits on the lower ledge. From now on we lay on the bare rock. We lay there all that night and all through the next day and night. That was the fifth day and night and the storm was still going strong with lots of snow. You understand? After five days Ferry Command assumed you were dead and wrote you off the books.

"So ended our dream of being found. We had to face the other thing. Death hadn't meant much to us up to then. Oh, we'd been close to it a good many times in the air but danger in the air is something different, everything happens very fast, your mind's fixed on your instruments, you haven't time for wondering what death may be like. Now here it was, not making a swift jump at us like all the other times but sitting right there with us, all about us, like another presence on the ledge, waiting patiently for us to give up our silly little struggle and chuck in. You could feel it. So we talked the whole thing over calmly. It's not so bad to die in a crash or in a hospital where they've taken you afterwards, or anywhere or anyhow so long as you're amongst people and the thing's marked and definite to all concerned. What's bad is the notion of perishing in a place like that rock, where your bones will never be found, nobody ever knowing what became of you. The loneliness, the awful loneliness of the thing.

"Our bones! By this time we ached in every bone, our shoulders and hips were chafed raw from all that hard lying, and to ease it we'd chucked all the stuff out of our pockets, the keys, the pocket-knives, the cigarette lighters, the pencils, the wallets containing our money and papers, the loose change, everything. You could see those things lying about the ledge whenever you scraped away the snow. And now you could see a meaning. You'd put aside all the things that had to do with the business of life. You'd written all that off. And now you could only wonder how long it would take to die, and what it would be like. We hoped we'd all go together. It was frightful to think of being the last to go.

"Once or twice in the nights, in that howling wind, it came to me that there was one way to make sure—to link arms and jump off the ledge together. A quick end to our pains and doubts. Why wait? But somehow that seemed too easy. We'd fought for life the hard way ever since we ditched the ship and—and, well, there was something mean about buying death cheap like that. I didn't mention any of this. None of us mentioned it, though we'd all thought the same thing. I know that because now our minds were too close for secrets any more. Aloud we simply admitted there was no hope and it was just a case of waiting for the end. There had to be something, though, for the time of waiting. It was Pearce who suggested prayer. Prayer together, you understand.

"To the ordinary run of men like us prayer's not a thing to shoot the breeze about. We'd heard of chaps ditched, afloat on a raft for days and weeks, and all of them taking to prayer aloud. It seemed a bit, well, hysterical. Or maybe it was just that it didn't seem quite the square thing, begging the Almighty for a favor when up to the pinch you'd been satisfied with the world and the flesh if not the devil. Anyhow Pearce made the suggestion and we talked it over. Pearce and Addison were Protestants—Baptist and Presbyterian—and I was Catholic. We'd never discussed religion. We'd never mentioned it except in the incidental way of three fellows who work together. Now we did. We compared our beliefs. And what struck us all was not the differences but the things that were the same. I'd always thought of Protestants and Catholics as two different kinds of humanity. So had Pearce and Addison. They'd even felt miles apart in their separate Protestant beliefs.

"But now after all we'd suffered together and what we were about to suffer further it seemed to us that in spirit we were one. There were no differences any more. Just as we'd thrown all the junk out of our pockets so we cleared all the small stuff out of our minds. And the feeling was wonderful. It was all so clear. Like taking off three pairs of dark glasses and seeing each other for the first time. I daresay I'm putting this badly. Perhaps you think we were all delirious with hunger and cold and exposure. Maybe you think I'm drunk now. I've never told all this to anyone and I don't know why I should be telling you. I don't want to embarrass you with these revelations. But I must tell you this. We three, we common ordinary men, found a deep understanding up there on that rock. More than that we found love—love in its true sense, the one pure thing, the kind that Christ meant every human soul to have. It came to us quietly. Like when you're waking slowly after a night's sleep and you open your eyes without thinking and you become aware that the sun's on the wall, that it isn't dark any more. And as we talked it over we wondered what kept all the world apart. We wondered at war. And we wondered at all the senseless cheating and lying and scrambling that goes on every day all over the place, as if the world was one big garbage heap and all of us a pack of rats.

"Well, I'll leave it at that. Perhaps you understand a bit of what I'm trying to say. You can understand this, anyhow. All three of us knew the Lord's Prayer. It was simple and it said everything. It was humble without whining. It was what we wanted. We repeated it aloud together every morning and every night that remained to us on the rock. On the sixth day the storm blew itself out and the sun shone. We crept out to get the benefit of it at mid-day. We even took off our boots and sunned our feet. That was a mistake, of course. The illusion of warmth or maybe just the further exposure started a pain in them and we suffered agony all that night. And through that night another gale came up and beat snow upon us, and all the next day. By that time our feet had lost all feeling again and we were thankful.

"We were getting feeble. Every movement was an effort. All our joints seemed to have gone stiff. We lay in silence except for the morning and evening prayers. In the daytime we looked at each other in the queer yellow light under the fabric. Our faces were gaunt and stubbled, our lips were dry and cracked and bleeding. In all that scrambling about the rock we'd cut our hands badly and we'd smeared the cuts with antiseptic jelly from the kit. They looked inhuman, all gentian-violet patches, and the fingers stiff as wood. Our fingernails had stopped growing with that first touch of frostbite in the ice—you know, as if our bodies had begun to die as far back as that.

"On the eighth day the snowfall ended but the clouds still hung low and black. There was a faint haze over the sea. We crawled out and tried to dig away the new snow on the ledge but we gave it up. We sat in a sort of a stupor with our backs to the rock, looking out over the sea. After a time Pearce said quietly, 'You'd think that was a ship.' He lifted a hand and pointed. We stared. Far out in the scatter of bergs and floes we could make out a small dark shape. In that haze it might have been anything. The ice had fooled us several times. Some of those bergs from the glacier had dark patches of gravel on their flanks and at a distance you could imagine a ship or anything you liked.

"Our minds were dull of course. We watched the thing for some time before the one absolute fact about it came to us. The object, the illusion, whatever you want to call it, was moving slowly north. North! Against the coastal current! We snapped out of our trance in a hurry. There was no sun for the helio-signal mirror. I took the pistol and fired off half a dozen flares at intervals of five minutes, and again we saw what useless things they are in daylight. A short flight, a thin wisp of blue smoke, a dull red spark falling into the sea, nothing more. The illusion in the distance drifted on towards the north and finally disappeared amongst the ice.

"False hope—there's a bitter thing, my friend. We needed our new spirit then. And as if that disappointment wasn't enough we found that water had leaked into our last little packet of barley sugar and dissolved it. Now we were down to a ration of milk tablets, nothing else. On very bad nights, when there was storm or severe cold, we'd been dipping into our reserve and eating two extra tablets apiece between dark and morning. We had to cut that out.

"The ninth day was cloudy and cold. We stayed under the fabric, clawing a handful of snow now and then to satisfy our thirst. And that night was very cold. We clung and shivered together, unable to sleep, listening to all the familiar racket, the distant thunder and plunge from the glacier, the pig-squealing of floes coming together in the dark. The current eddied around our rock and threw opposing masses of ice together in the channel behind it, and all that sound went echoing along the cliffs. You lay there and you thought, when death comes that will be the last sound in my ears.

"On the tenth morning the sky cleared and about noon we crept out and sat against the rock facing the sun. Suddenly there was a sound of motors. We stared into the sky and saw a plane about five miles to the west, like all the others flying at ten thousand feet, too far, too high to see the flares we shot or the glint of the helio mirror in Pearce's hands. It disappeared quickly. We gazed after it for a time. Nobody said a word but somehow the sun had no comfort any more. It was as if the sun had gone and there was only the cold wind. We crawled back under the fabric and lay there silent. Some time in the afternoon Pearce went out to suck water from a crack in the ledge. We heard him muttering. Then one plain word. 'Ship!' I thought, here we go again. We scrambled out, concerned more for Pearce than anything else, thinking his mind had gone. He was pointing seaward. And there it was again, that mysterious illusion of two days ago. This time the air was clear though, and if Pearce was mad so were we all, for by staring hard you could even fancy masts and a stubby funnel on the thing. I picked up the Very pistol. I knew it was useless but I slowly and solemnly shot off the last of our stock of flares, timing the five-minute intervals exactly by my watch.

"Nothing happened. But the illusion remained. This time it wasn't moving in that fantastic way against the drift. It wasn't moving at all. The ice pack had been pushed to seaward by the last hard gale off the land, and the object just sat there amongst a few bergs and growlers from that busy ice-factory up the bay. There was one last thing to do. I picked up the little helio mirror. The sun was in a good quarter and fairly high still. The mirror was four inches square with a small hole in the centre, and there was a separate sighting-disc, also pierced. You held the back of the mirror to your eye with one hand, and with the other you held the sighting-disc six inches or so in front of it; and you squinted through both holes at your object. Then you waggled the mirror slightly to make it flash.

"We took turns at it, one working the helio while the others tucked their hands under their armpits trying to coax some life into the fingers. Every half minute we passed the mirror from one to another. And aloud we said our prayer. For we knew this was the finish, one way or the other. We couldn't survive another cold night. We worked the mirror a long time. It seemed impossible for the glint of that small thing to be seen at ten miles or more. Once Pearce thought he saw a flash in reply. I didn't, nor did Addison. Anyhow it wasn't repeated. But after a time a speck detached itself from the illusion and swam slowly in towards the coast.

"We sighted the mirror on this smaller thing and kept it flashing, passing it quickly from hand to hand. The object came on steadily. And as it came on I began to notice a momentary flicker on each side, coming in a sort of rhythm. That could mean only one thing, a boat, and the wet oar-blades flashing together in the sun. So whatever the main illusion was, this at least must be true. Still, we couldn't believe our eyes. We felt that we had to go on flashing that little bit of polished steel in the sun or the whole dream would collapse. Long after we made out not only a boat but the figures of men, long after we saw the face of the steersman looking straight up at us, we kept the mirror flashing and flashing and flashing.

"Now, my friend, see how the Almighty works a miracle with just the odds and ends at hand. It was a ship all right. But it wasn't there looking for us or anything like us. It was a little old Norwegian whaler under charter to the U.S. Army, sent to establish a meteorological post in a fiord some miles to the north of us. Sent up in a hurry, you understand, a last-minute decision before the Greenland winter shut down hard. When we first saw her, two days back, she was on her way there. Now she was heading south. And mark this. She'd have passed our rock while we were lying under the fabric resigned to death, but something happened. Something went wrong with the old whaler's engines and they had to stop to fix it. There. Just there, ten miles abeam of our rock and in plain sight. She'd been sitting there motionless for an hour when Pearce went out and noticed her. You understand? As if she were just waiting there under orders, waiting for us to snap out of it and make our presence known.

"Now hear this. None of the crew had seen our mirror flashing. The man who noticed it was just a casual passenger, an army man, an American major who'd gone along to see the met-stuff put ashore. I suppose the crew were all too busy to concern themselves about a far glitter on the cliffs. But the army man had something on his mind. Earlier in the war the Germans had sneaked a ship to the east coast of Greenland and set up a weather post, with a radio set and two or three operators posing as Danes. Our people had located the thing and abolished it before the Luftwaffe got much benefit, but there was always a chance that the Germans would try again. When the American major noticed our shaky signals from the rock he watched them suspiciously. They seemed to be dots and dashes but he couldn't make out a word, of course. We weren't trying to send words. It was all we could do just to hold the steel up to the sun.

"He called the ship's officers and they watched and speculated. They stared through their best binoculars. At that distance they couldn't make out anything but the rock and the flash, and their verdict was pooh-pooh. Just a bit of ice winking in the sunlight on the cliffs. The engineers finished their tinkering and the skipper wanted to go on. It was a touchy job, navigating amongst the ice up there on the leading edge of winter, and the state of the old ship's engines worried him. He wanted to get south. But the soldier insisted. Something queer about that flashing on the rock. Signaling in some strange code. Another German met-post maybe, mistaking the whaler for something of their own. Anyhow they'd got to investigate. And at last they put off a boat's crew armed with rifles and tommy-guns, with the major himself in charge.

"That was how they came to us, armed and hostile, ready to blow us off our ledge at the first sign of anything German. We clawed and slithered down the rock to the water's edge and when they recognized our uniforms we heard them all exclaim. The major cried, 'Good God, boys, how long have you been there?' I tried to answer but my voice was just a croak. I held up my hands and let them count those ten stiff fingers and thumbs.

"And that's how we were saved. Saved by a combination of chances first and last that couldn't happen again I suppose in a million years. We were the luckiest men alive. Everybody told us that. After a time we found ourselves saying it. Just luck, you see. Just luck. The whaler's crew did what they could for us on the way to Bluey One—a fiord in south Greenland where there's an air strip, and from there we were flown to Montreal. The doctors at the Royal Vic worked over us for weeks—in my case months. In the end they were able to save our hands and most of our fingers. The feet were another story, 'specially mine. I'm thankful just to have lost my toes. Pearce and Addison got out of hospital some time ago and now I'm about to leave myself. That's why they let me out tonight. I'd promised myself a dinner with all the fixings as soon as I got well, in a place like this, amongst people like this. You know, people who don't know there's a war on."

Sam Cutliffe paused, with a strange little smile. There was a challenging glint in his sunken eyes. "I'm not like you with that lofty Bluenose attitude. You say money smells. So it does. It smells all over this room. And it smells good."

"You didn't think that way on the rock," I said.

"No."

"Then what became of it, that wonderful spirit you talked about? I'm not trying to be sarcastic. I was moved, believe me, when you told me about it. Because that's what we all want really—inside, of course, where it doesn't show. To throw all the junk aside and find the one pure thing. Love for each other, the kind that Christ preached, the kind that people like Gandhi have been preaching ever since, and nobody listening. What about all that?"

Sam looked away. "You see," he said carefully, "I haven't told you quite everything. There was one thing more. When we got down the rock to meet the boat and while we stood there with our arms stretched out as if in appeal to them not to turn into a dream and go off and leave us to die, we remembered something. It struck us all at the same time. The money. The money lying up there on the ledge. We'd each carried a pretty good sum, mostly in U.S. paper currency. We had to, in that game, hopping about the world in wartime when the U.S. dollar was the only thing that passed without question everywhere. And now we . . . well, we were going back to the world and we had to have money again. Life and money—you can't separate them. Not on this planet. Not in the kind of life you have to live. So we went back for it. Yes! We clawed and hobbled our way up to that ledge and we scrabbled for the wallets in the snow. There were coins lying in sight, in cracks, in the bare place under the dinghy fabric, the loose change of our travels, copper and silver, Canadian, U.S., British, Indian, Egyptian, God knows what else. We didn't bother with those. I daresay they'll puzzle some wandering archaeologist up there about a thousand years from now. We stuffed the wallets in our pockets and hustled back to the boat."

"I see," I said. "And that's all?"

Sam Cutliffe sipped the last of his brandy and shrugged. He looked unhappy. His gaze flicked about the buzzing dining-room.

"What else is there?"

THE STREET THAT GOT MISLAID

Patrick Waddington

Marc Girondin had worked in the filing section of the city hall's engineering department for so long that the city was laid out in his mind like a map, full of names and places, intersecting streets and streets that led nowhere, blind alleys and winding lanes.

In all Montreal no one possessed such knowledge; a dozen policemen and taxi drivers together could not rival him. That is not to say that he actually knew the streets whose names he could recite like a series of incantations, for he did little walking. He knew simply of their existence, where they were, and in what relation they stood to others.

But it was enough to make him a specialist. He was undisputed expert of the filing cabinets where all the particulars of all the streets from Abbott to Zotique were indexed, back, forwards and across. Those aristocrats, the engineers, the inspectors of water mains and the like, all came to him when they wanted some little particular, some detail, in a hurry. They might despise him as a lowly clerk, but they needed him all the same.

Marc much preferred his office, despite the profound lack of excitement of his work, to his room on Oven Street (running north and south from Sherbrooke East to St Catherine), where his neighbours were noisy and sometimes violent and his landlady consistently so. He tried to explain the meaning of his existence once to a fellow tenant, Louis, but without much success. Louis, when he got the drift, was apt to sneer.

"So Craig latches on to Bleury and Bleury gets to be Park, so who cares? Why the excitement?"

"I will show you," said Marc. "Tell me, first, where you live."

"Are you crazy? Here on Oven Street. Where else?"

"How do you know?"

"How do I know? I'm here, ain't I? I pay my rent, don't I? I get my mail here, don't I?"

Marc shook his head patiently.

"None of that is evidence," he said. "You live here on Oven Street because it says so in my filing cabinet at City Hall. The Post Office sends you mail because my card index tells it to. If my cards didn't say so, you wouldn't

REPRINTED BY PERMISSION OF OXFORD UNIVERSITY PRESS FROM *Canadian Short Stories*, EDITED BY ROBERT WEAVER AND HELEN JAMES.

exist and Oven Street wouldn't either. That, my friend, is the triumph of bureaucracy."

Louis walked away in disgust. "Try telling that to the landlady," he muttered.

So Marc continued on his undistinguished career, his fortieth birthday came and went without remark, day after day passed uneventfully. A street was renamed, another constructed, a third widened; it all went carefully into the files, back, forwards and across.

And then something happened that filled him with amazement, shocked him beyond measure, and made the world of the filing cabinets tremble to their steel bases.

One August afternoon, opening a drawer to its fullest extent, he felt something catch. Exploring farther, he discovered a card stuck at the back between the top and bottom. He drew it out and found it to be an old index card, dirty and torn, but still perfectly decipherable. It was labelled "Rue de la Bouteille Verte" or "Green Bottle Street".

Marc stared at it in wonder. He had never heard of the place or of anything resembling so odd a name. Undoubtedly it had been retitled in some other fashion befitting the modern tendency. He checked the listed details and ruffled confidently through the master file of street names. It was not there. He made another search, careful and protracted, through the cabinets. There was nothing. Absolutely nothing.

Once more he examined the card. There was no mistake. The date of the last regular street inspection was exactly fifteen years, five months and fourteen days ago.

As the awful truth burst upon him, Marc dropped the card in horror, then pounced on it again fearfully, glancing over his shoulder as he did so.

It was a lost, a forgotten street. For fifteen years and more it had existed in the heart of Montreal, not half a mile from City Hall, and no one had known. It had simply dropped out of sight, a stone in water.

In his heart, Marc had sometimes dreamed of such a possibility. There were so many obscure places, twisting lanes and streets jumbled together as intricately as an Egyptian labyrinth. But of course it could not happen, not with the omniscient file at hand. Only it had. And it was dynamite. It would blow the office sky-high.

Vaguely, in his consternation, Marc remembered how, some time after he first started to work, his section had been moved to another floor. The old-fashioned files were discarded and all the cards made out afresh. It must have been at that time that Green Bottle Street was stuck between the upper and lower drawers.

He put the card in his pocket and went home to reflect. That night he slept badly and monstrous figures flitted through his dreams. Among them appeared a gigantic likeness of his chief going mad and forcing him into a red-hot filing cabinet.

The next day he made up his mind. Pleading illness, he took the afternoon off and with beating heart went looking for the street.

Although he knew the location perfectly, he passed it twice and had to retrace his steps. Baffled, he closed his eyes, consulted his mind's infallible map and walked directly to the entry. It was so narrow that he could touch the adjoining walls with his outstretched hands. A few feet from the sidewalk was a tall and solid wooden structure, much weatherbeaten, with a simple latched door in the centre. This he opened and stepped inside. Green Bottle Street lay before him.

It was perfectly real, and reassuring as well. On either side of a cobbled pavement were three small houses, six in all, each with a diminutive garden in front, spaced off by low iron palings of a kind that has disappeared except in the oldest quarters. The houses looked extremely neat and well-kept and the cobbles appeared to have been recently watered and swept. Windowless brick walls of ancient warehouses encircled the six homes and joined at the farther end of the street.

At his first glance, Marc realized how it had got its unusual name. It was exactly like a bottle in shape.

With the sun shining on the stones and garden plots, and the blue sky overhead, the street gave him a momentary sense of well-being and peace. It was completely charming, a scene from a print of fifty years ago.

A woman who Marc guessed was some sixty years of age was watering roses in the garden of the first house to his right. She gazed at him motionless, and the water flowed from her can unheeded to the ground. He took off his hat and announced:

"I'm from the city engineering department, madame."

The woman recovered herself and set her watering can down.

"So you have found out at last," she said.

At these words, Marc's reborn belief that after all he had made a harmless and ridiculous error fled precipitately. There was no mistake.

"Tell me, please," he said tonelessly.

It was a curious story. For several years, she said, the tenants of Green Bottle Street had lived in amity with each other and the landlord, who also resided in one of the little houses. The owner became so attached to them that in a gesture of goodwill he deeded them his property, together with a small sum of money, when he died.

"We paid our taxes," the woman said, "and made out a multitude of forms and answered the questions of various officials at regular intervals, about our property. Then after a while we were sent no notices, so we paid no more taxes. No one bothered us at all. It was a long time before we understood that in some way they'd forgotten about us."

Marc nodded. Of course, if Green Bottle Street had dropped from the ken of City Hall, no inspectors would go there, no census takers, no tax collectors. All would pass merrily by, directed elsewhere by the infallible filing cabinet.

"Then Michael Flanagan, who lives at number four," she went on, "a most interesting man, you must meet him—Mr Flanagan called us together and said that if miracles happened, we should aid and abet them. It was he who had the door built and put up at the entrance to keep out passers-by or officials who might come along. We used to keep it locked, but it's been so long since anyone came that we don't bother now.

"Oh, there were many little things we had to do, like getting our mail at the Post Office and never having anything delivered at the door. Now almost the only visits we make to the outside world are to buy our food and clothes."

"And there has never been any change here all that time?" Marc asked.

"Yes, two of our friends died and their rooms were empty for a while. Then Jean Desselin, he's in number six, and sometimes goes into the city, returned with a Mr Plonsky, a refugee. Mr Plonsky was very tired and worn-out with his travellings and gladly moved in with us. Miss Hunter in number three brought home a very nice person, a distant relative, I believe. They quite understand the situation."

"And you, madame?" Marc inquired.

"My name is Sara Trusdale, and I have lived here for more than twenty years. I hope to end my days here as well."

She smiled pleasantly at him, apparently forgetting for the moment that he carried in his pocket a grenade that could blow their little world to pieces.

All of them, it seemed, had had their troubles, their losses and failures before they found themselves in this place of refuge, this Green Bottle Street. To Marc, conscious of his own unsatisfactory existence, it sounded entrancing. He fingered the card in his pocket uncertainly.

"Mr Plonsky and Mr Flanagan took a great liking to each other," Miss Trusdale continued. "Both of them have been travellers and they like to talk about the things they have seen. Miss Hunter plays the piano and gives us concerts. Then there's Mr Hazard and Mr Desselin, who are very fond of chess and who brew wine in the cellar. For myself, I have my flowers and my books. It has been very enjoyable for all of us."

Marc and Miss Trusdale sat on her front step for a long time in silence. The sky's blue darkened, the sun disappeared behind the warehouse wall on the left.

"You remind me of my nephew," Miss Trusdale said suddenly. "He was a dear boy. I was heart-broken when he died in the influenza epidemic after the war. I'm the last of my family, you know."

Marc could not recall when he had been spoken to with such simple, if indirect, goodwill. His heart warmed to this old lady. Obscurely he felt on the verge of a great moral discovery. He took the card out of his pocket.

"I found this yesterday in the filing cabinet," he said. "No one else knows about it yet. If it should come out, there would be a great scandal and no end of trouble for all of you as well. Newspaper reporters, tax collectors. . . ."

He thought again of his landlady, his belligerent neighbours, his room that defied improvement.

"I wonder now," he said slowly, "I am a good tenant, and I wonder. . . ."

"Oh yes," she leaned forward eagerly, "you could have the top floor of my house. I have more space than I know what to do with. I'm sure it would suit you. You must come and see it right away."

The mind of Marc Girondin, filing clerk, was made up. With a gesture of renunciation he tore the card across and dropped the pieces in the watering can. As far as he was concerned, Green Bottle Street would remain mislaid forever.

WE HIRE A WITCH

Kenneth McNeill Wells

A wiry little man with bull-like shoulders and a swarthy face, wandered in off the concession line one afternoon, and stood silently watching the work in progress at our house site. He spoke to no one, and no one spoke to him. An hour passed. The sun slanted westwards. The workmen prepared to go home. The little man still stood by the cellar hole, swaying a little on his short legs, spitting tobacco juice meditatively into a nearby mortar box.

"Well," I asked him finally, "what can I do for you?"

"Nothin'," he told me. "I kinda figgered I could do something for you."

"Yes?"

"Yeah, I'm a witcher."

"A what?"

"A water-witcher," he explained. "I witch fer water—I find water. I dig wells. Figgered you might want a good well on this place."

I wasn't impressed. Water divining was so much mumbo-jumbo to me. Still, we did want a well on the place, a good well that would fill with cold spring water and stay filled, regardless of how we used it. And I was curious to see how this water-witch would go about his business of water witching. I had never seen a water diviner at work.

"Go ahead," I told him.

The little man with the big shoulders went to his car and brought out a forked twig. "Hazel wood," he explained, with a shy smile. "Some call it witch-hazel wood." He went out on to the hillside, and with two ends of the fork held firmly in his two hands, and with the butt end of the twig pointing directly ahead of him, began pacing slowly back and forth across the field. I followed him, sceptical, but fascinated.

"What happens?" I asked.

"You'll see."

Back and forth across the field we went, back and forth, back and forth, while the sunset filled the western sky with fire, and the shadows lengthened over the darkening hills. Suddenly the water-witch stopped his pacing. The knuckles of his hands whitened with strain. The forked twig in his hands twisted like a snake. He seemed to be struggling. The forks splintered. The thick butt of the hazel wood branch shuddered downwards, as though something powerful and invisible was pulling it down.

"There is your spring," said the water diviner. "It's running strong, about six feet down."

I didn't believe him, and so he walked the field again, this time with an iron crowbar balanced across two fingers of his left hand. When he came to the spot where the twig had twisted, the thick end of the crowbar dipped suddenly. I leaned forward and grasped the bar just ahead of his hand. I felt the strong down pull.

"The spring is still there," he declared, with a sardonic grin. "An' it's still jest six feet down."

I still didn't believe him, and so the water diviner walked the fields yet a third time, this time with his heavy old-fashioned watch held motionless at the end of his watch chain, at arm's length, and breast high from the ground. When his pacing brought him again to the spot where the iron bar had dipped, where the twig had twisted, the watch began spinning on the end of its chain, at first slowly, and then rapidly, so rapidly that I thought that it would twist the soft gold links apart. I looked at his hand. It was rock steady. There was no sign there that he was helping his time-piece spin. Still I was unconvinced. I shook my head. It was all so impossible. It was still hocus-pocus to me.

"Look, Mister," stormed the diviner, his dark face glowing with rage, "for two dollars a foot I'll dig yer well fer you. If I don't find more water than you an' yer whole damned family can ever use, I'll pay you two dollars a foot fer diggin' on yer blasted hill!"

I accepted his offer.

Never was a man less like a man, and more like a woodchuck, or mole, than that little water diviner. He did not dig his way into the earth of our hillside. He burrowed into it, grasping his short-handled shovel but a few inches above the blade, and using it exactly as a digging woodchuck might use its paws. Dirt spattered out of the deepening well-hole in a steady shower that first littered, and then buried the grass and flowers around the well site. Down and down he went, knee deep, waist deep, shoulder deep. Soon only his bobbing head, then only the tip of his flailing shovel, and finally only a constant shower of flying earth remained to tell the passerby of the frantic activity that was going on in the bottom of the hole on the hillside.

At a depth of six feet, where sand met clay, he struck water, just as he had said he would. The water came in first as a thin trickle, and then as it cleared a way for itself, in an increasing stream. The water-witch called me to the side of the well-hole, and pointed at the rising flood. He said nothing. He just pointed, but out of the two slits in the ball of clay that was his head, his dark eyes glared triumphantly.

We had our water, but in order to hold it, we had to make a reservoir for it, to dig on down through the blue clay another twenty, or thirty feet.

The water diviner built himself a box-like arrangement of boards and scantlings, a few inches smaller than the well-hole. As he dug, he pulled this cage down after him, and built on to the top, so that he had always, from top to bottom of the well-shaft, a wooden shell to protect him from cave-ins that might otherwise have buried him alive. When he had dug to a point where he could no longer throw the clay clear of the well mouth, he rigged a gallows over it, and hooked on a pulley and a rope, and a heavy iron bucket.

It was our well-digger's misfortune that the helper I found for him was a neighbourhood farmer with a perverted sense of humour. It was this man's job to draw, at first by hand, and later with the help of a gray horse, the mud- and water-filled bucket out of the well, empty it, and return it to the digger below. All went well until he noticed that a knot in the bucket rope came to his hand just before the lowered bucket reached the head of the well-digger. From that time on there was no peace on the hillside above Moonstone Creek. There were bangs, and clangs, and yells, and curses, and shrieks of idiotic laughter.

The well-digger's helper had a new way of returning a mud bucket to a well-digger. He simply tossed it into the well-mouth, to fall with a clattering bang down the long wooden shaft, to stop when the knot reached his hand, with a sudden, shuddering jerk, within inches of the cowering digger's shaking head. In vain did the well-digger protest. This was his helper's way of returning the bucket to him, and return it this way he would, or not at all. Rather than be held up in his work by lack of a helper, for I could get him no other, he put up with this nonsense, but it was a shaken, and shaking man that came out of the well-hole each night.

"Gad, man!" his helper would exclaim, as the shaking, cursing bundle of clay that was a man rose out of the well-mouth at quitting time. "It's all in the way of a joke, and meant for no harm. Gad, man, and I wouldn't hurt a hair of your head, if you have hair at all under that filthy ball of clay that might or might not be a hat. Gad, man . . ."

The shaking of the well-digger would increase. He would chatter with impotent rage, wave his hands in the air, and then totter away to his car; yet somehow he managed to summon up enough nerve, or stubbornness, to continue. Day after day he returned to the job, digging himself deeper and deeper into the earth. Day after day, a hundred times a day, he winced from the heavy iron bucket that clanged down upon him from the well-mouth, never knowing when the oaf above might miss the knot and kill him with his fun. He dug until a second spring broke in on him, and he could no longer control the flood.

We had our well.

THE AWAKENING

Bruce Hutchison

On the morning of May 17, 1939, the French Canadian people repaired to the rock of Quebec where their life had begun. They covered the forgotten site of Champlain's Habitation, clung to Wolfe's trail from the Anse au Foulon, and spread across the Plains of Abraham. A race which had been conquered on this spot and remained forever unconquerable awaited its sovereign, who was the symbol of its defeat, its victory, and its sovereignty. From the river, this multitude, in gay holiday dress, looked like a gush of spring wildflowers. The King's first glimpse of Quebec revealed the perpetual crop of the Laurentian soil.

The figure of a young man in the admiral's uniform of the British Navy appeared at the rail of the liner as she neared the shore. The wife beside him had the soft, pink beauty of an English spring.

The Prime Minister and Lapointe stood together, bolt upright, on the wharf. In their identical Windsor garb of cocked hat and gold braid they reminded the observer inevitably of a tiny Tweedledum and giant Tweedledee.

From that hour onward, across the continent and back, until they sailed for home, the royal visitors were seldom out of King's sight. He treated them almost as his own children. He changed from Windsor uniform to evening dress, to morning coat, to country tweeds, in exhausting sartorial sequence. He fussed over every detail of the tour. Eager to be seen and photographed in the royal presence, he leaped from the moving train at a western station and would have fallen on the platform, perhaps injured himself, if a Mounted Policeman had not caught him in his arms.

Those were weeks when every drop of King's royalist blood tingled, when history thrust geography from his mind and he basked in a warm, sweet nostalgia. The Canadian springtime, the burgeoning earth, the cheering crowds, and the trusting young visitors who placed themselves entirely in his keeping gave King a month of rapture. Bliss it was in those days to be alive, but to be the sovereign's first adviser and the unofficial uncle of the Royal Family was very heaven.

No one who saw the Rebel's grandson as the loving guardian of his King and Queen, and at every hamlet along the way the crowds of Canada cheering the regal procession, could doubt the nation's course should war come to England. If the tour was designed to test that sentiment and to strengthen it, the results were conclusive. Canada's long isolationism, and King's, melted by the hour. As he admitted later, King had questioned two years before whether Canada would go into a European war under any conditions, and certainly he would have been unready to lead it. For him, for the nation, such questions were fully settled by this midsummer.

It was none too soon. The visitors had hardly left, and Parliament returned home expecting nothing more serious than the congenial sham battle of a general election, when the old specter returned after brief vacation. By the end of July, King faced "nightmare and sheer madness" on the march.

The thought of Canada fighting again in Europe was still nightmarish but it no longer appeared mad, for it had at least the final sanity of the inevitable. And when Germany's treaty with Russia was announced on August 21, King's no-commitment policy was dead.

As events moved at a gallop, the pedestrian of Ottawa strove desperately to keep up with them. Distinguished visitors from Britain continued to assure the Canadian people that talk of war was newspaper hysteria. Lord Beaverbrook remarked that his presence in Canada showed what he thought of these absurd rumors. King was not deceived but he was torn between his emotions and his reason. As strongly as he had resisted the thought of war he embraced it now, with one side of his mind, as unavoidable, while to the other it was still unthinkable.

At ten o'clock on the night of August 22, when he was about to board a train for Toronto to attend the funeral of a friend, King was handed a cable from London. The British Parliament had been summoned. As he hesitated to cancel his trip a second secret message arrived from Chamberlain warning him that the worst seemed likely to occur.

King decided to remain in Ottawa. He called Manion in Toronto, and as clearly as he dared on the wire, told him the facts. The same message was telephoned to Woodsworth in Vancouver and to John Blackmore, of the Social Credit Party, in Cardston.

The next day King proclaimed the War Measures Act, announced that Parliament would be summoned if the peace was broken, and assured the nation that the Government was ready for "any emergency."

On August 25 the Government called for army volunteers, while King, in a last despairing gesture, cabled to Hitler and Mussolini that "force is not a substitute for reason," to which the Italian dictator replied unblushingly that he was sparing "no effort to safeguard the peace of the world." The simple peasant of 1937 did not bother to answer.

At one o'clock on the morning of September 1, the Canadian Press telephoned Pickersgill, one of King's secretaries, to report that the German armies had crossed the Polish frontier. Pickersgill was living with Norman Robertson, of the External Affairs Department, and the two of them followed the press reports through that night of waiting. They decided that it was useless to rouse their chief, for he could do nothing. At six o'clock they telephoned Skelton, who called Kingsmere and got the Prime Minister out of bed. King received the news in silence.

What could he say? The illusions of his lifetime were broken. His philosophy of conciliation had never faced the necessity of force when conciliation fails. Now that extreme dilemma could be escaped no longer.

King dressed and ate a leisurely breakfast. Years of war stretched ahead. The thing was too big for haste or excitement. He made up his mind then, as he said afterward, that no single man could alter the process now in train, could win the war or lose it.

At that moment a new career began, the last career he had wished or foreseen. The man of peace must become a man of war. The life-long conciliator must use force. The apostle of humanity must shed blood. From those first hours he drilled himself in the conviction that the war must and would be won. It was fortunate, in the succeeding months, that he could convince himself of anything.

King motored to town, entered his office as calmly as if this were a day of routine business, and summoned Parliament for September 7 to authorize "effective co-operation by Canada by the side of Great Britain, if Great Britain should be engaged in war in the effort to resist aggression." His summons, deliberately vague, buried the corpse of noncommitments for good and with it the hopes of his sixty-five years.

For all practical purposes the nation was at war already. The Government was committed to fight and Parliament would sustain it. When Britain and France made their formal declarations on September 3, Canada remained technically neutral, but King used the radio to redeclare the Government's policy "in a struggle between the pagan conception . . . and a civilization based upon the Christian conception of the brotherhood of man."

Parliament, he repeated, must decide—that much was left of the old formula and it was important to King and the nation. He could not deflect the torrent of events by a hair's breadth. He could establish Canada's right to make its own decision as a sovereign state independent of Britain. The national status which had been his chief lifework must be given final confirmation in the test of war.

In the twilight period of technical neutrality King was called to his private telephone. The voice of Roosevelt in Washington asked him if Canada was at war. King replied that it was not. Turning to his own advisers in the White House, Roosevelt exclaimed: "You see, I was right!" Being legally neutral, Canada could receive American war supplies despite the Neutrality Act, which forbade such shipments to belligerents.

During the next week the United States rushed across the border what munitions it had to spare, including some airplanes invaluable for training purposes in times when any plane or the oldest gun was worth a hundred later on. Another interim dividend had been paid on the Roosevelt-King friendship, and Roosevelt's neutrality had become technical also.

Unknown to the public or even to the Cabinet, King was engaged in another struggle with neutrality under the most wrenching personal strains of his career. Skelton, his trusted adviser on foreign affairs from the beginning, insisted with all the power of his experience and integrity that Canada must remain neutral.

As King told that story in his last days, Skelton argued that the surrenders and the hypocrisy of appeasement, from Ethiopia onward, had undermined all the moral purposes for which the war ostensibly was to be fought. Since no moral question was involved, Canada, like Ireland, should keep out. Being a North American nation, it might exercise some mediation in the course of a conflict morally chaotic.

It was easy for King to reject this advice. He grieved to see as great a man as Skelton so broken by frustration and despair. According to his own account, King told Skelton bluntly that his counsel, whatever else might be said of it, was impossible. Apart from all other considerations, any Canadian government which attempted neutrality would be swept out of office by public indignation within a week. Canada, said King, "must go in with everything it has."

He had no intention of compromising with Skelton. He could not bear to break their old friendship by accepting Skelton's resignation. So for two days, with only Lapointe privy to their secret, King and Skelton wrestled with their consciences, in perfect amity and insoluble disagreement. At the end of the second day, Skelton, who could never be ordered, was at last persuaded. After the travail of that lonely and honorable decision he never wavered again. In Ottawa there was no more thought of neutrality. But it survived elsewhere and must soon confront King with another and worse trial.

On September 7, King met a Parliament whose mind was fully made up. It was a little puzzled to hear in the Speech from the Throne only that the Government desired power to defend Canada and to co-operate in the effort to "resist further aggression." The opening formalities were observed, the tribute paid to dead members, the usual reports filed, the committees appointed without a word of war. Next day, King left no doubt of his meaning—the adoption of the Address in reply to the throne speech would be followed instantly by a war declaration.

Coming from the conciliator, the appeaser, the man of peace, King's war speech of September 8 must be considered the most important he ever made. In form, wording, and style it was one of the worst.

Physically he was tired that day after the struggle with Skelton and the office work of a Government actually at war. His face was pale, his hand shook a little, and his shoulders twitched. Not trusting himself to speak without it, he read from a rambling and unwieldy manuscript, hastily thrown together without shape or order, yet minutely edited in every word. Parliament awaited a trumpet blast. From King it received a lawyer's brief.

Canada, on September 8, presented a picture curious and deceptive—the lusty young nation, heir to three centuries of battle on Indian frontier and foreign field; the pale and bookish little man who proposed to lead it in the final adventure. Could this flabby scholar, this student of political theory, this mere manager of practical politics change his entire nature overnight and become a warrior of the Canadian breed? Could the tiny creature now standing nervously by his desk stand in the path of Armageddon? Many men in Parliament and most of the nation doubted it.

Parliament and nation thought they knew King. They knew only one side of him and forgot that the old Rebel had been a tiny creature, too. The larger side had yet to appear and did not appear that day. King had yet to discover that other side of himself. He, Parliament, and nation must sound his full depths together.

Though this bumbling and lamentable speech did not indicate it, the change from the prophet of peace to the man of war already was under way. Having accepted the inevitable and emerged from the enervating weeks of suspense into the cold climate of action, King had begun to feel a new exhilaration.

In his own bloodless fashion he had always been a fighting man—the first fact of his nature, the last to be discovered by his people. As he stood before a silent and skeptical House he knew that this was not the kind of fighting he had expected or prepared for. The mission he must perform was the very opposite of all his plans. After his sane works of peace he must grapple with the nightmare and the madness.

His ego, at least, was equal to the challenge. He had demonstrated his mastery of Canada in peace. All that must fail and be forgotten on the record unless he could establish his mastery in war. Now he must exceed all his predecessors as the double master. He had the will to perform his task, the health, the vigor, the essential and encompassing armor of personal vanity in which no doubts must find an entering chink.

Of that the House had no doubts either. Even King's enemies knew that he possessed a full, a godlike confidence in himself. Had he the capacity to match it? Technically he had not. He knew nothing of war. He had never worn a uniform or carried a rifle.

In his estimate, that was of no importance, for he saw war in the round, as a political process far larger and more intricate than its physical weapons. Especially for Canada it was a political process. If it was mismanaged, the two Canadian races would fly apart, the weapons would break, the armies would falter. Other men could build the weapons and lead the armies in battle. His battle was of a different and more dangerous sort. If he failed, the nation itself might be destroyed.

In part from vanity, in part from cold calculation, he knew, or thought he knew, like Pitt a hundred and eighty years before, that a divided nation must be saved from its own division, that he alone could save it.

A rash presumption it might seem to Parliament and nation. Yet the political calculation was as solid as the vanity. No other English-speaking statesman could hope to hold, as he already held, the confidence of French Canada. No French Canadian leader would be accepted for a moment outside Quebec.

The successor of Laurier had even greater assets for this trial than his spiritual parent, was in a stronger position than Borden in the first war. King was not attached to one side or the other in the ceaseless contest of the two races, now entering a new and perhaps a disruptive phase. His years of compromise, mediation, and often cynical expediency, intended for another purpose, now served him and the nation well. In the crisis King was better prepared, without intention, than any other man. All the contradictions of his work and of his nature merged in the final contradiction of the peacemaker transformed into the civilian warrior.

Like a general whose forces are outnumbered by a powerful enemy, he was planning every move in the battle of politics with a clear reckoning of his own weakness, knowing above all that he needed time to build strength. For the moment it must be a Fabian strategy until he could persuade French Canada into a war for which it was not yet ready. In his judgment everything depended on that.

Hence this twisted and sinuous speech, this wriggling between forces not yet calculable, this deliberate buying of time. And hence, to all those who miscalculated King, this spectacle of a virile young people led by a weak old man.

That false impression was exaggerated by the confused introduction to King's speech, the endless citation of documents, the fussy recital of details that no one cared to hear. Even as a lawyer's brief the job was botched by the nerve-strain of its author. As he confessed, "I never dreamed that the day would come when, after spending a lifetime in a continuous effort to promote and preserve peace . . . it should fall to my lot to be the one to lead this Dominion of Canada into a great war, but that responsibility I assume with a sense of being true to the very blood that is in my veins. I assume it in defence of freedom."

Then, in another random stroke, he promised to treat all war profiteers as creatures of "the underworld" and warned any of his followers seeking political patronage to "keep away from me for I will never listen to you." Those were large promises. They were made good as in no former war.

Next came a strange public examination of his own conscience to justify the doctrine of force evaded in his philosophy: "I am inclined to agree . . . that force has never accomplished anything—and yet I am not so sure of that. I believe that force does not fundamentally change a situation and that the only thing that in the end will change a situation is persuasion. You can persuade men; you can convert them, but there have been times . . . when if force had not been opposed by force, there would have been no Christianity left to defend." Force was accepted with horror but his conscience was clear.

He was clear also on Canada's freedom to choose for itself, as he had always insisted. If it went to war it would act "voluntarily, not because of any colonial or inferior status vis à vis Great Britain but because of an equality of status." The work which Macdonald, Laurier, and Borden had begun, which King had carried forward since 1923, was now to be vindicated, just as his isolationism already was discredited.

Until the dinner hour and through most of the evening, King continued his endless digressions into the history of the last five years. He read pages of telegrams, public documents, and orders-in-council into the record as if the sheer volume of exhibits could prove his case, as if Canada needed any proof that it must fight. He proved over and over again that he had made no advance commitments to Britain, as if he or anyone could alter the commitment of history. He feebly defended his inadequate preparations for war on the ground that he had given the fighting services all the money Parliament would vote, as if his Government had ever sought more.

By slow circular movement he began at last to creep up on the real purpose of his speech and on the real problem of Canada at war. He would not yet commit himself for or against an expeditionary force in Europe but the commitment against conscription for overseas service was given without reservation, as the only basis of racial unity: "No such measure will be introduced by the present Administration." In those words King offered French Canada the guarantee without which it would not accept the war. Was it enough?

The question would be raised and answered, not without agony and tears, before the first snow fell on the rock of Quebec. By those same words, chosen to placate the two Canadian races, King had planted a bomb to explode within his Cabinet five years hence. His greatest crisis would take time to develop. Invisibly, it had begun.

This he could not surmise but he saw further than many experienced soldiers. Remembering the face of Hitler, which had so deceived him, King cried: "Where is he creeping to?" He was creeping into the northern communities that proposed to be neutral. If they would not fight, if Britain and France went down, all the neutrals would go down, too, and "the whole business of isolation" even in America "will prove to have been a myth . . . there will in time be no freedom on this continent. Life will not be worth living."

This on the eve of the phony war. King never doubted from the beginning that the war would be long and cover the earth. He had escaped from his own myth of isolation. As nearly as he confessed anything, this was a public confession of his errors.

The speech trickled to its end at last in an ooze of borrowed sentiment. As the last exhibits of the legal brief, the fourteen stanzas and seventy lines of Lowell's poem "The Present Crisis" were read laboriously into the record. Plastered like sweet frosting on the dry substance of that speech, they had a cloying flavor. If dry, the substance was solid. Canada was going into the war with all its strength, of its own will for its own survival.

As King slumped into his chair, exhausted, a gray and tragic figure rose on the other side of the House.

Woodsworth, the saint, knew that he had reached the hour of his martyrdom in politics. Like King, he had refused to face in his philosophy the dilemma of force. Unlike King, he could not and would not accept force when the alternative was destruction. The prophet of peace refused to vote for war.

This man had left the church. He was still a Christian, and war, he cried, was the "absolute negation" of Christianity. Being himself more Christian than the church, and closer to the spirit of Christ than any Canadian in politics, he looked with loathing upon the slaughter of innocents throughout the world. He was driven away from the world and back to the isolation of North America, where "there may at least be the seeds left from which we can try to start a new civilization along better lines" after the general suicide.

The same sort of choice had faced many saints. For Woodsworth it was peculiarly agonizing. Other saints could abandon this world as insignificant and turn toward another. Woodsworth's work had been in this world, his whole life of labor, poverty, and daily suffering had been devoted to the salvation of human beings here and now, and it had all been in vain.

The House, as it watched a man going to the stake as surely as Jogues or Brébeuf, could see the world's anguish carved deep on this worn face.

None, perhaps, could read it as well as King, who watched with anguish and doubts of his own. He had warned the House to respect Woodsworth. He had called Woodsworth, his opponent, "an ornament to any parliament." He had pleaded with him, as one Christian to another, to consider where the doctrine of nonviolence would lead when violence threatened to exterminate Christianity altogether. All in vain.

Looking straight at King, Woodsworth refused to surrender his principles. The House was silent. It was witnessing a personal tragedy within the larger tragedy of the times and it listened in decent respect to one whom it knew to be nobly wrong. But when Woodsworth cried out that he would be proud of his own sons if they refused to enlist and faced a concentration camp or a firing squad for their convictions, a member in the Conservative back benches shouted "Shame!" No one joined him in casting the first stone.

As Woodsworth sat down, alone and defiant, he had broken with his own Party, he had thrown away his leadership of the Left in Canada, he had deliberately jettisoned his career in politics, and he was the most revered member of the Parliament which rejected him. His tragedy and triumph were now complete. They had been ordered from the beginning. In the jungle of these times the path of the saint leads inevitably to the stake. With one side of his diverse nature King must have envied Woodsworth his martyrdom.

On the following day a practical politician replaced the saint as the leader of the Left. Through no wish of his own and with a visible pang at separating from the man he had followed and loved, M. J. Coldwell announced the C.C.F. policy in favor of the war.

Coldwell, if not a saint, was a man of high intelligence, deep culture, and a private life of pain and nobility. He revealed his stature in taking leave of his old leader and supporting a Government whose social philosophy he abhorred, whose foreign policy he could not refuse to accept. For Coldwell saw that if the war resulted from the bungling of capitalists, it could not be lost without destroying all the hopes of Socialism. The brave new world of the C.C.F. would be postponed indefinitely by war. Defeat would doom it for all imaginable time.

The C.C.F. repudiated neutrality. It, too, had its agony and doubt and Coldwell tried to dissolve them by an impossible compromise. The C.C.F. policy, which he now read, declared that "Canada should be prepared to defend her own shores, but her assistance overseas should be limited to economic aid and must not include conscription of man power or the sending of any expeditionary force."

Such a futile straddle lacked the grandeur of Woodsworth's act of faith and, on the other hand, any practical use in a war far larger than the C.C.F. could or would admit. It was the pitiful gesture, midway between Woodsworth's neutrality and total war, of puzzled men who had suddenly realized that their mild, reforming socialism had been living in a dream. In the torture of that discovery they gibbered and postured on the brink of the pit.

King also had lost his dreams. There was no time to regret them. Once embarked on the nightmare, his immediate concern was to carry the whole House and nation with him; above all, to prevent any break among the French Canadian members and thus in the vital tissue of the state.

The break came, but was too small to matter. Maxime Raymond, a sincere French Canadian who could never become a total Canadian, denounced all wars as contests of interests, not of ideologies (strange words today when Raymond's church confronts Communism). Since Canada's interests were not involved in this war, Raymond was against it, for it would "ruin" Canada.

Here was a voice out of the depths of the French Canadian nature. Had that nature grown beyond old bounds, had it learned, as King himself had learned, that there was no isolation for anyone?

Raymond had not learned. He still stood where King had stood before the nightmare and he hurled all King's old isolationist speeches at their maker. These were pinpricks, no more. The importance of Raymond on this occasion lay in his clear warning that war, whatever the Government might promise, would mean conscription. Quebec would never accept it. The final crisis, five years hence, was implicit in Raymond's speech and explicit in that of Liguori Lacombe, who moved a motion directly opposing Canada's participation in the war.

Like the C.C.F., the two lonely isolationists of Quebec were making gestures only, and they knew it. The real voice of French Canada poured out in the organ tones of Lapointe.

That great man had faced his own ordeal and grown with it. And what a growth! The peasant who had come to Parliament without a word of English had made that alien tongue his own. The son of the narrow Quebec earth had seen the vision of the greater Canada and inherited as well the legacy of the old world. The isolationist who had repealed the oil sanctions because Ethiopia was not worth the life of a single Canadian knew now that his hour and the hour of his people had come. Knew also that on him more than on any man the outcome of that hour must depend.

Parliament and nation beheld here the indigenous and authentic product of a people who had first seized Canada from the wilderness, who had clung to it and would never abandon it, who had loved it longer and better than any Canadians. And all the instincts of this race, all its leaders from Champlain to Laurier, spoke now through their heir and vindicator, but in larger accents, with wider vision.

The House listened and King sat transfixed beside a greater human creature as Lapointe, with massive shoulders heaving, huge hands clenched, and dark face contorted, proved that in him the conquered race had conquered itself. That was the true meaning of Lapointe in his hour. Others might quail. He looked into the pit unblinking.

It was not quite his finest speech, there was a finer to follow, but Lapointe used it, as no other man could, to speak in an alien tongue for his people to the other Canadian race, and then to speak to his people for the majority of Canadians. The minority, whom the majority might not understand, but without whom the nation could not survive, had found a voice understandable to Canadians of every tongue. Incarnate in this man the two souls of Canada were striving toward elemental fusion.

As a lawyer, Lapointe argued that neutrality was impossible in law. As a statesman, he pronounced it impossible in practice. As a practical politician, he affirmed that no government could live if it attempted to resist an overseas expeditionary force.

So much for his own people. He turned as their leader to the rest of Canada: "Sons of one country, brothers in one family, for the future of Canada is it not imperative that no section of Canada, no race, no creed, should inflict upon the other sections, the other races or the other creeds incurable wounds which might destroy our country forever?" If unity would be shattered by neutrality, it would be shattered as completely by the other extreme of conscription for overseas service. That French Canadians would never, never accept.

For himself and all the Quebec Ministers he gave the solemn undertaking that they would never be members of a government which attempted to enforce conscription. Looking hard at the Opposition, Lapointe asked: "Is that clear enough?" His question must be answered five years hence when

Lapointe would not be alive to answer it. Power was silent that day. He would answer in due time with honor.

No party denied Lapointe's proposition that conscription would split the nation, that no French Canadian would sit in a conscriptionist government, that the agitators for conscription were really agitating against a concerted war effort. Even this proposition would not satisfy some elements in Quebec and no one knew it as well as Lapointe. He could not convince them, but "I disdain them! They will not deter me from the path of duty, as God gives me the light to see it. I will protect them against themselves!"

In those words he had pronounced the certain verdict of history on his work—by evoking the best side of its nature, he had protected Quebec against itself.

"I have been told," he concluded, "that my present stand means my political death. Well, at least it would not be a dishonorable end and I am ready to make sacrifices for the sake of being right. But let me assure you . . . that if only I can keep my physical strength, fall I shall not; and my friends shall not fall either."

He had the strength to make good that guaranty and no more. The God he trusted had left him time to complete this one task only. It was enough for a single lifetime.

Also, there was more unconscious logic in the performance of the task, thus far, than most of his friends and enemies yet realized. Lapointe, it was said, had bungled the Ethiopian crisis as King's agent. If this was true it was equally true that by his action then he had made his action now politically possible. In the case of Ethiopia, and in all the years of isolationism, the Government had proved to Quebec that it would never enter any war which could be avoided, even by retreat and humiliation if necessary. Now Quebec could not doubt the necessity of war when Lapointe and his French Canadian colleagues accepted it. Their bona fides in this respect had been established beyond question. In the view of their people they entered the court with clean hands. That fact was vital and perhaps decisive in the dangerous events immediately following.

In Quebec City, a crisp gentleman of the law, knowing little of politics or politicians, read Lapointe's speech in the papers with approval. Of all Canadians, Louis St. Laurent was the last to suppose that he must shortly take up the torch dropped from Lapointe's tired hand.

King, then, was in complete control of Parliament and nation, with no reservation on their energies in the war except the no-conscription pledge. The Conservatives, through the gallant Manion, and through Stevens, in a chivalrous speech (Customs scandals, price-spreads, and all old feuds forgotten) had pledged their complete co-operation to the Government. The C.C.F. had made its own reservations, so impractical as to be soon forgotten. Woodsworth and two Quebec members only were against the war.

Even at that early hour, however, the first rumble of racial collision could be heard in the voice of J. E. Lawson, a Conservative of the old school, who needed only one paragraph to say that he did not subscribe to the no-conscription policy. Many others in Canada, sharing his view, were willing to keep silent for the time being. For the time being only.

The Lacombe motion of neutrality was rejected and the main motion, which meant war, was passed without a recorded vote, only Woodsworth rising to express his objection. The Prime Minister left the House to advise the King of Canada to declare war on Canada's behalf.

On Saturday night the cables went to London. No reply was received on Sunday morning. As the day dragged on, King waited impatiently at Laurier House for word that Canada was at war. He tried to reach London by telephone and could not get through. He went to bed, still waiting.

What had happened in London? Had all his messages gone astray? Had the Germans tampered with the telephone and cable? Would he face Parliament and the world on Monday, empty-handed and ridiculous? He lay awake until dawn. During the rest of the war there would be only one more sleepless night.

At 6 A.M. the telephone rang at King's bedside. The delayed message from London had arrived. The King of Canada had declared war on September 10. His Prime Minister at last could sleep, with the knowledge that a sovereign nation had made its own decision.

The decision was not quite unanimous. A French Canadian of smaller stature and large ambition even now was preparing to challenge Parliament's right to vote for the people. The final struggle of Lapointe's life was only a month away. And in English-speaking Canada King faced a movement, not yet organized, but strongly backed, to oust him, erect a coalition government, defeat Lapointe in Quebec, and divide the nation before it could begin to fight.

THE MOVIES COME TO GULL POINT

Will R. Bird

Four men were mending nets in a shack behind the fish wharf at Granny Cove. Spring had come grudgingly, but now the warm sun was melting the ice and sending steamy vapours from tarred roofs. The Cove front murmured with activity as all its men prepared for the sea.

The four worked in silence, seated on benches, half-hidden by the drab folds that hung from the cross-beams overhead, their hands flicking in and out among the meshes, tying, knotting, threading. All at once they paused and listened. There were new voices outside.

"Them's the two back from pulp-cuttin'," said Simon Holder. He was a small lean man.

"Wonder if they got their pay," said Dick Berry, a red-faced man with big bony shoulders.

The two working in the rear were young, and brothers, Ben and Matthew Crowdy, proud of being hired with Simon. Ben was only seventeen, and slim, but he carried himself as seriously as the other three.

"Ho, Willyum," shouted Berry as a man passed the open door. "Don't rush yourself. What's the word down along?"

The man came back and peered in at them. "Not much new," he said. "They're havin' movin' pictures . . ."

"Movin'!" Berry's mouth fell open. "How?"

"The man's got a machine'n engine to drive her. He's over't Gull Point tonight givin' a showin'."

"Over't Gull Point!" Berry rose from his bench, his red face glowing. "Simon, let's go over?"

"What's he chargin'?" asked Simon.

"Twenty-five cents, but he's got good pictures. There's one . . ."

"Don't tell us," blurted Matthew. "That would spoil it. What say we go, Simon?" He had a solemn face, like Ben, but his eyes were bright.

Simon left his bench and went outside. The others followed him and they stood, gazing at the sea.

The ice was breaking up. The warm sun had been aided by a strong wind off land and a lane of black water was steadily widening along the foot of the cliffs, while smaller leads angled in all directions, opening as the pack surged

FROM "SUNRISE FOR PETER" BY WILL R. BIRD. REPRINTED BY PERMISSION OF RYERSON PRESS, TORONTO.

and loosened. Southward, toward Gull Point, there seemed plenty of open sea.

"Risky," pronounced Simon.

"Chancy," agreed Berry, "but not too much."

"Wind's favourin', too," added Matthew.

There was a slow shrill screaming of the ice. Floes and pans were grinding together; the harsh noises never stilled.

Ben looked up. There were no clouds and the sky was a blue that seemed to reflect the endless ice.

"Looks fairish weather," he said, "but it's comin' tonight."

"You boys got money?" asked Simon.

They shook their heads and Berry grinned.

"That makes a dollar," Simon said gravely. "That's a lot of money."

"There ain't never been," said Ben, "movin' pictures up here. I never seen any in my life."

"Bet she's open to the Point," said Berry. "We'd do fine with a lugsail."

Simon rubbed his salt-bitten chin. They four were the best in the Cove. "Git geared," he said suddenly.

"It's six mile," Simon said an hour later. They had launched their dory and were well into the wide lead but the lug-sail was proving a menace. A stiffer breeze caught them and tipped the boat. He pulled the canvas in. "Mebbe we're fools."

They had lost much time. Matthew had broken a thole pin in his eagerness and they had not turned back to repair it. They had trusted in the sail, and his oars were idle.

"The wind'll be strong outside," said Berry. He was rowing and he grunted his words.

They were true enough. Once away from the shelter of the high black cliffs, the wind caught the dory and they swung along sharply. There were many wide lanes and the sea was running higher than it had seemed, and spray flung over them.

Simon steered with a long sweep and Matthew was seated next him, squatted low but ready to lend a hand. As they swayed with the dory all four seemed a jumble of sou-westers and oilskins.

They did not attempt conversation. The shrieking, jarring crashes of the ice mingled with the whistling of the breeze and drowned all lesser sounds. The rapidly-widening lane they were in became a sea of racing, tumbling water that spewed spray as it struck the dory. Simon's oilskins dripped and his cheeks were wet but his expression never changed. He was gauging every wave with the instinct of one born to the sea.

Suddenly each man braced himself for action. A loose floe hove in their path and the waves pitched it about dangerously. Simon and Berry used all their strength and skill as they managed to avoid it, but neither man spoke. Matthew was bailing instantly and they moved slowly until he had scooped from the dory the gallons of water shipped during the swinging manœuvre. It seemed, in that short time, to become night.

The rocky point behind them had cut off the sun as it sank rapidly, and with its going the wind keened to a penetrating chill. The darkness added greatly to their risks and Matthew peered ahead.

"She's started to fog," he shouted. "She's a bank now."

The shore, hazy before, had become mist-drowned, shrouded with a thick white creeping veil. It seemed to permeate the air.

"She's come behind the same," yelled Ben.

They were half their journey and a swirling blanket of gray vapours closed about them. They would have to chance their passage ahead where the contour of the coast veered so that the slow-moving field of ice might bar their way.

It was Matthew who first saw that they had entered a wide lane and were between shifting ice. He peered again.

"Keep straight on!" he cried.

Short waves were deluging the boat with freezing spray. Berry rowed with quick strokes, and the roar of wind and grinding ice filled the night.

The water became smoother. Matthew reached and touched Berry on the back and at the signal the bigger man changed places with him. They were tense and watchful; only men of their experience could know the risk of a channel between rafted ice. Deep booming sounds seemed to pass over them as though they had sunk in a trough of the sea, and it grew darker.

"Look!" yelled Ben. "She's closin' in."

There was a muttered undertone beneath the booming and their lane of open water had narrowed to feet in width.

They slipped awkwardly in their sealskin boots as each man scrambled onto the floe, but they secured footing and with desperate hurried strength dragged the heavy dory from the water. It taxed them to their utmost and no one spoke. The ice was an uneven surging field and a blurred grayness covered everything.

"She's bad," said Berry. "We should have . . ."

He did not finish. There was a crash of giant floes colliding and they were sprawled beside the dory. In an instant the night was a wilder chaos of wind and clamour.

"Watch out!" Simon's voice rose above the tumult like a cracking whip. "She's breakin'."

The floe buckled. It rose and lowered under them. There were sudden surgings that pitched them about. They seized the dory sides and pushed landward. The roaring of surf at the face of the floe came clearly.

"Watch her!" It was a scream more than a shout. The ice was parting.

The floe rocked and settled. Water sloshed over the ice, reached them. There was another settling.

"There!" yelled Ben.

The field had opened and the sea drove into the vent with foaming fury.

It poured over the ice to meet them. Then, its weight, and the driving surf, heaved the floe.

They slid backward in the wash. Ben, caught by the dory, fell, and water washed over him. He rose, sobbing with his immersion, clinging to the dory, and, as if a signal were given, they rushed the boat toward the open water. The lane had widened into a broad lead.

Again the floe surged, and the dory slid into the water. Ben leaped into it, tilting it dangerously. Matthew sprang in beside him, rocking it to a safer keel. Berry had given a great thrust forward to clear them from the ice and as he sprang he lunged against Simon, knocking him backward.

For a heartbeat it seemed they must capsize. The churning water had caught them as the dory took its plunge. Berry grasped his oars and threw his weight against the surge. Behind them, in the screaming murk, Simon was lost to view.

Ben had seized Simon's sweep and they toiled to bring the dory about. The lane was a smother of surf. Danger hovered over every move and the water boiled with changing currents.

They drove back alongside, catching, with perfect co-ordination, a minute lull at the ice edge, and Simon gauging their move, joined them. It was a risky plunge, challenging all their chances, but once more Berry's strength saved the dory and then they had swung away and Ben was bailing.

In the thick darkness the surf seemed wilder than before but the worst was soon behind them. Then, just ahead, a pin-point of light shone steadily.

Within ten minutes they were in calmer waters, and lamp glows began to pierce the gloom. They landed and hurried Ben, shaking and almost numbed with cold, to the nearest house.

"Us is from Granny Cove," announced Simon. "Ben were wet on the ice. Could us dry him here?"

"Sure, the stove's red-hot." A woman wrapped in a thick jacket and ready to leave for the hall where the movies were to be shown, answered them. "I'll git a rig for him to put on and his'll dry while we're gone."

Ben was shaking as with ague and tiny pools formed on the floor beside him as the warmth of the stove softened his frozen clothing. He drank a scalding mixture the woman provided and his trembling ceased. He stripped his sodden clothing and Matthew ranged it on a chair back alongside the stove. Then Ben dressed in a makeshift outfit and they followed the path the woman had taken.

The building where the movies were being shown was packed with people. It was a low-roofed structure and heated by a huge box stove. There were high odours of perspiration and many faces were beaded with moisture. Children were sandwiched among their elders and every seat was taken. Simon led the way along one wall and they stood against it, tightly wedged by others who crowded after. Ben struggled from the borrowed reefer that blanketed him.

"We're lucky," he gasped, "she's jist startin'."

There were gasps and murmurings as the lamps were extinguished and the hum of a motor began. Headings appeared on the screen and a dozen voices tried to read them.

"Let teacher read 'em," bellowed a husky voice at the rear.

" 'She Knew She Was Wrong'," a high-pitched voice shrilled in the darkness as "teacher" assumed her task. "Pretty Virginia . . ."

The audience had stilled. It was seeing the incredible . . . mirrored eating places . . . ladies with bare backs and cigarettes . . . bewildering dances . . . racing cars . . . a bathing beach teeming with thousands. And one face dominated.

"See that one!" said Berry hoarsely. "Her's . . ."

"Keep shut," ordered Simon in a sibilant whisper.

They watched the heroine driving in city traffic and there were cries of admiration.

"Ho!" shouted Berry. "Look at she." He clapped his hands.

"She's won'erful sharp in steerin'," responded Simon, "but . . ." He couldn't express himself.

"Her smokes," objected Ben.

Another picture began and all voices stilled. It was a story of rival airmen, and the planes in action did marvellous stunting. A flight of machines gave a thrilling performance, all manner of stunt flying.

Berry tensed, his big hands gripping a seat back. Simon breathed with sharp little intakes. Ben and Matthew gave shrill exclamations, unable to restrain themselves.

"They're hittin'!"

"No–yes–there!"

"Lookit–lookit–*lookit!*"

A dozen voices yelled with him. The airmen were shooting earthward at dizzy speed, headed toward each other.

There was a dull grinding sound and the screen went blank.

A lamp was lighted and the operator of the movie machine worked desperately with various tools. Then he came forward.

"Sorry, folks," he said, "but the machine's broke and I've got to send the piece away. I can't show any more."

There were sighs of disappointment but no one gave criticism. They began filing from the building and the night was filled with excited voices.

Ben went to change his clothes again and the woman insisted on them stopping to drink scalding tea and to eat slices of hard bread.

"Stay the night," she urged. "I've blankets enough to fix you up on the kitchen floor."

"No," refused Simon. "The fog's cleared and she's light as day. We've got a mortal sight of work to do, gettin' ready to fish."

Berry ate and drank hugely but said nothing. The unexpected ending of the show had given him vast disappointment.

It was breaking day as the dory swung to the wharf at Granny's Cove. The sea had been much rougher than they anticipated and they had been forced to keep near the shore line all the way. For hours there had been but the creak of boat timbers and the slap of heavy water; each was silent, and dull-minded.

A slight breeze stirred the morning. It was from the west and warm. There would be a perfect day. The sunrise began in a fire of orange and crimson that merged into soft pinks and changing blues. The heavens were a mass of colour.

The light spread over the hills and reached the sleeping houses. It found iced places in the hollows and they glittered like jewels.

They dragged the dory to its landing and stood away from it. Ben was bruised and stiff. Matthew had lost a mitten and each was conscious of clothing damp with spray.

"We're back," said Simon tersely, "but it were worth it."

"Sure," agreed Berry, yawning mightily. "That girl were a prime one."

"It must be great," said Matthew, "to live where you kin see won'erful sights all the time."

The light strengthened and the sea was blue as sapphire where the sun rays reached it slantingly. Still they stood, as if each were labouring with thoughts they could not put into words. Then Simon spat and faced them.

"I don't know what youse think," he said, "but takin' all them risks to make a picture don't seem right to me."

Matthew nodded gravely. "Us been thinkin' just that," he said. "It's for nothin' but pleasurin' and it's queer they ain't laws to stop it."

"Sure," added Ben, "there should be a law ag'in it. They might have been killed."

There was no further comment. Smoke began to curl from a chimney. Ben yawned again. They had expressed that which stirred them most, so they turned and filed soberly to their homes.

THE SCHOOL ON THE LITTLE WATER HEN

Gabrielle Roy

PART ONE

Deep within the Canadian province of Manitoba, remote in its melancholy region of lakes and wild waterfowl, there lies a tiny village barely noticeable amidst its skimpy fir trees. On the map you will find it called Meadow Portage, but it is known to the people who live thereabouts as Portage des Prés. To reach it you must cover a full thirty-two miles of jolty road beyond Rorketon, the terminus of the branch railroad and the nearest town. In all, it contains a chapel, visited three or four times a year by an aged missionary, polyglot and loquacious; a boxlike structure built of new planks and serving as school for the handful of white children in the area; and another building, also of boards but a bit larger, the most important in the settlement, since it houses at once the store, the post office, and the telephone. Somewhat further away you can see, in a clearing among the birches, two other dwellings which, together with the store-post-office, shelter all Portage des Prés's inhabitants. But I nearly forgot: in front of the largest structure, at the edge of the rough track leading to Rorketon, proudly stands a lone gasoline pump, complete with its large glass globe, ever awaiting the arrival of electricity. Beyond these few things, a wilderness of grass and wind. One of the houses, indeed, possesses a front door, inserted at the level of its second floor, yet since no one has bothered to build for it either a landing or a flight of steps, nothing could better express the idea of utter uselessness. Across the façade of the large building are painted the words "Bessette's General Store." And that is absolutely all there is at Portage des Prés. It is the image of the final jumping-off place. And yet the Tousignant family lived, some twenty years ago, even beyond this outpost.

To reach their home from Portage des Prés, you had to continue straight on beyond the gas pump, following the same crude road; at first glance you could scarcely make it out, but finally you saw how it ran thanks to two parallel bands of grass which remained a trifle flattened by the passage of the Indians' light buckboards. Only an old resident or a halfbreed guide could find his way along it, for at several points this track divided, and secondary tracks led through the brush to some trapper's cabin two or three miles away and invisible from the main trail.

You had, then, to stick closely to the most direct road. And a few hours later, if you were riding in a buggy—a little sooner if traveling in one of those ancient Fords which still operate in those parts—you should reach the Big Water Hen River.

There you left Ford or buggy behind.

The Tousignants had a canoe to cross the river. Were it on the further shore, someone would have to swim over to get it. You then continued downstream, wholly wrapped in such silence as is seldom found on earth—or rather, in the rustle of sedges, the beat of wings, in the thousands of tiny, hidden, secret, timid sounds, producing an effect in some way as restful as silence itself. Big prairie chickens, almost too heavy to fly, heaved themselves above the river's brush-covered banks and tumbled back to earth, already tired by their listless efforts.

Clambering out on the opposite shore, you crossed on foot an island half a mile wide, covered with thick, uneven grass, mud holes, and, in summer, enormous and famished mosquitoes swarming up by the million from the spongy ground.

You then reached another river. It was the Little Water Hen. The people of the region had had no great trouble in naming its geographical features—always in honor of its senior inhabitant, that small gray fowl which epitomized all its tedium and all its quietness. Apart from the two rivers already mentioned, there was the Water Hen—unqualified—there was Lake Water Hen. Moreover, the area itself was known as the Water Hen Country. And it was endlessly peaceful, there, to watch of an evening the aquatic birds rising up everywhere from among the reeds and circling together in one sector of the heavens which they darkened with their multitude.

When you had crossed the Little Water Hen, you landed on a fair-sized island with few trees. A large flock of sheep were at pasture there, completely free and unfenced; had it not been for them, you would have thought the island uninhabited.

But there was a house built upon it.

Built of unsquared logs, level with the ground, longer than it was wide, its windows set low, it stood upon a very slight elevation on the island's surface, bare to the four winds of heaven.

Here it was that the Tousignants lived.

Of their eight handsome children, shy yet tractable, one alone had journeyed as far as the village of Sainte Rose du Lac to be treated for a very bad earache. This was the nearest French settlement in the area; it was situated even further away than Rorketon, on the local railway which in some measure linked all this bush to the little town of Dauphin. A few of the other children had from time to time accompanied their father when, two or three times a year, he journeyed to Portage des Prés to get his orders from the owner of the ranch under his management.

It was the mother who traveled the most. Almost every year she of necessity went to Sainte Rose du Lac. If there were the slightest hitch, you could spend days getting there; all the same, since she quit her island approximately but once a year, this long, hard trip, frequently hazardous, always exhausting, had come to be regarded by Luzina Tousignant as her annual holiday. Never did she refer to it far in advance before the children, for they were, you might say, too attached to their mother, very tender, very affectionate, and it was a painful business for them to let her go; they would cling fast to her skirts, begging her not to leave. So it was better not to arouse this grief any sooner than necessary. To her husband alone one fine day she would announce, with an odd look half laughter and half sorrow, "My holiday is not far off." Then she would depart. And in this changeless existence, it was the great, the sole adventure.

II

This year it looked as though Luzina Tousignant could not undertake her usual trip. Her legs were swollen; she could not stand on them for more than an hour at a time, for she was a woman of considerable strength and weight, full of life, always on the go the moment her poor feet seemed a little better. Hippolyte Tousignant did not like to let her leave under such circumstances. And then too, it was the very worst time of year. Nonetheless, Luzina laughed when she began to talk about her holiday. In midsummer or midwinter, if it were necessary, one could get away from the island, and even without too much trouble. But in spring a woman alone could not possibly run into greater risks, dangers, and misery than on the Portage des Prés trail. Hippolyte long tried to persuade Luzina she should not leave. Compliant under all other circumstances, in this she remained adamant. Of course she had to go to Sainte Rose du Lac! What was more, she must consult a doctor there about the baby's eczema. One of the cream separator's parts had got dented; she would have it fixed. And for business reasons she would stay awhile at Rorketon. She would take advantage of that visit to get some little idea of what people were wearing. "For," Luzina would say, "just because we live in a wild country is no reason we shouldn't be in style every so often." She gave a hundred reasons rather than admit that she took some small pleasure in getting away from the empty horizon of the Little Water Hen.

And, after all, how could Luzina ever have seen a crowd, a real crowd of at least a hundred persons, such as is to be found on Saturday nights along Rorketon's main street; how could she ever have been able to talk to persons other than her husband or her children, who, the moment she opened her mouth, already knew what she was going to say; how could she ever have those rare joys of novelty, of satisfied curiosity, of glimpses of the world, had she not had a wholly different reason for traveling—an eminently serious and pressing reason! She was not a demanding woman; she was quite willing to relish the pleasures of her trip, but only to the extent that they were proper rewards for duty done.

She left toward the end of March. The Little Water Hen was still frozen hard enough to allow crossing it on foot; the Big Water Hen, however, was free of ice at midstream. The boat was drawn over the ice like a sledge until it could be launched in the open water. Luzina was installed on its bottom boards, a bearskin over her knees, warmed bricks at her feet. Hippolyte had rigged a piece of rough canvas above her, somewhat in the shape of a small tent. Thus fully sheltered and showing no sign of fear, Luzina was keenly interested in everything that happened during the crossing. From time to time she thrust her smiling face through the slit in the canvas and remarked contentedly, "I'm as well off as the Queen!"

Two of the children, one pushing and the other pulling, helped their father maneuver the boat on the ice, and it was a job that required a lot of care, since no one could tell at exactly what spot the ice would begin to yield. Without any of them getting too soaked, they reached the river's free-flowing water. Large chunks of ice were floating in the current; they had to paddle hard to avoid them and to make headway against the Big Water Hen's rapid flow. Then the boat was hauled up on the other side—not without trouble, for the footing was far from firm.

The youngest children had remained on the little island, and this was the moment for their final good-bys to their mother. All of them were weeping. Swallowing their tears, and without the least outcry, they understood that it was too late to dissuade their mother from her journey. Their tiny hands, never still even for an instant, fluttered toward Luzina. One of the little girls carried the baby in her arms and made the infant wave continuously. All five of them were huddled together, so that they made one minute spot against the widest and most deserted of the world's horizons. Then was it that Luzina lost a great part of her gaiety; she looked for her handkerchief but could not find it, so encumbered was she with heavy clothing. She sniffled.

"Be good," she urged her children, raising her voice which the wind carried, though not at all in their direction. "Mind what your father tells you."

They tried to talk from one shore to the other, but the conversation made no sense. The children recalled the things they had wanted and begged for the whole year through; despite their grief, these things they remembered very well.

"A blackboard, Mama!" cried one of them.

"A pencil with an eraser, Mama!" another implored.

Luzina was not sure she understood what they were saying, but, taking a chance, she promised: "I'll bring you picture postcards."

She knew she made no mistake in promising postcards. Her children were crazy about them, especially those which showed very high buildings, streets jammed with cars, and—wonder of wonders—railway stations. Luzina thoroughly understood their taste.

Her husband lending her a hand, her older boys going ahead to beat a path in the snow, Luzina Tousignant reached the trail, and they all stood waiting for the arrival of the postman who, once a week, if it were at all possible, carried the mail from Portage des Prés to an Indian reservation some fifteen miles further north on Lake Water Hen.

They were much afraid that they had missed the mailman, or else that he had decided, because of the wretched condition of the road, to postpone his trip a week. Pierre-Emmanuel-Roger and Philippe-Auguste-Emile came very close to hoping for such a mishap; so even did Hippolyte Tousignant, who suggested timidly: "The postman will not dare set out in weather like this. If you were to come back home, Luzina . . . we'd manage all the same."

"Come now, you know very well that won't do," she replied with a smile of regret, mingled with a hint of mockery, which above all seemed to reproach Hippolyte for his lack of practical good sense.

She looked fixedly up the trail, more determined than ever. After having overcome so many obstacles it would be a fine thing for her to have to return home. A very light snow, mixed with rain, began to fall.

"If only I could go with you," Hippolyte was saying, as he had said on all her previous departures.

And, just as she had the last time, she agreed: "Yes, indeed! To take the trip together, the two of us, what fun that would be! But, poor man, surely someone has to keep an eye on things and be in command while I'm not there."

They said no more.

Far away in the vast, changeless solitude a horse came into view, all in a lather, and on the seat of the sleigh behind it, a great ball of fur, from which emerged a sad yellow mustache, a thick cloud of vapor, and, held aloft, a swaying whip.

It was the postman.

He drew near. Now you could distinguish his bushy eyebrows from the brown fur of his winter hat; you could see the gleam of the silver thread which always hung from the postman's nose in cold weather; you could make out his tobacco-stained teeth when he gave his mare a throaty order. Having reached the little Tousignant group without a word of greeting, his frowning glance fixed on Luzina alone, he tightened the reins, stopped, and waited. For this Nick Sluzick was an odd character. In a country where people were often silent for lack of anything new to talk about, he beat everyone for taciturnity. He was said to have managed his business, accepted errands, done favors, fulfilled his postman's duties, made love, and procreated children—and all this without ever having uttered more than a scant dozen sentences.

Luzina was installed alongside this unsociable companion, he moving over a trifle to make a little space for her to sit down. Talkative as she was, Nick Sluzick's amazing uncommunicativeness ever remained her principal—indeed, her sole—trial throughout the journey.

Pierre-Emmanuel-Roger had brought a lantern, which he now lit and slipped under the covers at his mother's feet. He spread a bison skin over her and on top of it a piece of oilcloth to prevent the fur from getting soaked. With all her coverings, Luzina had almost totally disappeared, save for her eyes, which peered out from above a heavy muffler. They were clear, blue eyes, rather large, full of affection, and, at that moment, moist with sorrow. All four of them were looking at each other with the same expression of sad stupor, as though these Tousignants, so united in their isolation, were almost unable to conceive of being apart. And suddenly these people, who thought they had long exhausted every subject of conversation, discovered a wholly new one and began to chatter.

"Do be careful, all of you, about fire," urged Luzina, lowering the scarf which covered her mouth.

"Yes. And you be careful not to freeze on your trip," said Hippolyte.

"Above all, don't starve yourselves," Luzina added. "There's plenty of flour and lard. Just make pancakes if you don't feel much like cooking; and you, Pierre-Emmanuel-Roger, be a help to your father."

The two eldest were not the only Tousignant children to have compound appellations. As though better to people the solitude where she dwelt, Luzina had given to each of her children a litany of names drawn from the pages of history or from the occasional novel that came her way. Among the children who had remained behind were Roberta-Louise-Célestine, Joséphine-Yolande, André-Aimable-Sébastien; the youngest, a fifteen-months-old baby, answered to the name of Juliette-Héloïse.

"You'll be very careful that Juliette-Héloïse doesn't swallow any pins," cried Luzina.

It was the last advice she gave her loved ones. Nick Sluzick couldn't waste any more time. Of all human actions, none seemed to him more useless and unnecessary than saying good-by. Either you did not go away or you went away; in the latter case, the event itself was explicit enough not to require comment. He spat over the side of the sled. With one hand he twirled his long yellow mustache, with the other he picked up the reins. And they were off through the soft snow, lying uneven on the ground, here in hummocks, there in hollows, which was the road to Portage des Prés.

To describe the difficulties of Luzina Tousignant's journey, seated next to her unsociable muzhik, who only once opened his mouth and then to ask her to stay put on her end of the seat since otherwise the sleigh might upset; to tell how, when she reached Portage des Prés, she had to wait for a week before the next mail left for Rorketon; how she spent those seven days at the store-post-office, which also after a fashion served the settlement as an inn, since in case of need it could afford people who had no other place to go a single room, practically unheated and with little or no furniture; how bored Luzina was while she waited, exasperated at this mischance and greatly fearing that she would get to Rorketon too late; how, when she finally left Portage des Prés, there was a cold wind blowing which grew in violence and froze one of her ears; to recount these few mishaps might be interesting were it not that her trip home was to be otherwise rich in vicissitudes.

III

Once the serious purpose of her trip had been accomplished and her business finished at Sainte Rose du Lac, Luzina's most pressing desire was to get back by train to Rorketon, where she hoped to find promptly some means of returning home. She was made that way; all year long it seemed to her, shut off on her island, that never would she have her fill of seeing Rorketon's brightly illuminated shop windows, the electric lights which burned all night along its main street, the many buggies that thronged there, the plank sidewalks and the people moving about on them—in short, the intense life afforded by this big village with its Chinese restaurant, its Greek-rite Catholic chapel, its Orthodox church, its Rumanian tailor, its cupolas, its whitewashed cottages, its peasants in sheepskins and big rabbit hats—some, immigrants from Sweden; others, from Finland or Iceland; still others, and they were the majority, come from Bukovina and Galicia. At Rorketon Luzina gathered the material for the tales she would tell her family for month after month, practically until her next trip.

Yet once she had spent a few days at Rorketon, she had had all she wanted of it. Nothing seemed to her warmer or more human than that lonely gray house which, atop its mound between the willows, looked out upon nothing except the quiet and monotonous Little Water Hen.

She worried about the children. She wondered whether, while chopping holes in the ice on the Little Water Hen in order to fish for pike, as was their custom in spring, they might not all have fallen in and perished as they attempted to save each other. She pictured to herself a flood which might cover the whole island and force her husband and her poor children to clamber up upon the roof of the house. Hers was a mind extraordinarily adept at imagining, the moment she was away from home, all the mishaps which could befall her loved ones and to which reality, harsh as it was in that land, lent a certain verisimilitude.

She was on edge.

But the coming of spring had been unusually delayed that year by heavy snowfalls followed by rain and finally by renewed cold. The wretched road between Rorketon and Portage des Prés had become impassable. Even the mailman refused to chance it. Now in those countries of the North, everyone takes it for granted that when the mailman cannot get through, no one can get through. The mail in that awesome wilderness remains the great, the most important business, and only obstacles truly insurmountable can stop it.

Nevertheless Luzina everywhere made inquiries—at the post office, in the stores, at the hotel—to see whether someone might know of a person who was going to try to reach Portage des Prés in spite of everything. At that moment the town was full of travelers, detained in Rorketon precisely because of the bad condition of the roads. And so Luzina made a number of acquaintanceships; to some few of these she would even send letters later on, giving news of her return and of events at the ranch, so interested in her had these people seemed and so anxious to wish her well. Because of her affability Luzina had made a number of friends during her travels; she still wrote regularly to an old lady who had grown most affectionate toward her during the short train ride from Sainte Rose du Lac to Rorketon ten years earlier, a Madame Lacoste who lived in the province of Quebec. In fact Luzina said that meeting likable people was the real pleasure of traveling. She enjoyed being helpful to those who happened to be at hand, and to such good purpose that rarely did she fail to find in her journeying agreeable people ready to do as much for her. This time, however, no one could help her. She was advised to speak to the postman on the Rorketon-Portage des Prés route, who would deliver her to the place where Nick Sluzick took over the mail.

Now this Rorketon postman was the most baffling fellow of all. Ivan Bratislovski nearly always said he was going to do the opposite of what he did, a kind of peasant's stratagem against fate, which perhaps he thus hoped to best. And probably for the same reason he complained endlessly. At all hours of the day he was to be found in the Chinese restaurant, eager to pick a quarrel with anyone who might have dared deny that he, Ivan Bratislovski, lived a dog's life. Were you only to agree with him on that point, the little Ruthenian could prove himself most useful. Luzina was unaware of this method of appeasement. Having sent a small boy twice to ask the Ruthenian whether he would be leaving the following morning, she had been informed that "Ivan Bratislovski's horse had been injured, that the sleigh was very small to carry a woman traveling with a lot of belongings, and that, in any case, he was on the point of offering his resignation to the postal authorities." What this meant was that Ivan Bratislovski would shortly take his chances and start for Portage des Prés, which, of course, was beyond Luzina's guessing. Meanwhile a Jewish merchant from Dauphin arrived at the hotel where Luzina was staying. He was in a hurry, anxious to get to Portage des Prés with an eye to a deal in muskrat skins that might at any moment be snatched away, right from under his nose. He rented a horse and sleigh. The next morning he left, Luzina with him.

IV

The two travelers had scarcely passed Rorketon's last farmsteads when they found themselves in a lonely expanse, entirely covered with a thin layer of sparkling ice. The fine-grained, shifting snow was wholly imprisoned, as though in an envelope of brilliant cellophane. No breath of wind disturbed this frozen whiteness. Here was the hard and perfect motionlessness which the cold in its full virulence demands.

The road was as completely frozen as the fields, as all the countryside, flat and lifeless. At times it stretched out like a congealed pond, blue and level; the runners of the sleigh began to slide to and fro as though they were waltzing; in other places the frost had solidified the hollows and unevennesses of the road into a surface so rugged that the vehicle plunged, reared up, crashed down again in a straining effort strange to behold in a landscape so broad and unfeeling.

The horse was soon in a lather. The ice shattered beneath its shoes in long sharp splinters which cruelly wounded it. Luzina could scarcely bear watching the poor beast, and despite her desire to get home as soon as possible, she kept urging the Jew to spare the animal.

It took them hours to cover a few miles. The ice grew smoother and smoother. At one corner they took a little quickly the sleigh upset, tumbling Luzina, her suitcase, and all her bundles some feet off the road. Abe Zlutkin ran to her help. Her heavy clothing had protected her, her and her most fragile gift, which as she fell she clasped within her arms. She had not even a scratch. She began to laugh, and, after a thoughtful moment, Abe Zlutkin did too.

He was a small, swarthy man, active, thin, always worrying and calculating. He had barely left Rorketon at daybreak when he began regretting that he had taken this woman with him. She might be injured if they had an accident; were that to happen, her husband would probably claim damages. Because he had wanted the three dollars Luzina had offered, Abe Zlutkin half foresaw that he would lose hundreds. He had been shaken by that very fear when Luzina stumbled back to her feet, more nimble than ever, and began to laugh. At once optimism replaced anxiety in Zlutkin's changeable soul. Such a woman, healthy and fearless, could not bring bad luck to him who helped her. On the contrary, he should make the best of it, put himself under her star, which was certainly a fortunate one. A half an hour after the accident Zlutkin was still chuckling over it, filled with amazement and henceforward certain that his good deed would be repaid a hundred-fold, in fine furs, in choice skins which he would acquire at small expense in Portage des Prés.

Seeing him so well disposed, Luzina began to chat. She was on her return journey; the horse's every step, however hesitant, brought her nearer home; she was grateful to Abe Zlutkin; she could not prevent her generous nature from offering what she had to give, which amounted to the stories of half-a-hundred adventures in her life that might have been tragic and that always had—she never gave herself any reason why—the happiest possible endings. In the goodness of her heart she really hoped that by means of all her tales she could distract her companion from the dangers continually confronting them both. Yet she feared she might seem selfish if she talked only about her own good fortune. She asked the fur merchant whether he was married. Stout Luzina's motherly kindness, her warm, inquiring eyes, her eager interest in others, her whole nature invited confidence.

Abe Zlutkin took advantage of an interval when the road was a trifle less slippery to show her a photo of his wife. It portrayed a plump young Jewish woman of dark complexion. Abe bethought himself that he loved her dearly. For a moment the business he was in such a hurry to transact ceased tormenting him. Such was Luzina's power. She disposed people to become aware that they had reasons for being happy.

When they were tired of talking, they rested by reflecting on the pleasant things that had been said. Her life, at the only times when she could give it much thought, while she was jolting along on her travels, seemed truly wonderful. Dwelling so far from all the world, she had encountered human beings of all races and characters. The most exciting romance could not have offered her so great a variety of people: little old bearded Poles, Slav postmen, halfbreed guides, Russian Orthodox; once she had even made the trip home with the post office inspector. No one of them had ever treated her disrespectfully; Luzina had only to put herself under a human being's protection for him to behave toward her exactly as she wished. Moreover, traveling in itself had taught her lessons of an unexpected sort: it had shown her that human nature everywhere is excellent. The Jews were about the only folk she had had no opportunity to study; yet, deciding on the basis of her fur merchant that they were rather on the likable side, she let herself drift into a feeling of vague benevolence, lazy and easygoing, which embraced very nearly the whole human race.

But she had to resume the conversation. Zlutkin was becoming uneasy again; the road continued to be just as bad; the horse was limping. And, before they had covered much more ground, the sky began to cloud over. Strange red streaks, low on the horizon, foretold a change in the weather. The two travelers were obliged to find a stopping place. It turned out to be one of those solitary farms such as were to be found every three or four miles along the Portage des Prés road. The house was poor; it contained only one room, furnished in back, behind the stove, with a number of beds. Yet the moment Luzina entered their home, shivering with cold, the man and woman of the house came forward to greet her, smiling, their arms extended to relieve her of all her bundles. They led her to the stove and at once offered her food, all this with so much alacrity that she could not harbor the least doubt of the sincerity of their welcome, even though it was expressed in a foreign tongue. It was just as she had always thought: every human being, the moment necessity forces us to seek his kindness, eagerly offers it in our behalf.

After supper Luzina settled herself for an interesting evening.

The family were Icelanders, a people with whom she had not yet had occasion to become acquainted. She noticed that they constantly drank very strong coffee and that, instead of putting sugar in their cups, they placed a lump on their tongues or between their teeth before drinking the burning liquid. When they began talking in their own language, she was even more delighted. Peculiarities, customs, and a language that were foreign to her, rather than putting her off, seemed to give life an inexhaustible attraction.

She did not want to be outdone in amiability by such kindly hosts. So, even though she had no assurance that they understood her, she began giving an account of the road she would have to travel to reach her home on the island in the Little Water Hen. Visiting was what gave them the greatest pleasure, said she. Laughingly she granted that it was the habit of living so far away from people that made her become so talkative whenever she had a chance. When she laughed, through politeness the Icelanders pretended to want to laugh also. Thereupon she dug into her purse, seeking some little keepsake she might offer their children. She had only the crayons and the postcards bought for her own offspring; she hesitated a lot, but reflecting—and with good reason—that her own would not have hesitated to share their crayons with the young Bjorgssons, she beckoned to them, and the crayons were duly distributed. Seemingly the parents were touched, for they arose again to offer everyone coffee.

The next morning the travelers had a slightly less slippery road; the clouds, however, hung low; the sky was mottled. A little snow had fallen during the night. The wind swept strongly through this fresh snow, and there was reason to fear that a real gale was in the offing. They did not reach Portage des Prés until midafternoon, having twice wandered off the track, and they were pierced with cold, famished, their eyes scorched by the wind. The worst of the trip was still ahead of Luzina.

V

That North country, with its vast, sparse forests and its equally vast lakes, that land of water and dwarf trees, has, of all regions, the most capricious climate. From one day to another the ice melted on the trail between Portage des Prés and the Tousignant ranch; you could almost see the snow disappear. Another cold wave had been expected, but during the night Luzina spent at the settlement store a south wind had blown up. Almost warm, soft and damp, a wind swollen with hope—at any other time it would have rejoiced Luzina's heart. With this wind returned the fast gray teal, the green-necked mallard, the wild goose and its plaintive cry, the gallant little silver-bellied water hens, many sorts of duck, bustling and winsome, the whole great aquatic tribe, exquisite companion of spring and of man's assurance throughout these faraway realms.

In less than twenty-four hours, however, the whole countryside had turned into a kind of perilous marsh, deep and treacherous. Under the flaccid snow a man's foot found water everywhere, everywhere seeping water.

All the same, Luzina decided to leave. Either she would succeed in reaching home that very day, or else she would have to wait idly for weeks until the road dried out. For her children she still had some postcards, and, herself childlike, she could not wait to give them their present, so that she might watch their guileless eyes brighten with joy. For Hippolyte she had a handsome necktie, which he would have a chance to wear on his next trip, within a few months. She was itching with desire to tell about how the Bjorgssons had received her. Above all she had with her, this year like the other years, the gift of gifts, so precious that Luzina dared not entrust it to anyone and kept it scrupulously wrapped. This gift was supposed to be a great surprise for her family, which, truth to tell, rather expected it, since Luzina, ever generous, would surely come home this time with as much as she had always brought before. Her happiness, no more than the wind of springtime, the warm wind, alive and friendly, could wait to spread abroad.

Hippolyte would scold her for having taken to the road on so bad a day. So much the worse! Today you could still chance the trip; tomorrow opportunity might be lacking, or the trail might be even worse. She gathered her things together and through the store window began to watch for the moment when Nick Sluzick, lately arrived, would be ready to depart. As a matter of fact, she had not saved any time by journeying with Abe Zlutkin rather than with Ivan Bratislovski, because, whatever happened, Nick Sluzick had to wait for the mail brought by the latter before he could begin to distribute it over his own territory.

At last Luzina saw that the mail bags had been piled up on the back of the sleigh. Immediately, she rushed over to take her place beside a Nick Sluzick more gloomy than ever; without good-day or greeting, without comment or question, the ancient Ukrainian cleared his nostrils with his fingers, then briskly gave his mare the whip.

Today he was especially out of humor; he had had all the trouble in the world getting through certain stretches of the road, and he suspected that the return trip would be even more disagreeable. Not that Nick Sluzick feared the water holes for the sake of his own tough hide; it took more than an icy bath to disconcert him. But he did not like to see a woman running such risks. In general he had no fondness for lugging women along with him—women, children, breakable objects, in short anything fragile. In danger he preferred to be alone. When it came down to it, he always preferred to be alone. A man needed to be alone to ponder his own affairs. What was more, if this Water Hen Country were to be any more settled, in the end he, Nick Sluzick, would have to seek refuge further north.

They reached a veritable slough. Bella refused to venture into it. The old man raised his whip; from the tip of his red nose flowed the usual silver thread; to his mustaches clung the remains of the garlic sausage and bread he had devoured standing near the stove in the store, knife in hand, even though the merchant had invited him to share his own meal. Bella seemed to be measuring the water's depth with her bent leg, which she drew back up under her belly. The water came half-way to her body, about half the height of the sleigh, flush with its floorboards. Luzina lifted her most precious package above her head, thinking less of herself than of this irreplaceable gift. They had, however, passed through the deepest of the water. Luzina, her arms laden, quietly sank back into the seat.

Toward the end of the afternoon one of the Tousignant children, posted on the Little Water Hen shore, heard the summons on the bark trumpet whereby it had been agreed that Luzina would indicate her arrival at the bank of the Big Water Hen.

Immediately Hippolyte and Pierre-Emmanuel-Roger launched the boat. At that last moment two more children clambered in; Hippolyte had not the heart to send them back so eager were they to see their mother again. They rowed quickly; they raced across the little island. From afar they could already see the motionless sleigh and two human figures, one of them peevish, annoyed at the delay, and the other waving, excitedly perched on the seat.

They crossed the Big Water Hen; now they were within hailing distance, and they cried out to each other. And then, a bit thinner, a trifle pale, but laughing with shyness and emotion, her face wrinkled in joy, Luzina stepped out upon the ground. And in her arms, as happened whenever she returned from her business trips, Luzina carried the baby she had gone to Sainte Rose du Lac to bring into the world.

PART TWO

Within a radius of fifty miles around Luzina's home there existed in all but two government schools. The one to the north, lying within the Indian reservation, was open only to children of the Saultais tribe.* The other school was even further away, at the end of eighteen miles of impossible road. It was at the settlement of Portage des Prés. This settlement was growing; and since its population included twelve children, it had been able to make sure of a schoolmistress and a few books. From time to time, every two or three years, the inspector of schools came there to make his report, provided that a whole sequence of fortunate circumstances allowed him to complete the trip —in June, if it was possible for him, and if it had not rained for at least three weeks, and if his car could negotiate the last dozen miles of trail. Moreover, it was necessary that these twenty-one consecutive days of fine weather required to dry the Portage des Prés road should fall before the inspector's holiday, which began early in July. Even so, he had had to delay his holiday almost every time he had visited the Portage des Prés school. The settlement's advantages, however, did nothing to solve the educational problem on the island in the Little Water Hen.

Once more the ducks had started their long flight south. The wild geese also strung their way over the island, coming from even more secret retreats in the north; never would they nest closer than ten miles from the nearest human habitation; the terns, the water hens, the prairie chickens, the teal were on the wing. The skies over the land were furrowed with aerial rights of way, almost visible to the eye, with all the traffic in one direction. Soon the Big Water Hen carried little islands of snow; the river also took on a lively mien, as though it were in a hurry to be gone, thanks to the large white bundles it swept along in its course, allowing you to measure the swiftness of its current. Sadly Luzina saw the coming of another torpid winter, again without a schoolteacher and regular lessons. Even the Indian children had a better portion than her own; they had a school, Luzina would say.

* One of the formerly nomadic Indian tribes of the Prairies which at present, like all the other tribes that have made a treaty with the Canadian government, lives in an isolated area where it enjoys exclusive hunting and fishing rights. The whites are generally forbidden access to reservations.

But here, how could we manage? Then one evening, as he sat rocking in the kitchen, Hippolyte found a solution for the bewildering problem.

Never did Hippolyte rock alone; the moment he had sat down in the rocking chair three or four children came begging to climb aboard. He would plant one on each of his knees, two others on the big chair's arms, and, thus laden, spacious and sturdy, the rocker would set forth on a kind of voyage, for not only did it rock all these passengers, it also took them for a ride across the kitchen floor. All the while Hippolyte smoked; it was his hour of relaxation. Navigating at full speed and surrounded with thick smoke, the chair was almost at the door; Hippolyte was meditating, and suddenly he glimpsed the answer. It was easy enough; all you had to do was think of it. Hippolyte briefly interrupted his travels; he took his pipe out of his mouth; the smoke grew thinner. Without undue excitement Hippolyte gave utterance to the profound discovery which was to transform their existence.

"Now about the children, Mother. . . . I've been thinking; we could write the government!"

The moment they had been spoken, these words introduced into the Tousignants' little home a relief so satisfying, so obvious, that they were astounded they had not hit upon it long before. Hippolyte had the pleasure of seeing Luzina's countenance reflective in its turn, absorbed, then gladdened and, at the same moment, congratulating him, Hippolyte, for always knowing where to turn. The government, of course! How had neither of them ever thought of it before! All kinds of imposing images, solid and reassuring, summoned the government before Luzina's inner eye.

Its seat was Winnipeg, the most beautiful city, she asserted, that she had ever seen. She had been there on her honeymoon, on the way to the Little Water Hen. The government dwelt in a house built entirely of marble imported from Italy; Luzina had heard it said that its construction had cost several million dollars, and at this juncture she literally believed it. In all the world there could not be a Parliament much better housed than Manitoba's. This Parliament was surmounted by a statue of a man who had wings and came from France. Access to it was by a great stairway, likewise of marble. Almost everything was marble in that Parliament. On each side of the stair two life-sized buffaloes appeared ready to charge. The buffaloes were the emblem of Manitoba: beasts with great heads planted directly in their humps, without any length of neck or all neck-length, according to the point of view, and whose feet still seemed furiously to pound the prairie soil. They had been almost exterminated and now they symbolized the province's daring and belief in progress. It had been by Winnipeg's schools, however, that Luzina had above all been overwhelmed. Big schools several stories high, all windows. The government took care of them. The government which ruled from behind the two buffaloes was among the most advanced in educational matters. It had decreed compulsory schooling before there were enough schools for all the children or roads for them to reach what schools there were.

Full of confidence, Luzina tore a sheet of paper from her pad and wrote to the government. She dreamed of the bronze buffaloes. No other province in the world could have such powerful animals for an emblem. Canada itself had only a beaver. In this dream of Luzina's the buffaloes charged down from everywhere at once against the ignorance of backward lands. The next day, ice or no ice, Hippolyte was dispatched to the edge of the trail, across the two rivers, with the letter to give the postman on the mainland. He was the same fellow as before, that old character by the name of Nick Sluzick who, although he had been threatening for ten years to leave for quieter, less thickly populated country, had continued to ply between the province's most remote post office and the region's uttermost habitations, just at the edge of the everlasting tundra.

At the same spot six weeks later, Nick Sluzick grumblingly drew from one of his mail bags a letter addressed to the Tousignants. Pierre-Emmanuel-Roger, who had been sent to reconnoiter each Friday, found it in their letter box, the hollow of an old tree that had been killed by the frost. The letter bore no stamp. In its place there were initials—O.H.M.S.—and, in the opposite corner, a buffalo surmounted by a cross, the whole engraved in relief, black on white, and most impressive. At once Pierre realized its importance. He ran all the way from the letter box to the house, a little more than a mile; he might easily have taken a ducking in the Little Water Hen, so negligently did he look to see whether the ice beneath his feet was sufficiently firm. On the threshold Luzina was waiting for him, the temperature thirty below zero, her cheeks aflame.

"It's got the buffalo on it," Pierre informed her.

"The buffalo!"

She caught a glimpse of the vastness of the power to which she had had recourse. The handsome envelope Pierre coveted flew into tiny bits. "Dear Mrs. Tousignant," Luzina began to read. She did not understand much English but enough to grasp the good news. She seemed to gather that first of all the government apologized for having made her await an answer for so long a time. It said that, knowing almost no French, it had had to appeal to its Quebec colleague, Jean-Marie Lafontaine, who worked for Titles and Land and who had helped it translate Luzina's letter.

Surely the government had been put to a lot of trouble through her fault; Luzina blushed a little at what she had done. Moreover, the government explained, Luzina's letter addressed to the *Gouvernement d'Instruction* had taken a long while to reach the offices of the Department of Education and, among all its offices, that of Mr. Evans, who was in charge of precisely such requests as those Luzina had made. Hence it was he who was answering Luzina. She examined the signature and saw that it indeed corresponded with the much more legible, typewritten letters appearing below it. All this, however, was merely by way of preliminary, friendly as it might be. Luzina found the essential matter in the second paragraph.

In this second paragraph of its letter, the government made clear to Luzina that she had not been wrong in supposing it very much interested in education. It expressed itself as distressed to learn that in regions like that in which Luzina lived there seemingly were future citizens deprived of schools. All this must be changed as quickly as possible, and all this would be changed, promised the government, for it was certainly by means of education that a nation came into being. Consequently it declared itself ready to dispatch a schoolmistress to the island in the Little Water Hen, starting in May and for a period of four or six months, as the weather and the roads might allow, under two conditions:

First, that there be a small building, or at the very least a room in the house, which would serve as a school. Second, that the number of students be at least six, all of them having reached the age of school enrollment.

The government explained that it was obliged to be rather severe on this last point; if there were less than six pupils neither too old nor too young, it could only, to its great regret, encourage Luzina to wait until she had more children or until she had neighbors with children. If these conditions were fulfilled, it would send a schoolteacher and it would itself pay out of its own pocket the schoolteacher's salary. As for the Tousignants, it would be up to them to furnish the schoolteacher shelter, board, and hospitality.

Hospitality indeed! Her expression businesslike, her eyes shining, Luzina was quite ready to turn everything inside out in order to welcome her schoolmistress, whom she saw almost arrived, popping out from among the rushes, her small suitcase in hand.

She also realized how truly she had been inspired not to cease for a single year bringing future schoolchildren into the world. Had she had any need of encouragement, certainly this last educational regulation regarding the number of pupils would not have served as any brake on Luzina's career!

As things then stood, she could reply to the government that she had five children of school age, that a sixth, Joséphine-Yolande Tousignant, would be six years old during the month of June, and that it seemed to her, Luzina, that the government might overlook so light an infraction of the rules, seeing that Joséphine would be so close to her sixth birthday when classes began. It was her great hope, she wrote, that she would not be required to wait a whole year longer merely through Joséphine's fault. As far as expecting another family near enough at hand, she said that that would occasion a far longer delay than Joséphine's.

II

No sooner had the letter gone than Luzina wanted to see Hippolyte at work building the school. The quicker they fulfilled the government's conditions, the less likely, she thought, that they might be turned down. To her continuing great confidence in the government's power there was added—now that it had become more familiar to her—a certain small portion of mistrust regarding the accomplishment of its promises. "They won't be able to go back on their word if we set about building a school," reasoned Luzina. But according to Hippolyte there was no such great hurry. At least they must wait until the snow disappeared—even until the frost was somewhat out of the ground. "Don't worry, Mother," he promised, "the school will go quickly once I can put my hand to it." Nevertheless, she claimed that she could not sleep peacefully until the framework had been put in place. One never knew; there might be provincial elections, changes in the government. That kind, sympathetic Mr. Evans might himself be replaced. Luzina's nature, under the influence of the ambition, of the ups and downs introduced into her hitherto placid heart, knew both worry and exaltation.

The site to be chosen already preoccupied her. At times Luzina wanted the school right close to the house so that during her daily tasks she could overhear the grave, delightful murmur of the children reciting their lessons; then she imagined it a little further away, a small house alone and quiet, as was perhaps more suitable to a temple of education. The school where she had herself learned her letters had been situated in the open country, half a mile from the nearest farm. It had been the fashion in those days throughout the southern plains to place the school far from dwellings, as though it should remain apart from trivial daily life. Luzina saw herself, a tiny little girl, running breathlessly so she would not be late; two long, deserted miles stretched before her; on her arm jingled the small pail in which she brought her lunch; she could never sit down during the trip because of her starched apron; often she carried a fine red apple in her hand for recess time. Oh! those were the good days! Absorbed in her recollections, Luzina then had the weird notion of placing the school at the northern tip of the island, in a small poplar wood beyond the marsh. Kindly Hippolyte was ready to make many concessions regarding this schoolhouse project which she had been the first to formulate. But with good reason he objected that if they were to send the children so far for their studies, Luzina would have to prepare them a meal to take with them every day, that this would mean a lot of work, and that, moreover, he thought it a bit silly to have the children eat at the other end of the island when they had a table, a stove, crockery, everything they needed, right at home.

Yes, but had not Hippolyte himself, when he was a child, had to go two miles to get to school? Had not his school at home been absolutely isolated, as was almost always the case in the South?

True enough, his own little school had been all by itself on a lonely rise, flanked by its supply of firewood and two small cabins at a slight distance, one marked BOYS and the other GIRLS. Yet what was the reason for this remoteness? It was merely because each family on the Prairies fought to have the school at its front door. On this point no one would yield. So it had been necessary, to satisfy everyone, to locate the school as much as possible at the same distance from all the farms. Here, thank God, there was no reason for acting similarly. What was more, Hippolyte feared that the schoolmistress would not have footgear suitable for crossing the muskeg.

"If it's a city girl," said Hippolyte, "she is quite capable of arriving here in low patent leather shoes."

The moment it was a matter of sparing the schoolmistress, Luzina moved the school in closer. Moreover, she had not seriously entertained the idea of having it built quite that far away. She had proposed it as a matter of form, for the pleasure of savoring the future under its various, multiple, and changing aspects, which added a lot, Luzina thought, to the joy of planning.

At last the day came when Hippolyte asked, "Now about the school, have you finally decided, Mother? I'm about ready to sink the first posts."

She had not the heart, then, to have it at a distance. At bottom, Hippolyte was right. Quarrels were what put schools at a distance in the South. She went out, a shawl over her shoulders, and indicated a spot a small distance behind the house yet not at all far away, right to the rear of the kitchen.

"There," said Luzina.

It was settled; at last she could never change her mind again, and it came almost as a relief.

The school took shape quickly, a small square building constructed of round logs like the main dwelling. It lay slightly at an angle, between two white birches, closely linked to the house like some faithful outbuilding and yet having its own door and its two entrance steps. It had been quite a task to locate it between the two frail birches which Luzina absolutely refused to sacrifice and which she wished to have, as much as possible, on either side of its doorway.

It was really coming along nicely. The children were constantly rushing in with reports. "Mama, Father has cut out the space for another window frame. Father says that you need a lot of light in a schoolhouse. That makes three windows, Mama!"

Luzina rushed out to see. Half-way up a ladder, Hippolyte was driving nails. He had a supply of them in his mouth, and, when he spoke, he pinched his lips on one side and turned them up on the other. Almost all the children stood at the foot of the ladder; they watched the building progress with all the gravity and interest of city dwellers watching the progress of important public works. Luzina's gay nature, after that attack of doubts and nervousness which, at the outset, all great projects produce, had reasserted itself. Now that the school was under construction, just try telling her that anything could possibly go wrong! One day she began laughing, a fine, open laughter, satisfied with herself: "Well, Father Tousignant, I don't know whether there are many families like us, who have their own school and their own teacher, all to themselves!"

This it was that delighted her above all else: a school just for the Tousignant family, the feeling that they must be in some way specially well regarded by the government. The settlement had been required to wait until it had twelve children before obtaining a teacher. Other small places still had no school. Though little inclined to self-importance, she could not thrust away the notion that the government was on her side. Had it not already forgiven Joséphine's age? It had written that it would be enough to satisfy its regulations were Joséphine to have her sixth birthday during the three months following the beginning of classes. And no sooner had it granted this favor than the government wrote again, this time politely asking Luzina what name she expected to give the new school.

Promoted, as it were, to the posts of president and secretary of her own school board, of which she was sole member, Luzina had a lively feeling for her responsibilities. Oh! she would have to think up a fine school-name that would not disappoint the government! Luzina hinted to Hippolyte that he might cudgel his brains a bit, too. First they reviewed the geographical features of the area, considering what help they offered the imagination. A small river surrounded the island on its west and north sides—the Little Water Hen. It flowed into a larger river which completed the island's encirclement and which, naturally, was called the Big Water Hen. The island, because it belonged to a man named Bessette, merchant at Portage des Prés, was therefore known as Bessette's Island. The school, however, could not be named after the island's proprietor since, after all, his only interest was the profit he could extract from it and since he had done nothing to further education in his domain. On the contrary, Hippolyte recalled, if anyone had put spokes in the wheels it was certainly Bessette. Without telling Luzina, Hippolyte had already sounded the merchant out on the subject of the school. Yes, exactly that. And what had been the big moneybags' answer? He had replied that in the end the school would be expensive; that at the beginning the government, in order to seem generous, would pay the teacher's salary out of its own funds, but that later it would surely make the landowners foot the bill; that that would mean more taxes and that he, Bessette, already paid enough taxes as it was; that he was the only man who paid taxes in the whole area, and that he was fed up with it.

What a shame, remarked Hippolyte, that he should pay all the taxes, since the whole countryside belonged to him. "A profiteer!" was Hippolyte's summary of the man. Not only was he not satisfied with having acquired the whole island for next to nothing, by greasing the palm of someone in the government, but now he was against education because ignorance kept the people at his mercy. It would be better if everyone in the region joined in distrusting the merchant Bessette, Hippolyte concluded. Bessette had even let it be understood that he would make obstacles for the projected school, and how did we know if he might not succeed, because he had friends in the government?

Little vindictive on her own account, Luzina espoused Hippolyte's quarrels. "Oh well, if that's the way it is," said she, "you're right a hundred times over; never will we name our school after that man."

All the more so, as Hippolyte pointed out, because the name of the island was not at all Bessette's Island. Long before Bessette and the rest, the French missionaries had passed through the region, and they it was who had given places their right names.

That was true. The island was not really Bessette's Island. The local people referred to it thus because of the need to simplify things and to distinguish it from a group of small islands at the entrance to the lake which were called the Little Islands of the Water Hen. In reality their island was the Big Island of the Water Hen. The French had thus settled the matter at least twenty-five years before—men who came here to evangelize and civilize the Indians and to rescue them from the fur traders' exploitation, not to enrich themselves. Urged on by patriotism and by loyalty to the missionaries, Hippolyte suggested: "Why not call our school the Little Water Hen school, *l'école de la Petite Poule d'Eau,* Luzina!"

She was won over. *La Petite Poule d'Eau* was just right! How could they, once again, have so long remained blind to the evidence! The Little Water Hen! Thus would justice and truth be re-established. Then too, what name could be better suited to a school situated in the very midst of the water hen country? At the very time of these deliberations, had anyone been paying attention, he would have heard their wings slipping through the damp sedge grasses, their little quarrels, their sharp, wild cry, which no one any longer noticed, so much was it all a part of life there—that plaintive note, yet not without its sad sweetness. He would have seen thousands of gray wings passing through the monotony of water, sky, and sedges.

Luzina had had Bessette send her—she had to patronize him; his was the only store—some letter paper together with a ruled sheet to keep her writing even, and this she used for all her correspondence with the government. On this paper she informed the government of the decision they had reached. What was her disappointment when she received a fresh letter from the government and discovered therein the odd gibberish which was thenceforth to serve as reference and designation between Luzina and the Department of Education in all business dealings: *Water Hen S.D. n° 2-678!*

There must have been some misunderstanding. Attached like a child to that which had cost her so much effort and, finally, gave her so much delight, Luzina could not be consoled. "That's not the name I chose. They've changed my name," she lamented.

Hippolyte asked for a closer look at the letter. "No, they haven't," he pointed out. "Water Hen—*Poule d'Eau.*"

"But all those numbers, and the S.D.?"

"S.D. must be School District."

The numbers, however, for a long time held no meaning for them. In the end, Hippolyte believed that they must mean the two thousand, six hundred and seventy-eighth school in the province.

Nonetheless, Luzina would never have believed that the words could have lost so much in translation. In English their *poule d'eau* had become wholly unrecognizable. Yet she had received too much from the government not to swallow her disappointment. In her reply to Mr. Evans, she studiously applied herself to copy the figures, the abbreviations, and even the underlining of the reference. Then arose the question of the platform.

The school was almost finished. It had three windows, somewhat unequal in size, a door which closed fairly well, a floor of heavy planks, some a little thicker than others, but all exuding the good smell of pine. There was, however, the problem of the platform. Hippolyte came to ask Luzina's advice on this point, which was to embarrass them almost as much as the choice of the building's site.

"Mother, do you think I should build a platform?"

"A platform? Is that necessary?"

Obviously not. As for that, neither the school nor the schoolteacher were absolutely necessary. They had undertaken something in the realm of the not strictly necessary, and thus the problem became delicate. Hippolyte did not know how to make up his mind. The school which he had attended only a few years in all seemed linked in his mind to a platform. A platform was perhaps useful to the relationship between teacher and pupils. As he looked at it, the teacher should dominate the pupils, speak to them from on high, as it were. This must be the way to go about it: place the teacher higher than the students. On the other hand, perhaps platforms were now out of style. First question of all, had there been a platform in the school where Luzina had gone as a child? No, Luzina recalled, but that was no reason for giving up the idea.

They both sat down at two of the little school desks to reflect. Hippolyte had built these before fashioning the door, during the rains which had lasted three weeks on end; they were of pine, a little rough to the fingers, with cracks that caught the wool of your clothes, but they were of varying heights to fit the pupils' differing statures.

There was a fairly large one for Pierre-Emmanuel-Roger, four others which varied in size, and finally a tiny writing bench for Joséphine. Moreover Joséphine's little desk had two almost precise replicas stowed away at the back of the schoolroom, amidst piles of wood shavings. All the children had constantly surrounded Hippolyte the moment he had begun building the desks. Seeing them throng around him, Hippolyte had thought it a good idea while he was at it, and while the rain continued, to be somewhat forehanded. Thus it was that the school contained, in Hippolyte's words, "two spare writing desks." Hippolyte was truly skillful; with a penknife he had carved out a little hollow, almost perfectly round, in the upper part of each desk, to hold an inkwell; a groove, also, to take pencils and penholders. The top of each desk was not made of a single plank but of two, one of which, attached to the other with hinges, could be lifted, revealing a large, convenient box that would serve for storing books and papers. But all these conveniences did not solve the question of the platform.

The more Luzina thought about it, the more it seemed to her a platform was needed. The platform would be most suitable to the schoolmistress when she was seated; she would be easier to see and to hear. The platform was the thing that would make the school.

Meanwhile the Tousignants learned their teacher's name from a letter she wrote them. She was called Mademoiselle Côté. In a quandary as to the steps she should take to get to the Little Water Hen, Mademoiselle Côté had turned to the Tousignants for help; they seemed to be the only people who knew the complicated road to their retreat. At the Department of Education, the officials had only a hazy notion. All they knew was that school *n° 2-678* should be located on an island bounded by two rivers, some place between Lake Winnipegosis and a whole series of smaller lakes; that there must surely be some sort of communication with the outer world. Was it by means of roads, rivers, or lakes? The Department was under an impression that the whole area was perhaps served by a canoe with an outboard motor, which supplied the needs of the area's Indians, but this transport would be under the jurisdiction of the Department of Indian Affairs.

Surely, thought Luzina, Mademoiselle Côté had not been in contact with Mr. Evans who, obliging as he was, would have given her better directions. Poor Mademoiselle Côté must have had to deal with some other person who was not posted on the numerous letters Luzina had exchanged with the government. She was filled with anxiety. Mademoiselle Côté, ill advised, might well wander as far as Winnipegosis and there take the Indian boat, which, when it left Lake Winnipegosis, did indeed follow the Big Water Hen and thus passed by their front door. But it was a small, uncovered boat, without shelter in case of rain, always full of none-too-clean Indian women. And those people had lice. Serious storms sometimes swept over Lake Winnipegosis. From their little landing on the Big Water Hen, Luzina had often seen the government craft pass; its passengers were soaked, worn out by the bouncing the vessel had given them, and summarily scattered among the bags of flour and boxes of lard which the canoe also transported; such a fashion of traveling had seemed to her very primitive. There was another, much more agreeable way of reaching the Little Water Hen. Luzina set about explaining it, point by point, to her schoolmistress, and she hurried at the task. It would be a close thing, now, for Mademoiselle Côté to get the letter in time.

She should take the main-line train to Dauphin. There she would have to change, and it might be that she would have to await the accommodation from Rorketon for a half or perhaps a full day. Luzina explained why. The train on the Rorketon branch line sometimes hauled ties for the railway and often empty milk cans; at other times it left without any load at all. Which is as much as to say that you couldn't know beforehand the hour of its departure. However, if Mademoiselle Côté found it too long waiting at the station, she would be well received at one of Luzina's friends', a Madame Lallemand, formerly from the province of Quebec, who lived in a small white house right next to the hardware store belonging to a man named Harrison at Dauphin. Mademoiselle Côté need not have a moment's hesitation in taking a rest at that lady's house. She should, though, be careful not to remain there too long in case the branch-line train to Rorketon might be loaded quicker than expected. Mademoiselle Côté would spend the night at Rorketon. Luzina gave the address of another acquaintance, a Madame Chartrand, at whose house the teacher would find a clean room at little expense. But, Luzina pointed out, it was absolutely necessary to arrive at Rorketon on a Thursday in order to make connections the next day, a Friday, with the mail from Rorketon to Portage des Prés. Otherwise, Mademoiselle Côté would have to wait a whole week for the departure of the next mail, and that would not be pleasant. On arrival at Rorketon, Mademoiselle Côté would therefore look for the postman. His name was Ivan Bratislovski, and he was to be found at the Rorketon post office or saddlery-relay station. He was easy to recognize by reason of a wildcat hat which he wore almost until mid-June. It was as well that she should be on her guard against Ivan Bratislovski's unscrupulous overcharging of strangers. The price of the trip was two dollars, and she should not give Ivan Bratislovski a cent more, even if he complained that he was in desperate straits, which was not true at all. Apart from this weakness of boosting prices when he had an opportunity, Ivan Bratislovski was not dangerous. He was a man who knew his place. Mademoiselle Côté need have no fear of traveling alone with the small Ruthenian. And so with him she would reach Portage des Prés. There she would change mailmen. After leaving Portage des Prés, she would travel with their own Little Water Hen island postman, a Ukrainian by the name of Nick Sluzick. On occasion he also tried to exact more than the regular price from strangers. People of the region only gave him fifty cents, and it was thought to be enough, since Nick Sluzick had to make the trip whether or not he had a load. Mademoiselle Côté was free to give him a little more if she wished, but not much more. Perhaps Nick Sluzick would say that it took more gasoline for two people. No attention should be paid to this. Two persons required no more gasoline than one alone, and everyone on Little Water Hen island was eager to see the schoolmistress arrive and sent her thanks and welcome in advance.

At last it was finished. Luzina did not think she had forgotten any of the mishaps—any of the snares—which might waylay Mademoiselle Côté, but for all that she was none too proud of her letter.

She naturally liked writing letters. Writing the government had not given her too much trouble. Surely the government was in some degree responsible for the ignorance on the island of the Little Water Hen, since it had waited so many years before giving them a school. Moreover, the fact that the government knew scarcely any French had put her at her ease; it would not take any note of Luzina's mistakes in spelling. The government's replies, typewritten and in English, had not greatly disturbed her. It was the teacher's letter, in a beautiful handwriting absolutely straight and without erasures which, by revealing the perfection a letter might attain both in form and in content, overwhelmed Luzina. Thenceforward she would no longer be altogether happy about writing. But the lot had been cast. Luzina had settled the matter forever the moment she appealed for education. Her fate would now be to write, everlastingly to write, to write until the end of her days.

III

The government's gifts arrived. The big packing case contained a box of white chalk, English readers, and precisely six blackboard erasers. The wall map of the world had traveled separately. On thick, strong, glazed paper, affixed to a wooden cylinder, it weighed about fifteen pounds. Nick Sluzick had worked like a dog to stow it away in his old Ford—he had had to slip it into the back of the car at an angle, between the bags of mail; a goodly part of the map, however, had remained outside, and it had snagged all sorts of branches along the narrower stretches of the trail.

Hanging in the schoolhouse, the world map took up a whole section of wall. It rolled and unrolled on itself like a smoothly operating window shade. You had only to pull the string at the bottom for the south polar lands to appear; then followed Australia, New Zealand, that part of the world where, Luzina said, it was night when they themselves had day. What mysteries! Thereupon Nick Sluzick lugged out another map, this one of Manitoba and very detailed. Old Nick had thought that he was delivering wallpaper, and he wondered how the Tousignants could use so much paper in so small a house. Were they going to paper the sheepfold? The schoolmistress was already on her way. That evening, before they went to bed, the Tousignants had remarked, "By this time, Mademoiselle Côté has taken the train."

In the morning Luzina mused out loud, "Now she has arrived at Dauphin."

Toward the middle of the afternoon she said firmly, "Unless there were a lot of ties to load, Mademoiselle Côté must have passed Sainte Rose du Lac, and the train is traveling backwards."

For some time now, Mademoiselle Côté's room had awaited her. Here is how Luzina had managed to make free a room for the teacher's use: pushing and pulling, she had moved a small bed into her own room; with her own big bed close against the wall, she had succeeded in making room for this smaller bed as well; another bed had gone its way to the kitchen, where it was well enough concealed behind a length of faded drapery. In such fashion there came into being in the Tousignant house a room which seemed extremely large and rich, an astounding room which contained only one single bed.

Luzina had never done so much even for the Capuchin Father who came once a year to hear their confessions and celebrate Mass in the parlor next the kitchen. Of course he had himself feared above everything else that he might give trouble and he had asked to sleep on the sofa in the parlor. Yet Luzina might have been accused of giving herself more pains for the teacher than for the Lord, and she strove to justify herself. "Our old missionary," said she, "is used to a hard life, whereas our schoolmistress is perhaps a girl who until now has never known anything but ease and comfort."

Hippolyte had shaved. Two hours ahead of time he had already put on his party headgear. "I'm sure it's about time to get going."

The postman's hours were most uncertain. Yet never did he get as far as the Big Water Hen before the end of the afternoon, and it was still several hours before the time when the sun would begin to set.

"Yes, go," said Luzina. "You can just see that poor girl sink to her knees in the mud along the edge of the Big Water Hen without her having the least inkling of an idea as to how she might cross it."

She herself went off to give the schoolhouse a final inspection. On this large, almost unpeopled island, the little school had quite naturally become the place where she by choice went to seek solitude and silence.

Nothing was lacking either in the atmosphere or in the physical objects to promote learning. Hippolyte had not forgotten the blackboards; he had used a heavy tarpaper which served in those parts as an insulating material or as covering for roofs, and of which there had remained a roll after their house was completed. Chalk took fairly well on its coarse-grained surface.

Luzina climbed the single step to the platform. It occurred to her to sit down at the teacher's desk in order the better to visualize what was about to take place on their island in the Little Water Hen. Was it because she was sitting on the schoolmistress's own chair, up on the platform? In any case, Luzina's vision was much deeper and broader than usual. She saw progress reach them. Thirteen years ago she had come to this place over a track you could scarcely make out in the wilderness. Little by little the grass had been flattened by the passage of vehicles, and at the end of a few years you had been able to see a sort of road emerge, fairly well marked. Then they had begun to receive the mail once a week. Come, now! The year when the Portage des Prés post office had been opened, that same year the merchant Bessette had bought himself a car! Two years later, Nick Sluzick in his turn was rolling along in summer in an ancient Ford. And now a schoolmistress was on her way to the island in the Little Water Hen. Oh, there was no doubting it at all: civilization, progress were blowing in this direction like the thawing spring breeze.

No longer could Luzina sit still. She took the baby in her arms and, four other children trailing behind, went to the bank of the Little Water Hen and stood waiting. It was a very hot afternoon for May. There was a slightly damp southwest wind which sang over the great, silent countryside. Luzina at its head, the little group stood erect under the heavens, in that wind out of open spaces which made the baby's hair and blanket flutter.

It was a day the like of which Luzina imagined she had never seen; on both edges of the river and almost to its middle the tall leaves of the rushes stirred; the neighboring island was also covered with them, and they continued far into the distance, growing thicker and thicker together as they approached the broad waters of Lake Winnipegosis.

At that season the year's fresh sprouts had made little growth; so far they formed only that moist background of greenery which was Luzina's pleasure. But last year's dead reeds still remained standing. They were lank and sparse, with ragged plumes, over the tips of which a bird would sometimes veer in flight. Long stems hung broken at the middle, tangled and collapsing upon the living young tufts. A few leaves remained to them, blades pointed or broken and shriveled, ready to crumble away. All this dead vegetation was faded, of a soft, pale hue like straw, and, even when the wind was still, without seeming to stir, the dry water grasses emitted a rustling sound, a trifle sad, sterile, continuous. They might have brought to mind autumn's melancholy, had it not been for the sun, which drew from them glints of gold, and the birds of the South, innumerable amidst the high rustling stalks. From all directions Luzina heard the plopping of the divers and the sport of the ducklings, splashing as they clambered out of puddles. You saw very little of them; all by herself a small mother duck occasionally emerged and inspected the surroundings with her brilliant eyes. She uttered a few energetic quacks, then swam away, her tiny tailpiece poked a little into the air, angry at all those people along the shore. These little females were bold ones and put on a bold show. By contrast, on the higher part of the island behind Luzina, the ewes lamented more than was their wont; close to their newborn lambs, their bleating was apprehensive. Of all this, today, Luzina was more than usually aware; perhaps—as it seemed to her—tenderness and anxiety were always one and the same.

She shaded her eyes with one hand. In the distance a small group had just landed on Mosquito Island, and a canoe was moving forward, upside down, above the level of the rushes. Ordinarily the Tousignants were well equipped for crossing the two rivers. A boat was assigned to the ferrying of each and was permanently available. But the Big Water Hen craft was in need of repairs; so only one canoe was available that day, and a carry was necessary.

The boat drew nearer; beneath it Luzina recognized Hippolyte's legs and torso, and behind him two others bearing burdens, who must be Pierre and Philippe-Auguste-Emile. Other children followed; from among them Luzina picked out the figure which must be Mademoiselle Côté.

Immediately her heart began thumping within her and fear overcame Luzina. Her eyes gathered in the children standing around her. What did she know about this Miss Côté? Perhaps she was one of those old maids whose prop is discipline and who know how to achieve it only by smacking tender knuckles with the edge of a ruler. When about nine, Luzina had had such a teacher; she had quickly forgotten her, her nature far preferring happy memories. Yet here she was, come back to life, and associated in Luzina's mind with the multiplication tables—that spiteful schoolmistress with her long pointed stick which was intended in principle to point out the many lovely countries on the map of the world, not to lash trembling knees and fingers.

The approaching group had reached the bushiest portion of the island; Luzina could barely glimpse them. When they emerged, they were close to her, and her eyes feasted upon a slender, sensitive apparition such as no one had ever hoped to behold upon the island in the Little Water Hen. This old maid was neither old nor stern. She was a picture of sprightliness. A tiny straw hat, a real city hat, which she wore cocked over her right eye, thrust its red feather here and there among the reeds that in their turn threatened to catch it and tear it loose. She had to hold onto her hat with one hand, with the other protect her pretty suit from being spattered, and be careful not to step into puddles. Her busy hands were covered with gloves. Tucked under her elbow was a beautiful leather handbag. Her shoes had high heels—which explained why Hippolyte had several times had to rest the canoe and wait for the teacher, since because of those heels she had had to circle the large holes, look for hummocks solid enough to support her, and thus cover almost twice the distance he did. You would have thought she was coming to a post a step from the railroad station, in the very middle of a village, and under the noses of at least a dozen families eagerly watching her arrival. Never would Luzina forget this lovely sight.

The teacher drew nearer, seated now on the bottom of the boat. She pulled her skirt down over her knees, finding it a bit difficult to shelter herself from the splash of the oars which sent drops flying over her leather bag, her suit, her valise, and her small hat. "Do be careful, Hippolyte," Luzina wanted to cry out. She had shifted the chubby baby from her right arm to her left; she pressed it to her sturdy breast and prepared to extend her free hand toward the teacher. She was laughing, for emotion had that effect on Luzina. The more she was affected, the harder she laughed, and then the more she laughed, the less she could control her laughter. All this elegance, this refinement, this gracious atmosphere of life in the South which was today invading her island, all this, constricting Luzina's heart, impelled her to a sort of robust, continuous clucking. At the very river's edge, her feet in the mud, the fat baby making her awkward, she kept heartily shaking Mademoiselle Côté's small gloved hand, and amidst her fits of laughter all she could manage was a series of ingenuous questions: "Mademoiselle Côté? Is it Mademoiselle Côté? So you've arrived, have you, Mademoiselle Côté?" as though there could exist some doubt as to the schoolmistress's identity.

That young lady was far from wanting to laugh. It was a mere two weeks since she had received her brand-new teacher's license. In a white dress, her hair freshly curled for the occasion, she had been handed the rolled parchment, tied with a wide red ribbon, by an official representative of the Department of Education, who had congratulated her on her fine academic record. No matter how clever Mademoiselle Côté may have been, she never would have believed that Manitoba could be so huge and so thinly populated. To all intents, she had never left her big village in the South, along the shores of the Red River, save to attend the Winnipeg Normal School, though she had done brilliantly in geography as well as in everything else that could be learned from textbooks. Jogging today from postal relay to postal relay, from one broken-down Ford to another even shakier, had shattered her. For many hours, now, the poor child had not had the least idea of where she was. When she had reached the Portage des Prés settlement, she had espied, a little apart from the five houses of the hamlet, a small plank building which, if you were hard put to it, you might take for a school. She had thought that this was her school, and, her heart already heavy, she had steeled herself to ask the merchant Bessette for the key. The latter had laughed heartily. This was the village, he had pointed out to her, and they had had their teacher long since. Mademoiselle Côté was given to understand that her assignment was far less important than that at the settlement. She had continued jolting onward, this time in company with a small man who was probably dumb, since he expressed himself only in a variety of grunts. And now she beheld what she had yearned for with all her heart through so many years of devoted study, of prizes for excellence, and of magnificent illusions: so this was it, her first school, the bottom step in what she looked upon as the most meritorious, the most exalted of careers! But when you came down to it, where was the school? She hesitated between the four gray cabins of unsquared logs, the biggest of which, in her native South, could have served for nothing more than a hay barn or a small piggery. All around her reigned silence, water, the shrill chirping of the little silver-bellied hens, their wings spotted with gray. And Mademoiselle Côté's heart likewise lamented, lost in the wilderness; it, too, already sought its refuge. Her glance fell upon the children. Half the small Tousignants had Luzina's light blue eyes, laughing and tender; the other half, Hippolyte's brown pupils, slow and sleepy. Yet all these eyes, fastened upon the schoolmistress, displayed at that instant the same expression of loving anguish. Even the smallest of them, who would not yet be going to school, hesitated between fear and trust. All stood close to the pretty young girl like fawns which a single movement could put to flight but which the least caress could tame.

Mademoiselle Côté suddenly stooped down toward the small, wavering band; putting aside her bag, her suitcase, her hat, she opened her arms to Luzina's children. Joséphine was the first to come, that shy child who, at the mere sight of a stranger, felt compelled to slip away among the rushes; then Charles; then Edmond who, as he moved forward, trembled all over, and finally, little by little, the whole small brood, except Pierre, blushing and deeply embarrassed of a sudden, feeling that all these embraces were unseemly.

The young woman straightened up. And then you saw that she meant business, this Miss Côté, and that her youth would not stand in the way of firmness—quite the contrary. She had picked the school out from among the cabins, and she said in a firm, low voice: "I'm going at once to the schoolhouse to prepare the lessons."

"You must be tired. You could almost take a day's holiday before that," Luzina reluctantly suggested, moved by a feeling of justice.

"Begin with a day's holiday! No, indeed! I must get to work," said Mademoiselle Côté.

She was the first to move, straight toward the school, and already it was she who gave them all the lead.

IV

The class had been in session for about an hour. In her kitchen, Luzina from time to time heard an explosion of small voices; toward nine-thirty a burst of laughter reached her ears, that uncontrollable laughter of children at school, nervous, excited, suddenly extinguished; but most of the time she listened in vain; tiptoeing about, standing in the open doorway, she did not hear a sound.

Luzina was not one of those women who are greatly disturbed by her children's racket. Since her nerves were quiet and her temperament dreamy and inclined to see the rosy side of life, she easily became oblivious to their noise by telling herself stories. Of course these stories included sad episodes, even rather sinister bits of drama, but solely for the pleasure of resolving them at the end and of seeing everything rightly ordered in her heart. Occasionally she imagined misfortunes beyond remedy: Hippolyte suddenly was drowned; she was left a widow with ten children; two of her boys turned out badly and married Indian women; but all this she had devised with an eye only to the relief Luzina always felt when, laying her macabre tales aside, she was able to see how remote they were from reality. All usual sounds, the outcries of the hens and the children, stimulated Luzina in these excursions. This morning, it was the silence that upset her.

What could they be doing in the schoolhouse? What was it that had made them all laugh a moment ago? Above all, what tasks could they possibly be performing amidst such silence?

Toward ten-thirty Luzina needed some wood shavings to raise the heat in her oven, in which she was baking a molasses cake, and quite naturally she went to gather them around the school building, where they had fallen from Hippolyte's plane. Far from her the thought of spying on the teacher. Luzina was fully resolved to respect Mademoiselle Côté's independence. That very morning she felt she had settled for everyone the question of shared authority on Little Water Hen island. "In school," Luzina had declared, "you will obey your schoolmistress in all things." She would not be one of those women who take their children's part against the teacher, sympathize with them for some minor punishment they have undergone, and thus undermine the prestige of authority.

Her back bent, her head drawn between her shoulders, she was getting ready to sneak by the corner of the school without being seen through the open window when a very specific question stopped her in her tracks. "In what province do we live?" Mademoiselle Côté wanted to know.

What a question! Luzina had the answer on the tip of her tongue. Right next the building there was a stump, exactly under the open window. Luzina let herself sink onto it.

"What is our province called?" repeated Mademoiselle Côté.

None of the children answered.

Luzina began to feel embarrassed. "What a pack of ignorant dunces!" she thought. "You certainly ought to know the answer to that." She shaped it with her own lips, syllable by syllable. She concentrated her will on transmitting the word to the minds of the schoolchildren. "What a shameful business—not even to know where you live."

At last one voice piped up, shy and faltering: "The Water Hen, Mademoiselle."

Luzina recognized the voice—it was Pierre's.

"If that's not a disgrace, a big boy eleven years old!" said she to herself. "I'll fix him when he comes back to the house, he and his Water Hens!"

The teacher continued patiently. "No, Pierre, the Water Hen is the name of this region alone; I'm not even sure it's the right geographical name. I rather think that it's a local name. What I am asking for is the name of the big province in which is included the Water Hen and many other regions. What province is that?"

No inspiration came to the Tousignant pupils' minds.

"It is a very large province," Mademoiselle Côté helped them a little more. "It is almost as large, by itself alone, as all France. It stretches from the United States all the way to Hudson Bay."

"Manitoba!"

Edmond flung out the word; his sharp little voice had taken on the very accent of victory. On the other side of the schoolhouse wall, Luzina was fully as proud; her round pink face grew tender. Edmond, indeed! A little shaver not yet eight! Where did that one learn we live in vast Manitoba? But then he had his nose in everything, that Edmond, he was always rummaging around, busy listening to grown-ups. Luzina broadly absolved him for all his prying.

"Very good," said the teacher approvingly. "This province is in fact Manitoba. But it, with eight other provinces, makes up a very big country, which is called . . ."

"Canada," Pierre suggested, in a humble tone of voice, as though begging pardon.

"Yes, of course. Very good, Pierre. Since we live in Canada, we are? . . . Cana- . . . Canadi- . . ."

"Canadians," Pierre finished the word.

"That's it, quite right," Mademoiselle congratulated them.

Luzina agreed that Pierre had in some part redeemed himself. All the same, to have said that we lived in the province of Water Hen! What a fool child!

"We are Canadians," continued the teacher, "but we are, above all, French Canadians. Long, long ago, more than three hundred years ago, Canada was inhabited only by redskins. The King of France then sent a Frenchman to discover Canada. He was called Jacques Cartier."

The sun warmed Luzina, well sheltered against the wind, her back to the schoolhouse wall. She had crossed her hands. Enchanted, she listened to the lovely, old, old story she had at one time known and then, later, almost forgotten. It was beautiful! Even more beautiful than in the books to hear it told by the schoolmistress with all the skill, all the eager youthfulness she infused into the telling. Luzina wanted to laugh, to cry.

"The first settlers were French. . . . The governor of Montreal, Maisonneuve. . . . His colleague at Quebec was called Champlain . . . the explorers of the New World, almost all of them, were French: Iberville, De Groseillers, Pierre Radisson. Father Marquette and Louis Joliet had discovered the water highway of the Great Lakes. La Vérendrye had gone on foot as far as the Rockies. Cavelier de la Salle had traveled by boat to the mouth of the Mississippi. All this country belonged to France. . . ."

"The Water Hen, too?" asked Edmond.

"The Water Hen, too," the schoolmistress acquiesced, laughing.

Luzina likewise smiled indulgently.

Indeed yes, France was the mistress of the whole country! Like a good pupil, Luzina attentively followed the lesson, but she was, after all, far more advanced than the children; her memory, emancipated from household worries, liberated from almost all her life's history, dug up dates and certain battles which she rediscovered with delight. Even as she listened, Luzina had begun to spin on her own account the tale of the past.

Surely among those first settlers come from France there had been Tousignants, and people of her own family, the Bastiens. Luzina had been given to understand that the French colonists had been carefully picked; that no loafer or thief had been able to slip in amongst them. All good people. They had established themselves in what was formerly called Lower Canada and which was later to be included in the province of Quebec. The Tousignants and the Bastiens were of their number. Moreover, venturesome and courageous as Luzina for the moment saw them, some of those Lower Canada Tousignants and Bastiens had emigrated to the West, even as far as Manitoba. Already they were far, very far, from the places of their origin. But wait! said Luzina out loud. A Manitoba Bastien woman and a Manitoba Tousignant man had turned up who had in their blood the same tastes as their ancestors, *coureurs de bois* and *coureurs de plaine*. Nowadays you no longer went West, but there remained the North. No railways, no roads, almost no dwellings; they had been drawn to the North. No communications, no electricity, no schools—that had tempted them. Then again, how could you explain this folly, since no sooner were they settled in the North than they had set to work to make it seem like other places! They had left villages fully established—she, Saint Jean Baptiste on the Red River, Hippolyte the fine village of Letellier—and ever since they had toiled to transform the North, they had labored to bring there the customs, the atmosphere, the abundant life of the South. Perhaps they were among those builders of nations about whom Mademoiselle spoke with so much warmth. Oh, if that were the case, Luzina could not bear the glory of it without a few tears. Her eyes grew moist. She could not endure listening to the all-too-beautiful stories. Nor to the sad ones either. But it was the more beautiful ones which finally played the greater havoc with her heart. She crushed a little tear at the corner of a swollen eyelid.

Ah, but wait a moment! To have come to the Water Hen was not the best part of the story. The best part of it was to have been rejoined, on the island in the Little Water Hen, by the forebears, the former Tousignants, the unknown Bastiens, Lower Canada, history, France, La Vérendrye, Cavalier de la Salle. Luzina sniffled. That was progress, far greater progress than the postman's aged Ford, the store catalogues. What was she saying! For six months of the year the winds might howl without slackening; the snow could shroud the house to its roof; and it seemed as though the Tousignants on their island would never again be alone.

"My cake!" thought Luzina.

She fled, angry at herself, blushing to the roots of her hair and scattering shavings from her apron. What kind of woman was she so to neglect her duty! To each his task in life: to the teacher, the explaining; to the children, the learning; and to her, Luzina, the serving of them all.

V

The afternoon seemed long to her. At half-past two, school was adjourned for a recreation period. Luzina moved to the threshold of the house, fully convinced that the children would come bounding to her to tell her about the progress they had made. At noon she had not, as it were, had time to question them, having been wholly busy with the vast preoccupation of making them absorb a double ration, since now they were working with their brains. She waited for them on the doorstep, touched and indulgent as if after a long absence. It seemed to her she had been bereft of her children for as long a while as when she used to leave them for her trips to Sainte Rose du Lac.

Like a whirlwind, the whole class dashed by, right under her nose. They all flew in Mademoiselle's wake. They reached a part of the island a little ways off where there was a good piece of flat ground, there formed a circle, and began going through the motions of a game under the schoolmistress's leadership. The breeze carried to Luzina a few snatches of the old song Mademoiselle was singing: "*Savez-vous planter les choux . . . à la mode, à la mode et à la mode de par chez nous . . .*" How charming they were, those civilized children's games, amidst the same old wanderings of the sheep, their tiresome laments, and the water hens' eternal chirping! Luzina moved forward a little the better to see them execute the round. She herself had sung and acted out the song in other days; she knew it well. You began by planting the cabbages with your hands. Then with the feet. You finished with your head, and that was the funniest of all. And sure enough, they were laughing a lot over there. Mademoiselle was showing how to plant cabbages with your nose. In their eagerness to imitate, the children were all shoving their noses into the soil and sticking their buttocks into the air. They laughed with joy. Mademoiselle was able to make them laugh as Luzina had never heard them laugh. Seemingly she knew how to get anything she wanted out of them. Thus she clapped her hands together, and at once they stood in line, very serious, intent on walking the way she did.

Oh, but just wait! said Luzina to herself. At four o'clock it will be another story. Little used to constraint, the children would welcome a return to the freer atmosphere of the house. And then they wouldn't be such angels. Mademoiselle herself would be worn out. Poor tiny Joséphine must be very wearied. Just wait for four o'clock! thought Luzina.

At four they wished each other good afternoon in the classroom, the teacher and the children, then they went out together, and in a moment all of them were in the house. It was almost like Luzina's homecoming from one of her trips, except that now it was her turn to ask questions.

"Did you learn a lot, Edmond? So you knew the name of the province, eh?"

Sure, he knew the name of the province; it wasn't hard to know the name of the province. Edmond even knew that there were nine provinces.

"You didn't stick your fingers in your nose?"

You didn't even talk about fingers in the nose before nice, pretty Mademoiselle!

"Have you begun to read, Joséphine?"

Yes, Joséphine almost knew how to read already. Joséphine had only two or three little things to learn, and she would be able to read all the books ever written. Joséphine was way ahead in her studies; Mademoiselle had said so. Their greatest worry was the fear of seeing their normal daily life revealed to Mademoiselle by some inept remark of their mother's. And then, too, they were afraid of seeing Mademoiselle disappear. You never knew, she might go for a walk, she might go off a long ways, they might even lose sight of her. They all watched her, out of the corners of their eyes, ready to block her way. The moment she started to move, they clustered around her.

"Where are you going, Mademoiselle?"

Luzina intervened, her authority a bit tearful: "Now you let Mademoiselle alone. She's had enough of you."

Mademoiselle protested with a positiveness to match Luzina's exasperation: "Not at all! The children are so sweet. Let me have them a while longer, Madame Tousignant. We'll take a walk along the river bank. It will give me a chance to teach them something about things."

"Things? What next!"

"Yes, about birds, plants, insects," Mademoiselle explained.

"You're not going to keep on working twelve hours a day," complained Luzina.

"It's no more than a pleasure with such likable children," insisted the teacher.

"Likable! You don't know them," Luzina said. "They're perfect little devils."

The schoolmistress corrected her: "Nice children!"

How could the children disagree with a woman who described their true natures, their goodness of character, and whose keen insight located them at that high level of perfection she herself required of them!

"Hateful little brats!" complained Luzina. "If you begin to listen to them, they'll never leave you alone. Horrible children!"

"Good children," insisted Mademoiselle.

She hurried out. The children kept step with her as though they were all but a single person. Edmond left her side only when he ran a little ahead to pick some flower which he came back to offer her, bowing so low his forehead almost touched the ground.

"Thank you, Edmond; you are a thoughtful little boy."

She was explaining, "This must be mint. This, here, is wild mustard."

She knew all the things that children like to learn, the names of everything around them, the knowledge of which confers possession. Joséphine was trotting along behind the others, in her pink cotton dress, her stockings, and her best shoes.

Luzina's humbled authority fastened upon Joséphine who was unable to keep up with the others.

"Joséphine!" she cried out. "In any case, you're too small to learn about things. Come on back to the house! Do you hear?"

The child galloped all the faster, crestfallen, pretending not to hear.

"Joséphine!"

The little girl turned back. Her eyes were clouded. In the middle of the path, stamping her foot in anger at being delayed, she uttered her defiance: "The teacher said that I could learn about things too!"

What could she do? The little troop moved off into the rushes. Pierre held aside the higher stems, making a path for the young woman. The other children picked away the fluff from the dead bulrushes which kept sticking to her clothes; they kept brushing off her lovely suit. Out of breath, Joséphine cried out: "Mademoiselle, dear Mademoiselle, wait for Joséphine, wait for Joséphine!"

Now where on earth had they ever learned such loving thoughtfulness, a thoughtfulness they had never yet shown their own mother!

VI

The following summer there arrived on Little Water Hen island an amazing creature, prudish to excess, infatuated with hygiene, who had fixed ideas about everything; she was an Ontario old maid, speaking not a word of French, and a Protestant into the bargain.

She had bungled her whole trip north, and the journey had almost shattered her, especially that part of it spent in Nick Sluzick's bounding Ford;

she was breathless when she entered the Tousignant house, and the moment she caught her breath, it was to begin her recriminations. It seemed almost impossible that so many grievances could find utterance at the same time.

Miss O'Rorke had been wronged by the government which had given her no proper idea of the trap into which she was to set foot and was not a bit troubled at seeing a "lady" travel alone through such country; principally she had been wronged by the bandits along the way. These bandits, whom she described as though they had been a horde, in the end turned out to consist of one solitary individual, Nick Sluzick. According to Miss O'Rorke, he had purposely driven her at hellish speed through the open prairie and over stumps and boulders. Inured to hardship, whenever she experienced it anew the poor woman no longer had any defense against this old acquaintance save to pretend that she had never before encountered it. Had she known what she would be up against before she left, she would never have set foot on the island in the Little Water Hen. She had been offered good posts in civilized regions. She could have had a big village school. And she would have turned right around and left had it not been so complicated. She supposed, however, that once in this Water Hen district, all she could do was stay there.

Having said her say, Miss O'Rorke removed a large hat pierced by several long pointed hatpins. She thus revealed a tired-looking bun of hair, a severe, sorrowful face, and, behind dark-rimmed glasses, eyes expressive of a very dejected, very sad zeal, which were already ticking off the things that would have to be changed in the Tousignant household. At a glance she had discovered the water bucket, tidily covered with mosquito netting but furnished with a long-handled dipper from which everyone apparently drank, sticky flypapers cork-screwing down from the ceiling, and, above all, that miserable, half-hidden little bed in the kitchen—if you please! Miss O'Rorke did not like promiscuity. And she was preparing herself very soon to ask for her own water glass.

"What's she saying?" whispered Luzina.

She had understood very little of the new arrival's talk. Hippolyte was thought to have the better knowledge of English.

"What did she say?" Luzina asked again, in a low tone.

Embarrassed at the thought of repeating such unamiable words before the person who had said them, Hippolyte urged his wife to have a little patience. "Later on you'll find out," said he with his eyes, and he looked deeply hurt.

"What do you think she is?" again whispered Luzina.

"She might well be Irish," Hippolyte answered without raising his voice.

"A Catholic, do you think?"

"Think not."

"What will the Capuchin Father say?" worried Luzina.

Yet, put out as Luzina was, she did not give up hope of making a friend, in the long run, of their "Englishwoman." Miss O'Rorke was thus labeled, for once and for all, in the minds of the Tousignants, young and old, since to them everyone who spoke English sprang from the same distant and completely foreign origin, and it would not have been possible to modify this classification even had it been proved that Miss O'Rorke's lineage had lived in Canada as long as the Bastiens and the Tousignants. But even a foreigner could be amiable. Anxious to be on good terms with everyone, Luzina attributed all kinds of qualities to people; according to her, it was impossible not to get along together if you wanted to. She had been friendly with Irish people, with Ruthenians, with French. Why could they not manage with their Englishwoman? She had a long row to hoe ahead of her.

Miss O'Rorke had never tested the wisdom of the old saying, "When in Rome, do as the Romans do." Her teacher's soul would rather have led her to attempt the transformation of the whole world rather than to abandon a single one of her set ideas and trifling whims. In the present circumstances, she had a particularly bad run of luck. A strict vegetarian, she was stranded on an island where salt pork was eaten from one end of the year to the other. She slept lightly. In order to sleep, she needed perfect silence around her. Now the ewes and their baby lambs roamed freely all over the island, and they were endlessly calling each other. Certain lambs, separated from their mothers at birth, bottle-fed, and kept a few days in the warmth of the kitchen, had acquired a taste for the house. When Miss O'Rorke could not sleep, she would relight her lamp; these lambs would then gather before her window, trustful of this tardy light; they would thrust their muzzles against the fly-screen and ask asylum. Toward dawn, when they finally grew quiet, the ducks and the water hens took over Miss O'Rorke's torment.

In the morning the poor woman's face was haggard. And what was most enraging of all to her mind was the fact that the Tousignants seemed astounded that she had been prevented from sleeping.

"You not sleep?" Luzina inquired with so much concern that it looked suspicious.

"Ah, too bad, very too bad!" said Luzina, truly upset.

They had not heard a sound. If anything could have disturbed their sleep it would have been precisely the unwonted, inexplicable quiet which the poor woman seemed to wish. In a land of sheep, what was extraordinary about hearing them bleat!

It was well worth while, Miss O'Rorke bitterly lamented, to come to the ends of the earth in order to discover that they did not even possess the only advantages you might have had a right to expect there—silence and peace! Luzina could not believe her ears. As for silence and peace, it did not seem possible to her that anywhere else could one have found them to so great an extent as along the Little Water Hen.

Finally, however, Miss O'Rorke became aware that the island was very long, and an amazing scheme entered her mind—a mind extraordinarily inventive the moment her comfort was in question. She told Hippolyte about this very simple discovery. Her idea was merely to exile the sheep to the other end of the island, seven miles away, and to build around the flock an enclosure sturdy enough to keep them there forever. In this way she would have peace.

Because she insisted on winning the schoolteacher by kindness, Hippolyte could not forgive Luzina for Miss O'Rorke's unreasonable requests. "That old fool of yours imagines that we're going to build a thousand feet of fence and travel the length of the island twice a day just to satisfy her little fancies."

With the old fool herself, however, he took a different tone. She overawed him with her glasses constantly directed toward him, and the way they reflected the glare of the sun troubled his eyes. What was more, Luzina had urged that they should continue to coax her with gentleness. "Try to win her by good manners," urged Luzina. "That's always the best policy in the end."

"Well?" asked the schoolmistress.

"Well," said Hippolyte, and he undertook to explain that he was not altogether master on Little Water Hen island. It belonged to the merchant Bessette, and Bessette could have had no other reason for establishing his ranch on an empty island at the edge of nowhere than that there he would be freed of the necessity of raising fences. Fences were expensive, and Bessette had one thoroughly fixed principle: the least expense possible, the most profit possible.

"You see?" inquired Hippolyte.

But out of all this the old maid principally gathered that a man named Bessette was responsible for the noise which disturbed her sleep. She set to work to write him a few well-chosen words on the subject. There was no effort too troublesome for Miss O'Rorke once she had determined to change some little thing in this world where just about everything annoyed her.

Meanwhile it was discouraging to Luzina to see her refuse, at every meal, the salt pork, the red cabbage with vinegar, and the pancakes.

"Don't you like?" said Luzina, sincerely sympathetic; yet to speak English to an Englishwoman was torture for her, and when she was tortured, Luzina always had a desire to laugh.

When the worst of the heat was over, she conceived the idea of sending to Rorketon for a piece of fresh meat. The government had entrusted to her the task of extending hospitality to the schoolmistress, and she had no intention of shirking that task. She busied herself with settling, two weeks in advance, the itinerary of the meat, this being more difficult than it would have been in the case of a human being who could change vehicles under his own power.

Luzina ordered her meat by mail. At the same time she had to inform Ivan Bratislovski, also by mail, that he would have to pick up the meat at the butcher's, but only at the very last minute, so as to give the said meat a chance to remain as long as possible on ice; urge Nick Sluzick not to forget to ask his colleague Bratislovski for the piece of beef, since the latter was absent-minded and might very well take it back with him to Rorketon (this very thing had happened during the Capuchin Father's last visit); finally, remind both postmen to keep the beef well wrapped to protect it from the flies and extreme heat, not to put it in the mail bags, and not to sit on it.

Despite all these precautions, either because some of them were neglected along the way or because they were themselves insufficient, the piece of beef arrived in precarious condition. It was too bad; you could see at a glance that it would have made a fine roast. Luzina hoped in any case to disguise its odor with a good spice sauce. Miss O'Rorke must have had a refined palate and sense of smell; at the very first mouthful she made a face.

Hippolyte, little given to laughter, by nature indeed serious and humorless, for some reason or other found this business of the roast beef exceptionally funny; Luzina's three letters, the stages of the journey worked out in advance like a railway timetable, the ill humor of Sluzick, who above all else detested taking charge of fresh meat in midsummer, all these elaborate negotiations leading to nothing more than their Englishwoman's expression of martyrdom!

He burst out laughing. The embarrassment of hearing himself laugh in the midst of complete silence made Hippolyte laugh even harder. The eyes of all the astounded children shuttled from their father to poor Miss O'Rorke. Luzina had threatened them with at least ten punishments for every breach of the respect they owed their teacher. Here and there hesitant little chuckles began and were choked off. Suddenly Luzina herself let go her own irresistible wild laughter. Then all of them broke down. For fully five minutes, the Tousignants, freed of a long constraint, laughed their heads off at Miss O'Rorke who, very stiff, her lips pursed, crumbled a bit of bread while sighing for the day when she would at last shake the dust of this island from her feet.

Once the crisis was over, Luzina begged everyone not to let it happen again. "Perhaps she suspected we were laughing at her," said Luzina with a glance of obvious repentance at Miss O'Rorke.

In one way it was rather convenient that the teacher did not understand French. Luzina could, in her presence, give vent to lessons in politeness as direct and concrete as they possibly could be. "You can see perfectly well that she looks out of sorts. Do try not to stare at her. We don't know what may be on her mind from time to time."

Out of delicacy, nevertheless, when Luzina said such things, she looked elsewhere, usually at a religious calendar. Thus the poor woman had learned to recognize the occasions when the talk was about her and to associate them with Saint Joseph, for whom she already cherished no love whatever. These likable and kindly Tousignants were, of all the people she had ever undertaken to rescue from ignorance, the most stiff-necked.

Every morning there were protestations and tears. The children did not want to go to school. Miss O'Rorke the whole day long addressed them with patriotic speeches which they did not understand, and she was incensed because they had not grasped her comments. She called them "ungrateful children, very ungrateful children." According to her, the government could not be worse repaid for its kindness than by this Tousignant family: generously treated as it was by an English government, it intended to remain French. Where could you find anything worse in the line of ingratitude? "The government is English, the province is English," Miss O'Rorke tirelessly explained; "you should conform to the majority and the general will." Two or three of the pupils tried to run away from school every morning. Luzina had a job on her hands to recapture them. But she persevered. Education could be nothing other than a joy. Such great riches, so deep an experience might well warrant a few tears. She reasoned with the children: "Now, last summer you learned French with Mademoiselle Côté. This year, learn English; take advantage of it to learn English."

At bottom a great opportunist, Luzina at last discovered one merit in her Englishwoman: that was the English language. Although incapable herself of savoring it, Luzina held it to be no less a merit. If anyone had something to say against Miss O'Rorke, Luzina found an excuse for it: "Anyhow, she speaks English well."

Miss O'Rorke, however, possessed another, more meritorious virtue, although it was to remain substantially invisible to the Tousignants. Miss O'Rorke's heart, lonely and none too amiable, throbbed with an excessive loyalty to the British Empire, and especially to the United Kingdom, with the exception of Catholic Ireland, where she had never set foot. Fired by a passion fully as unreasonable, Mademoiselle Côté had caused its extravagances to blossom around her; Mademoiselle Côté had left as her legacy the names of personages as far from the Tousignants as the moon. Cavelier de la Salle, La Vérendrye, Radisson, Frontenac, the evil Intendant Bigot—all of them, even the bad ones, had a right to faithful remembrance. Perhaps Mademoiselle Côté retained the advantage of having been the first to come to the island. What opportunity to stimulate their imaginations could Miss O'Rorke find in her Act of Capitulation, in the French defeat, in her Fathers of Confederation and her Dominion of Canada? What was more, she was imprudent enough to attack Mademoiselle Côté's heroes. The English General Wolfe, according to her, had soundly beaten Mademoiselle Côté's Montcalm, who, Frenchman that he was, had gone to battle with lace frills on his shirt and had politely offered his enemy the first volley.

But it is impossible completely to withstand even an inept passion, and Miss O'Rorke's for the British Isles finally won her a small victory over the Tousignants.

VII

About two months and a half after her arrival, Miss O'Rorke was taking her Sunday stroll toward the end of the island where the sedges were thickest. She had got into the habit of mitigating her boredom by long solitary walks, which sometimes took her to the island's northern tip, the spot to which she had hoped to banish the flock of sheep and, failing in this, where she had intended to pitch a tent that she could herself use as a retreat. Like the first, this scheme had fallen through; confronted by Miss O'Rorke's announcement of her odd resolve, Luzina had begun to whimper, truly provoked and alarmed.

"What would people say? People would certainly talk."

"People! What people?" Miss O'Rorke had inquired; she now was beginning to learn a little French, based on Luzina's vivid vocabulary.

Unable to say exactly what people she had in mind, Luzina was still just as afraid of talk.

"People will say that we have mistreated you, and they will blame us."

And thus the last advantage by which Miss O'Rorke had hoped to benefit from her stay on Little Water Hen island slipped from her grasp. Here there was no solitude. Of course, the poor woman reflected, human beings and animals, when they are unfortunate enough to live in what is practically a wilderness, are condemned to living very close together. So that Sunday she set forth, her back turned on the four cabins. The clouds floated vaguely across the sky, slow to overtake each other, and the Big Water Hen, itself lazy and unruffled, reflected the clouds' continuous procession. The sheep, as sometimes happened with them, had of their own choice and in one solid mass emigrated toward the island's distant tip. There was almost nothing to ruffle Miss O'Rorke's calm. Here was one of those quiet, drowsy days when the island really seemed to be uninhabited. And then it burst upon Miss O'Rorke that there was no flag floating over the island. She must have been distracted indeed not to have noticed it before. She went back by the shortest possible route and stepped firmly into the kitchen.

"Mrs. Tousignant, there must be a flag here."

"What is she asking?" Luzina sought enlightenment from her husband.

"Now she wants a flag!" Hippolyte interpreted.

"A flag!" Luzina exclaimed with great affability. "True enough, we need a flag. But what sort of flag?"

"The flag of His Majesty the King," said Miss O'Rorke.

Luzina fastened on the word majesty. As far as British majesty was concerned, Luzina was rather behind the times; in this matter she had progressed no further than the old Queen Victoria, whom she respected because, Protestant though Victoria had been, she had borne nine children. To Luzina, large families seemed a purely Catholic obligation, which was not to be shirked since Heaven depended upon it. Victoria, who was not bound by such requirements, seemed to her all the more meritorious. It was as though Victoria had acted as she had only to set a good example and perhaps to comfort the other women of her Empire.

Eager to please, Luzina tore an old worn sheet into strips. These she dyed and assembled under the schoolmistress's instructions. So proud was she of her Union Jack that she would gladly have sewn a few others, now that she had the pattern. Meanwhile Miss O'Rorke had begun to plague Hippolyte. Seemingly it was not enough to have a Union Jack; it must be able to flutter freely in the breeze, firmly planted in front of the school and visible from all directions. Stimulated by the symbol of Empire, Miss O'Rorke had found fresh energy. Ultimately Hippolyte understood that the Englishwoman wanted a flagpole. Truth to tell, Hippolyte deliberately took a long time to understand Miss O'Rorke's wishes. Luzina and the children were vastly more interested in the flag. Beyond question it would help to define an area which otherwise might have passed for unexplored. Pierre-Emmanuel-Roger, following the teacher's specifications, trimmed a pole eight feet long. But then a difficulty arose; according to Miss O'Rorke, it was necessary to hoist the flag every morning when school opened and to lower it at the stroke of four. Hippolyte could not see why, once the flag was installed at the tip of the pole, it should not remain there indefinitely. Less stubborn, Luzina sewed a deep hem along one of the flag's edges. Pierre threaded a line through this hem; then he climbed the pole and affixed the line in such fashion that, depending on which end of the line you pulled, the Union Jack slipped to the top of the mast, came down, went up again. The hoisting and lowering of the flag could all be managed from below; it was no trouble to put the flag at half-mast or to raise it into the wind's full force, for the fun of seeing it whip and snap. They had at hand all that was needed to betoken mourning, holidays, days of rejoicing, of toil, of departure. In her own fashion Miss O'Rorke left her mark on the island.

One autumn afternoon, toward the end of October, they went to turn her back to Nick Sluzick. Despite the diversion supplied by the business of the flag, Luzina was not too upset at seeing the Englishwoman go. Just as they reached the mainland, the postman's Ford came bouncing along the river's edge. It continued without slackening speed, passing the little mound, slightly leveled off at the top, which, according to conventions unwritten but of long standing, represented the stopping point of their common carrier. They could see the mailman's heavy hands firmly grasping the wheel. His face danced up and down; his mustaches quivered; Nick Sluzick was dashing along as he used to in the old days when there was no one to pick up along the trail. As one the Tousignants raised their arms; Hippolyte whistled. At last the old fellow came to a stop, but a good ways off, in the middle of a muddy pool which had not yet fully dried out.

He had a quick eye. No one could accuse Nick Sluzick of not seeing the people who waited for him in the midst of this bare country. At a glance Nick had even recognized, in this exceedingly visible group, the woman traveler of last spring who had endlessly implored him to watch where he was going. As though Nick Sluzick needed someone to guide him over these roads he had navigated these past twelve years, the only man who could master them! Nick sat squarely on the center of the front seat; the back seat was covered with mail bags and large packages. Miss O'Rorke had to accept the narrow space beside him which the motionless postman neither offered nor refused. Nick Sluzick remained superbly aloof from what was going to happen.

At the Ford's first bound, the mail bags piled up to the coarse canvas top lost their equilibrium and began to tumble down toward Miss O'Rorke. She received their full impact upon her shoulders. Her hat went askew, and her glasses almost shot out of the car.

The unfortunate old maid was leaving, and without much feeling of relief after all. It would be no better elsewhere. For twenty-five years she had been knocking about, from job to job, and the next one in line was always a little more remote, a little deeper in the wilderness; the food was heavier and heavier, sentiments less and less refined, gratitude rarer and rarer. This post on the Little Water Hen had perhaps, all in all, not been too disagreeable. At a venture, unable to risk making a movement or even turning her head to look, because of the mail bags which weighed against her neck, Miss O'Rorke waved one hand outside the Ford, in the Tousignants' general direction.

Whenever she quit a place, in fact, she had a fairly painful time of it. With amazement she became aware that life had not been too bad in the spot she was leaving. It even seemed to her moderately pleasant. And finally she would come to believe that in that place alone existence would have been possible for her. Such was Miss O'Rorke. Her preference—gloomy and depressing—always was given to that which she had lost, and if there were crannies in this world which she lauded without respite, they were always those where she was certain never again to set foot.

Different though her nature was, Luzina nonetheless found certain people more likable at departure than upon arrival. Her Englishwoman—so unpredictable, eccentric, and disconcerting—at the moment of her going, became one more friend for her in this oversized, inadequately peopled world where, Luzina felt, you never could have too many friends.

Returning in Indian file, thoughts of Miss O'Rorke did not lessen the Tousignants' curiosity about their next teacher. Luzina brought up the rear, out of breath despite the briskness of the weather, her cheeks red, she herself a trifle saddened by the void Miss O'Rorke left behind her, but her eyes smiling at thought of the new schoolmistress who would take her place. She had reached the conclusion that they would never have the same teacher two years running; in a way this pleased her appetite for novelty. The great differences she had glimpsed in teaching methods as between only two schoolmistresses opened to her a vast field for conjecture. Without being aware of it, the whole family had already acquired a taste for living in suspense during the longer half of the year, busy thinking about what kind of teacher they would have next, as might some remote colony awaiting the arrival of its new governor. Change suited them. It added zest to life, afforded subject matter for long winter's conversations. "Perhaps she'll be a Hungarian," Luzina remarked one fine day. No one knew what could have given Luzina such an idea, but they all knew that Luzina had been thinking of the new schoolmistress. This attraction toward the unknown in their existence prevented too keen feelings of regret; to some extent it even militated against loyalty. "Certainly we'd be pleased if Mademoiselle Côté were to come again —no doubt of that," Luzina would say, yet at the same time she had an inkling that her heart would not welcome such a return. Of course it would be very nice to see Mademoiselle Côté once more, but not at the cost of missing a new teacher, still unknown to them, whom they were beginning to feel they could not forgo, at least until they had had a chance to know her.

By spring Luzina had exhausted all the possibilities. Their schoolmistress had appeared to her mind's eye in the guise of almost every nationality. She thought she had prepared herself for any possible surprise. Only one had she forgotten. The schoolmistress who arrived at the island early in May turned out to be a young man.

VIII

This young man landed on the island clad, at least, in appropriate garb. Luzina even thought it a bit exaggerated. She saw advancing toward her an odd silhouette topped with a colonial helmet, wearing a red-checked flannel shirt and heavy oiled boots; he was laden with an armory of weapons, rifles large and small. From his shoulder hung a game bag; to his back was attached a blanket roll. Surveyors off for a full three or four months' trip in trackless wilderness would have carried no more equipment. Luzina had another reason for being ill at ease; she was five months gone with child, and under the circumstances she found unbecoming the presence of a young man who could daily watch her girth increase. It had been embarrassing enough to submit to Miss O'Rorke's constant examination from behind her spectacles, and Miss O'Rorke had had no reason for alarm, because that summer Luzina was taking a rest.

He was a likable chap, however, without pretense, and seemingly at once pleased with the island. No glance he cast at Luzina hinted that he was curious as to whether she were fatter or more rotund than usual. Luzina would have found him wholly to her taste had he only shown as much interest in the schoolroom as he did in the chase.

He would ask Luzina to leave him a little coffee in the pot; he would then get up while it was still dark, help himself, and, presumably, find his way out into the rushes, since from the house where everyone was asleep you could hear the whistle of bullets in that direction. This was the hour when the little water hens, the terns, the ducks—creatures that took delight in the pale glow of dawn—were rousing. The sun would come up, the shooting cease. And yet the schoolmaster would not return. The children, seated at their small desks, would sometimes wait for him until ten o'clock, having long since finished the lessons he had indicated on the blackboard. What on earth could the teacher be doing? One morning Luzina sent out a search party in her anxiety. Here is what the children discovered: their instructor lay asleep, stretched out on a flat-bottomed boat among the reeds, with his cap over his face to protect him from flies and sun.

His teaching methods, moreover, were vastly curious. He gave the impression of considering the whole business a huge joke. "Learn what's on this page if you feel like it," he would say with a laugh, and he seemed to be slyly telling them, "Don't learn it if you are no more tempted to than I am tempted to teach you."

Luzina's children, however, were bent on learning.

Every evening each would seek out his nook and declaim for hours on end, this one a grammatical rule, that one an historical passage; and, in order to hear themselves, they would all yell louder and louder as time went on. Joséphine's voice was particularly ear-splitting. All this did not displease Luzina; it gave her, rather, the impression that her children were making great progress. But when they proudly informed their teacher that they "knew their lesson," Armand Dubreuil would begin to laugh. "Well, then, since you're so quick at it, get to work on the next page!"

To hear him talk, you would think the most intelligent course was adroitly to escape effort. After the passage of a few weeks, rather than making up the school hours of which he had cheated the children in the morning, Armand Dubreuil robbed them of another at the end of the day. At three o'clock, class was dismissed. Then, with his gun under his arm, he would disappear deep into the wooded part of the island. The prairie chickens' outcries made it clear that it was to them he was giving his attention. They fluttered over the ground or else ran for a bit, their bodies rolling comically on their spindly legs, almost as fat and awkward as barnyard hens. Bing! Bing! For hours you could hear the popping of the twenty-two rifle.

Evenings he would tell stories. He had quickly acquired Hippolyte's trick of sitting back on his heels and rocking to and fro while he smoked his pipe. From day to day Luzina postponed the remarks which she thought it her duty to address to him; it was very difficult; Armand Dubreuil was such a pleasant fellow. He was easygoing; you might have thought that he had always lived with them. He developed an interest in sheep raising; he would calculate the profits which would have been theirs had they been the owners of the hundred and fifty sheep. He was keen about everything except his school. Luzina sought for ways of remonstrating with him without hurting his feelings. Thereupon he would give the children a whole day off, alleging as excuse some holiday of which Luzina could find no mention whatever on the calendar. Miss O'Rorke's flag was far too often at half-mast. At last Luzina thought she had found a way to reprimand the teacher without irritating him. She began praising Mademoiselle Côté to the skies.

"That schoolmistress we had year before last—Lord! did she stick to her job! Do you remember, children, the lovely gold stars she would give you! With her, school started at nine on the dot. Nice, attractive, but my! what a hard worker! She had found the children way behind in their studies. To make up for lost time, she even had school on Saturdays!"

Armand Dubreuil laughed wholeheartedly. "My method is different," said he. "I don't believe in forcing children too much. Nature, you understand, is still the best teacher. Nature teaches us more than all the books. But it takes years to see the fruits of my method. Nature—that's my system. And it's the best."

Such was not at all Luzina's view of the matter. They had nature in plenty all around them; there would always be enough of that. Yet how could she discuss pedagogy with an educated young man who had an answer for everything and whom she was afraid of offending? She was made even more impotent when one day Armand Dubreuil artlessly began to call her Mama Tousignant. He knew her weak spot. The salt pork, the pancakes, the game stews—everything Luzina concocted—seemed excellent to him: "I've never eaten as well as in your house, Mama Tousignant. Do make me another cup of your fine coffee, Mama Tousignant."

Luzina complained to Hippolyte: "He's such a coaxer; he twists me around his little finger and I can't be as severe as I should."

Hippolyte likewise was worried, but for another reason. Never had such carnage been seen upon their island. Occasionally they had killed, for eating purposes, a wild duck or a fine prairie chicken, well fattened and fully grown. Never had they shot for the sake of mere practice. Now the schoolteacher was a good shot, and he should have been satisfied long since at the proof he had given of that fact. He continued to kill indiscriminately: water hens whose coarse flesh was scarcely edible; an unfortunate bittern, which had found asylum a few days earlier in one of the coves of the Little Water Hen, a long-shanked, melancholy, lonely bird that had shattered the air with its booming; and female ducks, almost certainly.

The hunting season had not yet begun, and Hippolyte feared difficulties with the government. In no case did he like trouble with the authorities, especially not now when they were in such official favor. They had received personal letters from the government. Luzina, you might say, was in direct and constant touch with the government. Now, less than ever, was lawbreaking in order. Bessette might report them to the Mounted Police, were he to think that he could thus succeed in closing the school. Hippolyte was deeply upset. Yet he had not the courage, either, openly to reprimand education personified. If anyone knew the law, it should have been the schoolmaster.

One evening he expressed what he had to say in a wholly tactful fashion. "Mother, when does the hunting season open?" Hippolyte inquired.

Astounded, Luzina replied, "But you know very well, Father; the season begins about September eighteenth."

"Yes, that's just what I thought," said Hippolyte. "I've been telling myself, these last few days, that the hunting season doesn't begin until the eighteenth of September. We're in July. So we have a good two months before hunting begins."

Armand Dubreuil was far from obtuse. Hippolyte's little stratagem made him laugh even harder than Luzina's reproaches. Sitting on the floor with his back to the wall and his short pipe between his teeth, he expounded to them his view of the law. "Can you people see any government inspector arriving on Little Water Hen island! You'd first of all have to go get him, show him the way, drag him out of swamps, lead him by the hand. Give him a rub-down, encourage him with hot toddies . . ."

Hippolyte was afraid of expressing too direct a rebuke and went off to take a stroll along the shore of the Big Water Hen. At its middle the river ran free; outside the current it was encumbered with sedges. They spread everywhere here, gaining ground from year to year, just as did the crops elsewhere, the tilth, the forest—a country really made for the birds. Each spring they came from the depths of Florida, two thousand miles as a bird flies, hastening and following a cunning course in order to reach this sure asylum! Perhaps more than two thousand miles! The mother birds must have remembered the water which came half-way up the length of the rushes. Here were the finest hiding places in the world in which to train their ducklings when first they began to swim, and then to show them how to fly from tuft to tuft. Hippolyte sighed heavily. He did not like to see young lives snuffed out before they had even learned to suspect danger. He did not like to see mothers snatched away from their broods. And to think of that long journey of confidence, from the depths of Florida, ending in disaster!

By now, however, it was very late in the day to become annoyed at Armand Dubreuil. He made himself increasingly at home with the Tousignants. To his heart's content he practiced a more and more extraordinary teaching method—laughter, indulgence, liberty. "There is nothing like liberty," he would say. "Why push the children so much? They'll always know as much as they need to. What good do you suppose grammar and history will do them in these parts?"

"Aren't you happy here?" he would then ask.

Certainly they were happy, but what had that to do with their little knowledge?

Inclined as she was to look at the pleasant side of things, Luzina could not help realizing that, as far as education was concerned, they were going from bad to worse. In the end, perhaps, all they would have would be someone who came to the island in the Little Water Hen to spend a pleasant holiday.

Yet at the beginning of August it began to rain, and Armand Dubreuil, unable to indulge his favorite pastime, had to fall back on his schoolwork. He began abruptly to be almost as zealous in its behalf as he had been about hunting. Everyone then could see what precious things he had denied his pupils by his earlier neglect of duty. Invariably he translated arithmetic problems into terms of sheep, and thus every calculation became a matter of immediate interest to all of them, and they all labored at its solution. He asked Luzina for a great variety of disparate objects: a perfectly spherical tomato, another smaller tomato, clothespins, and thread; then, with the help of these things, he showed that the earth was round, that it revolved on its axis wrapped in its threads of latitude and longitude and in the effulgence from the other tomato, which also revolved and was the sun. In this fashion the children understood what Luzina had already maintained: that it was night on one portion of the terrestrial globe while elsewhere the sun was shining. He was a good teacher—even an excellent teacher.

In the evening he sat in the kitchen with a book, very different in this respect from Miss O'Rorke, who locked herself up and even shoved a table against the door and seemed unable to erect enough barriers to protect her pathetic privacy, which was ever lacking something. The sight of an open book, of a person absorbed in reading, had always been soothing and alluring to Luzina. She asked the teacher if what he were reading was very interesting. It continued to rain, a heavy rain which beat down on the roof of the house. Armand Dubreuil began reading aloud the fictionalized account of a visit to the North Pole. And the Tousignant family, on the very edge of the inhabited world, lost all feeling of isolation in its enthralled concern for the sufferings, the cold, the loneliness endured by these imaginary personages.

Luzina was overwhelmed. She who so readily commiserated real misfortune, how could she fail to be stirred by the mishaps which novelists are so skilled at piling upon the backs of their creatures! The worst was that the moment one catastrophe had been averted, another began to threaten. Luzina was continuously afraid for the explorers on their perilous expedition. Yet it never would have occurred to her to spare her emotions by putting a stop to the reading. On the contrary, the more calamities there were to dread, the more eager she was to hear about them. Never would she have believed that you could be at once so happy and so anxious. The rain whipped at the windows. The reader's voice drowned out the gusts. The stove, barely alight, emitted a little warmth. They felt themselves secure, and their hearts contracted at the thought that others were in a different case. With tears in her eyes, Luzina begged, "A little more, Monsieur Dubreuil; let us at least learn how they find their way through the storm!"

She could not resign herself to the tepid comfort of bed while at that very moment the explorers were wandering lost.

Occasionally, as though the reader had some power of intercession with the author and could rescue Luzina's heroes from their discomfiture, she threatened the teacher: "Come, now! Don't you dare let another of them perish!"

After the odyssey of these explorers, not one of whom survived, Armand Dubreuil read the true and tragic adventures of forty convicts exiled to Siberia.

How cold and inhuman a spot was that Siberia! How far away! What hardhearted Czars were those Nicholases, Emperors of all the Russias! Luzina no longer heard the wind thrust at her own door or the coyotes howling at the full moon not very far from where she sat. She thanked Heaven she was in Canada, in a country civilized, well governed, and progressive. Even though she considered the characters in books quite as real as she was herself, not at all inventions of their authors' minds, Luzina blessed the talent that must have been necessary to make all this living thing vivid and clear. "Don't leave us hungry for more, Monsieur Dubreuil!"

He was completely transformed. As though to make up for lost time, he fed them double rations. The children never could complete the homework outlined for them on the blackboard. Joséphine alone held up in this marathon he had devised for them. Grammar, arithmetic, geography—everything at breakneck speed. Edmond had nightmares. They rushed from page to page without catching breath; hardly ever did the schoolmaster give them an hour's recreation. Everything he did he had to do to excess. All the same, Luzina had no intention of reproaching him now for this sudden zeal. Perhaps he was moved by remorse. Or else, as always, Luzina's formula of winning people with honey was at last bearing fruit.

Then Luzina brusquely awakened to the truth. One evening as he closed his book, Armand Dubreuil calmly announced that he was leaving the next day.

It was only the end of August; the schoolmaster was engaged until the end of October. The large box he had brought with him and which Luzina now knew was packed with books was far from having been emptied. Luzina was about to protest when, of a sudden, she wondered whether this were not some new form of teasing on his part; he was a great wag.

"You're not serious in your talk about leaving; you're trying to frighten us," she asserted.

He assumed an air of amusement. "All the same, I've a fine school in the South. A school with three grades, located in a large village. You wouldn't want to have me miss a chance of advancing myself, would you, Mama Tousignant?"

The next day she got up very early and found him already rigged in the same fashion as on his arrival, his blanket on his back, his rifles over his shoulder. He was adjusting under his chin the strap of his pith helmet. Luzina felt he was carrying the joke a little too far. "Why are you upsetting us this way, Monsieur Dubreuil?"

He laughed again. "There's no time to fool around if I want to catch old Sluzick."

She began brewing him some coffee; she still hesitated to believe him. "We're only in August; you could at least stay on until October. All this nonsense is just some more of your practical joking. . . . And the best hunting of all is in autumn." She hoped that that would lure him.

"Too bad, too bad! But my school in the South begins on the fourth of September. A school built of brick, if you please, and what's more, Mama Tousignant, your little Dubreuil has been appointed its principal."

He swallowed the last mouthfuls of coffee and moved toward her, smiling, teasing, his hand outstretched. "Many thanks and good-by, Mama Tousignant."

So it was true that he was leaving. To have been doubtful of it to the end made his departure all the harder. She had slept in peace; had she bestirred herself, perhaps she might have been able to keep him a bit longer.

"So soon! Already! Almost without giving us time to see you go!"

He had not always been conscientious, at least during the beginning of his stay. He had advocated bad principles—nature, indulgence, freedom. Yet perhaps he had been the best teacher of all. Henceforward they never would be able to see a tomato without remembering that the earth is round. Truly an odd master! He had said that it was not very important to learn, and yet it was he who had given them the strongest taste for it.

"Won't you come back?" Luzina asked. "Do try next summer!"

She had grown used to mothering him. She had mended his hunting trousers, often torn when he came home from the willow and hazelnut thickets. She had washed and ironed his shirts, kept cleaning his pipe ashes everywhere he went. Neither with Mademoiselle Côté, who was very fastidious, nor with Miss O'Rorke, who was grimly independent, had Luzina enjoyed these small pleasures. Above all had it been the schoolmaster's contentment at living with them which had won him Luzina's heart.

"We'll expect you next year."

"I've been appointed principal," he began again. "You understand, Mama Tousignant, I'm quite a learned fellow. I have my bachelor's degree."

She opened her eyes wide, without fully understanding what it was all about except that here was a further reason for hanging onto the teacher. Now, however, he left all seriousness behind. "Good-by freedom!" said he. "I'm a real fool! One hundred and fifty dollars a month, Principal Dubreuil. . . . I'm slipping my head into the noose. . . . Not a particle of all that is worth a single day on the island in the Little Water Hen!"

As he moved away, he turned and fixed his eyes on the small building Hippolyte had erected for the future and for knowledge.

What would be the outcome of all this? A great deal of sorrow, perhaps, for Mama Tousignant. What, indeed, would come of it? Discontent first of all, which lies at the root of all progress. And afterward?

"Would you like my advice, Mama Tousignant?" he inquired, still laughing but a trifle more serious than usual. "Close your school. You'll never get anything here except old battle-axes like your Miss O'Rorke or fellows like me who come because they want to hunt. And eventually you won't even see the likes of us. In the end, summer classes attract only misfits, and from what I hear that species is dying out in our profession."

He saluted her, with two fingers touching the visor of his helmet. He preferred leaving alone, with Pierre as his only companion, he being needed to bring the boats back to the near shores of the two rivers. He knew how to get along by himself. The countryside had become familiar to him, intimate, easy, like some way of life a man at first glance knows would fully content him and on which, for that very reason, he turns his back. If this happiness were not so easy, would you thus casually leave it behind, calmly and whistling some little tune?

"Monsieur Dubreuil!" Luzina called him back.

He was already at some distance, ready to take his seat in the boat. He put his hand to his ear, made a sign that he was listening. She cried out into the wind, "Come back, one of these days!"

She was far from understanding this last lesson he had sought to teach her, more ambiguous than all the others. But he had left alone, as he had wanted, when he had wanted. He had himself taken up the oars. It was as though one of themselves were leaving, and Luzina's heart was touched with anxiety. During the course of the winter she constrained herself not to think too much out loud of the teacher to come, and she did this out of prudence, in the hope, probably, of extracting from the future something even better by demanding little. Whoever might wish to come to the Little Water Hen would be well received and duly appreciated.

But the following summer no one came to the island.

IX

You might have doubted the existence of the English kings Miss O'Rorke had introduced into the island, and Mademoiselle Côté's heroes, however far afield they had planted the flag of France, and even Dubreuil's unhappy exiles, had it not been that the tiny schoolhouse remained. After its fashion it gave witness to a civilization which would have existed. A traveler coming to the island and seeing there one cabin more than was strictly needed by its population might have meditated on the tale it told of progress and decline. The little structure leaned at an angle; the bitter cold had wrenched its joints, and on one side it had sunk perceptibly. A pair of squirrels had succeeded in forcing an entrance between two logs which had pulled a trifle apart. On the blackboard you could decipher, as in truncated messages from the distant past, a few scraps of Armand Dubreuil's last lesson: "Nouns . . . *al* . . . in the plural . . . cept *bal, chacal* . . ." The brush had obliterated the rest. The map of the world was hanging askew.

Luzina had several times remarked, "We mustn't let the school go to wrack and ruin." Yet one day, not knowing where to stow away a bag of grain, Hippolyte had leaned it against a corner of the schoolroom. Pierre used it to store his fishing apparatus. Wolf traps were hung up there. The school was in process of becoming a lumber room. And the summer ran its course like the Water Hen itself, sleepy amidst its rushes. No longer was it necessary to wash every morning, and why wear shoes now? Pierre gave up his books. Often had he been humiliated and provoked; in school he had felt very backward for his age. Now he was relieved at last to be able to devote himself, a man full-fledged and unharassed, to the important business of life—the sheep, fishing, firewood. Meanwhile Joséphine had become schoolmistress on Little Water Hen island. She would lead a row of four or five small Tousignants into a corner of the kitchen or outdoors under a birch tree, and she would announce, with a serious mien strangely reminiscent of Mademoiselle Côté: "School will now begin." Then she would insist that they greet each other politely.

Luzina's heart swelled at seeing the children repeat last year's lessons from morning until night. And as though to embitter her regrets, the Department of Education continued to send pamphlets and communications of one sort or another. The government people seemed unaware that the Little Water Hen school was closed. Other blackboard erasers arrived, and then a packet of letters from New Zealand children forwarded through the courtesy of a Miss Patterson of the Department. This consisted of answers to letters written two years earlier by the Tousignant children under Miss O'Rorke's direction. In order to create and maintain cordial relations between the various subjects of the British throne, Miss O'Rorke required the pupils in every school through which she passed to write letters to their small cousins in South Africa, Australia, Newfoundland, or some other portion of the Empire "on which the sun never set."

That summer the Tousignants still received a magazine published by the Department of Education. Luzina was leafing it through one morning when abruptly she gave an exclamation of shock and pride. The letter Edmond had written two years ago to a little New Zealand friend was there before Luzina's eyes, in the full dignity of print. It was headed, "A Water Hen District Student Describes His Life for Us."

Luzina remembered Edmond's letter very well. Into it Miss O'Rorke had injected many ideas of her own, especially toward the end, where she had Edmond say that he was happy to belong to a great Empire. She had of course helped with spelling and punctuation. All the same, a number of the short sentences were wholly Edmond's. A greater friend of originality than one might have imagined, Miss O'Rorke had respected their un-English way of saying things. Luzina unraveled some part of it.

"I am at the Little Water Hen. My mother is Mrs. Tousignant. My father keeps Bessette's sheep. One has a hundred and forty-nine sheep. One is far from the big train. Never in all my life have I taken the big train. But my mother takes the big train. She gets babies. And how do you like New Zealand, you, my little New Zealand friend? Have you sheep? I like New Zealand. Do send me your photograph. I'll send you my photograph if I have one. I have another little new baby. One has a lot of babies. Have you a baby?"

And it was signed in full, Rosario-Lorenzo-Edmond Tousignant.

"Heaven's sake! Heaven's sake!" Luzina was in an ecstasy.

Edmond's friend's answer appeared on the same page, and had as title, "A Few Words from Bill McEwan."

More fortunate than Edmond, Bill McEwan had his picture in the magazine; it had been taken near his home, in a clearing amidst huge trees, and showed him leaning against a small plank structure. Apparently this New Zealand was rather similar to the Little Water Hen; he also mentioned sheep.

Luzina ran off to find Hippolyte in the sheepfold. She was waving the paper in the air. "Edmond's letter!"

What was Luzina talking about! To the best of Hippolyte's knowledge, Edmond had not left, so why the talk about letters? Luzina spread the open pages before Hippolyte's eyes. He was busy. With his hands he continued to take care of a sick lamb. He began reading a few words. "I am at the Little Water Hen. My father keeps Bessette's sheep. . . ."

Hippolyte was prey to a strange emotion. At first he felt embarrassed that his business, through Edmond's doing, should, as it were, be common knowledge even as far away as New Zealand. But now that this sin of pride had been committed, all he could do was endure the celebrity it carried with it as best he might, without seeming too puffed up about it. And such had been almost exactly Luzina's feelings. To see it proclaimed throughout the whole Empire that she had so many babies had not, at first sight, wholly pleased her; perhaps you did not win fame after the fashion you might have chosen. All the same, burdensome or agreeable, the fact remained that it was through little Edmond that they had attained it, and you could not long be cross with him over such a gift. That the letter should have been written in English, however—a tongue foreign to them, just barely understandable, far from their normal lives—was what after all gave them the greatest pride. And that honor they could relish to their hearts' content.

"So well written a letter, and not even in his own language!" said Luzina.

This child of theirs, moreover, had never done them anything but credit.

"Already in Mademoiselle Côté's time," Luzina recalled, "he answered questions well."

From a long way off she could hear: "The Little Water Hen, too, Mademoiselle?" "Of course, Edmond dear, all this, this whole country belonged to France."

Like all happy ages which ever pass too quickly, the days of the school seemed to have gone by at breakneck speed. She also heard, deep in her motherly satisfaction, a burst of laughter, perhaps a warning. "And will the little Tousignants on Water Hen island have much use for grammar and spelling?"

Well, this is what use they had for them: they wrote letters even to New Zealand; they made themselves known afar; they had friends elsewhere, in distant parts of the world; was that not an answer?

"And then, later," insisted the schoolmaster's mocking voice, "they will little by little forget what they have learned, and what good will the school have done you!"

That was the most forthright of the threats he had caused to hover over her, and it was the one she dreaded most. To forget seemed to her worse than not to have learned. To forget was to allow something that had been yours to be lost, and that was more serious than not to have tried to better yourself. Forgetting was no more nor less than thanklessness. And yet once, during an evening, they had all tried to call to mind the name of the Governor General of Canada, which they had known perfectly well.

"We did know it; we'll surely remember it," said Luzina. "Let's try hard."

But no one of them could think of the Governor's name. It seemed to be right there, in their memories; still, it amused itself by hiding, and all their efforts could not bring it to the surface. Joséphine, so loyal in remembrance, said nothing. Edmond himself declared he had forgotten. That Governor's name was, after all, not too great a loss. Hippolyte grumbled that it would not prevent their eating or sleeping in peace, but Luzina continued to rack her brain. On several occasions in full daylight they saw her sitting, her eyes vague; she was dredging for that Governor's name, which must begin with a T. One day you lost the Governor's name, said she, and the next day you lost something else. Then she began to reflect that if one of them held onto the knowledge they had acquired, all would not be lost. Her glance fell on Edmond. "Either they will little by little forget," Armand Dubreuil had said, "or they must keep on learning." Edmond was the best informed among them. Assuredly his was the right of guardianship over their knowledge. Whereupon, one evening when she was not seeking it, Luzina hit upon the Governor's name. It was Tweedsmuir. Her fear, nonetheless, had been keen, and it remained so. Edmond was to spare them from such alarms in the future. Meanwhile Luzina's imagination brushed away the difficulties; she did not fully envision the fact that to get schooling Edmond would have to leave them, live far away. Later on it was too late to back water. Hippolyte had agreed, thinking to please Luzina; and Luzina could not reverse herself for fear of saddening Hippolyte. Autumn was already close at hand. From day to day the birds were flying higher. They were practicing for their long flight. One of these mornings, when you got up, you would be astounded at the unwonted silence which reigned over the deserted sedges. At dawn, when no one yet suspected anything, the birds would have gone, and at the hour when their going was discovered, they would already be far away; they would have covered a good stretch of the road to Florida, where, it seemed, the sun shone bright the year round and where there were always flowers. Even the life of a young bird had its mysteries. They seemed to want things that they had never known.

About the time of year when the birds emigrated from the North, the first of the Tousignant children departed.

X

For four years now, Joséphine had been buoyed by a great ambition: to walk about on high heels, with a light and graceful tread like Mademoiselle's; to do her hair with tiny curls in front like Mademoiselle; and, what was much more difficult, to become as learned as Mademoiselle.

The very day of Mademoiselle Côté's departure, Joséphine had followed her all the way to the mainland, weeping large tears: "Whatever is going to become of us!" Yet at the last minute she had pulled her book out from under her apron and had asked: "Do at least explain this page to me before you go, Mademoiselle."

"You're now quite capable of learning by yourself," Mademoiselle Côté had encouragingly told her. "Learn a little something every day."

The whole winter through, seated in one corner of the kitchen and reading aloud, Joséphine had worked her disconsolate way to the very last page of the second reader. And she then had requested another.

She had not been overfond of the Englishwoman. The Englishwoman had not been nice, like Mademoiselle; she was not lovely-looking, like Mademoiselle. But almost equal to Joséphine's loyalty was her passion for learning. She learned from the Englishwoman because there was no one else at hand to teach her and because Mademoiselle had urged her to study hard. She knew her *Mother Goose*. She knew it all by heart, without understanding more than a half-dozen words. Yet mangling these brief tales in verse, one mistake leading on to another, without pause, full steam ahead, Joséphine was considered to have a very good knowledge of English on Little Water Hen island.

Armand Dubreuil's arrival had disappointed her. She had never thought it possible that a man could be any good at teaching. That, however, was no reason for her to abandon her tactics which consisted in learning from whoever might know a bit more than Joséphine. She took it upon herself to stalk him while he was hunting.

She would suddenly pop up in front of him, having hidden behind trees the better to keep tabs on him. "I've learned the page you told me to learn," Joséphine would announce.

She stared at him with a disapproving look in her eye; he was far from being a good schoolmaster. He took very little trouble with his explanations. You had to do it almost all by yourself. What was the difference? He was better than nothing.

"Good, very good, Joséphine. You're really a little wonder. Now go ahead and learn the next page since you're so quick at it."

"At least ask me a few questions to see if I know it," Joséphine would insist.

During the evening, her instructor still had the small girl underfoot. She would interrupt his tales of the chase; unbending, tenacious, she would force him back into his teacher's role: "What does it mean when it says the *subject* of a sentence?"

"Joséphine is a pest. In that sentence, Joséphine is the subject. She is the one who is doing the talking. She is the one who acts, and bothers me."

Though he had great faults, Armand Dubreuil made the things he taught clear. Then, too, Joséphine suspected that he, also, would be leaving soon.

She buzzed around him like a bee, eager to extract all the information, all the knowledge he possessed.

Before he went, Armand Dubreuil gave them all little presents. "And you, my small nuisance, what in the world will I give you?"

Without hesitation, determined to get what she wanted, she had answered, "Your grammar." And the schoolmaster gave it to her.

What complications were to spring from this dry-as-dust gift of Joséphine's! Her head between her hands, resolved to learn, she jousted with unintelligible texts. No longer did she teach on Little Water Hen island; in vain did her pupils, Héloïse, Valmore-Gervais, and tiny Marie-Ange, stand in line and ask her to play school. Joséphine had to attend to her own advancement. One day her piping, afflicted voice drowned out all the competing sounds in the house at an instant when Luzina was busy with a score of other things.

"Mother, what is an indirect object?"

Luzina stopped stirring her broth. The void that opened in her mind dizzied her. An indirect object! Come! She must have learned that in her day! An indirect object! It was far off, much further off than the Governor's name, and even that she had again forgotten. Probably it was lost forever. Quite the coward, Luzina told Joséphine, "Ask your father."

As for him, he did not believe he had ever known what an indirect object was. "Ask your mother."

Joséphine grew impatient. "Now, Mother! I want to know!"

Suddenly it was more than Luzina could stand. She became angry. Could she do everything!—bring up eleven unmanageable children, cook for them, mend their clothes, take care of their father who was almost as unreasonable as they, and, over and above all that, still remember her grammar? God in Heaven! No one person could have done all that! What was more, she was sick and tired of this grammar business. She had heard all she wanted to hear about it.

"I'm going to burn that wretched book, that's all there is to it," Luzina decided.

Burn Joséphine's grammar! No sooner had Luzina grasped the meaning of her threat than she at once turned repentant, kindly, persuasive. What had come over her! For this long time she had lived in the midst of her children, kindly, indulgent, herself as unharassed as a child, imagining that they would become well educated, would know a great deal more than she did herself. She had never had an inkling that they would ask devastating questions, would find her ignorant.

"I'm going to show you how to sew," she offered in an excess of goodheartedness. "Get a needle and thread. It's much more useful to know how to sew than to learn grammar."

"I'm going to be a schoolteacher," said Joséphine.

"All right, then." Luzina wanted to conciliate her. "Teach your little brothers and sisters. You know a lot. Show them what you know. Play school some more."

"I'm going to be a real schoolteacher," Joséphine continued.

Then a very sly defense strategy occurred to Luzina. "Like the poor Englishwoman, I suppose! You want to waste your life going from one wretched school to another, like our old Miss O'Rorke. There is nothing more miserable than being a schoolmistress."

"I'm not going to be a schoolmistress like Miss O'Rorke," said Joséphine with asperity. "I'm going to be a schoolteacher like Mademoiselle Côté."

"To become a schoolteacher," Luzina pointed out, "you'd have to go to a convent for years and then more years. You'd be shut in and far from home. You'd have to do what the sisters told you, all the time. And even before that, you'd have to leave all alone with old Nick Sluzick and travel alone on a big train. A little pussy like you! Do you think that makes sense?"

Quite unaware of what she was doing, Luzina had opened before Joséphine precisely the road to the great things she wanted to undertake. And indeed it was the road Joséphine would follow. She would sit up beside the mailman in the region's biggest automobile. Joséphine had seen no other. She would travel for miles and miles—a hundred miles, perhaps. She would arrive at the settlement which was ten times bigger than all the buildings at the ranch put together. She would go even further. Wait a minute! Joséphine would go as far as Rorketon. There it was ten thousand times bigger than at Portage des Prés. And at Rorketon there were the trains. Joséphine sank deep into a kitchen chair, just as though she were installed aboard the train, and she saw all southern Manitoba coming toward her. Her braids swung to and fro with the train's jolting. Joséphine rolled along faster and faster. She blinked her eyelids as though she felt full on her face the locomotive's scorching blast. She arrived at Winnipeg. Joséphine got off her train at the capital of Manitoba. At this juncture in her trip, Joséphine reached something so colossal that she gave up any attempt at comparison with what she knew already. Quite simply, Joséphine remained suspended in the midst of the unknown, the tip of her eager tongue rubbing against her lip.

"It's well enough for the boys to go far away to school," conceded Luzina. "But a little girl does not need education as much as all that."

Joséphine cut her off short. "Mademoiselle was a girl, and she was even better educated than Monsieur Dubreuil."

"No, no, no," argued Luzina. "Monsieur Dubreuil said so himself. He has his bachelor's degree."

"You said yourself," Joséphine reminded her, "that Mademoiselle was the nicest girl in the world."

"Oh! That one!"

Luzina glanced distractedly at Mademoiselle Côté's old room. Miss O'Rorke had occupied it and turned it upside down with her mania for moving the furniture around every other day. Armand Dubreuil had transformed it into an arsenal. Finally the Capuchin Father had slept there, and yet it still was called "Mademoiselle's room." Their first teacher had left it more than four years ago, but she remained ever with them, never to be ousted, beyond criticism. She answered through the children's mouths. She won in every argument. Basically it was she who finally had pulled Edmond away and then Charles. And now it was clear that she would have Joséphine.

Luzina sat down at the big kitchen table to write to her sister Blanche, who lived at Saint Jean Baptiste, where there was a convent. She asked her whether she would be willing to take Joséphine, "a good small girl, studious, hard-working, handy, not too bothersome, stubborn as they came, but stubborn in her desire to learn. . . ." And from time to time, exasperated by the effort every letter exacted, Luzina demanded silence around her, addressing her remarks principally to Joséphine. "Obstinate girl! The sisters won't put up with the things I've put up with. . . . You'll see that it won't always be fun at the convent. . . ."

Luzina had laughed so much in her life that the wrinkles and expression of her face were fixed in a pattern of good humor. Her scoldings and complaints never seemed very serious. Just like those aged Indians whom you can't imagine sad because their eyes, from exposure to the sun, seem always to twinkle with engaging slyness, poor Luzina was fated to be seriously misconstrued. "Mama is always gay. Mama takes things well," her children would say.

It was spring, though the weather remained quite cold, when the family ventured forth to deliver Joséphine to the mailman. From the elevated seat of the ancient Ford, Nick Sluzick saw a strange sight. The whole Tousignant tribe was coming toward him in single file. The father and one of the sons carried a box made of dark wood which, from a distance, looked exactly like a small coffin. In their midst walked a little girl dressed all in black. The group, only partly visible above the rushes, moved along as though at a burial. Hoisted to shoulder height, the wooden box jolted through the air.

What had got into them today?

Waiting upset the old fellow's nerves. It would be at least five minutes before the Tousignants could reach him, and those minutes gave Sluzick ample time to ruminate upon his life's quest for happiness.

Some fifteen years earlier he had arrived in this country utterly without neighbors, and it had been his reasonable belief that he would live there in peace. Nobody knew how to read or write in those fine old days, and no one suffered because of it. Progress, civilization, which was what people called nuisance and botheration, had all the same begun to overtake them, little by little, in the North. At first people had taken it into their heads to get letters, then mail-order catalogues. Mail-order catalogues! Just about the silliest thing in all the world! They were cumbersome; they filled a mail bag in no time at all, and why? I ask you! Just to demonstrate to you that now you needed a whole stack of things you had gotten along perfectly well without: lamps with incandescent mantles, aluminum saucepans, enameled stoves. Enameled stoves, if you please! People had sunk to that! What was more, every spring the population increased to the point that it amounted to an epidemic. And with all their brood, the Tousignants had conceived the idea of having a schoolmistress.

His knees crossed, one leg projecting outside the car, Nick spat overboard, aiming at a dent in the mudguard.

Ugh! He should have understood that life was no longer livable in these parts the very day when he had lugged out that crazy old woman who tried to show him the road to the Little Water Hen! For five years now he had constantly been carting people back and forth. He was under a running fire. No sooner had he brought someone here in May than October was upon him and he had to carry that person all the way back. It was a fine thing to have left the heart of the Carpathian Mountains and to have crossed almost the whole of Canada only to end up with traffic as congested as it was getting to be here. Hadn't it happened, one fine day last year or the year before, that he had taken on a soldier of some kind? The chap had called himself a schoolmaster, but don't try to tell Nick Sluzick that there wasn't spy work of some sort in that business. Nick Sluzick had turned around and seen his Ford loaded to the brim with instruments of warfare. Enough to finish the old car off. It was already a wonder that the ancient vehicle ran at all. On every trip he had to crawl underneath, replace a piston, get a new wheel, unscrew the carburetor; he almost had to take it apart and put it together again for each trip. He could not be expected to lug along baggage, people, mail bags, and spies into the bargain. Nick Sluzick would sell his car that very day, while it still was in good order. Today it was in the prime of its life. Nick would get rid of it. It was a fine little car. Everything about it had been put in shape like new. It could keep on going indefinitely. So Nick would sell his old rattletrap, and then, the quicker the better, he'd clear out for Fox Island, thirty-five miles further north. He had brought in every one of these Tousignants, one after the other, when they weren't more than ten or twelve days old, the size of rabbits. He had had a dog's time getting them there alive. They cried with cold, with hunger. Once, during the thaw, he had just avoided drowning one in a flooded stretch of road. He had almost lost one in the snow, with a March blizzard raging. It was a miracle if two or three others had not been born in his arms, on the trip out, those people always being in such a hurry. Yes, in all truth, Nick Sluzick had had troubles enough to deliver the Tousignant population alive; he had no intention now of carting them, one by one, away from their island.

Joséphine had just taken her seat between the mailman and Hippolyte, who was to see her to Rorketon. There, the conductor would be requested to take care of Joséphine and himself to put her on the Winnipeg train, he having done as much already for Edmond and Charles. Aunt Blanche was to go to the capital to meet Joséphine. Swollen with her own importance, Joséphine felt a love throb in her heart which embraced very nearly all mankind.

The mailman's nose was running copiously; his catarrh had become so bad that, summer and winter, Nick Sluzick distilled a silvery liquid which hung in threads between the hairs of his nostrils and the bristles of his mustache, crisscrossing in an intricate network and supplying him with a kind of diminutive muzzle, fine-meshed yet tough. Joséphine, however, who was off to be educated, felt a wholly fresh forbearance for the people of the region, dirty for the sole reason that they knew no better. Today something strange was gnawing at Joséphine's heart. Her great affection for all humanity was already fastening especially on the unfortunate, the ignorant whom it would later be her mission to teach. She turned toward the postman the little face of a schoolmistress who understood things.

Nick grabbed the wheel. The Ford bounced over a big mound, tumbled into a water hole, clambered up the side of the trail. Luzina had started running to catch up with it. Both arms outstretched, she stumbled against a boulder; she could still make out the fine white piping on Joséphine's black dress. She stopped. Her eyes grew wide. Luzina suddenly saw much more than a detail of her daughter's clothing. For a long time it had been she alone who had traveled. Almost every year she had departed and hurried about her business in order to come home with one more child against a wilderness to be peopled. Now she remained behind, and it was the children who were leaving. After a fashion, Luzina was seeing life. And she could not believe what her stout heart told her: already life, to which she had given so abundantly, little by little was leaving her behind.

XI

She could no longer keep up the pace. She had more children, but at far greater intervals, and soon it seemed that that was finished. The children, however, continued to go their ways. After Joséphine, André-Aimable and Roberta-Louise. Where had the latter picked up her compelling desire to become a nurse? The only explanation was that one communicated to the next the ancient illness with which Mademoiselle Côté had infected the house. Hardly had Joséphine left when Héloïse had set herself up as schoolteacher for the Little Water Hen. She taught that there were nine provinces, that the world was big, ten thousand times as big as Portage des Prés. How true that was, alas! Edmond and Charles were at school at the academy in Saint Boniface; one of Hippolyte's uncles, a parish priest, was paying their board and lodging. Edmond was studying literature; Charles had progressed as far as rhetoric; in her letters Joséphine spoke of compound addition and of botany. She had been given a medal by Bishop Yelle, Bishop Beliveau's coadjutor.

There had been a time when Luzina could direct her children's studies: *a, e, i, o, u;* another period when she succeeded more or less in keeping up with them. Evenings, the kitchen turned into a study hall. There the pupils spread out their manuals and notebooks. "Mama, the ink bottle." Luzina snuffed the lamp; you must take good care of your eyes if you wanted to do your lessons properly. She fetched her own homework, the family mending. If she had to get up to find thread or another needle, she did it quietly, on tiptoe. She would sit down again at education's edge. And she would grasp her small share of it. While she patched the seat of a pair of trousers, she would pick up a requirement of grammar, a snatch of history. Frontenac informed the commander of the British fleet: "I shall answer you with the mouths of my cannon!"

From her corner, Luzina spoke her approval: "Well answered." Her needle flew. In the length of time it took to repair Edmond's pants, the English were repulsed. How pleased she was at the ill-tempered old Governor in those days gone by! Having never seen a fleet or a cannon, Luzina had no muddled images in her pleasant reconstruction of history. After all, it was not so much the victory of one side or the defeat of the other that interested her, but rather the fact of learning. She would store a date away, in the same fashion as she would set aside a spool of thread or a scrap of cloth, saying to herself, "I must remember that." And she had done it to such good purpose that from time to time she could produce some bit of information precisely when it was of use. Mademoiselle Côté herself had been taken aback by this. "Do you realize, Madame Tousignant, that you have a great deal of natural ability?" For having said this alone, Luzina could have thrown her arms around the teacher's neck. Luzina was not an unhappy woman; she did not believe she had any reason to complain. Her life seemed to her as good as she deserved; and yet there were times when she had felt a brief twinge in her heart, that sadness at not being wholly understood which is common to all who dwell upon this earth. So it was, in all truth, the keen joy of having had her shy taste for learning discovered and not held up to ridicule—it was that joy which the teacher's kindly words had made sparkle in Luzina's eyes, suddenly alight with gratitude. After the evening's lessons, she went to bed almost as overexcited as the children; she repeated to herself what she had heard; her housewife's tasks complicated her life as a pupil; her two sets of cares became intertwined. She began to progress more slowly. And then, abruptly, she was left behind. Never again would she be able to catch up with the children. Syntax, Latin, Greek! The Bishop's medal!

Occasionally Luzina would still enter the small schoolhouse. The birches had grown and cast a great deal of shadow over the windows which Hippolyte had wanted opening on as much light as possible. Within the tiny room the light was now green and sad. In order to mount the platform, Luzina had to clamber over lengths of stovepipe, coils of rope, and she had to push aside a grindstone. The school smelt of mold, the smell of old, damp paper. Luzina pulled the string of one of the large maps sent long ago by the government. Manitoba hung in front of her, almost as big as the wall. Here and there the sturdy paper had come somewhat loose from its muslin backing; there were places where Manitoba was swollen in blisters, like those maps on which mountain chains are shown in relief. Here, however, it was the even plain that rose, sank back, split open. An underwater glow played over the old map, wrinkled as it was and spotted with green. You might have imagined that it sought to show Luzina a world which everywhere had reasons for growing sorrowful. At the very bottom of the map Luzina saw an area fairly black with the names of rivers, villages, and towns. That was the South. Almost every village had its geographical rights in the South. Luzina's finger went exploring along the lines of longitude and latitude. Lovingly she would now and then seek to smooth out the map's wrinkles. At last she would discover Otterburne, the precise spot where André-Aimable was studying apiculture with the Viatorians. Her finger moved along further. Here, at Saint Jean Baptiste, she located young Héloïse, whom Aunt Blanche had sent for the moment Joséphine had made sufficient progress. Luzina moved upward to find Roberta-Louise at the Dauphin hospital. The old map seemed to her almost a friend—and likewise a thief. It oozed moisture. As she stroked it lightly and warmed it with her hand, Luzina extracted from it little drops of humidity, thin, cold, which under her finger gave her a strange impression of tears. Then Manitoba seemed to her to grow bored. So vast, so little bestrewn with names, almost entirely given over to those wide, naked stretches which represented lakes and uninhabited space! Emptier and emptier, bare paper without a printed word, the further you went into the North. It seemed that all the place names had clustered together on this map as though to warm each other, that they had all crowded together in the same corner of the South. There they even had to be abbreviated, so small was the available space, but up above they stretched out at their ease, with room to spare. Mademoiselle Côté had taught that three-quarters of Manitoba's population all dwelt within this little portion of the map that Luzina could cover with her two hands. That left very few people for the North! So vacant in that portion, the old map seemed to want to take vengeance on Luzina. In large letters it bore the name Water Hen River. It was silent, however, regarding the existence of the island in the Little Water Hen.

Luzina sat down briefly at the schoolmistress's desk, high up on the platform. Joséphine must be a big girl by now. Her Aunt Blanche wrote that she had won another prize. In a competition sponsored by the Manitoba Association of French Canadians, she had been given the award for French established by the Manitoba Federation of French Canadian Ladies. "I wish you could have seen her," wrote her aunt, "in the white dress I made her for the prize-day ceremonies at the convent." Some day soon Luzina would receive a small photo ordered from Winnipeg as well as one of Héloïse, and she would see that the younger girl was also looking well. Edmond had landed an "accessit" in English. He, likewise, had always had an aptitude for English. *Accessit!* In one of the teacher's desk drawers there was still a small dictionary. To be certain she could lay hands on it when she needed it,

Luzina had insisted that it was better to keep it in its proper place, which was Mademoiselle Côté's drawer. She looked *accessit* up. "Honor awarded in schools or in academies to those who have come closest to winning a prize. . . ." So! It was not the prize itself, but only an approach to it! Luzina had thought that it was more than that. Perhaps Edmond had had the ground pushed out from under his feet by some teacher's pet. Poor Miss O'Rorke! Where was she now? Luzina had heard from her once. Miss O'Rorke had written that she felt old and that she was thinking of retiring at last and going back to her beloved Ontario and civilization. She inquired after Edmond. She would have been pleased to have learned that he had won an accessit in English. Poor Englishwoman! With the passage of time, Luzina had made her a real friend of her heart, the only woman in the world perhaps fully to understand solitude. Suddenly she thought she heard a rustling sound, as though someone were turning a book's pages. She glanced toward a dark corner of the schoolroom. It was only some field mice nuzzling a discarded copy book. For five years now Blanche had been saying that she would some day come to see this famous Water Hen Country and that she would bring the girls with her. Never having had any daughters, Blanche claimed that the Good Lord Himself had sent Joséphine and later Héloïse to be the consolation and pride of her life. As for Hippolyte's uncle, the parish priest, he talked about his nephews as though he had somehow succeeded, by himself alone, in bringing them into the world. Luzina would love to have seen him, now and again, sitting with his belly all swollen alongside the postman in a blizzard; and it was "Smack your horse, my old Nick Sluzick, if you want me to get there in time . . . and you, too, Ivan Bratislovski, smack your horse!"

She saw herself again, jolting over the hardened crust along the wretched trail. Would she arrive in time? Would she not arrive at all? She did take precautions; she tried to depart at least a week early. After all, she could not leave the family to its own devices indefinitely. She changed relays hurriedly. Sometimes the joltings and anxieties of the trip hastened nature's processes. She was not yet at ease even when at last she had clambered aboard the train. This was not the moment for relaxing. She was on the verge of begging the engineer to put on speed. The old peg-legged conductor knew her; every five minutes he would come ask her whether she felt all right. The wheels turned, the locomotive whistled. Before coming into the world, Luzina's children knew every kind of terror, every means of transportation, and, finally, this last stretch by train which, with its whistle blasts and the hammering of wheels on rails, seemed especially to stir them up. Almost always Luzina reached the Sainte Rose du Lac hospital at the last possible moment. No sooner had she entered its front door than old Dr. Magnan arrived on her heels, out of breath. He would scold her: "For Heaven's sake, have you set out to populate the Little Water Hen all by yourself! . . ."

Luzina returned to the present. She found herself sitting alone in the tiny schoolroom; she smiled for an instant at recollection of her ancient prowess.

Then at once she rejoiced to think that some few of her children had escaped from the difficulties she had known.

Her resentment against Hippolyte's uncle turned into gratitude. Even he himself could not know from what a wilderness he had extricated them. Thinly peopled as it was, the Little Water Hen Country had nevertheless found means to empty itself.

Luzina's nearest neighbors, halfbreeds named Mackenzie, who for six months had been living on the mainland two miles from the ranch, at about the spot where the postman left the mail, had just decamped.

Their departure, moreover, had dealt the final blow to Luzina's hope of some day seeing her little school reopen. In her negotiations with the government, she now dealt with a Mr. Stewart J. Acheson. Whatever had happened to that good Mr. Evans? Luzina missed him; his successor was far less accommodating. He required at least seven pupils of enrollment age, and that meant between six and fourteen, with no leeway at all. Of small Tousignants within those age brackets there remained only four at home. But the Mackenzies had six children. They were almost wholly wild, half-naked, grimy, speaking the Lord knew what language—a little English, a smattering of French, and probably some Saultais mingled perhaps with a few words of Cree. No matter! Luzina had cast a greedy eye in their direction. She had paid the Mackenzies a visit. A small log hut, dirty, smoky, furnished with straw mattresses lying directly on the floor. The family's Indian blood was particularly apparent in the mother. Shifty eyes, hypocritical, timorous. Luzina had been friendly, enthusiastic. She had brought with her fresh butter and pembina jam the better to persuade the halfbreeds of the advantages of education. "If we write the government—both families together—we can force their hand; we should be sure of getting a schoolmistress." Wasted effort. The halfbreeds regarded school as something like prison, a dungeon complete with bars. Luzina had then made the blunder of introducing the law into her pleasant descriptions of education. All children between six and fourteen were supposed to go to school. That was the law, and a serious business. You made yourself subject to fines and other penalties if you evaded the law. The government had inspectors who came to ferret out recalcitrant children in their own homes. The government had a long arm.

Perhaps she thus succeeded in making the Mackenzies clear out sooner than they would have in their normal routine of sudden moves. Placed where game most abounded within an area of forty miles, they possessed three other cabins similar to that where they occasionally sojourned along Nick Sluzick's route. Then, too, it was a simple matter for them to break camp. Like the Indians, they owned almost nothing, and that little—a stove and some pots—they gladly left behind them so that they might the more freely leave.

XII

The winters seemed to become harsher and harsher along the Little Water Hen. That year, before the end of October snow covered the entire island. Everywhere stiff whiteness. The tufts of reeds, rounded under their mantles of snow, resembled frozen sheep; and thus the winter landscape in some fashion reminded you of summer. The wind, however, was terrifically violent. In its sweep across so many an icy plain, so many motionless rivers, lakes frozen solid—space held captive and affording it no other obstacle than spindly sedge grasses—the wind acquired an insane velocity. The Tousignant dwelling, with its thick walls, its squat length, its small windows near the ground, was the first house the northwest gale encountered on its journey from the North Pole. The gale belabored it furiously, as though there were some absolute need to make an example of this spearhead of man's encroachment which, were the wind to leave it alone, would tomorrow find reinforcement, sturdier means of resistance.

Only twice a day did they dare open the door and face the elements. Hippolyte, heavy and bulging in his sheepskin, lantern in hand even at midday, set out for the sheepfold. It was not far off, about a hundred feet, but more than once it happened that Hippolyte could reach it only on snowshoes, holding his hurricane lantern in front of him like a man trying to find the road at night in some strange country. The wind never ceased. No sooner had they succeeded in beating a path from the house to the outbuildings than the fresh snow blotted the path out. One blizzard would blow itself to an end, only to be followed at once by another blast out of the North. Here were most powerful enemies arrayed against the island's only living beings: a few hundred sheep, squeezed into a confused, astonished mass, almost invisible in the twilight of their shelter, a few domestic animals, and in the house five human beings in all. Of Luzina's large family there remained to help the father only Pierre and Norbert; for Luzina herself there was Claire-Armelle, the surprise package.

She had had this surprise at the age of forty-six. One evening, four years earlier, Luzina had gone to find Hippolyte at the sheep pen. She had sat down on one of the bars of the enclosure's fence as she used to in the old days when she was still a young woman and when, not having enough children to keep her busy, she would get bored in the house and, in the middle of the working day, go out to chat with Hippolyte. Seeing her perched upon the fence, he had known at once that she had news. And she, for the first time in years, had recaptured her fine, open laugh, rich and a trifle dovelike.

"We couldn't have hit it worse if we'd tried for a hundred years," said Luzina. "This time, my man, your wife's holiday comes plumb in the middle of February!"

And, in very fact, the "surprise" and her mother had traveled in weather seldom experienced even in Manitoba's frozen wasteland. Snow, wind, bad roads, excessive cold—all had joined forces against the two voyagers. Perhaps this was why Luzina so greatly cherished her surprise. Together they had outfaced more misery than many a human being encounters throughout his whole lifetime. Perhaps it was even more because Luzina firmly believed that no power in the world could separate her from her little Claire-Armelle.

The winter continued its rigors. In December the snow, almost daily shoveled to either side of the doorway, made a sort of tunnel at the end of which for a brief moment you could see the sun's red face; whereupon the light faded away.

Then it was that Luzina conceived the idea of having Joséphine's former tiny school desk brought into the house and placed near the stove. The school was buried in snow up to the tops of its three small windows; its door was completely covered. Even when it had been freed of its encumbering snow, it refused to open. It had sagged of its own weight, and water had collected on its surface and frozen it solid to the jamb. They had to force it with a pickax and pour boiling water into its joints. Hippolyte had grumbled that if Luzina was so keen about having Joséphine's desk, she should have told him so before winter. One day, all the same, he came in carrying the rough little piece of furniture in his arms; it was damp from its long stay in the schoolhouse, and here and there it was powdered with snow.

Joséphine's tiny desk! Despite her obstinacy in asking for it during the last several weeks, Luzina would not have believed how eager she was to see it again. In her mind's eye the house was—for an instant—full of children, as in days gone by, each in his corner, studying his lessons out loud. Joséphine was the shrillest of all—yet she herself in those days had not adequately understood her little girl's ambition and had sometimes teased her for wanting to become as learned as Mademoiselle. She rushed to the sideboard to find Joséphine's most recent letter. It was Joséphine's first year as a teacher. She had written: "Dear Mama, when I went into my classroom this morning and I saw the children's faces turn toward me, I certainly thought of you. This happiness I in large part owe, dear Mama, to your spirit of sacrifice, to your devotion. . . ."

During her lifetime Luzina had read as many novels as she had been able to lay her hands on. Almost all of them had made her cry, were their endings sad or happy. It was simply that stories' endings, in themselves, induced in her regret beyond consoling. The lovelier the tale had been, the more did she grieve to see it end. Yet in what novel issuing from an author's pen had she beheld a better-managed ending, one more satisfying than that which crowned her own life—and one to make her weep more tears! "Deep thanks from the bottom of my heart . . . your devotion . . . your self-sacrifice . . . you it was who gave us a taste for learning. . . ." Joséphine expressed herself as well as they do in books. Her even, careful handwriting lent weight, as Luzina saw it, to sentiments already so well put. The summit of all difficult things for her consisted in apt words written in a steady hand with letters clear and well shaped. Respectfully she recognized this in the most unfamiliar expressions Joséphine used: the ideal, vocation, fulfillment of personality. She lingered over it also in Edmond's letters, but here it was less striking; Edmond did not have a fine handwriting. To think, though, that he was finishing his medical studies at Laval University, in that same city of Quebec from whence Mademoiselle Côté's old Governor had replied with the mouths of his cannon! Could they even have suspected, in the days when they heard about Frontenac at the Water Hen, that Edmond would one day with his own eyes see the citadel of French resistance! And thus Luzina glimpsed, at times, her own strange greatness through this ultimate distance separating her from her children.

Nevertheless, a little further on in Joséphine's letter she wrinkled her forehead: "Now that I'm earning something," Joséphine wrote, "I shall assume responsibility for the education of one of the children. It's certainly my turn. You realize that we can't neglect little Claire-Armelle. So I hope that within a few years you'll be able to send her to me. . . ."

No, certainly not! The priest uncle had had three children. Aunt Blanche three more. Dr. Pambrun of Saint Boniface had had Edmond, whom he was helping in his studies. The South had attracted others who had been keen to live nearer their fellows. Some few were not very far away, true enough, married and settled at Rorketon and Sainte Rose du Lac. All of them, what was more, were eager to have Luzina and Hippolyte near them. "Why continue to live on the Water Hen?" they asked. Luzina had made a grand tour to see them all again. But at Winnipeg she had felt lost. It was not at all the city she remembered from the days of her honeymoon. The Parliament building had seemed fearful to her, icy, and the buffaloes even heavier than she recalled them. Moreover, she could never again have all her children around her. When she would be in the South, she would think of those who were at Rorketon and on the ranch; at Rorketon she missed those at Saint Jean Baptiste; from Saint Jean Baptiste her thoughts would flit to Dauphin; and so it went. It was during her visit in civilized parts, likewise, that she best heard the plaintive, monotonous call, the persistent call, of the little water hens. She had come back the quickest way she knew with her small Claire-Armelle, who had accompanied her on the great tour.

This one the good Lord had given her to be the staff of her old age.

Yet the days were long. Writing to every corner of the land did not wholly use up the winter hours. The snow fell against the panes in moist flakes which were kept from sliding down by the black wooden mullions; little by little these supports piled the snow up until it almost blocked each pane. You could look outdoors through a narrow strip of glass just the width of the eye peering through it. The metal doorknob was covered with rime and colder to the touch than an icicle.

To while away the time, Luzina one day took the small "surprise" by the hand and led her to Joséphine's writing desk. Still heavy and plump, Luzina could just squeeze onto one edge of the desk. The wind was howling. Close beside her tiny daughter, Luzina began showing her her letters. "That's A," said Luzina. "A like your brother Aimable, A like little Armelle."

In a short time, in two or three years perhaps, the pupil had a better hand than her teacher. At least Luzina thought so. The content of the letters, all the things she must not forget to remind them about—health, good conduct, generosity of heart—remained Luzina's province. But for that which would be visible to the mails, to the postman, to that intermediary between herself and her children's pride, which must not be wounded, Luzina turned to Claire-Armelle.

From then on the letters which left the Little Water Hen were written along the usual slope, but the envelope bore another calligraphy. It was a handwriting extremely careful, childishly accurate. When they examined the envelopes closely, Edmond and Joséphine could make out the not wholly erased pencil lines which Luzina had drawn to help the small girl write straight.

And Luzina's educated children momentarily felt their hearts contract, as though their childhood back there, on the island in the Little Water Hen, had reproached them for their high estate.

WHITE MUSKY

Scott Young

On the last Tuesday in April, Black Ab Magee was sawing wood behind the house when he heard a car coming in low gear through the mud of his lane. The day was raw, with low fast clouds, but Black Ab had laid aside his sweater while he sawed. Now he put the sweater back on and walked around the house. He was pretty sure he knew who had come, and he was right. The truck from the government muskellunge hatchery was standing by the front gate, and John McManus was getting out of the driver's seat.

Black Ab's big boots squished in the waterlogged soil as he walked, and his overalls flapped against his thin legs. John McManus, long-nosed, smiling, taller than Black Ab and almost as thin, waited for him at the truck. The two men shook hands warmly.

"How've you wintered, Ab?" John asked.

"Not bad, John. How about you?"

"Gets worse every year. The more money I get, the more desk work I have to do. Sure glad it's spawning time."

Black Ab had worked with John for twenty-two years—ever since John had come here, a raw-boned, diffident young man, to organize the first milking of the great muskellunge in Irishman's Lake—yet they had little more than that to say to each other. Perhaps it was because they knew that when men are friends there's no use jawing about it.

It was different, though, when the company came. News of a strange car travels fast on those rolling back roads, and these farmers, whose forebears a hundred years ago had fled an Irish famine to the Kawartha country of hills and lakes in central Ontario, knew the hatchery truck from years past and liked to listen to the kind of talk it brought.

Red Ab Magee, Black Ab's cousin, skirted the new green of his winter-rye field, climbed a couple of cedar-rail fences, and got there in time for the after-dinner tea. Fat and thin, bearded and shaven, young men and old, O'Connells and Fees and Deyells and McQuades came, too. They all crowded into Black Ab's kitchen, sitting on the rocking chairs and the black-leather settee and the floor, and some stood against the wall. Black Ab's three boys, home from school for the noon meal, sat in the wood box by the kitchen range, and his littlest girl sat on Black Ab's knee.

Prompted by a question here, or a comment there, Black Ab and John told stories then of the forty- and fifty-pounders they'd milked of spawn in other years. They talked of the battle scars they'd found on these ferocious fish, of the musky that had been starving until they removed the sucker stuck in its throat, of net-smashing monsters they hadn't been able to milk because they couldn't subdue them without hurting them.

When Black Ab was telling of a five-foot fish, he rubbed his whiskery chin and chuckled and said, "Wonder where that old lady keeps herself in the summertime. Some of those Yanks I guide would sure like to know, and for that matter so would I, so I could take 'em there and see the fun."

From his tone of voice, you knew he was really on the side of the fish like a fight manager who will send his boy against anybody in the world and never figure on his losing. Red Ab Magee, in a rare moment of perception, put his finger on that.

"You'd think them fish was personal friends of yours, Black Ab."

"All my friends is fish," said Black Ab, "and some of my cousins, too."

There was general laughter at that, a single soprano from Black Ab's large and comfortable wife, Minnie, a high giggle from the little girl on Black Ab's knee; and one of the Deyells said, "Wonder what you'll find down there this year, Black Ab?"

"Something interesting. We always do, eh, John?"

John smiled and nodded and there was a thoughtful silence, because everyone there understood the feeling that Black Ab Magee and John McManus had for these fish, from twenty-two years of guarding their birth and babyhood.

About two o'clock Black Ab and John got up, and the neighbor men got ready to go. Black Ab rolled up his oilskins and kissed Minnie and got in the truck beside John. They waved good-by and drove a couple of miles to pick up Lanny O'Connell. Young Lanny's wife didn't look too happy about it, but Lanny had known they'd be coming any day, and he was ready. From Lanny's they drove seven miles to the Duke of Bedford Tourist Camp on the north shore of Irishman's Lake.

John had the keys to one of the cabins and to the camp kitchen, and by midafternoon the men had unloaded the truck and were checking and mending nets in the sun on the grassy hillside. Lanny went back into the bush to cut some poles which would be pounded into the soft lake bottom to hold the nets. There was no one else around. The owner of this camp never came out from the city until the middle of May. The musky-milkers always had the place to themselves for the weeks they were here.

On the second morning, in a hard cold rain, they set out to stake nets. Black Ab, sitting in the stern of a skiff, handling the five-horse outboard which towed a punt full of nets, pointed at a huge snapping turtle climbing a gravel cliff on shore to lay her eggs. An early loon flew high overhead, cackling madly, and Lanny exclaimed, "Listen to that darn' loon laugh!"

"That loon ain't laughing," Black Ab said. "He's serious!" The three of them laughed hard at the old joke, and Black Ab had the feeling that always came with springtime and musky-milking and the awakening of the world again—the feeling that made him tell jokes, and laugh hard at others' jokes, and feel good. He felt good now, and the rain beat down on their oilskins and soaked the cotton gloves that would have been soaked soon anyway, and finally Black Ab nosed in to where they'd stake out the first net.

They worked with the precision of a gun crew. Black Ab and John placed the first stake and held it while Lanny pounded with the mallet; then they unrolled more net until they came to another stake to pound, and still another, until a single net like a fence stretched fifty feet out from the shore. That was the lead net. The heart net was easier. They set the stakes in a rough square with the nets strung between them. It was open at the entrance from the lead net and had a funnel-shaped passage leading to the final net, the pound net.

The big fish, nosing into the shallows to seek spawning places, would hit the lead net and turn out to go around it. They'd hit the heart net and circle it, looking for a way out, and the first outlet they'd come to would lead them along an underwater funnel and in through the bottom of the pound net. Fish being what they were, they circled there until the spawners came, seldom going back to the depths to find the small hole through which they had entered.

The three men staked out one net that morning, another that afternoon, the remaining two the following day. Lanny drove the truck to town for groceries and also brought back some beer, and they played three-handed cribbage that night in the cookhouse, stopping occasionally to throw more wood into the roaring kitchen range, uncapping beer as they needed it. They quit at ten and went to bed in cots right there in the kitchen because it was too cold to go to the cabins. The next morning at eight o'clock, after John had telephoned his hatchery to send a truck at noon for the first spawn, they set out to milk the muskies.

Black Ab, as usual, handled the skiff and Lanny bailed. The boats had been in water only these three days and were not yet watertight. John sat in the punt, towed behind the skiff over the choppy, gray water, which on this morning's reading was nine degrees warmer than freezing. It was in the first net, that first day of milking, that they found the albino muskellunge.

Black Ab saw her first. Looking ahead to the string of nets stretching out from the shore, gauging his wind and drift, he saw the long, rolling flash of white, and immediately he thought it might be the albino. In the instant it takes a man's mind to call up the possibilities, he thought of the times he had seen her before, the crashing, bait-smashing fight of her, and how he had kept silent to protect her from men who would want to boat such a sensational freak. He said nothing to these others who had never seen her or heard of her, because maybe it had not been the albino at all, maybe just the white belly of another large fish.

He brought the skiff quickly alongside the pound net and grabbed one of the stakes and stood up to look down into the ten-foot-square enclosure. He saw her clearly.

"Look in there, John," he said. "See it?"

The white shape swirled near the surface again, and they all saw the murderous undershot jaw.

"By the Lord Harry!" Lanny burst out. "It's a white musky!"

Black Ab jerked on the punt's towrope and clambered into the punt beside John. He pulled the punt into the passageway between the heart net and the pound net and flipped off the lines that lashed one corner of the pound net to a stake. He and John hauled on the heavy black nets.

Their gloves were soaked immediately, and the punt heeled far over with the weight of the net. They pulled it in until the bottom of it was only about eighteen inches under water. The white musky, splashing and threshing, was the largest fish in the net. Black Ab's expert eye estimated it at twenty-five pounds as it plunged furiously among the hundreds of other fish.

"It's the damnedest queerest-looking fish!" Lanny burst out.

"I never saw one before," John said, turning. "Have you, Ab?"

Black Ab nodded his head in quick jerks, but he said nothing. He was angry that this fish should be caught in a simple net and he cursed himself for being angry because, after all, she wasn't hurt and she could be released when her purpose was served. And yet he felt apprehensive and tense.

He picked up a large landing net, and John did the same. With quick selective sweeps through the dashing fish, they scooped out the unwanted varieties, flipping bass and sunfish and perch back into the water. The egg-eating carp were tossed to the floor of the skiff and the mud cats to the floor of the punt. After two or three minutes of fast work, only muskellunge were left in the nets.

"Let's get a look at her first," John said. "You bring her, Ab." He reached for the pile of enameled dishpans in the punt, placing one to his left in the stern.

Black Ab dipped his landing net into the water and moved it gently until it enclosed the head half of the albino; then he got his free hand under her belly and lifted her into the punt.

John took her flailing tail in his left hand, and clasped her to him with his right elbow, the way a man would hold a banjo. She struggled, and the men grunted and held hard, and her tail whacked the side of John's face.

"Steady, baby," said Black Ab gently.

The struggle ceased for a few seconds and John cupped his right hand under her belly and pressed slowly toward her tail, forcing the first thousands of eggs into the pan. They were the normal golden yellow. He pressed again and again, pausing occasionally to hold on hard when the albino rioted in his arms, while Black Ab struggled to keep her head in the enclosing net. The level of the eggs in the pan rose until the stream lessened and finally stopped.

The two men still held the big white fish in their arms. Usually when a fish had been stripped it was released. The only ones put back in the trap were females not quite ready to spawn, or males not yet needed for their fertilizing sperm.

"I think we should put her back in the trap," John said.

"We've got her eggs," Black Ab said. "Don't need nothing more."

John said, "If we let her go, sure as hell somebody is going to say why didn't we keep her."

"You mean for a zoo, or something?"

"Something like that."

Black Ab's anger at the albino came back. Maybe John sensed the way he felt.

"I've got to remember I'm working for the department," John said. "I wouldn't be doing my job if I didn't hold this one at least until someone told me to let her go."

John moved his end of the albino out over the side of the punt and, after a second's pause, Black Ab upended the landing net. The albino slid back into the water and lay sluggish with shock. Then she moved slowly against one side of the net, a few inches under the water.

With the eggs waiting in the pan, there was no time for talk. Black Ab dipped the net again and came up with one of the males. He was almost as hard to hold as the albino. The forcing process was the same, and when this fish had contributed his fertility to the eggs of the albino he was released gently in the open lake. Black Ab had another male ready, and then another, until John said that should do it. Black Ab dipped water from the lake and poured it carefully against the sides of the dishpan, so as to cause a minimum of disturbance among the eggs as it settled around and over them, reproducing as closely as possible the conditions of a normal nesting place.

John moved the half-full dishpan up under the punt's short deck and said he'd take over the hoisting while Black Ab did the milking. They switched often like this to rest. Black Ab placed a dishpan beside him and turned to receive the next female as John picked one from alongside the albino and slowly lifted her from the water.

They worked in silence, releasing all fish which gave eggs or sperm, returning others to the net. A few males they didn't need were left in the net in case there was a shortage of males another day. From six females they took about three quarts—roughly two hundred thousand eggs—and then they dumped the nets out of the punt back into the water. While Black Ab secured the nets to the stakes, he watched the albino sink slowly in the water.

They worked the other nets and pulled in to the jetty two hours later, their hands red and stiff from the cold. John carried seven dishpans of spawn to the boathouse, Black Ab hoisted the motor off the skiff to a rack ashore, and Lanny tossed the egg-eating carp into tubs to be killed, and the mud cats into fruit baskets to be picked up by anyone who wanted a free meal.

"Ab," John said, when he came back from the boathouse, "when did you see her before?"

Black Ab was brief. "Saw her get caught once and break a line and get away. Saw her make a pass another time. That's all."

Lanny came up. "I'll get the fire on," he said. "Got some frogs' legs I froze last year. Brought 'em down. I'm hungry."

"What I'll do," John said, "is phone Toronto and see what to do with her."

The men walked toward the cookhouse together.

When the man at the government buildings in Toronto was on the line, Black Ab listened to the conversation.

"It's a musky, all right," John said. "Pure white except for the fins and the tail."

There was a pause while the man in Toronto spoke.

"Well," John said, "Black Ab Magee here, he helps me every year with the musky-milking—he guides a little, too, between farming—he says he's seen her before a couple of times . . . Yeah, it sure is lucky, then . . . Well, sure, all right then, see you tomorrow morning."

John hung up the telephone. "That was the Deputy Minister of Lands and Forests. He says there's some sportsman's show has been asking for a big musky to put into a traveling aquarium. Figures they'd be tickled to death to get a rare one like this. He'll be up tomorrow to pick her up."

Black Ab set his stockinged feet on the floor and began pulling off his oilskins, seeing in his mind a scene near a boggy shore here on Irishman's Lake three years before, when an American he was guiding suddenly had jumped to his feet after a cast, fighting his rod and reel, and a great white fish had surged into the air, shaking in a mad dance at the spoons dragging from one side of its great jaws. He told the story.

"A doctor from Cleveland, the guy was," he said. "He hooked her on an old set of buffalo spoons."

"I'll bet she put up a fight," Lanny said.

Black Ab grinned. "The guy got one look at her and froze on the reel when she ran. She took everything, line and all."

John pulled three bottles of beer out from under the table and opened them. Lanny set a couple of frying pans at the back of the stove. Black Ab, in pants and shirt, hung his oilskins near the door, drank his beer and opened another bottle.

As a guide, he always kept track in his mind of where the big fish hit, because except for spawning time muskies live out their lives in the same hundred-yard stretch of water.

Sometimes, if he liked a fisherman, he'd tour these places where he knew big ones lived. He'd seen some of these ferocious fish hooked four or five times without being landed. But only one other time had he taken someone to where he'd seen the albino. It was a woman whose husband had been drunk for days in the lodge from which Black Ab did his guiding in the time he was able to take off from his farming; a fading woman in her thirties who sometimes had a look of desperation about her. He had wondered since what possessed him to take her to where the albino was, and the only thing he could figure was that it was the kind of thing people do sometimes, showing a hoarded treasure to try to ease someone in pain.

He'd chosen her bait. He'd skillfully directed her casts. But at the last moment, when he saw the albino following the bait in, he had withdrawn the prize, yelling, "Reel harder!" The bait had jerked ahead just as the big white fish struck. With a turning flash of white, half out of the water, she was gone again.

He had shielded the albino after that day. When they got back to the lodge and the woman said she'd had a strike from a fish that looked white, some people remembered that the Cleveland doctor, the year before, had said the same thing. Guests and guides asked Black Ab where they'd seen the fish. "Down by Muskrat Island," he said. "Right across the south face of Muskrat."

For days, Muskrat's south shore had been so crowded with boats that there was hardly room to cast, and since the woman and her husband had left, no one but Black Ab knew that the albino's home waters were really a good mile from Muskrat Island.

Black Ab thought of the albino flailing now at the strong nets that enclosed her. He thought of the luck of any fish's birth and survival: the luck that kept a piglike carp from finding and eating the eggs; the luck that in the case of this albino was multiplied, after birth, a million times because her color would catch the eye of any fish coming in to feed. And when she got bigger she'd stayed away from the cunning hooks and twirling baits. For twenty years, she'd been free, and then in the urge of propagation she'd hit the lead net and nosed into the heart net and then into the pound net, and now she was caught and a man in Toronto was coming to get her.

"What color would the egg be, that started the albino, John?" Lanny asked.

John, usually patient and courteous, seemed as preoccupied as Black Ab. "Damned if I know," he said briefly.

Black Ab took a third bottle of beer. Lanny tossed frogs' legs into the melted butter in the frying pans.

The truck from the hatchery, driven by a voluble, freckled kid, came just after they'd eaten. John told him where to find a tank that would hold the albino tomorrow for the trip from the nets to the jetty. The people in Toronto would bring a bigger tank, to take her from there. The boy wanted to go out to see the albino but John told him he'd better get back with the eggs. Black Ab thought briefly of the process of growth, from eggs to clouds of black fry, then to fingerlings, and finally to adults, released in open water, the perils of babyhood beaten by the care of men.

If they'd let the albino go, they'd have talked about her interminably. Now they scarcely mentioned her. They played cribbage in the afternoon and even Lanny, rebuffed by the silence, played without talking. They went to bed early, and Black Ab lay awake. He wanted to talk to somebody but now he couldn't talk to John, because John wasn't a farmer who owned his own land and did as he pleased. John worked for the department, and for the first time it was a barrier between the two men. The thought of talk turned Black Ab's mind to the sessions in his kitchen at home, telling the Deyells and McQuades and Fees and O'Connells and Red Ab, his cousin, about the queer ones. This was one he wouldn't enjoy talking about. He slept, finally, with a sense of oppression, and he had waked up and got the fire going and was outside in the warm spring morning when a truck from the hatchery, a larger truck from Toronto, and a car full of men arrived at nine o'clock.

The four men in the car piled out, dressed in city suits and topcoats and hats. John and Lanny came out of the cabin and Black Ab walked up with them. John introduced him to Norman Dahl, the deputy minister, a fit-looking middle-aged man. Black Ab and Dahl shook hands. The other three men were from the Department of Travel and Publicity. "Manna from heaven," one of them said, his voice rising above the general excited talk.

"We'll take the fish in the tank truck," Dahl said. "We can change the water along the way every few hours. The show is in Detroit right now. I think we can run this baby right down there. A great break for us, for publicity."

Black Ab said, "Guess it is."

"Did you eat breakfast?" John asked Dahl. "Haven't got much here, but we could dig up something."

"We ate," Dahl said. "Thanks all the same. We'd like to get back as soon as we can. That's why we came so early. I've got an appointment this afternoon but I really wanted to see this thing. Would it put you out too much to go straight to that net, get the fish, and bring her to shore? Then we can get going."

The freckled driver from the hatchery had brought a small tank which fitted in the punt, to bring the albino ashore in. Lanny loaned the deputy minister his oilskins, then stood with the others at the kitchen door as the skiff towing the punt churned away from the jetty.

The deputy minister sat with John on the middle seat of the skiff. He seemed excited, and he kept looking ahead to the nets they were approaching. He seems like a nice enough guy, Black Ab thought, although he wasn't sure exactly what kind of a guy he had expected to be a deputy minister. Black Ab noticed that John didn't talk much but lifted his head occasionally with a reluctant half-smile on his lean, thoughtful face to nod agreement with what his superior was saying.

Black Ab brought the skiff up close beside the pound net and pulled on the punt's towline and clambered in. John followed. Dahl was standing up in the skiff, rolling easily with the boat's movement, looking into the net exclaiming about the albino. Black Ab unlashed the line from a stake and he and John began hauling the net into the punt. The net grew quickly shallower and the albino flashed and whirled and spun with the other fish; with them and yet apart from them, like the star of a dancing show pirouetting among the lesser lights of the chorus.

Black Ab quickly picked up a landing net. "I'll hoist her out."

"We'll take her just as we would if we were spawning her," John said. "Bring her tail up toward me and I'll grab her and you hold her head in the net and we'll ease her into the tank."

Black Ab dipped the landing net carefully toward the albino. Because of the masses of smaller fish, which usually were cleared out before this operation began, it was harder to get the albino. Finally he caught her, reaching well outward as he did so, both hands on the handle as he hoisted the struggling fish into the air.

"This way!" yelled John suddenly.

Black Ab completed the motion he had started, straining on the looping, sidewise swing. The net flashed in a quick arc over the square bows of the punt and there was a monstrous splash as the albino hit the open water, a streak of light as she disappeared.

"Why–" yelled Dahl. "Why, you damn' dumb Irish farmer! Why, I'll be–"

John McManus didn't speak. He took out a handkerchief, blew his nose vigorously, then pulled his hat over his face and sat down.

Black Ab's face took on a sudden merry smile. "Now, wasn't that a damn' queer thing to do?" he said.

"Damn' queer isn't the word," Dahl spluttered. "It was, it was–"

"All the same," Black Ab said, "that's what I done."

And that night, when news of the albino should have been startling sports-page readers in Toronto, when the first astonishing word should have been passed over the loud-speaker at the sportsman's show in Detroit, Black Ab sat at his kitchen table in the flickering lamplight. The word had traveled through the valley of Irishman's Lake, and Red Ab Magee was there from his farm, and so were O'Connells and Fees and McQuades and Deyells.

Black Ab told them he'd been fired, and why, although he didn't look as sad as he would have if it had happened another way. The room shook with laughter when he described the faces on the jetty as he brought the skiff and punt and the empty tank and the speechless, angry deputy minister back from the nets, and how fast the Toronto men struck off out of there for the city, mad as hornets.

"John drove me home," he said.

"He did?" said one of the Deyells.

"Did he say anything?" asked Red Ab.

Black Ab grinned. "Just as he let me out at the gate he said that the deputy minister had said what I was officially–a damn' dumb Irish farmer. As far's he's concerned, he said, all very unofficial, he said, I'm just an Irishman, and let it go at that."

They all laughed again, and his boys stopped even the pretense of doing homework on the kitchen table to grin at their dad, and the littlest girl reached up from his knee and rubbed her hand softly over the whiskers on Black Ab's cheeks and chin.

VIGNETTES OF FRENCH CANADA

Thomas B. Costain

THE FIRST SETTLER

I

Quebec in 1620. It must be confessed at once that the cradle of New France was little different from what it had been at the start. Perhaps the dreams and hopes and determinations of the loyal souls who clung to the base of the rock had already created an atmosphere of solidity, but physically it was far removed from a realization of Champlain's vision. Seven years later the resolute founder gave the population as sixty-seven, including children, and so it may be assumed that at this stage there were no more than fifty people in the settlement.

The huddle of hastily constructed buildings still stood among the walnut trees, but they were beginning to leak and show signs of collapse. Other houses had grown up around them, all of which were just as unsubstantial and dreary. Along the waterfront were wharfage facilities and some rude storage sheds.

Between the summit towering overhead and the little settlement hugging the riverbanks there was nothing but a steep, winding path; in summer nothing to break the browns and greens, in winter no cheerful glimmer of light against the solid blanket of snow. The summit was bare also. Some efforts had been made to clear the ground, and the stumps of what had once been noble trees now cluttered that lofty expanse, waiting for the settlers who would haul them out and set oxen to plowing the ground.

Off to the east the high line of the hills sank rather sharply until it leveled off in a thick tangle of woods where the St. Charles joined the St. Lawrence. Here, where Cartier had built his forts, the Récollet fathers had established themselves in a log building surrounded by a square palisade. The Récollets were an offshoot of the Franciscans, the order which St. Francis of Assisi had conceived to aid the lowly and tend the sick and cheer the downtrodden. The original purpose of the founder had been obscured over the centuries, and the Franciscans had become powerful and even wealthy. The result of this had been the breaking away from the parent body of dissenting groups for the purpose of getting back to the original conception. The most rigid of these were the French Récollets, known sometimes as the Franciscans of the Strict Observance, a mendicant body wearing the pointed capuche and dependent on charity for their daily bread. It happened that a Récollet convent had been established near Brouage, and on one of his visits to his home Champlain went there and made clear how much the colony needed spiritual assistance. The Récollets agreed to send out a group of their members, but with the understanding that the expenses of the venture would be provided, they themselves having not so much as a single coin. Champlain at this point stood at the peak of his organizational powers. He visited Paris, where the States-General was in session, going from bishop to bishop and stating his needs. The leaders of the French Church, despite a feeling of contempt among them for the lowly friars, subscribed the sum of fifteen hundred livres to be used in the purchase of vestments and supplies. Four of the friars had volunteered eagerly for the mission, Joseph le Caron, Jean d'Olbeau, Denis Jamay, and Pacifique du Plessis.

II

"I hope the cutting is good. Now for the sewing," said Catherine de' Medici, Queen Mother of France, after her favorite of the three sons who succeeded each other on the throne, the weak and vindictive Henry III, had seen to it that his chief political opponent, the Duc de Guise, was assassinated. The Queen Mother seems to have had grave doubts about the sewing. She had long been in bad health, and there were many who declared that after the massacre of St. Bartholomew's, which she instigated and managed, she never knew real peace of mind. Whether or not the ghosts of the slaughtered Huguenots came back to haunt her dreams, it is certain that she strove hard to keep at a distance the one enemy she feared, death. She kept about her always a large staff of physicians and listened hungrily to the advice they gave her. All to no avail: she did not live to see the results of the sewing (they were most disastrous) but died thirteen days after the body of Henry of Guise lay stretched on the floor of the royal anteroom.

One of the physicians who thus failed to do anything for the guilt-ridden Queen bore the name of Hébert. He had a son called Louis, and it is likely that the boy had opportunities to see court life with his own eyes. It was not an edifying spectacle at this point in French history, but it had one advantage: the royal chambers buzzed continuously with talk of the great country across the Atlantic. The boy grew up with a deep desire to keep far away from royal courts and to have a personal share in the settling of Canada.

He followed his father's example and became an apothecary, perhaps as a means to an end. At any rate, he was the first to answer the summons and sail with the Sieur de Poutrincourt when that gallant gentleman voiced the need for an apothecary in his company for Acadia. The disastrous ending of that venture did not lessen Hébert's enthusiasm. He reopened his shop in Paris, but his mind was fixed on a land where mighty rivers flowed through the silence of great forests and he took little interest in the mixing of laxatives and the rolling of pills. When Champlain came to him in 1616 and offered what seemed like splendid terms to go to Quebec as resident physician and surgeon for the company, he accepted gladly. He was to be maintained for three years and receive a salary of two hundred crowns a year. Hébert promptly sold his shop and his house in Paris and the next year took his wife and family of three to Honfleur for embarkation.

Here a shock awaited him. The Boyer element was in the saddle at the moment, and the only sentiment which prevailed was the desire for more and still more profits. The bewildered Hébert was told that Champlain had exceeded his authority and that the agreement would not be honored. He would receive only one hundred crowns a year for the three years, and after the term of the arrangement expired he must serve the company exclusively for nothing. He must never dabble in the fur trade, and if he became a raiser of produce he must sell everything to the company at prices they would fix.

The brusque gentleman who informed him of this late change of heart on their part had an agreement drawn up for Hébert to sign. He realized that he had no choice in the matter. He had disposed of his shop, he had cut loose from his snug moorings, and now he could not turn back. He signed the scandalously unfair paper and took his worried family aboard the ship for the New World.

The ship landed at Tadoussac on a warm summer day, with the sun bright overhead and an invigorating breeze blowing across the majestic river. The first settler went ashore with hopes so high that no thought of the chicanery of the directors came up to disturb him. It did not matter that the chapel in which a Récollet father said Mass was a flimsy structure made out of the branches of trees and that a cloud of mosquitoes descended upon them. It did not matter later that the Indians who watched them land at the dilapidated supply sheds in Quebec were dirty and practically naked and openly sullen. This was the New World, and to stout Louis Hébert the great wall of rock above the tumble-down houses in the grove was a symbol of the new world which would rise about it. He was so anxious to begin that he could not tolerate a day's delay. Up the steep pathway he led his family to inspect the ten acres which had been allotted to him on the crest. There they spent the first night under a tree. The exact spot where the tree stood is still pointed out to curious visitors.

Louis Hébert soon demonstrated that he was of the true pioneering breed. No repining for him over the lost ease of his comfortable shop on a fashionable street in Paris, no sulking over the bad faith of the company. He set to work at once and cleared a considerable stretch of the land. The temporary house he set up for his small family and the one domestic who had followed them out was soon replaced by a permanent one, a substantial structure of stone. All that is known of this first real house to be reared on Canadian soil was that it was of one story, the length thirty-eight feet, the width nineteen feet.

Here the Héberts seem to have been happy. Certainly they were industrious. The vegetables they grew on their fertile acres soon supplied all of the less fortunate families on the riverbanks; and for this, under the terms of the unfair agreement, they received no pay. At the same time the head of the family acted as physician and dispenser to the whole colony.

With Champlain he was always on the best of terms, not blaming the founder for the repudiation of the first agreement. It is said that Champlain, who was now fifty years of age and was beginning to fill his doublets with a degree of amplitude, plodded up the steep path frequently to visit the Héberts, his dog Matelot at his heels. There was another reason for the frequency of his visits: he liked to look down over the river and the country which stretched to the south and to think of the day when all this land would be as thickly settled as Normandy or Touraine.

As physician to the colony Louis Hébert had his reward in the love and often expressed gratitude of the people he served. Fortunately he was to receive more tangible evidences. In 1621, when a proper legal system was inaugurated in Quebec, he was appointed King's procurator in the first court of justice. In 1623 he was given full title to the land on the summit and was admitted to the ranks of the minor gentry. The following year he received an additional grant of land on the banks of the St. Charles, with which went the title of Sieur d'Epinay. He had become reasonably prosperous. His children had grown up and married and had built around the comfortable parental home. Paris had become no more than a dim memory; the new life had been infinitely more satisfying than an existence on the edge of the royal court.

The first Hébert daughter, Anne, married Etienne Jonquit but died soon after in 1620. The second daughter, Marie Guillaumette, married Guillaume Couillard in 1621, a carpenter who had arrived in Quebec a year before the Héberts. They raised a family of sturdy children, and from this fine stock a line descended which has never been broken and has played a prominent part in French-Canadian history.

It was a severe loss to the colony when Louis Hébert suffered a fall and died on January 25, 1627.

THE MAN WHO WAS ALWAYS FIRST

I

Of all the Frenchmen who listened to the call of the wild, Etienne Brulé was perhaps the most rash but also the most daring and enterprising. The records do not supply a description of him, but it is not difficult to achieve a mental picture of this wild and unfortunate man. It is known that he was extraordinarily strong. In his last appearances among white men he was dressed like an Indian, his powerful torso bared to the waist and tanned as brown as walnut. His hair, it may be guessed, was shocky and coarse. His eyes, when he became angry, which was often, had a reddish glint in them. He had gone native, living as the Indians did, taking brown-skinned wives wherever he went and putting them away as his fancy dictated. Father Gabriel Sagard, who was his friend, acknowledged sadly that Brulé was "much addicted to women."

After the failure of the expedition against the Iroquois, Brulé began on the travels which would have made him famous if his achievements had not been blotted out by a final act of treachery. He went down the Susquehanna and reached the northern tip of Chesapeake Bay. On his way back he was captured by the Iroquois but made his escape by a lucky accident. He had been the first to ascend the Ottawa, crossing to the Mattawa and following its course to Lake Nipissing and the French River, thus establishing the route to the Huron country. He had also been the first to set eyes on Georgian Bay. Making his way through the Inner Passage, he had reached Lake Huron.

His failure to return to Quebec convinced Champlain that his onetime servant had been killed. No one could have been more completely alive and active. Brulé's first move after returning to the Huron country was to lead a party past Michilimackinac and so out to the waters of Lake Superior, the Grand Lac. Some historians believe that to his list of "firsts" should be added the discovery of Lake Michigan. If he failed to reach it, Michigan was the only one of the Great Lakes that he overlooked. He saw all the others first.

He took no notes, he drew no maps, he wrote no stories of his travels; but the verbal reports he gave of what he had seen left no doubts as to the truth of his statements. In all probability there was no serious purpose back of his wanderings. He liked to be on the move, to have a paddle in his hands, his eyes fixed on the farthest horizon. Had he shared the scientific interest of the men who came after him and followed the trails he blazed, his name would have headed the list of early American explorers.

II

It was known to Champlain that Kirke's ships had been guided up the St. Lawrence by Frenchmen, and he encountered two of these renegades when he reached Tadoussac as a prisoner on his way to England.

The English commander had left a garrison at Quebec under Lewis Kirke and was taking all his important prisoners of war with him. Champlain, the most unhappy and weary of men, was allowed to go ashore when they reached the mouth of the Saguenay, and it was here that the two men were pointed out to him as having belonged to the party of four who acted as guides to the enemy. The governor's indignation caused him to approach the guilty pair, who hung back with a shamed air and seemed anxious to get away. To his astonishment and sorrow, he recognized one of the brown and unkempt fellows as Etienne Brulé!

Champlain's ire mounted to such a height that he proceeded to berate the pair at great length. A full version of what he said is contained in the *Relations*. It unquestionably has been rephrased, for it is a well-rounded and somewhat stilted harangue and not in the heated terms in which Champlain probably expressed himself. The picture of the scene that is given, however, can be accepted as an accurate one. It is recorded that Brulé, holding his head down and shuffling in the extremity of his embarrassment, made no defense save to say that he knew the French garrison had no hope of resisting successfully and so it had not seemed to him wrong to act with the English.

The former servant of the governor, whose exploits in the field of exploration had been so creditable and, in fact, astounding, but who now would be remembered chiefly for this act of treachery, slunk away and was never seen again by men of his own race. Word of his doings reached their ears, however, and it is possible to tell briefly of his last days.

When he guided the English ships up the estuary to the foot of the rock, his period of achievements and, yes, glory came to an end. From that stage on he failed to add anything to his record. Apparently the urge to set out on new quests had left him. No longer was he filled with a desire to plant his moccasined feet on new trails or to dip his paddle in strange waters. He went back to the Huron country and spent the balance of his days there, a slothful and degraded existence. Perhaps he became bitter of temper and quarreled with the tribesmen in whose midst he lived. He had settled down in the village of Toanché on Penetanguishene Bay, a spot of great natural beauty. One day the Indians turned on him and by force of numbers (he was a man of considerable personal strength and could not have been worsted in single combat) succeeded in beating him to death. Having killed him, they decided they might as well benefit in the usual way. They cut up his body and boiled it in the kettles, and then they gathered in a wide circle and proceeded to consume all that was left of this ungovernable young Frenchman (he was only forty-one when he came to his end) who, in spite of everything, deserves to be remembered for the greatness of his exploits.

THE KING'S GIRLS

"Some of them are *demoiselles* and tolerably well brought up," wrote Talon to Colbert in France, in speaking of the 109 King's Girls who had been sent to New France that year. He had asked for young ladies, knowing that those who had come earlier had too often deserved the comment of Marie de l'Incarnation, *canaille*.

The King's Girls were the young females who were shipped out to provide the unmarried men of the colony with wives. It was not a new idea when

Louis the Paternal Tyrant began it: the English had sent King's Girls to Virginia and the Spanish to their colonies in the Indies. It was a situation made to order for writers of romance, and many stories have since been published over the years about girls of great beauty and good family who ran away from home and escaped by joining the colonial shipments, always finding the husband of their hopes and dreams.

It is doubtful if any girls of the nobility came to Canada under such circumstances. The closest approach to a romantic atmosphere, in fact, is contained in the brief reference above by Intendant Talon. The *demoiselles* he mentions were girls with good backgrounds and even a little education. They were wrangled over and selected and married, probably to military officers or men of more than average property. They were happy or unhappy thereafter according to their dispositions and the luck they had had in finding compatible mates.

Many hundreds of the King's Girls were sent out over the two decades when the need for them was felt. As many as 150, in fact, arrived at one time. They came mostly from the northwestern provinces of France, from Normandy, Brittany, and Picardy. The preference seems to have been most decidedly for peasant girls because they were healthy and industrious. Girls from the cities did not prove as satisfactory; they were inclined to be lightheaded, lazy, and sometimes sluttish, and the sturdy young habitants had no desire for wives of that type even though they might be prettier and trimmer than the broad-beamed candidates from the farms.

It is very doubtful if any girl of high degree fleeing from an elderly suitor (the reason most often employed in the romantic stories) or for political reasons could have succeeded in enrolling for Canada. The candidates were looked over carefully, their birth certificates were examined, and their recommendations from parish priest or confessor were read and considered. There were a few occasions when mistakes were made and girls were admitted who had either been guilty of loose conduct or had criminal records. The exceptions had been frequent enough to justify the comment of Marie de l'Incarnation and to explain the slighting descriptions of an officer named La Hontan who visited the colony and wrote a book which contains the fullest information available on this matrimonial traffic. There were even a few cases where women who had been married were brought out. What happened to them when they were caught is not explained. Probably they were submerged in the ducking stool or publicly whipped before being sent back. A wife's status under French law was pretty much that of a chattel. It was almost impossible, for instance, for her to regain her freedom. Infidelity on a husband's part was not acceptable as an excuse. Only if he beat her with a stick thicker than his wrist could she claim the right of separation.

It is La Hontan who tells what happened when the girls arrived in the colony. They landed, of course, at Quebec, where they were looked over by the local swains. There were sometimes bitter complaints that the best were snapped up in Quebec and the culls were then sent on to Three Rivers and

Montreal. On first landing, after making the long journey under stern duennas appointed by the government, they were placed in three separate halls for inspection. What basis was used for determining to which hall a girl should be sent is not stated, not even by that arrant gossip, La Hontan. Were they divided according to weight or coloring or even according to social background? Whatever the arrangement may have been, it permitted the authorities to direct the young men who came seeking brides to the particular hall where they were most likely to find a suitable choice.

The girls had the privilege, of course, of refusing any candidates who might want them. It is on record that they did not hesitate to ask questions of the embarrassed swains who paused in front of them; presuming that the girls were drawn up in lines or elevated on platforms like slaves at an auction or as they were on occasions in the French provinces when the glove was up for a Giglet Fair and candidates for domestic service were scrutinized by questing employers. Among the questions they were likely to ask were the following:

"How many acres do you have cleared?"

"How many rooms are there in your house?"

"Does it have wooden floors? How many windows? Does the hearth draw well?"

"Have you a proper bed and plenty of blankets? How wide is it? Is it made of cypress wood or sassafras or cherry?"

"Have you a horse? How many cows, pigs, and sheep? How many chickens?"

"How much money have you saved?"

"Are you addicted to drink?"

"Are you of clean habits?"

It was seldom, however, that they carried things to the point of a refusal, for that was a chancy proceeding. They had come out to find husbands, and it behooved them to take advantage of an offer. They did not want to be among those who were passed over by all the shuffling, staring, arch males who filed through the halls. Some, alas, failed to find favor and had to be content with domestic service for the rest of their lives. An unwanted King's Girl was a tragedy, her lot sadder than that of a confirmed spinster, for she had publicly proclaimed her willingness to be chosen. She invariably became soured and ill-tempered, the target of sly jokes and innuendoes as long as she lived.

La Hontan says the plumpest girls were taken first, and this undoubtedly was true. The bachelors wanted healthy partners who could be depended on to do their share, or a little more, of the work. A bad complexion or a squint could be overlooked if the figure was buxom.

The truth might as well be stated at once: there was little of romance in the coming of the King's Girls and their absorption into the life of the colony, little more than at a sale of livestock. The marriages followed immediately after the selection, priests being on hand to conduct the ceremony and notaries to make out the necessary papers. The girls would be dressed in their best; but their best, poor forlorn waifs, would not be very gay or suitable. Some undoubtedly would have nothing to wear but the cardinal cloaks they had used on the sea voyage, with the hoods folded back. None of them would have the finery of a bride with parents to fit her out properly: gloves with drawstrings of silk, three-cornered hats with jaunty pompons on top, whalebone stays to make her look slim or *criardes* to stiffen out her skirts. Perhaps a few of them would be lucky enough to have trussing chests, the equivalent of the modern hope chest, with a few treasured odds and ends in the secret compartment, the *till*, as it was called.

The men, on the whole, would be better dressed. They would have on their long-tailed coats (of red cloth in Quebec, of course) with turned-up cuffs and immense side pockets or, if they had saved up enough to be a little festive, a cool ratteen capot which was made with stiffeners and flared out from the waist.

Each couple was given an ox and a cow, two pigs, a pair of chickens, two barrels of salted meat, and eleven crowns in money. This started them off well.

The result of these hasty marriages was to create a belief that the bracing climate of Canada was particularly advantageous to women. "Though the cold is very wholesome to both sexes," wrote Dollier de Casson from Montreal, "it is incomparably more so to the female, who is almost immortal here." The need for children was considered of such importance that the innumerable letters carried back and forth across the Atlantic, many of them in the King's own hand, were concerned largely with the problems of multiplication. It was even believed that marriages between Frenchmen and Indian girls could be a useful factor, and Mère Marie was said to favor the idea of finding husbands among the colonists for the Indian maidens. Talon conducted an inquiry into this before he returned to France the second time. But he reached an adverse opinion. The young squaws, he reported, did not bring many children into the world because they nursed them too long. This was a fortunate finding: otherwise the resourceful monarch would have found some ingenious regulation for the encouragement of miscegenation.

Talon's reports on the King's Girls were more favorable. In 1670 he stated that most of the young women who had arrived the year before were pregnant already. His information proved to be perfectly sound. In the following year nearly seven hundred children were born in the colony.

THE MAIDEN AT CASTLE DANGEROUS

October 22, 1692

The particular section of Canada which was most open to Indian attack lay along the banks of the St. Lawrence from Three Rivers to Montreal and beyond. In this vulnerable area stood a fort which was called Castle Dangerous because of the excessive peril in which its inhabitants existed. This was Fort Verchères, which was on the south bank of the river, about twenty miles below Montreal. It was therefore only a short distance from the Richelieu River, the route taken by Iroquois war parties. The mouth of the Richelieu was always under watch and guard, and the wily redskins had fallen into the habit of leaving the water before reaching the junction point with the St. Lawrence and striking inland. After a few miles they would find themselves in sight of the fort and blockhouse (connected by a covered passage) of Verchères. It had suffered so many attacks and alarms that the inhabitants thereabouts lived in constant dread.

Castle Dangerous belonged to the Sieur de Verchères, who had been an officer in the Carignan regiment. He had settled down with more good will and determination than most of his fellow officers and had been reasonably successful over the years.

A curious spell of overconfidence seems to have invested the Verchères domain on this morning of October 22. The seigneur was on duty at Quebec and Madame de Verchères was in Montreal. It had been a good season in spite of the constant alarms which had kept men as well as women indoors. The fields were high with waving corn, the pumpkins were ripe and yellow, the last of the melons remained to be gathered, and the trees were laden with fruit. The sun had been so bright and cheerful this fine October morning that the settlers had decided to risk gathering this bountiful harvest. They were out in the fields, and the cheerful sound of their voices could be heard from all parts of the cultivated area as they labored with sickle and hoe.

The fourteen-year-old daughter of the family, Madeleine, was at the wharf on the riverbank, which was close to the main entrance of the fort. The settlers had a name of their own for wharves, calling them *mouille-pieds*, which meant "wet feet"; but this did not concern small Madeleine (from the descriptions available she seems to have been petite and rather pretty) because she was probably expecting her mother from Montreal and so would not have dared put on her best kid-topped shoes with tasseled drawstrings. A hired man whose name was Laviolette was with her.

A sound of musket fire reached them from the direction of the fields where the settlers were at work. Laviolette, with his greater height, could see more of what was happening than the girl. In a voice of great panic he cried: "Run, mademoiselle, run! The Iroquois!" She saw then that the fields had filled almost in the winking of an eye with naked top-knotted warriors screeching their triumphant battle cries and killing the unarmed workers as fast as they could run them down.

She turned and made for the fort, followed by the man Laviolette. Her mind was filled with supplications to God and the Holy Virgin but at the same time busy with thoughts of what might be done. There were only two soldiers in the fort, she knew, in addition to her two brothers, aged twelve and ten, a very old man of eighty or thereabouts, and a number of women with infant children. They reached the fort uninjured in the face of a heavy spatter of Iroquois bullets.

"To arms! To arms!" cried the girl.

Outside the gate were two weeping women who had seen their husbands cut down and killed by the fierce marauders, and it required a firm hand and a display of confidence, both of which the child managed to achieve, to get them inside. Madeleine closed the gate herself and drove the crossbeams into place.

She found the two soldiers in the blockhouse, which was safer than the somewhat dilapidated fort. One had hidden himself and the other was standing over a budge barrel of powder with a lighted fuse in his hand.

"What are you going to do?" she cried.

The man answered in a quavering voice, "Light the powder and blow us all up."

"You are a miserable coward!" said the girl, driving him away from the ammunition supply.

She proceeded then to instill courage into the huddled group about her. They must fight as though they were all soldiers and numerous enough to hold the Indians off, she said, and perhaps God, Who was watching them as she spoke, would send them help in time. The rest were encouraged by her words. First her two young brothers and then the soldiers in a shamefaced silence took guns to the loopholes and began to fire on the Indians in the fields. By running from one loophole to another, while the women loaded the guns for them, they were able to create the impression that a sizable garrison held the fort.

Neither time nor space is available to tell in full detail the story of what followed. For a week the little band of defenders kept up their brave pretense. The four men, counting the octogenarian, the two boys, and the petticoated commander slept at intervals only and never at night. They stood guard in the bastion of the fort and at the loopholes in the blockhouse in the daytime, firing briskly when the bronze skin of a hostile warrior showed in the fields or in the cover of the trees. At night they paced the platforms to keep awake and kept up encouraging cries of "All's well!" at regular intervals. The gallant little band was so successful in its pretense of being an adequate and alert garrison that the Iroquois, still lurking in the woods, did not risk an attack. It became known later that the redskins held a council of war and decided that the chance of carrying a fort so well defended was slight.

During this week of effort and strain the meager garrison took their orders without question and drew their inspiration from the girl of fourteen. In the desperate moment of time when she had first seen the war party issuing from the trees she had ceased to be a child. An adult resolution had taken possession of her. Knowing the full weakness of her tiny band—the soldiers had displayed their clay feet in the first moments of the attack, her brothers were still children, the old man could do no more than dodder about the loopholes—she drove them with a fierce energy and never allowed them a moment's ease. She slept little herself and consumed the cold scraps of food which the women prepared with an eye on the fields and the line of trees. She preached at them and prayed with them when their will to go on wavered. She sometimes swayed unsteadily with the weight of the musket which she always carried (and used also to good effect), her face became pale and wan, her eyes were shadowed and deep-sunken. But never for a moment did she give way to her fears.

On the night of the seventh day a party of forty men arrived from Montreal under the command of Monsieur de la Monnerie, a lieutenant in the French army. They stopped at the landing place and hailed the fort, not knowing whether the defense still held out but fearing very much that they would find the Iroquois in possession. Madeleine had been dozing with her head on a table, her gun still in her arms. She roused herself and mounted the bastion.

"Who are you?" she demanded.

The answer came back in an unmistakably French voice, "It is La Monnerie, who comes to bring you help."

In a voice which seemed for the first time to show emotion, Madeleine ordered the gate to be opened. Leaving one of the soldiers there to keep guard, she ventured out alone into the darkness. When she met the lieutenant on the path, she stopped and saluted him.

"Monsieur," she said in a voice high-pitched with the first hint of hysteria, "I surrender my arms to you."

She was ready to drop with fatigue but she remained a good commander to the end. Her first thought was for those who had shared with her the long vigil. "Monsieur," she said to La Monnerie in a tone of great earnestness, "it is time to relieve them. We have not been off our guard for a week."

When she told the story later of these remarkable seven days, she made no mention of what followed immediately after the arrival of the rescuing party or of the emotions she felt. It may be assumed, however, that she did not allow herself to break down and that her tears were held back until she reached the privacy of her room. It may also be taken for granted that she slept the clock around and that the effects of her seemingly unending vigil were not easily shaken off. Did the maturity of character and mind which she had summoned so resolutely continue to govern her thereafter, or did she slip back into the fancies and humors of girlhood? One thing may be accepted, perhaps, that she began to insist on some grown-up privileges. It would be pleasant to think, for instance, that she was allowed to wear her kid-topped shoes whenever she chose and that she was allowed the right to have *considerations* on her skirts, the panniers which were deemed proper only when girlhood had been put behind.

Her full name was Marie Madeleine Jarret de Verchères and she was fourteen and a half years old when she thus earned for herself a place in Canadian annals with Adam Dollard and the heroes whose shades are in his train. She was summoned by the Marquis de Beauharnois, who held the post of governor when she was a young married woman, and told her story at his request, with proper dignity and simplicity. She was treated with the consideration she had earned and given a pension, a small one. Her husband was Thomas Tardieu de la Naudière, and she brought a number of children into the world. They lived in rather less parlous times and had no opportunity to emulate the deed of this remarkable girl who had become their mother.

THE TWO GREAT BROTHERS

I

March 2, 1699

Iberville knew that he had solved the mystery as soon as he saw the waters on the Gulf turning color. The brilliant blue in which they had been sailing had become grayish and the surface was distinctly agitated. He had no doubts that these were signs of a heavy inflow. Somewhere ahead, then, he would find the mouth of a great river; the Mississippi, he was sure—the Hid River, as the Spanish had begun to call it since La Salle's failure.

Later in the day the great French Canadian—for by this time Iberville had acquired a reputation which put him first in the esteem of his own people—saw a break in the banks ahead, marked by two tall rocks. Between these natural sentries a great body of water was rolling down with inexorable majesty. No Frenchman ever set eyes on the Mississippi without recognizing it; nor, in all probability, did anyone else. It could not be mistaken now, this turgid and magnificent stream, carrying to the Gulf the surplus water of the prairies and so much of the mud from the Ohio, the Missouri, and the Arkansas.

The small company, staring with fascinated eyes at the goal of their long voyage, crossed themselves in thanksgiving. Iberville, who had brought Bienville with him, the younger brother who was destined for great things also, found himself in a conflict of emotions. He was triumphant, of course, for he had come almost straight to the mouth of the river. At the same time he must also have been sad, thinking of the three brothers, Jacques, François, and Louis, who had died in battle and would never know that it had fallen to the lot of the Le Moynes to complete the work of La Salle.

Iberville's reputation as a military leader had grown out of a series of unusual exploits. He had led another land expedition to Hudson's Bay, which had been successful but had resulted in the death of the seventh brother, Louis, known as the Sieur de Châteauguay. Louis had been distinguished for bravery, even in this family of brave men. His was a young and heroic form of courage, reminiscent of that great figure of the preceding century, the Chevalier Bayard. It had led him to advance gaily and audaciously across open ground in an attack on the English fort, and a bullet had cut him down.

The exploits of Iberville were on the sea after this last land invasion. In charge of two small ships of war, the *Envieux* and the *Profond*, he won a naval battle off the St. John River and immediately after captured Pemaquid. Leaving these waters, he sailed to Newfoundland, taking possession of the island and sacking the towns and villages with realistic thoroughness. This unpleasant task over, he led a fleet of four ships of war into Hudson's Bay to take Fort Nelson and so made the French sweep complete. His lasting reputation is largely based on his brilliant success in this undertaking.

His flagship, the *Pelican*, carrying forty-four guns, became separated from the rest of the small fleet and found itself confronted on the somber waters off Fort Nelson with three English vessels, the *Hampshire*, the *Daring*, and the *Hudson Bay*, carrying 120 guns between them. Great naval commanders have always had two qualities, audacity and initiative. Iberville had these assets in a superlative degree and, because of the daring strategy he employed, he scored what is probably the most noteworthy victory in French maritime history; which, it must be added, is a rather barren page.

Keeping to windward of his opponents by the boldest of tactics, he sank the *Hampshire*, captured the *Hudson Bay*, and sent the *Daring* into hasty flight. The capitulation of Fort Nelson followed, and so the French, for the time being, had all of the great bay in their possession.

It was after this that Louis XIV, perceiving he had in Iberville an iron leader who always carried out his orders and always won, decided to make one more effort to seize the mouth of the Mississippi. His preference was to send some court favorite with a lofty title in nominal command, with Iberville to do the work, but he was finally persuaded that this habit of divided command always led to trouble. He gave in, and the brilliant young French Canadian was appointed to an undivided leadership.

II

After a week's slow progress up the Mississippi in small boats, the little party saw a wide curve in the river ahead of them. Standing in the prow of the leading *chaloupe*, Iberville had been keeping an observant eye on this exotic land in its spring stage of extravagant blossoming, realizing perhaps that someday a miracle would happen hereabouts. Now he looked closely ahead, and it came to him that the land above the bend was exactly what he had been seeking. It was low at the water's edge but rose slowly and steadily back from the shore. His hand shot out triumphantly to show where the remains of Indian huts marked the southern end of a portage. It was apparent to Iberville that this was the site for the great city he proposed to establish, a view in which his keenly observant younger brother fully concurred. It is perhaps superfluous to add that on the land they studied from the deck of the *chaloupe* there now stands a much larger and finer city than anything their imaginations had conceived, New Orleans.

Great military leaders have confidence in themselves or they would not dare the improvisations and risks by which battles are won. Iberville was no exception. It was only because he had a belief in his star that he had adopted such bold offensive tactics and had attacked the three ships which came against him on Hudson's Bay. It is not unlikely, however, that his assurance had been dampened somewhat by his reception at court before the command of the Mississippi venture was entrusted to him.

Louis XIV had kept such close personal supervision of Canadian affairs that he had come to regard the men and women of the colony as puppets moving in response to his tugging on the strings. The most colorful and effective of the puppets, the most rambunctious in its response to the pressure of the royal fingers, had been Iberville, but the King still seemed to consider him no more than a rather astonishing automaton. There had been no thought, apparently, of making use of his spectacular talents in any task which did not have to do with America.

Knowing the King's attitude, Iberville was still unwilling to accept the minor role in which he was being cast. To sit in a fever-ridden jungle and wait for a tiny post to grow into a flourishing colony was not a part that the hero of New France was prepared to play; he was too pre-eminently a man of action for that. Leaving Bienville in charge of the land operations, the bold Pierre sailed off to keep watch and ward on the sea. For seven years thereafter the eighth son remained in command of small forts, first at Biloxi, then at Mobile. He grew sallow from malarial infections in his veins and many times his patience wore thin, for nothing seemed to happen and his resources were so slight that he could do no more than hold his ground against the activities of Indians under such tribe names as the Bayougoulas and the Quinupissas who were as hostile as the Iroquois.

In the meantime the legend of French invincibility on land had been rudely jolted by the appearance on the European scene of English armies under the command of a great general named Marlborough. This unusual soldier defeated the French and almost annihilated one of the Sun King's armies at the battle of Blenheim, thereby breaking the power of Louis in Germany. Two years later he won another tremendous battle at Ramillies, which resulted in freeing the Low Countries from French invasion. The Sun King, as stubborn as ever and still unshaken in his confidence, recruited new armies and continued to entrust them to the command of generals who shared his reactionary ideas. It did not occur to him, apparently, to make use of the French Canadian who had never lost a battle on land or sea. Too many Frenchmen of high degree clamored for the command of regiments and brigades, and even armies, for a place to be made for Iberville.

Fate then intervened to remove the latter forever from any of the enhanced glory which he might have won in the continental wars. He was not to live long enough even to see the first crude settlement at the bend of the Mississippi nor to observe any material results from his rediscovery of the mouth of the Father of Waters. Sailing in the Caribbean with the sixth Le Moyne, Joseph de Serigny, he cast anchor off Havana Harbor. Three members of the crew had died with suspicious suddenness, and the two brothers suspected they had the plague on board. The suspicion became a certainty when the port surgeon visited the ship. The latter found, moreover, that the plague, which is no respecter of rank or authority, had visited the captain's cabin as well.

Iberville was taken ashore and placed in quarantine. The foul disease quickly strengthened its hold. He tossed for days in torment, babbling in his delirium. Only at brief intervals did reason pay him a fitful return. His brother was not allowed to come ashore, and so the brave Pierre faced the inevitable end alone. What were his thoughts during the brief moments when sanity returned? Despite the disappointments he had suffered, he knew that he had not yet reached the peak of his powers and he did not want to end his days so soon in a stinking Spanish lazaret. He raved perhaps of the great plans he had shared with his remarkable brothers, shouting "*Pointez à couler bas!*" as in his fevered fancy he stood on the quarter-deck of the *Pelican*, murmuring in lower tones of Longueuil with its four towers and high walls, which all of the valiant sons had loved so much.

There were only five of the Le Moynes left when the body of the great Iberville was put in the death cart and hurried away to an unmarked and never identified grave.

III

Twelve more years passed. The Mississippi colony, now located near Mobile, languished in great discomfort and privation, and nothing seemed to come of what they were attempting to do. A miracle would be needed to turn the palisaded shacks in which Bienville and his discontented men existed into a flourishing outpost of empire.

The miracle came to pass. A spectacular banker from Scotland named John Law persuaded the Duc d'Orléans, who had become regent of France on the death of Louis XIV, that a get-rich-quick scheme of his contriving was the tonic the country needed. The regent authorized the launching of a huge investment concern in 1717 called the *Compagnie de la Louisiane ou d'Occident*. The public was offered subscriptions in it at a price of 500 livres a share (there were 500,000 shares), and as there had to be tangible assets back of the company, it was given sovereignty over all of North America west of the Mississippi. The riches of Louisiana were dangled before the eyes of investors, and the people began to buy shares so eagerly that the value went up and up and one of the great booms of history started. In a very short time the whole nation was in the throes of a madness which later caused the scheme to be called the Mississippi Bubble.

In the meantime, of course, something had to be done to turn Louisiana into a bonanza land. The ever-loyal Bienville, sitting so patiently in his toy fort, received hurried instructions. He must provide at once a capital for the El Dorado into which Louisiana was to be turned, a place to which could be sent the shiploads of settlers the government was packing out immediately, and the soldiers and the King's Girls, and the mountains of supplies and building materials, and the guns. There could be no manner of delay; the first ships were sailing at once.

The genius for organization which had been dormant in Bienville all these years came to life. Remembering the land on the broad bend of the Mississippi which his great brother, now moldering in a Spanish grave, had selected as the best site for the projected capital, he moved his men there at once and set them to work. The place which had served as the terminal point of the portage was cleared off and made into the Place d'Armes of the new town. The north side of the square, looking down to the river, was selected for the cathedral; although for the time being the young leader could contrive nothing more than a shrine under a canopy of canvas. On each side of the square he built frame *casernes* (barracks) for the soldiers who were coming on the first ships. At the southwest corner he raised a hasty single-story building which would serve for administration purposes.

Streets were then cut through the woods and underbrush and small houses were run up hastily. With the addition of a great many tents, the capital of the new El Dorado (named New Orleans for the regent) was capable of housing in one way or another all the people due to arrive. Here was a second miracle, a man-made one, the credit for which belongs to Bienville.

Then the ships began to arrive at the mouth of the river and the place was quickly overrun. The new arrivals were a thoroughly unsuitable lot, as Bienville saw at one glance. His work as governor of this hastily thrown together metropolis was not going to be easy.

Back in France the Bubble burst. The company failed, thousands of investors were impoverished, John Law had to leave France in great haste and secrecy. The only thing that did not vanish was the capital of the new empire which Jean Baptiste le Moyne de Bienville was building and which was now crowded with disillusioned people. This part of the experiment had to go on.

A real and enduring miracle came about. Slowly the town grew as ways were found to use the resources of the river lands. Permanent buildings were erected, churches and schools as well as private residences of charm and individuality. The first personal wealth produced sent the possessors out to fine houses and plantations along the streams and bayous. Bienville never returned to Canada, he never married, and when he was allowed finally to retire he was an old man. He went to Paris to spend what was left of his life.

He was eighty-seven years old when Louis XV, who had very slight consideration for the obligations and responsibilities of kingship, decided to hand Louisiana to Spain. Bienville tried to intercede, to convince the King that the charming civilization which the people of the colony had created would wither and die under alien rule. The King would not see him, and the ministers were unsympathetic. Bienville died before the transfer was carried out officially, and it was generally believed that the blow had broken his heart.

THE DEATH OF THE GREAT BISHOP

May, 1708

Bishop Laval was dying. Quebec, which had always maintained an air of gaiety and sophistication even when a scowl above a black cassock had carried authority, paused and pondered what it would mean to be without him. A deep sense of impending loss took possession of the people of the town.

Visitors had always been impressed with the volatile spirits of Quebec. They had commented on the gay air of the town and, in particular, on the beauty and charm of the women. This had been in no sense an exaggeration. Often in the late evening hours, the still, cold air would fill suddenly with the high notes of feminine voices and with the last snatches of song as social circles dissolved and the members took their way homeward. The shadows cast by the high palisade Frontenac had built back of the heights were seldom untenanted, for here young lovers went for walks, and often the crunch of slow footsteps on the snow would evoke the same sharp *Qui vive?* as the old governor had heard from the sentries in the stone towers.

But the people of Quebec were as devout as they were gay, and so the loss of the old bishop was going to be deeply felt. They had been on his side in the main when they found that he and his successor were at odds. Laval had been so sure of the fitness of the Abbé Saint-Vallier that it had come as a shock to find that the new bishop did not share his convictions at all on certain points. Saint-Vallier was not inclined to place much importance in the seminary which he, Laval, had founded with so much enthusiasm and which he felt should be the very heart and core of spiritual life in the colony. A decree had been passed which limited the institution to the education of priests, and the number of directors had been reduced casually to five. The new bishop had accepted fifteen thousand francs from the King for the erection of an episcopal palace and the funds had been used for the purpose, so that now Laval in his bare little corner of the seminary could see the tall windows and fine glass of his successor. Saint-Vallier had been an ardent supporter of Denonville, even when the mistakes of that well-meaning but weak governor had brought Canada to the brink of ruin.

Troubles had multiplied on the head of the old man since his return from France. A scourge had carried off a quarter of the inhabitants of Quebec.

The seminary had burned down, and Laval, desperately ill at the time, had been carried half clad from his bed. It had been necessary for him to accept on behalf of himself and his staff the hospitality of the episcopal palace; although he had cringed no doubt from the evidences it presented of easy living. When the walls of the new seminary were halfway up, another fire swept the neighborhood and the work had to be started over again. The Spartan old prelate had removed himself before this from the comparative magnificence of his successor's abode.

Fortunately, because two such men could not have lived in peace together, Saint-Vallier had now been absent from Canada for the better part of ten years. The King, who generally had a shrewd grasp of the situation in his favorite colony, which was also his pet extravagance, had realized the danger in the open lack of unity between the two men. Perhaps he also had been disappointed in Saint-Vallier. At any rate, he summoned the new bishop back to France in 1700 and kept him there on various pretexts. In 1705 permission was granted him to return, and he set sail for Quebec in a ship called the *Seine*, which was taking out a million francs. Getting wind of this tempting cargo, perhaps, an English ship chased and captured the *Seine*, taking all the crew and passengers back to England. Saint-Vallier had been a prisoner of war ever since and he would remain in England for two years more. In his absence two of his assistants attended to the executive duties, but for spiritual guidance the people had turned back to Laval. He ordained the new priests, he presided at confirmation, he visited the sick and attended the dying. His face, wrinkled with age and reduced to boniness by the rigor of his fasting, was seen everywhere in spite of the infirmities which had gripped him.

The old prelate's asceticism had increased rather than diminished with the years. He still rose without fail at two in the morning and dressed himself hurriedly in the cold of his room. The tendency to varicose veins had become worse with the years, and as a result an unsteadiness had developed in his legs. It had become necessary to bind them every day, and in this he would allow no help. Stooping with great difficulty in the dark (for the use of candles was an extravagance) and groaning from the pain he was inflicting on himself, he took a long time at the task. Not until he was dressed would he light the charcoal in his brazier, and even in the depth of winter he allowed himself no better than a feeble fire, above which he would huddle as he turned to his morning devotions. At four he would be ready to set out for the cathedral, where he would celebrate the four-thirty Mass.

He could no longer venture out alone as he had done when he was young. An *engagé* at the seminary, Houssard by name, devoted himself to the service of the stern old man. Houssard would come to the bishop at four, his eyes heavy with sleep, to escort his master through the darkness of the streets. Sometimes the bishop was too weak to walk and Houssard would take him on his back. They must have cast a curious shadow when the *engagé*, carrying the thin figure pickaback, emerged on stumbling feet from the twisting and narrow streets into the full light of the moon.

The prelate spared neither himself nor the back of the devoted Houssard, for always he must go to the cathedral for later services on Sundays and saints' days. He must attend all funerals and respond to every request for his presence. The people of the town had become well accustomed to the sight of the old man being thus carried wherever duty called him. Nothing could be said to convince him that the time had come for him to rest.

He continued thus to tend the spiritual needs of the ill and the dying until it became only too apparent that his own end was close at hand. This was in 1707, and during the summer of that year it seemed that he could not rally from the weakness which had seized him; but he did, and even presented an appearance of physical improvement. He smiled again and spoke much of the future and of all the things he intended to do. This improvement carried him through the winter.

Spring was late the next year. On Good Friday, Houssard carried the ailing prelate to the cathedral. There was still ice on the streets and a bitter and unseasonable wind had risen and was twirling the snow about the eaves of the houses and making it almost impossible for the eye to see the top of the spire. It was not surprising that the bishop's feet were frozen before they reached the comparative warmth of the cathedral. The old man said nothing about it until it was too late to take the necessary steps. Even had he done so, it is doubtful if any measures could have been taken to relieve him, for the swollen veins in his legs gave at best a poor circulation of the blood. Gangrene set in and he suffered terribly during his last few days on earth.

He did not complain, but the intensity of the pain wrung exclamations from him. "O God have pity on me!" he cried. "O God of mercy, let Thy will be done!"

He had no thought that his accomplishments had set him apart. The humility he had shown in his later years seemed to accelerate, in fact, as the end drew near. Someone made the suggestion that he do as the saints had so often done and voice a last message for the people he was leaving.

The dying man shook his head slowly from side to side.

"They were saints," he whispered. "I am a sinner."

He died early in the morning of May 6, 1708. There had been no gaiety in Quebec for many days, nor would there be for a long time thereafter. The spiritual father of the colony had been taken away, and with bowed heads the people prayed long and earnestly that his benign influence would not be lost to them.

THE LITTLE GHOST

Gwen Ringwood

Kathy Preston gently removed her son's glasses without waking him, recovered a Cub cap, a comic book and a toy pistol from between the bed and the wall. Then she walked into the next room, to pat and tuck at the two small pig-tailed girls. As she moved to the baby's crib, the familiar, wordless prayer for her children's safety welled up in Kathy's mind, and then behind it, slipping in unbidden, undesired, was the little ghost.

"Oh, no! Go away . . . go away," Kathy protested silently, "you aren't three years old any more. You'd be eight now, going on nine. I couldn't have done anything. I couldn't have taken you." But the little ghost remained, motionless, alone, the tiny face crumpled in a despair that seemed as old as grief itself. "Oh, I wish I'd never had that awful party," she thought as she stroked her baby's soft cheek.

The party dated back five years, to the summer after VE Day when Kathy had taken Stephen and Sue to Balsam Lake for six weeks. She chose Balsam because Mary Arnold and her children would be there and because it was a short trip by bus. Kathy just had the two older children then.

As they unpacked in the rough cabin, four-year-old Stephen squealed with delight. "Daddy would like this place, wouldn't he?" "Oh yes," Kathy agreed, "Daddy would think this is wonderful." Daddy was somewhere in northern Germany wondering when he'd get home.

Kathy and Mary soon settled themselves and their children into an aimless pleasant routine of going to the beach, getting the mail, swimming in the rather weedy lake during the lazy sunny afternoons. After five, they would separate to their respective cabins to get supper.

One evening, returning from their swim, Kathy and the children were somewhat startled to find an old woman peering into the cabin windows. Huddling close to her were three small children.

"Hello," called Kathy, a little louder than necessary. The stranger turned quickly.

"Oh, how do you do? Don't mind us pokin' about, will you now. I understand this cottage is for sale. Are you the owner?" Kathy vaguely placed the accent as London, East side.

"No, I just rent it." Kathy tried not to sound annoyed.

REPRINTED BY PERMISSION OF OXFORD UNIVERSITY PRESS FROM *Canadian Short Stories*, EDITED BY ROBERT WEAVER AND HELEN JAMES.

"You don't know what they're askin' for it?"

"No. The storekeeper could tell you."

The old woman moved away from the house, the children with her. "No matter. Just havin' a look, passin' by." She was short and stout, almost dwarfish, with a large ruddy face that had a kind of calculating, cold cheerfulness about it. Above the face was a straw hat covered with pink roses that flopped a little as she talked.

"Are these your grandchildren?" Kathy looked at the three quiet youngsters for the first time.

"Never had any of me own," the old woman snorted. "These are my wards. This one is government." She pointed at a small boy. "The other two is boarded with me private. I've four more down the way."

Kathy gasped. "You take care of seven children?"

"That's right. My niece gives me an 'and lately. Why, I've kept children for years—government, private, anywhere from a week old up to six years. At six they get into the Institutions. This one goes to the Sunlight Home this fall, so he'll be leavin' old Mrs Midden. That right, Robert?" Robert nodded miserably.

"These are the two oldest," Mrs Midden explained, indicating Robert and a skinny vacant-looking little girl. "Have a lot of trouble with this girl. Elsie. Steals. Be glad when she's old enough for the home."

"Hello, Elsie," Kathy said. She looked down at the third of Mrs Midden's wards. "And what's your name, dear?" Her voice sounded falsely sweet in her own ears. Two brown eyes in a flower-like face stared solemnly at Kathy. "I'm Kristie," the child said in a husky, attractive whisper.

"Yes, that's Kristine," said Mrs Midden. "I've had her since she was three months. She's past three now. We don't know where her mother is; her uncle pays."

Kathy knelt beside the little girl, pushing the straight brown hair off her forehead. "Kristine . . . that's a pretty name. You're a nice little girl, aren't you, Kristine?"

"Yes, I am," the child's brown eyes searched deep into Kathy's.

"Hey, you kids, do you want to teeter-totter?" Stephen demanded belligerently, but the three little strangers crowded closer to their guardian.

"Are you staying at the Beach long?" Kathy asked.

"Only till Saturday."

"It's fun at the Lake, isn't it, children?" Kathy asked brightly. Her fingers closed gently around Kristine's arm. "How thin she is," Kathy realized with a shock. "How thin they all are."

"Well, we must be gettin' back." Mrs Midden waved her walking stick towards the huddle of cabins near the highway. "Come along, children."

Kathy found herself moving after them.

"Mrs Midden, I was wondering . . . I'm Kathy Preston . . . I thought maybe you'd bring all the children here for a picnic supper on Friday. My friend would bring her two boys. We could have a bonfire."

"When, Mommy? Shall I get the wood? Right now, Mommy?" Kathy's youngsters pulled at her in wild impatience.

"That sounds lovely, dearie," Mrs Midden decided after a pause. "I'll tell you now, I'll bring along the milk and you make up some sandwiches. We'll be looking forward to it, won't we, children?"

So they settled for three o'clock on Friday and the old lady, with the three quiet children sticking close to her, shambled off down the path like a giant crab. Looking after them, Kathy noticed that Mrs Midden's bare legs were twisted with varicose veins that had broken into ugly sores.

Friday was a golden sunny day. Stephen and Sue industriously piled wood for the bonfire. Mary arrived early with her two brown red-cheeked boys and a basket of fruit. Promptly at three Mrs Midden, followed by her seven wards, came up the path. The children, dressed in faded, ill-fitting cottons, were all very clean. Between them they carried five quarts of milk.

The party lasted for three hours. Kathy and Mary watched their own children race and tear from swing to gate, climbing, shouting, fighting and tumbling like puppies. But the seven visitors huddled together in a circle, heedless of Mrs Midden's urging to "go on now and have a good time of it". Kathy couldn't decide whether they were sub-normal or badly nourished or just plain shy. Certainly Robert, nearly six, was not much taller than Mary's three-year-old Brad, and Robert was the oldest of the seven.

The party seemed such a flop that Kathy decided to serve the lunch at once. As usual Kathy's and Mary's children gobbled some sandwiches, gulped their milk, ate an orange, wasted a hot dog or two, hoarded some cookies and begged to resume their play. But Mrs Midden's wards ate seriously and steadily, never refusing anything that was passed to them. As the food was passed again and again, Mrs Midden kept admonishing Kathy. "Don't give them any more, Mrs Preston, or I'll have them all sick tonight. You can't fill them up you know. They'd never stop eating. Go on all night if you'd let them. You'd never fill them up, you know."

Kathy and Mary exchanged startled glances, realizing that these were children such as they had never seen—hungry children, hungry from a long time back.

"Here's a cookie for you, Kristie," and Kathy bent to touch the soft straight hair. Kristie's blue dress had been handed down and not altered to fit her. She took the cookie hesitatingly. "Thanks," she whispered.

Mrs Midden looked around the circle proudly. "And what do you think of my little brood, Mrs Preston?" For some reason she had chosen to ignore Mary. Kathy swallowed.

"They're awfully nice."

"That one ain't never come along just right." Mrs Midden pointed at a fine-featured little boy whose co-ordination seemed poor.

"Do they get cod liver oil?" Kathy asked suddenly.

"Every morning I gives them each a tablet—government orders."

"Perhaps if you had a doctor see the little boy," Mary said. "I know a very good man who–"

Mrs Midden interrupted haughtily. "You'll think it strange, Mrs Arnold, but I don't hold with doctors. I've never had a doctor for any child that's been in my care, and that's thirty years of looking after children, and well looked after they've been too."

Kathy glanced at the pitiful little group, at the old woman's legs with the ulcerating veins, and turned away. She changed the subject.

"I think you're wonderful to manage so well," she gushed.

"Oh, I keep them in line all right. You have to. But they have a good time of it with old Mrs Midden, don't you, duckies? Elsie gives me the most trouble. She pilfers . . . food, bread, anything. To be expected of course . . . child of a brother and sister, she is." The last was in a perfectly audible whisper.

"Come on, Elsie, let's you and I start a game," Mary said suddenly, pulling Elsie to her feet. Kathy gathered up two more. "Let's all play." And in a little while she and Mary were teaching the children to play "Ring Around the Rosy" and "Drop the Handkerchief". Their own four joined in noisily. They were rewarded finally by hearing Elsie and Robert squeal with excitement, while the smaller ones jumped up and down uncertainly. "Choose somebody, Kristine," Stephen ordered, "choose the cat," and the little girl tugged at Kathy's dress, looked up at her, and smiled for the first time, slowly, trustfully.

Then Mary passed out the candies. The party was suddenly noisy, greedy, spontaneous, like all the other children's parties they had given. There were quarrels to settle, tears to dry, shouts to shush. At six, Mrs Midden announced that it was time to go home.

Kathy set about collecting milk bottles. "Kathy, look here." Mary's voice was low. Kathy turned. Mary had taken up a little boy. He clung to her like a small animal attached to its mother. Kathy had a lump in her throat. "I know," she said. She moved away and almost knocked Kristine over. "Hi, Kristie. Did you have fun at the party?" The little girl nodded. Kathy reached down and lifted her in her arms. She was startled to feel the child's slight body settle against her, clinging, just as did the boy in Mary's arms.

They walked almost home with Mrs Midden and her wards. Mary carried the little boy and Kathy carried Kristie. Kristie's tiny arms crept around Kathy's neck, and Kathy could feel the small bones under the child's soft flesh. And Kristie snuggled closer and closer to her, as if driven by a desperate physical need for shelter and warmth. As they walked, Kathy crooned nursery rhymes and repeated the child's name: "Kristie, Kristie, dear little Kristie, darling."

Kathy's and Mary's own children ran back and forth like outriders to the procession, acting particularly silly out of pique at their mothers' strange absorption in the outside children. As they approached the run-down cabin, a dark, rather flashy-looking girl came down the steps. "Here we are, Hilda," called Mrs Midden. "And a wonderful time we've had, too."

Mrs Midden was vociferous in her thanks. She said not many people had bothered, she said they'd talk of this for many days to come and she had each child say "Thank you". When Robert hesitated, her voice cracked over him. Kathy disengaged Kristie's arms from around her neck, slowly, reluctantly put her down.

"Good-bye, Kristie," she whispered. The little girl looked at her, not understanding. "Good-bye," Kathy said. She turned quickly, waved at them all, and hurried after Mary. The two women looked at each other, their faces stiff with repressed feeling. "Good-bye, good-bye," they called, waving like puppets.

"Come on, kids, race you home," Mary shouted.

Kathy turned to wave again. Kristie stood looking after her, and standing so was as terribly alone as if lost in a parched and limitless desert. When Kathy waved, the tiny face crumpled in despair.

"Come Kristine," called the niece Hilda. "Hurry up now." But the child remained motionless and alone.

In the next six years Kathy often told herself that she had tried to do something about the children. When she returned to the city, she had telephoned a few people, consented to act on a committee if it were formed, expressed delight when told that a welfare survey was even then in progress. She talked to a doctor about malnutrition and thought of asking Mrs Midden and the children to tea and of having him drop in at the same time. But this seemed a Judas-like gesture and she didn't do it.

She never saw Mrs Midden or the children again. When her husband came home from overseas, they moved to another town, had another child, and then another, watched Stephen and Sue enter school, begin to grow up. Why, Stephen was a Cub now, and Sue took piano lessons. Kathy often told herself that Mrs Midden's brood were none of her affair, that she had probably imagined the children's fear and hunger.

But tonight, bending over the baby's crib, Kathy realized suddenly that she could never explain to herself about the children, never forget the party, and that in all the days to come she could never wholly escape from Kristie's despair. Kathy knew, too, that from time to time, haunting her joy in her own children, slipping in behind her fear for them, arriving unsought and undemanding, would come the little ghost. "I couldn't have taken you," Kathy protested. "I couldn't have. There was no room, Kristie, no room." But it was no use. As she stood in the summer night, listening to the breathing of her four children, Kathy knew that even when they had gone from her, even when she was old, she would sometimes look up to see Kristie standing there, looking after her, her face crumpled in the old despair. And Kathy's heart would cry out for the child she had lost, for the thin arms that had once closed round her neck. In imagination she would run back and kneel beside the still, forlorn little figure and hold it close. "Oh Kristie, Kristie, my daughter," her heart would cry, even when she was old.

THE SPECULATIONS OF JEFFERSON THORPE

Stephen Leacock

It was not until the mining boom, at the time when everybody went simply crazy over the Cobalt and Porcupine mines of the new silver country near the Hudson Bay, that Jefferson Thorpe reached what you might call public importance in Mariposa.

Of course everybody knew Jeff and his little barber shop that stood just across the street from Smith's Hotel. Everybody knew him and everybody got shaved there. From early morning, when the commercial travellers off the 6.30 express got shaved into the resemblance of human beings, there were always people going in and out of the barber shop.

Mullins, the manager of the Exchange Bank, took his morning shave from Jeff as a form of resuscitation, with enough wet towels laid on his face to stew him and with Jeff moving about in the steam, razor in hand, as grave as an operating surgeon.

Then, as I think I said, Mr. Smith came in every morning and there was a tremendous outpouring of Florida water and rums, essences and revivers and renovators, regardless of expense. What with Jeff's white coat and Mr. Smith's flowered waistcoat and the red geranium in the window and the Florida water and the double extract of hyacinth, the little shop seemed multi-coloured and luxurious enough for the annex of a Sultan's harem.

But what I mean is that, till the mining boom, Jefferson Thorpe never occupied a position of real prominence in Mariposa. You couldn't, for example, have compared him with a man like Golgotha Gingham, who, as undertaker, stood in a direct relation to life and death, or to Trelawney, the postmaster, who drew money from the Federal Government of Canada, and was regarded as virtually a member of the Dominion Cabinet.

Everybody knew Jeff and liked him, but the odd thing was that till he made money nobody took any stock in his ideas at all. It was only after he made the "clean up" that they came to see what a splendid fellow he was. "Levelheaded" I think was the term; indeed in the speech of Mariposa, the highest form of endowment was to have the head set on horizontally as with a theodolite.

As I say, it was when Jeff made money that they saw how gifted he was, and when he lost it—but still, there's no need to go into that. I believe it's something the same in other places, too.

The barber shop, you will remember, stands across the street from Smith's Hotel, and stares at it face to face.

It is one of those wooden structures—I don't know whether you know them —with a false front that sticks up above its real height and gives it an air at once rectangular and imposing. It is a form of architecture much used in Mariposa and understood to be in keeping with the pretentious and artificial character of modern business. There is a red, white and blue post in front of the shop and the shop itself has a large square window out of proportion to its little flat face.

Painted on the panes of the window is the remains of a legend that once spelt BARBER SHOP, executed with the flourishes that prevailed in the golden age of sign painting in Mariposa. Through the window you can see the geraniums in the window shelf and behind them Jeff Thorpe with his little black skull cap on and his spectacles drooped upon his nose as he bends forward in the absorption of shaving.

As you open the door, it sets in violent agitation a coiled spring up above and a bell that almost rings. Inside, there are two shaving chairs of the heavier, or electrocution pattern, with mirrors in front of them and pigeon holes with individual shaving mugs. There must be ever so many of them, fifteen or sixteen. It is the current supposition of each of Jeff's customers that everyone else but himself uses a separate mug. One corner of the shop is partitioned off and bears the sign: HOT AND COLD BATHS, 50 CENTS. There has been no bath inside the partition for twenty years—only old newspapers and a mop. Still, it lends distinction somehow, just as do the faded cardboard signs that hang against the mirror with the legends: TURKISH SHAMPOO, 75 CENTS, and ROMAN MASSAGE, $1.00.

They said commonly in Mariposa that Jeff made money out of the barber shop. He may have, and it may have been that that turned his mind to investment. But it's hard to see how he could. A shave cost five cents, and a haircut fifteen (or the two, if you liked, for a quarter), and at that it is hard to see how he could make money, even when he had both chairs going and shaved first in one and then in the other.

You see, in Mariposa, shaving isn't the hurried, perfunctory thing that it is in the city. A shave is looked upon as a form of physical pleasure and lasts anywhere from twenty-five minutes to three-quarters of an hour.

In the morning hours, perhaps, there was a semblance of haste about it, but in the long quiet of the afternoon, as Jeff leaned forward towards the customer and talked to him in a soft confidential monotone, like a portrait painter, the razor would go slower and slower, and pause and stop, move and pause again, till the shave died away into the mere drowse of conversation.

At such hours, the Mariposa barber shop would become a very Palace of Slumber, and as you waited your turn in one of the wooden arm-chairs beside the wall, what with the quiet of the hour, and the low drone of Jeff's conversation, the buzzing of the flies against the window pane and the measured tick of the clock above the mirror, your head sank dreaming on your breast, and the Mariposa *Newspacket* rustled unheeded on the floor. It makes one drowsy just to think of it!

The conversation, of course, was the real charm of the place. You see, Jefferson's forte, or specialty, was information. He could tell you more things within the compass of a half-hour's shave than you get in days of laborious research in an encyclopædia. Where he got it all, I don't know, but I am inclined to think it came more or less out of the newspapers.

In the city, people never read the newspapers, not really, only little bits and scraps of them. But in Mariposa it's different. There they read the whole thing from cover to cover, and they build up on it, in the course of years, a range of acquirement that would put a college president to the blush. Anybody who has ever heard Henry Mullins and Peter Glover talk about the future of China will know just what I mean.

And, of course, the peculiarity of Jeff's conversation was that he could suit it to his man every time. He had a kind of divination about it. There was a certain kind of man that Jeff would size up sideways as he stropped the razor, and in whose ear he would whisper: "I see where Saint Louis has took four straight games off Chicago"—and so hold him fascinated to the end.

In the same way he would say to Mr. Smith: "I see where it says that this 'Flying Squirl' run a dead heat for the King's Plate."

To a humble intellect like mine he would explain in full the relations of the Keesar to the German Rich Dog.

But first and foremost, Jeff's specialty in the way of conversation was finance and the money market, the huge fortunes that a man with the right kind of head could make.

I've known Jefferson to pause in his shaving with the razor suspended in the air as long as five minutes while he described, with his eye half closed, exactly the kind of a head a man needed in order to make a "haul" or a "clean up." It was evidently simply a matter of the head, and as far as one could judge, Jeff's own was the very type required.

I don't know just at what time or how Jefferson first began his speculative enterprises. It was probably in him from the start. There is no doubt that the very idea of such things as Traction Stock and Amalgamated Asbestos went to his head: and whenever he spoke of Mr. Carnegie and Mr. Rockefeller, the yearning tone of his voice made it as soft as lathered soap.

I suppose the most rudimentary form of his speculation was the hens. That was years ago. He kept them out at the back of his house—which itself stood up a grass plot behind and beyond the barber shop—and in the old days Jeff would say, with a certain note of pride in his voice, that The Woman had sold as many as two dozen eggs in a day to the summer visitors.

But what with reading about Amalgamated Asbestos and Consolidated Copper and all that, the hens began to seem pretty small business, and, in any case, the idea of two dozen eggs at a cent apiece almost makes one blush. I suppose a good many of us have felt just as Jeff did about our poor little earnings. Anyway, I remember Jeff telling me one day that he could take the whole lot of the hens and sell them off and crack the money into Chicago wheat on margin and turn it over in twenty-four hours. He did it, too. Only somehow when it was turned over it came upside down on top of the hens.

After that the hen house stood empty and The Woman had to throw away chicken feed every day, at a dead loss of perhaps a shave and a half. But it made no difference to Jeff, for his mind had floated away already on the possibilities of what he called "displacement" mining on the Yukon.

So you can understand that when the mining boom struck Mariposa, Jefferson Thorpe was in it right from the very start. Why, no wonder; it seemed like the finger of providence. Here was this great silver country spread out to north of us, where people had thought there was only a wilderness. And right at our very doors! You could see, as I saw, the night express going north every evening; for all one knew Rockefeller or Carnegie or anyone might be on it! Here was the wealth of Calcutta, as the Mariposa *Newspacket* put it, poured out at our very feet.

So no wonder the town went wild! All day in the street you could hear men talking of veins, and smelters and dips and deposits and faults—the town hummed with it like a geology class on examination day. And there were men about the hotels with mining outfits and theodolites and dunnage bags, and at Smith's bar they would hand chunks of rock up and down, some of which would run as high as ten drinks to the pound.

The fever just caught the town and ran through it! Within a fortnight they put a partition down Robertson's Coal and Wood Office and opened the Mariposa Mining Exchange, and just about every man on the Main Street started buying scrip. Then presently young Fizzlechip, who had been teller in Mullins's Bank and that everybody had thought a worthless jackass before, came back from the Cobalt country with a fortune, and loafed around in the Mariposa House in English khaki and a horizontal hat, drunk all the time, and everybody holding him up as an example of what it was possible to do if you tried.

They all went in. Jim Eliot mortgaged the inside of the drug store and jammed it into Twin Tamagami. Pete Glover at the hardware store bought Nippewa stock at thirteen cents and sold it to his brother at seventeen and bought it back in less than a week at nineteen. They didn't care! They took a chance. Judge Pepperleigh put the rest of his wife's money into Temiskaming Common, and Lawyer Macartney got the fever, too, and put every cent that his sister possessed into Tulip Preferred.

And even when young Fizzlechip shot himself in the back room of the Mariposa House, Mr. Gingham buried him in a casket with silver handles and it was felt that there was a Monte Carlo touch about the whole thing.

They all went in—or all except Mr. Smith. You see, Mr. Smith had come from down there, and he knew all about rocks and mining and canoes and the north country. He knew what it was to eat flour-baked dampers under the lee side of a canoe propped among the underbrush, and to drink the last drop of whisky within fifty miles. Mr. Smith had mighty little use for the North. But what he did do, was to buy up enough early potatoes to send fifteen carload lots into Cobalt at a profit of five dollars a bag.

Mr. Smith, I say, hung back. But Jeff Thorpe was in the mining boom right from the start. He bought in on the Nippewa mine even before the interim prospectus was out. He took a "block" of one hundred shares of Abbitibbi Development at fourteen cents, and he and Johnson, the livery stable keeper next door, formed a syndicate and got a thousand shares of Metagami Lake at three and a quarter cents and then "unloaded" them on one of the sausage men at Netley's butcher shop at a clear cent per cent. advance.

Jeff would open the little drawer below the mirror in the barber shop and show you all kinds and sorts of Cobalt country mining certificates—blue ones, pink ones, green ones, with outlandish and fascinating names on them that ran clear from Mattawa to the Hudson Bay.

And right from the start he was confident of winning.

"There ain't no difficulty to it," he said, "there's lots of silver up there in that country and if you buy some here and some there you can't fail to come out somewhere. I don't say," he used to continue with the scissors open and ready to cut, "that some of the greenhorns won't get bit. But if a feller knows the country and keeps his head level, he can't lose."

Jefferson had looked at so many prospectuses and so many pictures of mines and pine trees and smelters, that I think he'd forgotten that he'd never been in the country. Anyway, what's two hundred miles!

To an onlooker it certainly didn't seem so simple. I never knew the meanness, the trickery, of the mining business, the sheer obstinate determination of the bigger capitalists not to make money when they might, till I heard the accounts of Jeff's different mines. Take the case of the Corona Jewel. There was a good mine, simply going to ruin for lack of common sense.

"She ain't been developed," Jeff would say. "There's silver enough in her so you could dig it out with a shovel. She's full of it. But they won't get at her and work her."

Then he'd take a look at the pink and blue certificates of the Corona Jewel and slam the drawer on them in disgust.

Worse than that was the Silent Pine—a clear case of *stupid incompetence!* Utter lack of engineering skill was all that was keeping the Silent Pine from making a fortune for its holders.

"The only trouble with that mine," said Jeff, "is they won't go deep enough. They followed the vein down to where it kind o' thinned out and then they quit. If they'd just go right into her good, they'd get it again. She's down there all right."

But perhaps the meanest case of all was the Northern Star. That always seemed to me, every time I heard of it, a straight case for the criminal law. The thing was so evidently a conspiracy.

"I bought her," said Jeff, "at thirty-two, and she stayed right there tight, like she was stuck. Then a bunch of these fellers in the city started to drive her down and they got her pushed down to twenty-four, and I held on to her and they shoved her down to twenty-one. This morning they've got her down to sixteen, but I don't mean to let go. No, sir."

In another fortnight they shoved her, the same unscrupulous crowd, down to nine cents, and Jefferson still held on.

"They're working her down," he admitted, "but I'm holding her."

No conflict between vice and virtue was ever grimmer.

"She's at six," said Jeff, "but I've got her. They can't squeeze me."

A few days after that, the same criminal gang had her down further than ever.

"They've got her down to three cents," said Jeff, "but I'm with her. Yes, sir, they think they can shove her clean off the market, but they can't do it. I've boughten in Johnson's shares, and the whole of Netley's, and I'll stay with her till she breaks."

So they shoved and pushed and clawed her down—that unseen nefarious crowd in the city—and Jeff held on to her and they writhed and twisted at his grip, and then—

And then—well, that's just the queer thing about the mining business. Why, sudden as a flash of lightning, it seemed, the news came over the wire to the Mariposa *Newspacket*, that they had struck a vein of silver in the Northern Star as thick as a sidewalk, and that the stock had jumped to seventeen dollars a share, and even at that you couldn't get it! And Jeff stood there flushed and half-staggered against the mirror of the little shop, with a bunch of mining scrip in his hand that was worth forty thousand dollars!

Excitement! It was all over the town in a minute. They ran off a news extra at the Mariposa *Newspacket*, and in less than no time there wasn't standing room in the barber shop, and over in Smith's Hotel they had three extra bar-keepers working on the lager beer pumps.

They were selling mining shares on the Main Street in Mariposa that afternoon and people were just clutching for them. Then at night there was a big oyster supper in Smith's caff, with speeches and the Mariposa band outside.

And the queer thing was that the very next afternoon was the funeral of young Fizzlechip, and Dean Drone had to change the whole text of his Sunday sermon at two days' notice for fear of offending public sentiment.

But I think what Jeff liked best of it all was the sort of public recognition that it meant. He'd stand there in the shop, hardly bothering to shave, and explain to the men in the arm-chairs how he held her, and they shoved her, and he clung to her, and what he'd said to himself—a perfect Iliad—while he was clinging to her.

The whole thing was in the city papers a few days after with a photograph of Jeff, taken specially at Ed. Moore's studio (upstairs over Netley's). It showed Jeff sitting among palm trees, as all mining men do, with one hand on his knee, and a dog, one of those regular mining dogs, at his feet, and a look of piercing intelligence in his face that would easily account for forty thousand dollars.

I say that the recognition meant a lot to Jeff for its own sake. But no doubt the fortune meant quite a bit to him, too, on account of Myra.

Did I mention Myra, Jeff's daughter? Perhaps not. That's the trouble with the people in Mariposa; they're all so separate and so different—not a bit like the people in the cities—that unless you hear about them separately and one by one you can't for a moment understand what they're like.

Myra had golden hair and a Greek face and would come bursting through the barber shop in a hat at least six inches wider than what they wear in Paris. As you saw her swinging up the street to the Telephone Exchange in a suit that was straight out of the *Delineator* and brown American boots, there was style written all over her—the kind of thing that Mariposa recognized and did homage to. And to see her in the Exchange—she was one of the four girls that I spoke of—on her high stool with a steel cap on—jabbing the connecting plugs in and out as if electricity cost nothing—well, all I mean is that you could understand why it was that the commercial travellers would stand round in the Exchange calling up all sorts of impossible villages, and waiting about so pleasant and genial!—it made one realize how naturally good-tempered men are. And then when Myra would go off duty and Miss Cleghorn, who was sallow, would come on, the commercial men would be off again like autumn leaves.

It just shows the difference between people. There was Myra who treated lovers like dogs and would slap them across the face with a banana skin to show her utter independence. And there was Miss Cleghorn, who was sallow, and who bought a forty-cent Ancient History to improve herself: and yet if she'd hit any man in Mariposa with a banana skin, he'd have had her arrested for assault.

Mind you, I don't mean that Myra was merely flippant and worthless. Not at all. She was a girl with any amount of talent. You should have heard her recite "The Raven" at the Methodist Social! Simply genius! And when she acted Portia in the Trial Scene of *The Merchant of Venice* at the High School concert, everybody in Mariposa admitted that you couldn't have told it from the original.

So, of course, as soon as Jeff made the fortune, Myra had her resignation in next morning and everybody knew that she was to go to a dramatic school for three months in the fall and become a leading actress.

But, as I said, the public recognition counted a lot for Jeff. The moment you begin to get that sort of thing it comes in quickly enough. Brains, you know, are recognized right away. That was why, of course, within a week from this Jeff received the first big packet of stuff from the Cuban Land Development Company, with coloured pictures of Cuba, and fields of bananas, and haciendas and insurrectos with machetes and Heaven knows what. They heard of him, somehow—it wasn't for a modest man like Jefferson to say how. After all, the capitalists of the world are just one and the same crowd. If you're in it, you're in it, that's all! Jeff realized why it is that of course men like Carnegie or Rockefeller and Morgan all know one another. They have to.

For all I know, this Cuban stuff may have been sent from Morgan himself. Some of the people in Mariposa said yes, others said no. There was no certainty.

Anyway, they were fair and straight, this Cuban crowd that wrote to Jeff. They offered him to come right in and be one of themselves. If a man's got the brains, you may as well recognize it right away. Just as well write him to be a director now as wait and hesitate till he forces his way into it.

Anyhow, they didn't hesitate, these Cuban people that wrote to Jeff from Cuba—or from a post-office box in New York—it's all the same thing because Cuba being so near to New York the mail is all distributed from there. I suppose in some financial circles they might have been slower, wanted guarantees of some sort, and so on, but these Cubans, you know, have got a sort of Spanish warmth of heart, that you don't see in business men in America, and that touches you. No, they asked no guarantee. Just send the money—whether by express order or by bank draft or cheque, they left that entirely to oneself, as a matter between Cuban gentlemen.

And they were quite frank about their enterprise—bananas and tobacco in the plantation district reclaimed from the insurrectos. You could see it all there in the pictures—the tobacco plants and the insurrectos—everything. They made no rash promises, just admitted straight out that the enterprise might realize four hundred per cent. or might conceivably make less. There was no hint of more.

So within a month, everybody in Mariposa knew that Jeff Thorpe was "in Cuban lands" and would probably clean up half a million by New Year's. You couldn't have failed to know it. All round the little shop there were pictures of banana groves and the harbour of Havana, and Cubans in white suits and scarlet sashes, smoking cigarettes in the sun and too ignorant to know that you can make four hundred per cent. by planting a banana tree.

I liked it about Jeff that he didn't stop shaving. He went on just the same. Even when Johnson, the livery stable man, came in with five hundred dollars and asked him to see if the Cuban Board of Directors would let him put it in, Jeff laid it in the drawer and then shaved him for five cents, in the same old way. Of course, he must have felt proud when, a few days later, he got a letter from the Cuban people, from New York, accepting the money straight off without a single question, and without knowing anything more of Johnson except that he was a friend of Jeff's. They wrote most handsomely. Any friends of Jeff's were friends of Cuba. All money they might send would be treated just as Jeff's would be treated.

One reason, perhaps, why Jeff didn't give up shaving was because it allowed him to talk about Cuba. You see, everybody knew in Mariposa that Jeff Thorpe had sold out of Cobalts and had gone into Cuban Renovated

Lands—and that spread round him a kind of halo of wealth and mystery and outlandishness—oh, something Spanish. Perhaps you've felt it about people that you know. Anyhow, they asked him about the climate, and yellow fever and what the Negroes were like and all that sort of thing.

"This Cubey, it appears, is an island," Jeff would explain. Of course, everybody knows how easily islands lend themselves to making money—"and for fruit, they say it comes up so fast you can't stop it." And then he would pass into details about the Hash-enders and the resurrectos and technical things like that till it was thought a wonder how he could know it. Still, it was realized that a man with money has got to know these things. Look at Morgan and Rockefeller and all the men that make a pile. They know just as much as Jeff did about the countries where they make it. It stands to reason.

Did I say that Jeff shaved in the same old way? Not quite. There was something even dreamier about it now, and a sort of new element in the way Jeff fell out of his monotone into lapses of thought that I, for one, misunderstood. I thought that perhaps getting so much money—well, you know the way it acts on people in the larger cities. It seemed to spoil one's idea of Jeff that copper and asbestos and banana lands should form the goal of his thought when, if he knew it, the little shop and the sunlight of Mariposa was so much better.

In fact, I had perhaps borne him a grudge for what seemed to me his perpetual interest in the great capitalists. He always had some item out of the paper about them.

"I see where this here Carnegie has give fifty thousand dollars for one of them observatories," he would say.

And another day he would pause in the course of shaving, and almost whisper: "Did you ever *see* this Rockefeller?"

It was only by a sort of accident that I came to know that there was another side to Jefferson's speculation that no one in Mariposa ever knew, or will ever know now.

I knew it because I went in to see Jeff in his house one night. The house —I think I said it—stood out behind the barber shop. You went out of the back door of the shop, and through a grass plot with petunias beside it and the house stood at the end. You could see the light of the lamp behind the blind and through the screen door as you came along. And it was here that Jefferson used to sit in the evenings when the shop got empty.

There was a round table that The Woman used to lay for supper, and after supper there used to be a chequered cloth on it and a lamp with a shade. And beside it Jeff would sit, with his spectacles on and the paper spread out, reading about Carnegie and Rockefeller. Near him, but away from the table, was The Woman doing needlework, and Myra, when she wasn't working in the Telephone Exchange, was there, too, with her elbows on the table reading Marie Corelli—only now, of course, after the fortune, she was reading the prospectuses of Dramatic Schools.

So this night—I don't know just what it was in the paper that caused it—Jeff laid down what he was reading and started to talk about Carnegie.

"This Carnegie, I bet you, would be worth," said Jeff, closing up his eyes in calculation, "as much as perhaps two million dollars, if you was to sell him up. And this Rockefeller and this Morgan, either of them to sell them up clean, would be worth another couple of million—"

I may say in parenthesis that it was a favourite method in Mariposa if you wanted to get at the real worth of a man, to imagine him clean sold up, put up for auction, as it were. It was the only way to test him.

"And now look at 'em," Jeff went on. "They make their money and what do they do with it? They give it away. And who do they give it to? Why, to those as don't want it, every time. They give it to these professors and to this research and that, and do the poor get any of it? Not a cent and never will.

"I tell you, boys," continued Jeff (there were no boys present, but in Mariposa all really important speeches are addressed to an imaginary audience of boys)—"I tell you if I was to make a million out of this Cubey, I'd give it straight to the poor, yes, sir—divide it up into a hundred lots of a thousand dollars each and give it to the people that hadn't nothing."

So always after that I knew just what those bananas were being grown for.

Indeed, after that, though Jefferson never spoke of his intentions directly, he said a number of things that seemed to bear on them. He asked me, for instance, one day, how many blind people it would take to fill one of these blind homes and how a feller could get ahold of them. And at another time he asked whether if a feller advertised for some of these incurables a feller could get enough of them to make a showing. I know for a fact that he got Nivens, the lawyer, to draw up a document that was to give an acre of banana land in Cuba to every idiot in Missinaba county.

But still—what's the use of talking of what Jeff meant to do? Nobody knows or cares about it now.

The end of it was bound to come. Even in Mariposa some of the people must have thought so. Else how was it that Henry Mullins made such a fuss about selling a draft for forty thousand on New York? And why was it that Mr. Smith wouldn't pay Billy, the desk clerk, his back wages when he wanted to put it into Cuba?

Oh, yes; some of them must have seen it. And yet when it came, it seemed so quiet—ever so quiet—not a bit like the Northern Star mine and the oyster supper and the Mariposa band. It is strange how quiet these things look, the other way round.

You remember the Cuban Land frauds in New York—and Porforio Gomez shooting the detective, and him and Maximo Morez getting clear away with two hundred thousand? No, of course you don't; why, even in the city papers it only filled an inch or two of type and anyway the names were hard to remember. That was Jeff's money—part of it. Mullins got the telegram, from a broker or someone, and he showed it to Jeff just as he was going up the street with an estate agent to look at a big empty lot on the hill behind the town—the very place for these incurables.

And Jeff went back to the shop so quiet—have you ever seen an animal that is stricken through, how quiet it seems to move?

Well, that's how he walked.

And since that, though it's quite a little while ago, the shop's open till eleven every night now, and Jeff is shaving away to pay back that five hundred that Johnson, the livery man, sent to the Cubans, and—

Pathetic? tut! tut! You don't know Mariposa. Jeff has to work pretty late, but that's nothing—nothing at all, if you've worked hard all your lifetime. And Myra is back at the Telephone Exchange—they were glad enough to get her, and she says now that if there's one thing she hates, it's the stage, and she can't see how the actresses put up with it.

Anyway, things are not so bad. You see, it was just at this time that Mr. Smith's caff opened, and Mr. Smith came to Jeff's Woman and said he wanted seven dozen eggs a day, and wanted them handy, and so the hens are back, and more of them, and they exult so every morning over the eggs they lay that if you wanted to talk of Rockefeller in the barber shop you couldn't hear his name for the cackling.

SOME ARE SO LUCKY

Hugh Garner

I met Ethel Walton last week. It was strange, because it happened as I had always pictured it would. I left the office rather late, and was standing on the curb waiting to flag a taxi when my eyes strayed across the busy street. There she was, coming out of the doorway of a department store. I hurried through the rain to intercept her.

"Hello, Ethel," I said, when I caught up.

"Why–hello," she answered, searching my face for a clue to my identity.

"You don't remember me, do you?"

"Your face looks familiar–" she began.

"Rod. Rod Murphy."

"Oh, of course," she answered, smiling. She brushed some raindrops from the collar of her coat. It was apparent that she was waiting for me to speak; she was not quite sure who Rod Murphy was.

"Fifteen years is a long time between meetings," I said. "It's strange that two people can live in the same city that length of time and never meet."

She smiled an uncertain smile. Her looks hadn't changed a bit; except for a few small lines at the corners of her eyes she was still the same. A little thinner, maybe, but her beauty was preserved, as it so often is in some slim dark women.

"Do you remember the night I took you to see Cab Calloway?"

Her face lighted up with recognition. "Of course," she answered, her voice animated now that she recognized me. "Sure! Rod Murphy!" She took a step back and looked me over. "You've certainly changed," she said. "Why, when I knew you, you were–well, you seemed like a little kid. You've grown a lot heavier since then."

Laughing, I said, "Some of us do."

"What are you doing these days?" she asked, pulling me by the sleeve until we stood in the shelter of a doorway.

"Oh, nothing much. I've been in the insurance business for years."

"Married?"

"I'm too old to get married," I said. Suddenly I wanted to tell her that marriage had never occurred to me since the last time we had seen each other. I wanted her to know what she had meant to me in those days. And behind my confession I wanted her to see that some of the things planned for myself—for us—had come true. . . .

"Here comes my car," she said, holding her hat as she leaned out from the doorway to peer down the street.

"Let me take you somewhere for a drink."

She set her face into a thoughtful expression, pursing her lips like a Frenchwoman does. "Not tonight, Mr. Murphy," she answered. "I've got to get home."

"How about another night then?" I asked, hating myself for insisting, but unwilling to let her disappear again.

"All right," she answered, overcoming her reluctance. "Tomorrow night . . . same time. Right here." She began running towards the car stop.

"Here?" I shouted.

She turned her head slightly and nodded. The street car drew to a halt at the corner.

It was during the winter of 1934 that I first met Ethel Walton. There was a dance at the Odd Fellows' Hall; one of those twenty-five cent affairs run by an out-of-work impresario. The orchestra was a rattletrap troupe that banged out tunes like Sleepy Time Gal, Sugar, and You Didn't Know The Music—I Didn't Know The Words, from second-hand orchestrations. The hall was bare and cold, its only decorations being a few fly-specked paper lanterns left around the lights since the last Hallowe'en dance.

Alex Myers, Jim Sturdy and myself made our way to a corner beside the orchestra, where we sat down on some varnished kitchen chairs to watch the girls come in.

The memory of that dance stands out vividly in my mind. Even to the fact that we three young fellows were out of work, and that my quarter admission had come from gathering five empty milk and ginger-ale bottles from under the cellar stairs, and collecting the deposits on them from Muldoon's grocery store.

We rolled cigarettes from Alex Myers' package of tobacco, and sat back at our ease, passing remarks about the girls as they wandered in through the door. We didn't pay much attention to it in those days, but looking back it seems to me that most of the girls came stag. That is understandable to anybody who was twenty-one years of age in 1934.

Jim Sturdy would say, "Here's Molly Anderson coming. I wonder if she's got enough money with her to buy me a coffee if I take her home?"

Alex and I would laugh.

Then Alex would remark that Dot Bannerman had arrived, and that we'd all better dance with her, once, because she was having a birthday party on the following Wednesday, and it might be too cold a night to stand around the corner.

As the benches around the hall began to fill up, Jim and Alex wandered away, leaving me alone. I sat back on my chair, listening to the orchestra tuning up, and watching the small crowd that was gathering at the door. I recognized most of them, from schooldays or because they lived in the same neighborhood as me.

The young men wore dark suits and their hair was either carefully waved or plastered down with Brilliantine and parted in the middle. The girls were attired in ankle-length skirts that year and "shirtwaists". Most of them had their hair cut in a shingle bob.

Two girls pushed through the crowd at the door, and looked around for a seat. The only empty seats were the few chairs in the corner where I was sitting. One of the girls pointed in my direction, and they came across the floor.

The one who had pointed was plump and blonde, while the other one was a slim girl wearing a grey skirt and red sweater, with long dark hair combed straight back and ending in a series of natural waves clipped together with a butterfly bow on her neck.

I looked around the hall, expecting to see every male eye turned upon the dark girl, but apparently she was crossing the wide expanse of floor, noticed only by me. It was amazing, but pleasant too, like a stranger's intimate smile. I fell in love with her that moment; before speaking to her, before knowing who she was, how she talked, whether she was married or single, whether she had teeth behind those beautiful lips.

"Are these chairs taken?" asked the blonde girl, pointing to the two empty chairs my friends had left.

"Help yourself," I answered, unable to keep my eyes from her companion's face.

They sat down and stuffed their coat checks into their handbags. Then they fixed their hair, turning this way and that while they stared at their reflections in their compacts.

"I hope it warms up in here. I'm almost froze, aren't you, Ethel?" asked the blonde.

"Me too," the dark one answered. When she turned to speak to her friend I saw that she had beautiful small white even teeth. I repeated her name to myself: Ethel.

It is not a pretty name, Ethel—in fact it is quite plain. But to me at that moment it was the most beautiful woman's name in the world.

How did this happen to me? Who can say? Who can gauge the lightning? Who can place their finger on the *one* thing that makes a young man fall in love? Who can say whether it was her hair, eyes, carriage, cleanliness or complexion? Was it her smile, her laugh, the habits of her hands? Was it the swell of her bosom, or the drape of her skirt across her hips? Was it all these together, or was it something apart from her? An emotional or chemical reaction within this young man perhaps; something that can be explained only with scientific detachment and the aid of retorts or psychological theorem?

Whatever it was, I fell in love.

In a few minutes the orchestra began to play, with a loud sudden noise against the naked walls of the hall. The couples drifted on to the floor. Pete Timmons was skirting the dancing couples, coming to ask one of the two girls sitting near me to dance, and I was suddenly afraid that if Ethel accepted him she'd be lost to me forever. Tapping her on the shoulder, I asked, "Would you care to dance?" using "care" instead of "like", and watching my enunciation as carefully as though taking part in an oratorical contest.

She looked at me, then turned again in the direction of the tall handsome figure of Pete Timmons who was approaching fast. She had seen him coming, and had been waiting for him. She hesitated as long as she could before standing up, then with resignation walked to the edge of the floor.

Putting my arm about her, we started off. When it was time to turn her on a pivot in the corner she resisted my efforts. Drawing away, I saw that she was staring over my shoulder, and knew without looking that she had eyes only for Pete.

The dance was a failure. My shortcomings were apparent to me, as if I were standing in her place, looking at myself. A skinny runt in a fifteen-dollar hand-me-down suit, and socks with knots of grey darning wool on the heels. A dancing partner who was so unsure of himself that he bumped into every second couple on the floor. And, besides, a young man who was too stupid or tongue-tied to be able to talk.

I wanted to talk. To tell her that I knew her name. To ask where she lived, and why she had come down to our neighborhood to dance. I wanted to let her know that she was the most beautiful girl in the world. To let her see all the things stored up inside me: the integrity and ambition and surety for the future. I wanted her to hear the smart repartee I had learned; to know that I had read many books, and had won a fifty-dollar scholarship in my last year at school. I wanted to blurt out that Pete Timmons was a nobody, and that soon I would be out and ahead of everyone in the hall . . .

It sounds crazy now, but all lovers' protestations are built of such artlessness and ostentation. They are formed of words as decorative and vain as a peacock's tail feathers, but their promise is a chimera that begins as truth and only becomes a lie with its unfulfillment.

When the music stopped she moved off through the crowd without a word. Making my way to the door I stood outside on the steps, letting the winter air cool my face, still able to feel her in my arms, my brain filled with the clean sweet smell of her hair.

There were dances with other girls that night, but these others were only partners in a ritual. No matter who they were, or what they were saying, my eyes were open only for the sight of this dark-haired girl whom I had met a few brief moments before.

She danced with many young men, filling me with a fierce jealousy at the sight. She moved past me, talking and laughing, impervious to the fact that I was alive, unable to hear the beating of my heart.

During a Paul Jones the music stopped, and we found ourselves a yard or so apart. She smiled, and I smiled in return, knowing that she chose to dance with me rather than with the fellow on my right. But her smile was for someone else, and when she noticed me she stared above my head as if I wasn't there.

I saw her many times that winter, for she came to the Odd Fellows' Hall every Saturday night. We danced together a few times, and she told me where she lived—in a neighborhood much better than mine. The lack of money prevented me from asking to take her home, or for a date, but I saw her just the same. Not only at the dances, but in my dreams, in every crowd at the skating rink, boarding street cars, entering the movies. She was everywhere I looked, for my eyes could see no one else.

In the spring I began work as a clerk in an insurance office at twelve dollars a week. Part of my first week's pay went as the down payment on a new suit, and the following Saturday found me at the Odd Fellows' Hall, feeling the self-esteem that comes to a young man with new clothes and change in his pocket.

We danced the first two dances together, my shyness gone now, able to laugh and talk without a feeling of inferiority twisting the words in my mouth. She seemed surprised at my new effusion, but laughed at what I said, and looked at me instead of the other dancers.

During intermission we made our way to the small soft-drink counter in the lobby and had a Coke. We stood on the stone steps leading to the street and talked about our jobs and the coming of the warm weather. The air was balmy, and there was the fresh scent of grass from the nascent lawns across the street. A group of children played along the sidewalk, their shouted, "Bluebottle, Bluebottle, Redbottle!" loud against the soft ceiling of the night. I knew, somehow, that such happiness would never come to me again, and I wanted the earth and everything upon it to stop, for fear that its spinning should break the spell.

She let me take her home from the dance, and we stopped at the Greek's and had a coffee and something to eat. Sitting in one of the plywood booths, I was proud to be with her, and jealous of every passing glance aimed in her direction. Everything about her was beautiful, even her small imperfections; the curl of hair on her forehead, the stain of lipstick on one of her front teeth, her beautiful eyes, the shape of her mouth, her gaiety, her loud laugh, the shape of her ears.

We walked along her street and she chatted about her neighbors and friends, describing other young men she knew. She told me about walking back from a car ride the week before, when the man she was with had been "too fresh". I got the idea that she did not walk back very often.

These things brought a bitter-sweet pain to me, like a knife being turned in my ribs, but I smiled and nodded, and pretended that it was funny to hear about them.

Upon reaching her house we stood on the front steps and talked for a minute or two. She yawned and said that she had better be getting in; she had a date to go driving in the morning. I couldn't bear to think of not seeing her again for a whole week, and I blurted out an invitation to accompany me to see Cab Calloway and his orchestra on the following Tuesday night.

She thought for a moment as though weighing my invitation against another date before she said, "O.K., call for me here at eight."

I mumbled something that sounded like, "Sure. I'll be here, don't worry," and set off down the street.

She shouted after me, "Didn't you forget something?" but when I turned to go back she opened her front door and entered the house, leaving her laughter dancing outside.

On the Tuesday evening I dressed carefully, standing before the cracked mirror in my room and plastering every vagrant hair on my head into place. I wondered if she had remembered our date; feeling certain that it must be forgotten by now.

During my preparations a timid little voice was telling me that I would be a fool to go. Her mocking laughter kept returning to me, until I was sure that her acceptance had only been part of the whole cruel joke.

At half-past six I was ready, and sat around the house for another half hour in impatient indecision. I tried to reconstruct the final moments of our last meeting, analyzing what we had said and giving this or that little remark of hers a meaning and importance out of all proportion to its worth. But the beauty of her face evaded me, and she remained a vague girlish figure topped by a blur where her face should have been.

When the crawling hands of the clock reached seven I left the house and walked along the streets, whistling some long-forgotten tune, and being careful not to scuff the bright shine on the toes of my new tan shoes.

A clock told me that only a half hour had gone by as I approached her street, so I entered a lunch counter and toyed with a cup of coffee to kill the time. It seemed very important to me not to reach her house until the precise moment of eight.

The fire-hall clock was striking the hour as I knocked on her door. The front hallway was dark, but a middle-aged woman was moving around in the lighted kitchen at the back of the house. My knock sent up a clamor of children's laughter and the sound of running steps on the stairs. A man's angry voice shouted, "Shut-up!"

There was the sound of the inside door being opened, the front door creaked, and I was face to face with Ethel. What ran through my mind at that moment is forgotten, but I remember standing on the porch and staring at her, until she said, "Come in, Rod. I'm pretty near ready."

She led the way along the hall and into the living room, while I followed her, swinging my hat in my hand with a nonchalance I did not feel.

"Dad, I want you to meet a friend of mine, Rod Murphy."

"How do you do, sir?" my voice whispered to the forbidding figure who glowered from his chair beside the window.

Her father grunted something, and ignoring my outstretched hand, picked up several loose pages of the evening paper and left the room.

She took my arm and said, "Don't mind him, he's mad tonight. He hasn't picked a winner all week."

"Oh, that's all right," I replied hastily.

"Take a chair; I won't be a jiffy," she said, turning to leave the room. There was the sound of her feet running up the stairs.

I sat down and looked around me. The room was furnished much better than our front room at home. There was a new console radio against the wall, and I listened to Arthur Tracy, the Street Singer, singing Stars Fell On Alabama. My fingers made sure that the knot in my tie was tight, and I turned my trouser legs over my knees to protect the crease. Comparing the Walton's house with our own only heightened my feeling of inferiority. Her father's actions did not surprise me—it was no more than I deserved for having the temerity to call on his daughter.

When Ethel came downstairs she said, "Let's go, Rod."

Her mother shouted from the kitchen, "Don't be late again tonight!"

"No," Ethel answered.

That was the closest thing to an introduction I ever had with Mrs. Walton.

On our way to the car stop Ethel paused beneath a street light and asked me if her stocking seams were straight. This request seemed to me to create an intimacy that was as binding as a ring. When we began walking again Ethel laughed and pulled me over to the outside position on the sidewalk, saying, "I'm not for sale, you know."

On our way downtown in the street car she told me a little joke she had heard at work. It was more silly than bawdy, but I laughed at it heartily, ignoring the small shock it gave me to hear such things from her. It may sound foolish, but nothing she could have said to me right then would have changed me one bit. Some things may have pained me, but I would still have loved her. That's how it was between us.

Once, when I was just a kid, I found a drunken woman lying on the sidewalk, and helped her up some stairs to an apartment over a store. She was filthy, mentally and physically, and every second word she uttered was obscene—not the mild feminine obscenities, but the riving ones of a completely corrupt mind.

When we reached her door it was opened by a gray-haired mild little man who said, "Thank you, son. Thanks very much."

I asked him if the woman lived there.

"Yes, son, she's my wife," he answered without shame.

Between us we half dragged, half carried this woman into a room and laid her on a couch, where she thrashed in delirium, shouting filth at the top of her voice.

I nodded to the man and turned to go, trying to convey my sorrow to him. He pressed my shoulder in farewell and walked over to where his wife lay on the couch. Before closing the door I heard him say, "Quiet, Bella—quiet, dear. You're all right now, dear. Nothing's going to hurt you, darling."

To that!

I have never forgotten the incident. He was a man who *loved* a woman. Long after all beauty and cleanliness and decency had gone, he still loved her. And that is the way I would have loved Ethel—that is the way I am sure I would have loved her.

We sat together in the darkened theater. I could feel Ethel's nearness, and was conscious of the warmth of her body and the perfume of her hair. My arm was asleep around her shoulders, yet I was afraid to move it away. She sat hunched down in the seat, laughing with the crowd at the antics of the comedian upon the screen, half rising when the action quickened, giving little gasps of fright now and then or squeezing my free hand in hers.

When the lights went up for the vaudeville I pulled my deadened arm from her shoulders and let it hang beside me until the re-awakened circulation coursed through it with the pricking of a thousand pins.

Ethel enjoyed the stage show with the uninhibited joy of a child, laughing at the obvious slapstick, yet missing the more subtle humor of the acts. It was upsetting to me, in a way, but it had no more effect on my love for her than has the finding by a mother of a birthmark on her baby.

After the show we stopped off downtown and had a sundae apiece, before taking the street car home. Ethel went over the picture and the vaudeville, mentioning every little thing that had made her laugh, and laughing again at the memory of it. So did I, because I was happy and wanted her to see that we liked the same things.

When we reached her house we stood on the front porch and she allowed me to kiss her, giving her lips to me in gratitude or because it was easier to aquiesce than resist. The events of the evening overwhelmed me, and I, like a fool, poured out my feelings for her, telling her of the love that had grown from the first minute we met at the Odd Fellows' Hall. I said many more things that night, things which no man wants to remember years after the incident is past.

I asked her to marry me—on twelve dollars a week!—and she broke from my grasp, stepped out of the shadows, and laughed a loud pealing laugh. Something broke up inside me at that moment, and I had an impulse to hurt her as she was hurting me. And I felt the frustration of not being able to make her see that my feelings were deeper than those she would ever evoke from another man.

All I could say was, "Ethel, don't laugh like that! Ethel!"

She turned from me in disgust and entered the house, leaving me standing on the porch.

I don't remember going home. Perhaps I walked the streets half the night. My mind was not conscious of the physical steps taken by my stumbling feet. My sorrow, like a narcotic, filled my thoughts with a wild fanciful reliving of the few minutes before she left me at her door.

My mind seethed with self-loathing for the blurting out of my feelings, and I wondered if any man since the earth began had acted as foolishly.

All the advice that is given to unrequited lovers came to mind: "There's lots more fish in the sea", and "Don't worry, you'll forget her in a week", but they proved to be poor anodynes. I wanted Ethel, just as she was and with all her faults. And all the philosophers on earth could not have talked me out of my need for her.

The next few weeks were a nightmare—of unnecessary trips through her neighborhood, and phone calls in which I'd hang up the receiver before the phone was answered. I contemplated suicide and lay awake night after night drugging myself with dreams or asking myself why fortune had been so unfair. And gradually, as my family and friends had said it would, my pain became a dull ache, and I was able to live once more.

I didn't see her again for fifteen years.

She met me, as promised, last Thursday night. She looked radiant; her hair neat and sparkling beneath a cute spring hat, and her still lovely figure trim in a grey tailored suit. I thought, her husband certainly got the breaks —how can one man be so lucky, and another not?

We entered a nearby cocktail lounge, and were shown to a table far back in one of its darkened corners.

When we were seated I asked, "What are you drinking, Ethel?"

She scanned the liquor list. "I think I'll have a Tom Collins," she said.

When the waiter brought our drinks we talked for a minute or two about the weather and such things. Finally I asked her how she was getting along.

"Just great, Rod," she answered.

"That's good. You're married, I suppose?"

"Oh yes. I've been married now for fourteen years."

"Any children?"

"One," she answered. "My Bobby is twelve now—going on thirteen."

"Did you marry anyone I know?"

"I don't think so. My husband's name is Blanton—Ernest Blanton. Do you know him?"

I thought for a moment. "No, I don't think I do, Ethel."

Some young women came in and sat down at the table next to us. They could have been schoolteachers or nurses, or perhaps girls from an office across the street. I noticed that Ethel was estimating the cost of their clothes, and mentally comparing the price with that of her own. She was watching the way they were drinking, copying their mannerisms. "I should have ordered the kind of cocktail you get in those glasses with a stem," she said. "They look nicer, don't you think?"

"Drink your Collins then, and I'll order you a Martini or a Manhattan."

"A Manhattan sounds good," she said, draining her glass.

After I had ordered the drink I said, "You haven't changed much."

"Me?"

"You don't seem much older than you were the last time I saw you."

"I feel older though."

"Has your married life been happy?"

"Most of the time. We've had our little spats now and again." She told me a long story involving herself and a boy who had been rooming in their house. The way she told it to me, her husband had grown jealous over a mild friendship that existed between them and the young man had been forced to move.

"Does your son go to school?" I asked.

"Sometimes. He's a little devil! Since I've been working he's been getting away with murder. His teacher sent the nastiest letter the other day– Wait until I find it–" She searched her bag, but without result. "I must have left it at home," she said. There followed an explanation of why her son hadn't been attending school as regular as he should, and how snippy the teacher was getting to be. "I'd like to see her bringing up a kid these days," she finished.

One of the young women at the next table placed her wrap over the back of the chair, so Ethel stood up and I helped her do the same with the jacket of her suit.

"And you're still a bachelor?" she asked, as we sat down again.

"Yes."

"I guess it's not so lonely for a man. You can always get a girl when you want one, can't you?"

It sounded like a dirty joke. I nodded my head.

"What business did you say you were in, last night?"

"Insurance," I answered.

"You look pretty prosperous. I guess a lot of people have bought insurance since the war? Of course there's a lot of walking in it–ringing doorbells and things."

"I'm not a salesman," I said, laughing.

"Oh!"

She told me that her insurance collector had a hard time finding her in when he called.

"How much do you carry?"

"Oh, let me see. I never was one for that sort of stuff. I think it's ten thousand dollars."

I guessed that it would be more like a quarter of that amount.

"What does your husband do, Ethel?"

"He works for a packing company," she answered. "They wanted him to go on the road–selling, you know, but he'd sooner stay in the plant. He's got a good job–they only work a forty hour week."

I motioned to the waiter to bring her another drink. These little lies she was telling were so obvious that I wondered why she bothered. But it was rather sad listening to them, for they were the pride-saving untruths of a little girl.

"I like these Manhattans," she said, simpering a bit. "Ernie always has a bottle of rye over the week-end. That is unless we come downtown to one of these spots or go to a party. I was at a party the other night, and guess who was there?"

"I'm afraid I can't."

"Willie Barnard."

When the name didn't register she said, "You know him, don't you? The disc-jockey. You know, he has a program in the afternoons. Plays records and cracks jokes."

"I think I've heard of him. I'm not usually home during the day."

She nodded as if accepting my explanation. "Of course his name isn't really Barnard," she went on. "That's his professional name. You knew he was a kike, didn't you? Sure. His real name's Brodsky."

Her words took me back to a night fifteen years before. The beautiful girl sitting next to me in the street car was telling me an off-color joke. Her use of the word "kike" now did not shock me as much as the other had. Perhaps I had begun to expect such vulgarisms, or I was becoming immune to things like that. I stared at her and wondered if I was becoming immune to her.

The drinks were beginning to take effect. She was leaning with her elbows on the table, her eyes showing sparks of brightness through the brown of the iris. "We've got a lot of influential friends," she stated.

"I'm sure you have, Ethel," I agreed, wishing she'd keep her voice down.

"You didn't used to be such a big-shot when I knew you," she went on argumentatively.

I laughed and said, "I'm not a big-shot now, either."

"No, you're damn right you're not. I used to watch you sometimes, hanging around the corner of our street. I could have twisted you around my little finger," she said, smiling with the muscles of her face.

I glanced at the tables near us, but nobody seemed to have noticed anything wrong. Ethel held up her empty glass and signalled the waiter.

She placed the glass down carefully and turned her head in the direction of the girls at the next table. After looking them over for a moment she sniffed disdainfully and turned to me again. One shoulder of her suit coat had slipped from the back of the chair, and she reached her arm around and pulled it up, twisting the collar in the process. I leaned across and straightened it. "You know what they are?" she asked, pointing behind her at the table full of girls.

I was afraid they would hear her. "Sure, Ethel, sure," I answered, knowing that *she* didn't.

"You know everything, don't you? You're a big-shot, Mr.– Mr.–"

"Murphy."

"That's Irish, isn't it?"

"It was, away back," I answered.

"I guess you made your money during the war, didn't you, Mr. Murphy?"

"Let's not get involved in any arguments, Ethel, please. We came here to talk over old times. I thought it would be nice seeing you again. You know how crazy I was about you, back in those days."

"Oh yeah! Who're you kidding! You haven't answered my question, Mr. Murphy," she continued, straightening up and trying to appear dignified. "What did you do during the war?"

"Does it matter?"

"Sure it matters. My husband worked from nineteen-forty-one in the shipyards, see?"

"Fine, fine," I answered as the waiter placed the new drinks before us.

"What did *you* do, sell insurance?"

That made me angry. Keeping my voice as low as possible I said, "No, I didn't sell insurance, and I didn't work in a shipyard. I was in the P.B.I."

"Never heard of it," she said. "What does P.B.I. stand for?"

"The poor bloody infantry," I told her. "Now let's forget the war."

She drew back and lifted her glass to her lips. After she'd placed it back on the table she said, "You didn't need to swear!" She set her mouth in a pout. At one time this facial gesture may have been cute, but now it was out of character. It was the vain groping of a woman for something lost, like a grandmother with hennaed hair.

I sipped my drink and studied her. Outwardly she was the same, but there was a change somewhere. It was impossible to tell whether the change was hers, or in my feelings toward her. Had the last fifteen years coarsened her, or had she always been coarse, while I had been too blind to see?

"What do you think you're looking at?" she asked.

"I was just thinking back a few years."

"Do you remember when you proposed to me? That was the funniest thing ever happened," she said, tipping back her head and laughing.

I laughed with her to show I didn't care, but I felt like a traitor. It wasn't fair to that poor foolish kid who had stood on her front porch that night and declared all his hopes and dreams. Suddenly the memory of it nauseated me. It was as though he had poured his life . . . all that was decent and good in him, down a sewer.

I finished my drink and said, "I guess you'll be wanting to run along soon, Ethel, won't you?"

She laughed her strident laugh. Some of the other patrons looked over at our table.

"You're not trying to get rid of me, are you?" she asked, in a vain attempt to be coy.

"No, not at all," I lied. "It's only that I have a dinner engagement later, and I thought that you'd like to be getting home."

"I don't have to go home yet," she said. "If it's the money you're worried about, tonight's my pay-night and I can buy my own drinks." She opened her handbag and placed a small wad of bills on the table.

"Put your money away," I said sharply, noticing the girls staring at us from the next table.

She snatched up the money and returned it to her bag. "I just wanted you to know that I'm no cheap-skate," she said. "I can pay my own way."

"Sure. I realize that."

"I thought you and me'd have a good time," she said. "I phoned my husband that I was going to stay at my mother's place tonight. My mother's been sick for a year now." She gave me a secretive little wink.

"I'm sorry to hear that about your mother."

"We could have a few more drinks and then we could go to your place, couldn't we?" she asked, bending over close.

God knows I'd dreamed of Ethel and me together a thousand times, but suddenly she no longer attracted me in this or any other way. I was glad she had said these things, however, for it was the final snap that released me forever from the spell I'd been under so long.

"I've got to go now, Ethel. It seems that we haven't talked about half the things I'd planned. Perhaps we'll meet again some other time."

"Running out on me, eh? I ought to have known you would." She leaned across the table and I noticed for the first time that she was ugly. Under the beautiful shape of her face was an ugliness I'd never seen matched before.

"Go ahead, run home, little boy!" she snarled. "I don't need you—I've got plenty of boy-friends!" Her coat had slipped from the back of the chair, and it lay trailing on the floor. Her hair, the hair I had thought so beautiful a short time before, was coming undone under her hat, and a vagrant wisp shook across her forehead as she talked.

"Can I get you a taxi, Ethel?" I asked.

"No, I don't need anything from you. Get out of my sight, that's all!"

The waiter came from behind the bar and brought me the check. I paid him and walked out into the warm spring evening without a backward glance.

A voice that I recognized as my own was saying, "You're lucky. You're the luckiest man on the face of the earth!" I walked along the still-warm pavement, feeling good, feeling free, feeling that something dirty and vicious was dead, feeling fifteen years younger than I had an hour before.

BEATING THE SMUGGLING GAME

Thomas Chandler Haliburton

"I shall never forget a talk I had with Ichabod Gates here, and a frolic him and me had with the tide-waiter. Ichabod had a large store o' goods, and I was in there one evenin' a-drinkin' tea along with him, and we got a-talkin' about smugglin'. Says he, 'Mr. Slick, your people ruin the trade here, they *do* smuggle so; I don't know as I ever shall be able to get rid of my stock of goods, and it cost me a considerable of a sum too. What a pity it is them navy people, instead of carryin' freights of money from the West Indgies, warn't employed more a-protectin' of our fisheries and our trade.' 'Why don't you smuggle then, too,' says I, 'and meet 'em in their own way?—tit for tat—diamond cut diamond—smuggle yourselves and seize *them;*—free trade and sailors' rights is our maxim.' 'Why,' says he, 'I ain't jist altogether certified that it's right; it goes agin my conscience to do the like o' that 'are, and I must say I like a fair deal. In a gineral way a'most, I've observed what's got over the devil's back is commonly lost onder his belly. It don't seem to wear well.' 'Well, that's onconvenient too, to be so thin-skinned,' said I; 'for conscience most commonly has a hide as thick as the sole of one's foot; you may cover it with leather to make it look decent-like, but it will bear a considerable hard scrubbin' without anythin' over it. Now,' says I, 'I will put you on a track that will sarve you without bringin' corns on your conscience either. Do you jist pretend to smuggle and make believe as if you were agoin' the whole hog in it. It's safer and full out as profitable as the raal thing, and, besides, there's no sort o' risk in it in the world. When folks hear a thing is smuggled they always think it's cheap, and never look into the price; they bite directly—it's a grand bait that. Now always onload your vessels at night, and let folks hear a cart agoin' into your place atween two and three o'clock in the mornin'; fix one o' the axles so it will squeak like a pig, and do you look suspicious, mysterious, and oneasy. Says you (when a chap says, I guess you were up late last night), ax me no questions, and I'll tell you no lies. There are so many pimpin' eyes about now, a body has to be cautious if he don't want to get into the centre of a hobble. If I'm up late, I guess it's nobody's business but my own I'm about, anyhow; but I hope you won't make no remarks about what you see'd or heerd.

" 'Well, when a feller axes arter a thing, do you jist stand and look at him for a space without sayin' a word, inquirin' like, with a dubersum' look, as

FROM "THE CLOCKMAKER" BY THOMAS CHANDLER HALIBURTON.

if you didn't know as you could trust him or no; then jist wink, put your finger on your nose, and say mum is the word. Take a candle and light it, and say, foller me now, and take him into the cellar. Now, says you, friend, don't betray me, I beseech you, for your life; don't let on to anyone about this place; people will never think o' suspectin' me, if you only keep dark about it. I'll let you see some things, says you, that will please you, I know; but don't blow me—that's a good soul. This article, says you, a-takin' up one that cost three pounds, I can afford to let you have as low as five pounds, and that one as cheap as six pounds, on one condition—but, mind you, it's on them tarms only—and that is, that you don't tell anyone, not even your wife, where you got it; but you must promise me on the word and honour of a man. The critter will fall right into the trap, and swear by all that's good he'll never breathe it to a livin' soul, and then go right off and tell his wife; and you might as well pour a thing into a filterin' stone as into a woman's ear. It will run right thro', and she'll go a-braggin' to her neighbours of the bargain they got, and swear them to secrecy, and they'll tell the whole country in the same way, as a secret, of the cheap things Ichabod Gates has. Well, the excise folks will soon hear o' this, and come and sarch your house from top to bottom, and the sarch will make your fortin'; for, as they can't find nothin', you will get the credit of doin' the officers in great style.'

"'Well, well,' said Ichabod, 'if you Yankees don't beat all natur'. I don't believe on my soul there's a critter in all Nova Scotia would 'a thought o' such a scheme as that; but it's a grand joke, and comports with conscience, for it paralls pretty close with the truth: I'll try it.' 'Try it,' says I, 'to be sure; let's go right off this blessed night and hide away a parcel of your goods in the cellar—put some in the garrat and some in the gig-house. Begin and sell to-morrow, and all the time I'm in Liverpool I'll keep a-runnin' in and out o' your house; sometimes I'll jist come to the corner of the fence, put my head over and draw it back agin, as if I didn't want folks to see me, and sometimes I'll make as if I was a-goin' out, and if I see anyone a-comin' I'll spring back and hide behind the door; it will set the whole town on the lookout—and they'll say it's me that's a-smugglin' either on my own hook or your'n.' In three days he had a great run o' custom particularly arter nightfall. It was fun alive to see how the critters were bammed by that hoax.

"On the fifth day the tide-waiter came. 'Mr. Slick,' says he, 'I've information th—' 'Glad to hear it,' says I; 'an officer without information would be a poor tool—that's a fact.' Well, it brought him up all a-standin'. Says he, 'Do you know who you are a-talkin' to?' 'Yes,' says I, 'I guess I do; I'm talkin' to a man of information, and that bein' the case, I'll be so bold as to ax you one question—have you anything to say to me, for I'm in a considerable of a hurry?' 'Yes,' said he, 'I have. I'm informed you have smuggled goods in the house.' 'Well, then,' says I, 'you can say what many gals can't boast on, at any rate.' 'What's that?' says he. 'Why,' says I, 'that you are *miss*informed.'

"'Mr. Gates,' said he, 'give me a candle—I must go to the cellar.' 'Sartainly, sir,' said Ichabod, 'you may sarch where you please. I've never smuggled yet, and I am not a-goin' now to commence at my time of life.' As soon as he got the candle, and was a-goin' down to the cellar with Gates, I called out to Ichabod. 'Here,' says I, 'Ich, run quick, for your life—now's your time;' and off we ran upstairs as hard as we could leg it, and locked the door; the sarcher heerin' that, up too and arter us hot foot, and bust open it. As soon as we heerd him a-doin' of that, we out o' the other door and locked that also, and down the back stairs to where we started from. It was some time afore he broke in the second door, and then he follered us down, lookin' like a proper fool. 'I'll pay you up for this,' said he to me. 'I hope so,' said I, 'and Ichabod too. A pretty time o' day this, when folks can tare and race over a decent man's house, and smash all afore him this way for nothin', ain't it? Them doors you broke all to pieces will come to sunthin', you may depend; a joke is a joke, but that's no joke.' Arter that he took his time, searched the cellar, upper rooms, lower rooms, and garrat, and found nothin' to seize; he was all cut up, and amazin' vexed and put out. Says I: 'Friend, if you want to catch a weasel, you must catch him asleep; now, if you want to catch me a-smugglin', rise considerably airly in the mornin', will you?' This story made Ichabod's fortin' a'most; he had smuggled goods to sell for three years, and yet no one could find him in the act, or tell where onder the sun he had hid 'em away to. At last the secret leaked out, and it fairly broke up smugglin' on the whole shore. That story has done more nor twenty officers—that's a fact."

THIS STUBBORN BREED

Joseph Lister Rutledge

The conference Braddock had called at Alexandria to formulate a general plan of campaign seems to have been conceived under an unlucky star. It might have brought about a union of provinces able to show a solid front to any enemy. It might even have resulted in a United States without the necessity of revolution. But it didn't, for each colony brought to the gathering its prevailing prejudices and piques; its conviction that its own interests were paramount, and its reluctance to combine or contribute to any less self-centered purpose. So the results were something less than negligible.

Braddock had died miserably and unavailingly at the forks of the Ohio. Governor Shirley of Massachusetts, possibly the shrewdest politician of the conference, had introduced a plan for an attack on Niagara. It was sound in conception and might have brought him the military glory longed for. Instead it was easily checkmated by Canada's new governor, Vaudreuil, who was hardly even Shirley's equal as a strategist but who recognized the importance of this threat. William Johnson, sachem of the Mohawk tribe and named by them Warrachijagey, "he who does much business," did indeed gain a victory over Baron Dieskau. This bit of business, however, had been achieved more by inadvertence than by military skill, of which Johnson had little, or by shrewd planning, which for once seemed to be lacking. So even Johnson's victory was without tangible results. It left him fifty miles short of Crown Point, his objective, and it left the fortress itself still firmly in French hands.

There had been other plans proposed and approved at Alexandria. The most important of these again stemmed from Governor Shirley. It covered one phase of a belief that dominated all his actions. He was married to a French wife whom he had met some years before while on a mission to Paris, but this association had not changed his view that the French influence in the New World must be completely destroyed so that Canada could never again be a threat to the English colonies.

The first move in that campaign should be the destruction of Fort Beauséjour, which dominated the isthmus joining Acadia to the mainland. Shirley was convinced that the intrusion of this fort on what was rather obviously Acadian territory was an initial move in a plan to regain the whole. He believed, as had several governors of English Acadia, that the French would never rest until this land had been restored to them. His own thinking and all experience had convinced him that New England would never be safe should France once more control Acadia. Shirley may quite possibly have gone even a step farther and have feared that the British, who had been content to trade Louisburg for Madras for reasons of their own, might on some other occasion be ready to exchange Acadia for some remote advantage, thus again sacrificing the interests of the colonists.

That is pure assumption. But it is a possible one. It gives support to Shirley's open determination to make Acadia as completely and effectively British as might be, as it was now almost completely French. This as an assurance against just such a possibility. The forty-odd years since the Treaty of Utrecht had awarded Nova Scotia to the British had not achieved that end. This partially because the terms of the treaty, thus loosely defined, had set the limits of Acadia "according to its ancient boundries." These boundaries themselves were highly uncertain. The French had included in Acadia almost everything in sight. While they possessed it, they argued that not only did it comprise the whole Acadian peninsula but also Isle Royale, later Cape Breton, as well as present-day New Brunswick and a substantial part of the state of Maine. Thus it appears in early French maps and documents, while four separate censuses had included the mainland in the enumeration.

But when the Treaty of Utrecht awarded Acadia to the British, it shrank amazingly, and overnight. According to the revised views of French authorities, Acadia really included only the outer part of the peninsula. Obviously, they argued, it could not include the isthmus of Chignecto, which was the only possible route between Cape Breton and the mainland. This, of course, left Cape Breton, as well as the lands of New Brunswick and Maine, outside the new confines of Acadia.

All this resulted in a highly complicated argument. British and French commissioners meeting in lengthy session in Paris explored all the views and took evidence that filled four large volumes. They then dispersed, having decided nothing, so that eventually the boundaries had to be sought in less dignified ways.

If ever a conquered people were treated with consideration by their captors, it was the Acadians. That is not to argue any exceptional virtue on the part of the conquerors but rather a shrewd understanding of the situation that existed and a reasonable appraisal of the best way to meet it. If the reasons were practical rather than sentimental, the net result was generous and understanding treatment for people who represented a very stubborn breed indeed. This conquered people retained their land and freedom and the assurance of the exercise of their religion. The loyalty oath required of them was generous to a fault. If they preferred to leave, there was nothing to hinder them and they were permitted to take their goods and chattels with them.

The often-repeated French claim that they were refused permission to leave the country simply will not hold water. There were roughly nine thousand Acadians congregated in five or six centers. They outnumbered their captors more than three to one, and the latter were scattered everywhere about the country.

Unquestionably the English would have regretted to see the Acadians leave, for the double reason that their going would leave the country all but devoid of sustenance, while if they moved with their possessions to Cape Breton they would increase the strength of Louisburg and so make an attack on Acadia appear almost a probability. If the Acadians didn't go, it was because they did not want to go.

As early as 1720 Governor Phillips, then in command in Acadia, wrote the British Secretary of State explaining the utter impossibility of preventing the Acadians from leaving. "Once joined in a body," he wrote, "with the help of the Indians to favor their retreat, they can march off at their leisure, by way of Bay Verte, with their effects, and destroy what they leave behind without danger of being molested."

The problem was not one of keeping them, for French efforts to induce them to move to Cape Breton or New Brunswick were effective only where force was used or where they were threatened with the anger of the Church. The problem was to assure their loyalty while they remained.

A few years before the conference at Alexandria, Shirley had written the British Prime Minister, the Duke of Newcastle, that if a thousand French troops should land in Nova Scotia all the Acadians and all the Indians would rise and join them. Since he felt so strongly, it was reasonable to assume that the New England governor was somewhat prejudiced. In that same year—1745—however, the French governor and intendant were expressing similar views. Writing the Colonial Minister, they urged: "The inhabitants wish to remain under the French dominion and will not hesitate to take up arms as soon as they see themselves free to do so . . . that is as soon as they have powder and other munitions of war and are backed by troops for their protection against the resentment of the English."

The beating heart of this continuing antagonism to the English was not any governor or official, whether English or French, but a priest, as strange and malignant a figure as appears in Canadian history. It was the Abbé Joseph Louis le Loutre. He had come from the Seminary of the Holy Spirit in Paris to be a missionary to the Micmacs at Shubenacadie. He became the vicar-general of the Bishop of Quebec, with the whole of Acadia as his parish. While he was serving at Shubenacadie he blandly pledged himself to the governor of Nova Scotia that he would maintain good order and keep the French inhabitants faithful to their allegiance to Britain. The promise troubled him not at all. The Abbé le Loutre, whatever else he might have been, was a strong man, dowered with all the less admirable human qualities. He was a man of boundless egotism, with a lust for domination. There is no softer word to describe it. He was a man of unwavering opinion. His hatred of the English, even if we do not know what passion of mistaken patriotism caused it, was deep and abiding. It was bitterness and fanaticism in its very essence, and it was the moving spirit of his life.

He was a priest who had come to think in terms of violence. He could order a man scalped and with satisfaction could mark with his own hand and his own knife the course the scalping knife should take. He could set a price on such cruelty—a hundred livres for each English scalp—and could record with obvious care his two-year total, eleven thousand livres for "expenses and scalps."

He was not sensitive to treachery. It was to him a skilled profession. He could and did send emissaries under the flag of truce to the rough breastworks the English had raised at Beaubassin, and when Captain Howe came forward to meet them he could have his minions shoot him down in cold blood and then disown the act and lay the blame on savage exuberance. He could use his religion as a weapon to achieve his ends. When the unhappy Acadians had been induced by craft to cross from Beaubassin into French lands and, finding no subsistence there, pined for their deserted farms and petitioned Governor Duquesne for permission to return, he dealt with them sternly. They could remove their signatures from the appeal or have "neither sacrament in this life nor heaven in the next." He sent the Micmacs, to whom he had come as missionary, to watch the settlements at Chignecto and Windsor and Shubenacadie, and to destroy anyone who strayed beyond the slim protection these afforded. There were few, if any, like him in the great company of priests who move through the pages of Canadian history, more often than not adorning them with unparalleled accomplishment and sometimes touching them with a selfless devotion that has its own lonely splendor.

The Abbé le Loutre was not of this number. He did not do God's will but his own. He did not serve the Acadian people in wisdom or kindness or understanding. He worked to make his dream of dominion come true at whatever cost. A strange, strange figure of seemingly unvarnished evil. Yet in the day of Acadia's deepest sorrow, when some exiled themselves to a France they did not know and could not understand—a France that had no place for them—there Le Loutre found them at last and served them with a simple and unselfish devotion.

But one cannot think of him so. There are too many dark shadows in his past, and Governor Cornwallis, a man of gentle and generous impulse, was to describe him best: "a good for nothing scoundrel"—this he said as he placed an offer of a hundred pounds on his head.

It is understandable that where Le Loutre was, there also was trouble. His activities centered about Beaubassin near the head of the Cumberland Basin, an offshoot of Chignecto Bay. Here was the easiest point to lure the Acadians back to French lands, where they could be held pending the time that the word went out to retake Acadia for France.

Governor Cornwallis recognized this danger and moved to meet it. He sent Major Lawrence with four hundred men to take Beaubassin and to set up a post there to control this strategic territory. It was a bigger force than Le Loutre controlled, but the wily priest was far from beaten. If he couldn't hold the land, he could make it a desert. With his own hands he fired his village church, where he had said Mass so often. He urged his white and Indian followers to do as much for the village, and soon a hundred and forty homes were in flames. Too late the Acadians realized that they had been tricked again. There was no other course left but to follow where Le Loutre might lead.

He led to misery and to long months of cold, hunger, and loneliness. Even their fellow Frenchmen of the region were wearying of them and were happy when the authorities began to erect a post to face Fort Lawrence across the Missuguash River. Here Le Loutre put his dispossessed Acadians to work. It was a deal not unlike some we have known in our world today, in that the workers were fed—sparsely, it is true, but fed—but they were not paid. They were thinly clad, and winter was upon them. Soon it became obvious that they must receive wages enough to provide their most pressing needs. There were certainly those who still looked longingly homeward. For these Le Loutre had another approach. "If you go," he said, "you will have neither priests nor sacraments, but will die like miserable wretches." That was not true, of course, for under English rule they always had been guaranteed, and actually had, their priests and sacraments. But in their current misery, who was to remember that?

By spring those who survived saw the fort taking martial shape, and in the months following it became a place of first importance, commanding as it did the isthmus from Bay Verte to that of Fundy. On the strength of this new authority, Governor Jonquière issued an order. All Acadians were forthwith commanded to "take an oath of fidelity to the King of France, and to enroll themselves in the French militia on pain of being treated as rebels."

Small wonder that Governor Shirley, learning of such words, should have felt that the attempt to reoccupy Acadia, which he had feared for so long, was closer than he had thought. There was ample evidence. Only the year before the then Governor Duquesne had written to the Abbé le Loutre at Beauséjour: "I write both yourself and M. Vergor to devise a plausible pretext for attacking them." Meaning, of course, the unsuspecting English.

The M. Vergor mentioned was the commander of the fortress of Beauséjour, a dingy creature if there ever was one. He was the friend and confidant, the henchman of François Bigot, the intendant who did not pick men for their courage or their character, and so could use Louis duPont Chambon, Sieur de Vergor, who certainly had neither; but Vergor's day in the sun was drawing to a close, as will appear.

In Halifax, Major Lawrence, now Colonel, had also become the acting governor of Nova Scotia. He was the same who had taken Beaubassin and had built Fort Lawrence. He was a man shaped in a less gentle mold than his predecessor, Cornwallis. Perhaps he had seen that turning the other cheek had not served with people trained under the cracking whip of the Abbé le Loutre. Just as Shirley had wanted to move against the French and needed Cornwallis' aid, Lawrence now wanted to move and needed the aid of Shirley. He sent Lieutenant Colonel Monckton to Boston with a letter. It was direct and forceful: "Being informed that the French have designs of encroaching still further upon His Majesty's rights in the province," the letter said, ". . . I think it high time to make some effort to drive them from the north side of the Bay of Fundy." As a practical detail he suggested that Shirley should supply two thousand men for the purpose.

Never was there a happier exchange of opinion, for Shirley's letter, which crossed that borne by Monckton, suggested that the French of Canada might be driven out of Nova Scotia, and Shirley added: "I will endeavor to send you such assistance from this province as you shall want."

With two men of direct action sharing the same opinion there was little suggestion of delay. Shirley, as commander in chief of Massachusetts as well as governor, commissioned John Winslow to raise two thousand volunteers. Rather characteristically, perhaps, when the first regiment was formed Shirley appointed himself its colonel. He still had the thirst for glory. However, he admitted rather sadly that it was a nominal rank. The real commander of the first battalion was Winslow, with George Scott heading the second and Lieutenant Colonel Monckton in over-all command.

It was five o'clock on the morning of June 2, 1755, when a settler who lived near the Bay of Fundy, about two leagues from the fort, appeared before the startled sentry at the gateway. What he had to say was scarcely believable. He had been up before dawn at the hopeless task of tilling his infertile acres when, looking up where the morning mists were lifting from the water, his startled eyes saw an impossible vision—a great fleet of forty ships riding at anchor, waiting for the tide to permit them to enter Beaubassin.

Startled as they were, unbelieving as they were, the guards hurried him in to the presence of the equally startled Sieur de Vergor, who commanded the fort with its thirty-two guns and mortars and its one hundred and fifty regulars of the Canadian marines.

Vergor was all but paralyzed with fear, and his first and almost only thought was to hurry off couriers to Quebec, to the St. John River, to Louisburg, and to Isle St. Jean, the only points from which he might hope to secure assistance. So intent on enterprises more profitable to himself, he had done nothing toward strengthening the defenses of Beauséjour, which should have been equal to challenging the attacking force—something in the neighborhood of two thousand, including the garrison of Fort Lawrence.

It was a strong position and might readily have been made virtually impregnable but for the acquisitiveness of De Vergor and the fact that the Abbé le Loutre was more interested in pressing some buildings at Rivière du Lac. This left few of the Acadians except the old and the incompetent to work at the fort itself.

Jacau de Fiedmont, there being no military engineer present, had been deputed to act in that capacity. He did his best, but it was in the face of a vast spirit of inertia. He writes in his journal of the siege that "the confidence that peace would continue was so deeply impressed on the minds of those who lived in the district that it was impossible to awaken the slightest alarm. We continued," he observes, "to enjoy a sense of security as perfect as though we were residing in the center of Paris."

That happy sense of security was ill founded. Perhaps, had the fort been strengthened in accordance with the original plans, or if leadership had been different, there might have been a more heroic story. But the Sieur de Vergor had wasted no money or effort in strengthening defenses; nothing, at least, beyond some wails for help.

There was no reason to expect that he would. Louis duPont Chambon, Sieur de Vergor, was the son of that Governor Duchambon who had been in command at Louisburg when that great fortress was attacked by William Pepperrell and Commodore Warren. The father's far from inspired defense of that great fortress can only be considered minutely impressive in comparison with the even feebler showing of the son at Fort Beauséjour.

It must be admitted that De Vergor was not given command by reason of outstanding military qualities. It was an appointment straight from what we of today would speak of as "the pork barrel." While acting as a young officer at Louisburg, De Vergor had met and become an intimate of one who, among other notable qualities, was a capable debaucher of his associates. François Bigot, then intendant at Louisburg, had discovered young De Vergor and found in him a kindred spirit. As intendant of all Canada, Bigot had succeeded in having his favorite appointed to the command at Beauséjour. It was one of the plums that were within his gift. He did even better than that. He saw to it that De Vergor was also given charge of its supply and financing. This provided opportunities neither very complex nor very novel. Loyalty to the French King, it appeared, did not always mean that one might not at the same time defraud him. The practice was often simple. Sometimes it involved charging the King for supplies that existed only in the mind of the commander; sometimes selling actual supplies that had been sent to meet the requirements of the garrison.

De Vergor had not devised these niceties of administration for himself. Prior to his departure to his new post Bigot had written him with a candor that bespeaks their community of thinking. "Profit, my dear Vergor, by your opportunities," wrote the intendant. "Trim, cut—you have the power—in order that you may very soon join me in France and purchase an estate near me."

De Vergor had cut and trimmed as ordered. So nothing was finished, nothing was adequate. We know of these lacks through the journal of Lieutenant Jacau de Fiedmont, which has remained to tell of these events. De Fiedmont was working feverishly to repair the lack in the face of an overwhelming apathy. "It was after seven in the morning," he writes, "before the men came to work, and very few of them did a hand's turn." There were some more determined spirits. It is recorded that Abbé le Loutre was to be seen about "in his shirt sleeves, with a pipe in his mouth, directing the Acadians in their work of strengthening the fortifications." De Fiedmont and Le Loutre had this much in common—a single-minded will to defeat the English. It was not so with the Acadian defenders. When word came from the governor of Louisburg that no help was to be expected from that source, these defenders were profoundly unwilling to sacrifice in vain.

When their lesser protests were disregarded, De Fiedmont's journal records, "The settlers went in a body to the commandant, to demand that he should capitulate, saying that if there were any opposition to the decision they had reached in the matter, they would no longer respect the garrison, whose threats they did not fear in the least, and would turn their arms against the officers and the soldiers, and deliver the fort to the English."

It was not a laudable gesture, but it had become rather typical of a people who through terror and misunderstanding had grown accustomed to siding with the winner. At least it was a challenge that demanded some courage. The commandant had no equal courage to reply; no decisiveness to meet an open threat. There had been no direct assault, and the cannon fire that had touched the fort had done relatively little damage and occasioned few casualties, yet De Vergor had seen enough. When in reply to his request for terms Monckton agreed that the commander and his garrison could march out with "arms, baggage, drums beating, fuses burning," he was satisfied.

So also were the Acadians. They had been treated with customary gentleness. They were assured that they "would not be molested for having taken up arms," on the assumption that they were compelled to do so.

Commander de Vergor did not fare so well. He lost a profitable position that he had not yet fully capitalized. On his return to Quebec he was tried by court-martial but was acquitted, possibly through the support of his good friend Intendant Bigot. One more inglorious moment was reserved for Louis Chambon de Vergor before his name was happily forgotten. It was he who raised the curtain on almost the last dramatic scene of New France in the New World.

The fall of Beauséjour and the adjoining fort of Gaspereau, which was even more hurriedly abandoned, hadn't settled anything. The three hundred Acadians, supposed subjects of Britain, who had been part of the garrison, had been forgiven and permitted to return to their old lands and presumably to their old allegiance. Probably it seemed to them that everything had settled down into the accustomed ways as had happened so often.

There were factors, however, that the simple-minded Acadians simply could not evaluate. There was Governor Shirley's fixed conviction that France was still planning to repossess Acadia. Shirley would argue for the removal of the priests and the most troublesome of the Acadians and the substitution of colonists from New England. There was the fact that, for the time at least, Charles Lawrence was the acting governor, and Lawrence had been brought up a soldier and had imbibed the strict traditions of that caste and the belief that sentiment was not a sound substitute for basic realities.

He had learned by long association that the Acadians were an obdurate people, impossible as allies and dangerous as the neutrals they claimed to be. There was threat of stormy action in Europe and there was the more present threat of a great French fleet harboring at Louisburg. There was the knowledge, too, that Halifax, born with such high hopes, had not been able to keep its people enthused. Men had grown older and many of the colonists had been too old in the beginning. The hard reality of clearing the forest and sowing the land, and waiting endlessly for the harvest, had been too much for many.

The innumerable Micmac raids, stimulated by Le Loutre, that had bloodied pioneer doorsteps had been too hard a challenge for the uncertain and timid. They had drifted away. Halifax, after six years, was scarcely as large as it had been when the new colonists had first landed. Now word had come that the great expedition of Braddock, which was to have challenged the power of the French in the west, had ended in Braddock's death and his overwhelming defeat. And while all this was so, Lawrence had word that the French at Louisburg were receiving both information and supplies from the so-called neutral French in Acadia.

Lawrence was a stern but not a hard man. He merely held to a seemingly undebatable point stated long ago on unchallengeable authority: "He that is not with me is against me." He decided to put an end forever to a neutrality that wasn't neutral. He sent word to Monckton to hold his forces at Beauséjour, and he ordered the elected delegates of the Acadians to appear at Halifax for an accounting.

Lawrence met the delegates with a stern face. He told them he had but one word for them: Their people must take the oath of allegiance without qualification. The representatives were not unduly disturbed. Faced with such demands before, they had refused and the roof had not fallen on them. A night to think over their answer didn't change their opinion, though it sobered them a little. They protested that they would do nothing against the British. It was a familiar response. It had been given before, but at a word from Le Loutre or the suggestion of pressure they had done what they were told. Reluctantly perhaps, at times, but still as they were told. Now once again the representatives of the people faced authority and refused to take the oath.

Lawrence was in an unenviable position. Given a blank refusal, he had relatively little authority to challenge it. There had indeed been such refusals in the past, and Britain had done nothing on those occasions. Perhaps they had considered some definite action, but there had always been the fact that it would probably be costly. If Lawrence gave any of this a thought it does not appear. He notified the Board of Trade in England that he had ordered the Acadians to elect a new group of representatives to appear before him to accept the oath for their people. Should these also refuse—he did not ask permission but stated—he would "rid the province of such perfidious subjects."

There is nothing new in this proposal to expel a difficult and intractable population as a necessary measure of successful conflict. It has been part of warfare through all generations, and it certainly was not unknown in the days under review. Louis XIV, sending Frontenac back to Canada, had accepted with enthusiasm Callières' proposal to dispossess the English in New York and either deport them entirely or scatter them among the various colonies so that never again could they be united. Louis had actually charged Frontenac to put this plan into effect and, had it been possible, it would have been done.

Sir William Phips, had he been successful at Quebec, might have done something of the kind. There are documents relating the various plans, if not of moving the whole Canadian population, at least of removing their spiritual leaders. With a people so devout this was almost the same thing. Louisburg when first built had needed population sorely, and when the Acadians about Canseau, and more or less under the protection of the English, had refused to go, the King's thoughts had turned to the small French settlement at Placentia Bay, Newfoundland. These people had had no will to leave, but Governor Costebelle had received orders from Louis XIV's own hand that willy-nilly they should be moved to Louisburg.

Perhaps it might even be remembered that the United Empire Loyalists, who could not see eye to eye with the American colonists in revolutionary attitudes, may not have been expelled by law, but being profoundly out of accord with the thinking of the majority, they found life intolerable and they had no option but to leave their lands and possessions and to seek the shelter of a political system with which they could agree.

This is not to argue that a strict right existed to justify such happenings, only that it was accepted practice. Indeed the evacuation of whole populations certainly has been known in our day and, had these actions been carried out with a patience and humanity equal to that evident in this sad incident, it is not doubtful that a world conscience might have accepted it, regretfully perhaps, as a necessary military precaution.

The sober truth is that most of our thinking on this unhappy incident is not derived from accepted records but from the imaginings of a New England poet more deeply moved by a romantic situation than by the truth of history. He made Evangeline a living figure of protest of whom people might think with nostalgic fervor. He built that imaginary figure into a reality that could be crystallized in poignant monuments. He spoke to his own New England world that, with him, could still see the embattled farmers standing nearby and could still hear the shot that echoed round a world. This was something he knew, something that flowed in his blood, coloring his thinking and perhaps distorting it a little, however he tried to make his record just.

Henry Wadsworth Longfellow knew Concord well and perhaps couldn't be quite free of the prejudice that made the Englishman the traditional enemy. He didn't know Grand Pré or Beaubassin and could not recognize the patience that, however great, must sometimes have an end. And Acadia had known it for thirty-odd years. But Longfellow, whose great romantic story has moved generations of people, never thought to make it clear that there had been a long probation and that its sad end was the result of a failure to understand that no one can serve two masters.

The poet's story failed, too, in making what to history is an obvious point —that the English had no will or wish to dispossess the Acadians. They did not even realize that when they had returned Louisburg to the French they had made expulsion inevitable, since it left the threat of French imperial dreams on this continent naked for anyone to see; and William Shirley and his like saw it clearly. Should France recover not only Louisburg but Acadia as well, the "woful years" would begin again. New England could not be safe, nor could any of the coastal colonies, with an unassimilated enemy on their defenseless flanks. That was the judgment, and not any act of Monckton or Lawrence or Winslow.

Argue it however one may, tragedy isn't less tragic because in a considerable measure it is deserved. So there remains the bitter final chapter of a devoted people, who were gentle and industrious and kind and devout, but who added to those qualities an amazing stubbornness and a wholly blind loyalty. All that they really asked was to be left alone. That could so easily have been had they not entrusted these loyalties to the man who could destroy them, the Abbé le Loutre. Of him that fine historian, Dr. George M. Wrong, was to write a fitting evaluation: "He was the priest in politics, who brings to secular affairs the burning conviction that his enemies are the enemies of God."

The new representatives of the Acadians had been elected. They understood why, and were not unduly perturbed by the knowledge that they would again be asked to take the oath of allegiance. It was a game with which they were more than passing familiar. Always in the past refusal to agree had resulted in compromise of one sort or another, and there was no realization that the situation had changed. They were not people of learning or experience, these Acadians. They were simple folk whose horizons were their own farms' acres. How could they sense that a life-and-death struggle of two warring ideologies was shaping before their eyes? Perhaps it is not surprising that after almost forty years of efforts to conciliate them they should not recognize easily that the days of conciliation were over.

Governor Lawrence had met with his council, and the word had gone out throughout the province that an unqualified oath of allegiance should be demanded of everyone who had not already taken it. The Acadians responded according to their old accepted practice. Deputations from various districts went to Halifax to protest the stern directness of the oath. They wanted a stipulation freeing them from the obligation of bearing arms. They argued that their priests should be free of any form of supervision. They completely overlooked that it was the Abbé le Loutre and those who were under his direction who had brought them to this pass. They had no explanation as to why many among them had joined with French troops to defend strongholds or to attack English garrisons. They did not recognize, apparently, that among them were those who actively or passively had been a part of many a bloody raid on an English community.

Governor Lawrence was a stern man, but he had no wish to push the Acadians to desperate action. He was ready to make some concession for the moment in regard to demanding military service from the Acadians. He reminded them of the long years of considerate treatment with no compensating results. He urged them to understand how impossible it was to continue such treatment without the assurance that they would be loyal to the English Crown. It was to no end. Le Loutre and his associates had done their work too well. In the hearts of a simple and deeply devout people, the English had been made to appear a people beyond the pale of God. Subservience to such had but one end, eternal damnation. So the Acadians had been taught, and so they believed. The sum of it was that the representatives of a people stolidly refused to take the oath. One cannot escape a grudging admiration for a stupidity so consistent.

Governor Lawrence, standing before them white-faced and stern and unrelenting, spoke his quiet words of doom. "Then," he said, "you are no longer subjects of the King of England but of the King of France. You will be treated as such and removed from the country."

They could not believe the words they heard. They were so different, so direct, so final. But little by little the sense of reality came to them. It was the time to appear to submit. Such an attitude had not failed in the past. So the delegates returned and again faced the governor, but now it was a sterner figure. He didn't plead or argue any more. He faced them gravely, realizing only too well that these were old tactics. Concede only where concessions become imperative.

It was mid-July, and Acadia basked in the sun, a promised land indeed. But there was no promise for frozen hearts. They waited for what might come. It came with the march of feet. The King's soldiers in five companies covering the favored lands the Acadians had made their own. For a while they seemed to do nothing. At Fort Cumberland, which had once been known as Beauséjour, young Colonel Monckton waited for the hour while John Winslow and his blue-uniformed New England soldiery sailed away for the Basin of Minas.

The men of the section were bringing in the harvest when Winslow's summons came to them. They were to gather at the church in Grand Pré to hear the King's orders. Winslow was a kindly man and had no love for his task, but he was a soldier under orders, and he was supported by the bayonets of his New England militia. He read the sober words to a hushed and unbelieving people.

"Your lands and tenements and cattle and livestock of all kinds are forfeit to the Crown with all your other effects, except money and household goods, and that you yourselves are to be removed from this province."

Over the murmur of words his voice went on:

"Through His Majesty's goodness I am directed to allow you the liberty of carrying with you your money and as many of your household goods as you can take without overloading the vessels you go in."

There were other details. "I shall do everything in my power that all these goods be secured to you—and also that whole families shall go in the same vessel; so that this removal . . . may be made as easy as His Majesty's service will permit. . . ." And the words went on. "It is His Majesty's pleasure that you remain in security under the inspection and direction of the troops that I have the honor to command."

Day followed day and the "prisoners of the King" still waited, still unbelieving. There was danger in the growing desperation of this group. So they were separated; the younger and more dangerous were sent aboard five Boston ships then lying in the river nearby. Thinking they were being separated from their families, they had to be prodded aboard by the bayonets of Winslow's soldiery. It was weeks later that the ships, laden with united families, sailed away. Winslow sighed in relief. "This affair," he wrote to a friend, "is more grievous to me than any service I was ever employed in."

From his post not so far distant Captain Murray wrote to Winslow, congratulating him on the success of this first movement. "I am extremely pleased," he wrote, "that the poor devils are so resigned. Here they were more patient than I would have expected." He added, "But I long to see the poor wretches embarked and our affairs a little settled."

Ships were few and slow. In November, Winslow reported that nine vessels had sailed, carrying fifteen hundred and ten persons. It was December before all the six hundred remaining had been at last embarked. Winslow, too, was happy to see the end of an unpleasant task. "It hurts me to hear them weeping and wailing," he said. "Thank God, the transports are gone at last."

When the last of the vessels had sailed away to distribute their unhappy burden among the English colonies, their cargoes of human souls were totaled. It was a little over six thousand. Many had escaped and had joined with the guerrilla bands or had gone to Canada or Isle St. Jean. Many lurked in the forests and eventually drifted back to their old haunts.

Maybe it was the end of an ordeal for these, as it was for Winslow, but the ordeal did not end so swiftly for the many. It was idle to expect that the English colonies would rejoice at their coming. They were a troublesome people; all the reports made this very clear. They were Catholics in what were mainly Protestant communities, and in days when tolerance wasn't ranked among the virtues. Virginia would have nothing to do with them but promptly shipped the six hundred who were assigned to her to England, where they languished until the end of the Seven Years' War permitted their return to France. South Carolina felt the same way, as did Georgia. The best the Carolina governor would do was provide a couple of ships and send them on their way. These finally found a harborage about the St. John River.

The colonies that were more familiar with the Acadians treated them no better. Maryland, it is true, with its large Catholic population, did treat them with some humanity, but it could not care for many. New England did its sober unappreciative best. It accepted the expatriates because somebody had to, but it scattered them in unhappy little groups in scores of localities so that they might not form their own communities again. Many took the long road to Quebec.

Perhaps a quarter of them reached there or scattered near the border. They had no better treatment here, and many were close to starvation. The intendant Bigot did see in their unhappy plight an opportunity to approach the French court for aid. But when the aid arrived he saw to it that little was wasted on these unhappy exiles, while the bulk of it found its way into his own coffers.

In the story of Evangeline, many of the Acadians reached Louisiana, as indeed they did, drawn by the need to be with other Frenchmen. In the bayou country about St. Martinsville they created, as closely as they could, a replica of their old home. There they are living today much as they lived in Acadia two centuries ago, for the real desire of their hearts was for a status quo—a world that didn't change.

When one remembers their lovely country along the shores of Fundy, it is not hard to understand. But it was a hopeless ideal. Worlds do change and people cannot continue to live in the past, however gracious. When the wars were over, many found their way back and were not disturbed. After them came many others of this lonely, stubborn breed, to find their homes again, home to the old life, and the old lovely land, and the old certain religion —but not to the old priest.

The Abbé le Loutre, whom Captain John Knox had known well and was to speak of as "a most remarkable character of inhumanity," had suffered the chastening of eight years in a Jersey Island castle, a prisoner of the English he hated, and had then returned to the service of his people in France.

But in the Acadian pulpit where the bitter man once stood was another abbé speaking to these returned folk. The Abbé Jean Sigoigne had a different message. "To France may go your hearts," he said, "but to England must go your fealty and faith." How easily such words two centuries earlier might have taken from the book of history one of its unhappiest chapters.

THE WHITE MUSTANG

Edward A. McCourt

I

The boy had run all the way from the upland pasture and his thin eager face was damp with sweat. His father was standing at the shady end of the barn sharpening a mower knife, and the grating noise of granite drawn over steel sounded loud in the afternoon stillness. The boy stopped directly in front of his father, shoved his hands deep into the pockets of his faded blue denim overalls and spat in the dust that lay thick around his bare feet. Some saliva dribbled over his chin and he quickly wiped it away with the back of his hand, hoping that his father had not noticed. "Dad—what do you think I saw way up on the Hog's-Back?"

His father held the mower knife upright and began methodically testing the triangular blades with his thumb. "What, Jed?"

"A horse—a grey horse! I figger maybe it's the one the Judsons lost and Mr Judson said he'd give five dollars reward to anyone who found him! Gee, Dad, can't I ride up and see? If I got the five dollars I'd be able to send for the twenty-two in the catalogue. It only costs six thirty-five delivered and I've got a dollar and a half now."

The words burst out with a kind of explosive force that left the boy breathless and red in the face. He inhaled deeply, making a sucking noise, and scuffed the dirt with his bare feet. His father picked up the sharpening stone and eyed it critically.

"Not today, son," he said. "It's a long way up to the Hog's-Back on a hot day like this."

Jed turned away and looked at the big poplars down by the creek and tried not to think of anything at all. "But maybe tomorrow," his father said. "You could start right after breakfast. Only—"

"Gee, Dad—that'll be great! I could be back for dinner easy."

"Only you see, Jed, I can't figure how Judson's horse could have got up to the Hog's-Back. Not from their side anyway. It's a mighty steep climb and there's no grass to lead a horse on. You're sure you saw one up top?"

"Gee, yes, Dad, just as plain as anything—standing right on the skyline. Honest it was a horse. Grey, nearly white I guess, just like the Judsons'. I was 'bout half a mile up in the pasture picking strawberries when I saw him."

REPRINTED BY PERMISSION OF OXFORD UNIVERSITY PRESS FROM *Canadian Short Stories*, EDITED BY ROBERT WEAVER AND HELEN JAMES.

His father leaned the mower-knife against the wall of the barn. As if a cord holding them in place had suddenly given away, his long limbs relaxed and he collapsed on the ground, his back miraculously against the wall of the barn, his legs straight out in front of him. From his overalls' pocket he pulled out a blackened pipe, held it between thumb and forefinger and looked at it without saying anything. Then his eyes crinkled at the corners. "Son, I don't figure that was the Judson horse you saw at all."

Jed knew that his father was playing a game. Dermot O'Donnell loved to play games. Jed laughed out loud and sprawled in the dust at his father's feet. "Then whose horse was it?"

"No one's, Jed. You've seen the white mustang."

"What white mustang, Dad?"

Dermot's heavy eyebrows shot up and threatened to disappear into his hair-line. "Child, child, what do they teach you in school anyway. Nothing that matters or you'd have heard of the white mustang!"

He tamped down the tobacco in his pipe and struck a match along the leg of his overalls, all the time wagging his head slowly from side to side. "There's hardly a puncher in the plains country clear from the Rio Grande to Calgary who hasn't seen the white mustang at one time or another. Mostly at night of course, when the moon is shining and he looks more silver than white. You can get closer to him too, but not very close at that. But sometimes they see him in the daytime, only away off, and he doesn't stand long then."

"And has nobody ever caught him?"

"Not yet, Jed. You see, he's no ordinary horse. Seems like he never gets any older. And some fools have shot at him, but they either missed or the bullets went right through him and did no hurt at all. Anyway, no one has ever even slowed him up. And you can't catch him on horseback. Once, so they tell me, they took after him in relays—down in the Texas Panhandle it was—and chased him three days without a stop. But the white mustang never turned a hair. At the end of the three days two horses were dead and a lot more windbroken for life. But they never got within half a mile of the mustang and every so often he'd turn round and laugh at them the way a horse does if he's feeling extra good. Last I heard he was down in Wyoming working north. Way I figure it, no ordinary horse could get up the Hog's-Back from the Judson side. I guess it's the white mustang all right."

"Will you give me five dollars if I catch him?"

"Five dollars is it? Five dollars?" The pain in Dermot's voice was almost real. "Jed, if ever you catch the white mustang, you'll find him tame as a turtle-dove. And when you get on his back he'll take you away—just like flying it'll be, I think—to a country you've never seen where the grass is as green as the spring feathers of a mallard. And in a little glen so close to the sea you can hear the waves wash on the rocks, you'll find a beautiful princess with long golden hair waiting for you. And she'll get up behind you and put her arms around your middle and the white mustang will bring you back like he's a flash of lightning. And I'll build a house for you and the princess in the poplars down by the creek, and the two of you will be able to help your mother and me. And all your children—you'll have a grand houseful of them in no time—will learn to ride on the back of the white mustang, and when their time comes they'll ride away on him to be kings and queens all over the world. But mind you, Jed, no one has ever yet laid a rope on the white mustang."

Jed spoke thoughtfully. "I think I'd sooner have five dollars."

Jed's father was the most wonderful man in the world and his laughter was the most wonderful part of him. He laughed now, silently at first, then in a series of staccato explosions that culminated in a sustained gargantuan bellow. Jed laughed too; he always did, listening to his father. Then he ran away and lay down on his back in the middle of the grove of poplars where his father was going to build the house for the princess, and looked up through the tree-tops at the blue sky and thought of the things he would do with the twenty-two rifle.

II

Jed did not ride up to the Hog's-Back the next day. For the heat-wave broke in a drenching rain that began as a thunder-storm over the mountains and spread out across the foothills in a steady, settled downpour. Jed tried not to show his disappointment. He knew that the rain was needed badly, that without it his father's small crop, already stunted and parched and clinging precariously to life, would have been burnt beyond hope of recovery in a week or less. But such considerations were of the theoretic and remote, of small weight beside the immediate loss of a day's adventure and five dollars at the end of it.

Late in the afternoon Jed put on the high rubber boots and oil slicker which were among his most prized possessions and climbed up the path through the pasture and beyond until he was no more than a mile from the Hog's-Back, an immense arching hill-top that seemed as remote as a mountain-peak and almost as inaccessible. There was no path beyond the fenced upland pasture, and the long slope above was steep and treacherous underfoot. Jed had been up to the Hog's-Back only once; his father had taken him there one cool spring day, and the memory of what he had seen from the summit was like a lovely haunting dream. Now that he had been granted permission to go alone, the delay seemed to eat at his stomach and leave a hollow ache unlike any other pain he had ever known. Once, when he looked up, the swirling mists far up the slope seemed to part for a moment, and he glimpsed a whiteness that was no part of the elements. It was a whiteness that you didn't see in horses very often, and its outlines, vague and indistinct though they were, suggested the existence of something strange and portentous behind the wavering curtain of mist. Then the clouds closed in again and there were no more breaks. At last, when the rain had penetrated his slicker at a dozen points and was running in cold rivulets down his back, Jed turned away and half-walked, half-slithered down through a tangle of undergrowth to the comparative level of the pasture below.

He was quiet at supper that night. His mother had made his favourite dish of beef stew with puffy white dumplings floating in the gravy, and for a while there was no time to talk. But when the dessert came—pie made of dried apples and Saskatoon berries—Jed stopped with the first mouthful impaled on his fork and looked at his father. "Dad, is the white mustang very big?"

Dermot chewed a mouthful of food and swallowed. "Not big, Jed. A mustang is never big. But he *looks* big—like everything that's uncommon. Take Napoleon now. You'd measure him for a uniform and he was a small man, a runt—not much over five feet, I guess. And then you'd stand back and look at him and he was big. He was the biggest man you ever saw." That was another thing about Dermot—he made you feel that he had known Napoleon very well in the old days. Or Robin Hood or Brian Boru, or whoever he happened to be talking about.

Jed's mother filled Dermot's cup to the brim with strong black tea.

"What nonsense are you stuffing the boy's head with now, Dermot?" she asked. She was a small frail woman, the physical antithesis of her husband. But there was the same look in her dark eyes, a kind of remoteness in them that made her concern for the immediate seem casual at best.

"No nonsense, Mother, no nonsense at all. He hears enough of that at school."

"I wouldn't say that in front of the boy, Dermot," she said. "Maybe he'll learn enough at school to help him keep one foot on the solid earth. Dear knows it's more than he'll ever learn at home."

But she spoke without malice. And she looked at Dermot and Jed in a way that seemed to make no difference between them.

Next morning the sun shone from a clear sky and the mists rose from the earth in steaming exhalations that vanished before the cool wind blowing from the north-west. The ground underfoot was soft and spongy—muddy where there was no grass—and the grass itself washed clean of dust so that it looked as if it had turned green again overnight. Jed dressed quickly and hurried into the kitchen for breakfast. "It's a swell day, Dad," he said.

His father set a pail full of milk on the shelf in the little pantry adjoining the kitchen. "A fine day indeed, Jed. And I know what's in your mind. But I'll have to take Paddy and ride out to the far pasture this morning to look for the yearlings. They didn't come up with the cows and I'm thinking the fence may be down. But you'll be able to make the Hog's-Back this afternoon. It'll be a cool day I think."

Jed did not protest the delay. He knew what his father was thinking, that the grey horse would be gone anyway and that half a day would make no difference. He swallowed the lump in his throat and ate breakfast quietly but without appetite. After breakfast, when Dermot had ridden off down the valley to the far pasture in the flats, he amused himself snaring gophers in the little patch of wheat just across the creek. But it was not a pastime that he ever really enjoyed. He got a thrill from seeing the grey-brown head pop up from the hole in the earth—from the quick savage pull that trapped the victim—from the feel of weight at the end of the long line of binder-twine as he swung it through the air. But what had to be done afterwards was not so pleasant. Particularly he hated taking the string from the neck of the battered carcass, covered with blood and insides as it so often was. This morning his attempts were half-hearted and mostly unsuccessful. After a while he threw his string away and returned to the house. He felt hungry, and there were cookies in the big green tin on the bottom shelf of the cupboard, and milk in the earthenware jug that always stood in the coolness of the cellar steps. He poured out a cup of milk, sat down at the table and ate his way steadily through a plateful of cookies. His mother was busy at the small work-table by the window. Jed finished his last mouthful of cookie and pushed back his chair.

"Mom?"

"What is it, Jed?"

"Mom, did you ever hear about the white mustang?"

"Only what your father told you." Mrs O'Donnell lifted a pie from the oven, using a corner of her ample gingham apron to protect her hands from the heat, and set it on the work-table. She stood beside the table looking out of the window, and her voice was so low that Jed could hardly hear her.

"Your grandmother used to tell me a story about a white horse. The son of Finn rode away on him to fairyland where he lived with a beautiful princess. They called her Naim the Golden-haired. But he got lonely and rode back on the white horse to his own country. He knew that he shouldn't get off the white horse, but he wanted to feel the turf under his feet. And the white horse ran away and the son of Finn turned into an old man. That's what happens to people when they come back to earth."

Jed emptied his cup and set it on the table. "It's a funny thing, Mom. An awful lot of people believe in the white horse, don't they?"

His mother turned from the window without speaking. After a while Jed went back outside. He walked part way up the path to the pasture, then cut across to where the creek, rising from a spring far up in the hills, ran over rocks and gravel to the valley below. He sat on a flat rock and let the water trickle over his bare feet. The water was cold, but he liked the sensation of numbness stealing through his feet—first the instep, then the toes, heels last of all. Even better he liked the pricking feel of returning warmth when he drew his feet out of the water and warmed them on the surface of the rock. He stayed there for a long time, until he heard his mother's high "coo-ee" and knew that it was time for dinner.

Dermot was late getting home. So late that Mrs O'Donnell put his dinner away in the warming oven of the big range and brewed a fresh pot of tea. Jed waited stoically; but when he saw his father approaching up the valley trail he shouted at the top of his lungs and ran down to open the gate for him.

"Gee, Dad, I thought you were never going to get here!"

Dermot slid down from the saddle and stretched prodigiously.

"It was just as I thought—fence down and the yearlings miles away. Paddy has had a hard morning."

"He's too fat," Jed said. "He'll be all right in a little while."

He emptied a tin pail of oats into the manger feed-box while Dermot unsaddled the sweating pony. They went into the house together without saying anything. Mrs O'Donnell was setting Dermot's dinner on the table. "You're late, Dermot," she said.

"I am late, Mother. And I'm thinking it would be as well if Jed waited till morning now. Paddy needs a couple of hours' rest at least. And the grey horse is sure to be far away by this time."

Mrs O'Donnell spoke with unusual sharpness. "Paddy can have his rest and there still will be plenty of time. The evenings are long and the boy will be home before dark."

Jed's heart gave a great leap. His father grinned at him. "And they tell you it's the women-folk are over-anxious about their young," was all he said.

III

It was after two o'clock when Jed went to the barn to saddle Paddy. He threw the heavy stock-saddle over Paddy's broad back and pulled the cinch tight. There was quite a trick to tightening the cinch. You had to pretend you were all finished so that the little sorrel would relax his distended belly. Then you gave the cinch-strap a quick sharp pull and took in about three inches of slack. As soon as the saddle was securely in place Jed shortened the stirrups and tied a lasso to the cantle. He could not throw a lasso very well, and anyway the Judson horse was a quiet nag that could be led on a halter-shank. But the lasso looked impressive, and it was a good idea always to be ready for anything.

He rode Paddy to the water-trough and let him drink a few mouthfuls. His mother came to the door and he waved to her and she waved back and smiled. "Don't be late, Jed."

"I won't," he shouted. "So long, Mom!"

For nearly an hour he rode upwards without pause, the pony stumbling often in the damp uncertain footing. The valley slid farther and farther away below him until at last Jed was able to see over the opposite side to the great plain itself. He stopped at last, not because he wanted to, but Paddy was blowing heavily. He dropped to the ground and squatted on his haunches while Paddy stood quietly beside him with bowed head. Jed could no longer see his own house because of an intervening swell in the seemingly regular contour of the hillside, but other houses had come into view—Joe Palamiro's shack near where the valley ran out into the plain, and the Peterson place, easily identified because of the big windmill, right at the edge of the plain itself. And he could see, far out on the plain, a row of tall gaunt red buildings —grain elevators—standing like guardsmen on parade, and beyond them a second row, over the horizon itself, so that only the upper halves of the elevators were visible. Another time Jed would have been tempted to linger, trying to identify familiar landmarks when seen from an unfamiliar angle. But now, after only a minute or two, he stirred restlessly. Paddy tossed his head and began to nibble at a few tufts of grass growing around the base of a boulder. Jed leapt to his feet.

"All right, you old geezer," he said. "If you can eat you can travel. I'll lead you for a while."

He unfastened the halter-shank from the saddle-horn and started up the hill on foot, Paddy crowding close behind. There was no trace of path anywhere and Jed had to pick his steps with care along deep dry gulches channelled by the rush of water in springtime, over glacial deposits of shale and boulder, past dwarfed poplars and evergreen. There were flowers blooming on these upper slopes that he had never seen before, but he could not stop to look at them now. In spite of the uncertain footing he went up quickly. The sweat gathered on his forehead and ran down his face in salty trickles, for the sun was hot now and the wind had almost completely died away. But the Hog's-Back was close at hand; already Jed could distinguish objects on the skyline—a stunted bush, a pile of rocks forming a natural cairn, a single tree as incongruous in its lonely setting as a human figure would have been.

Now that he was almost at the top Jed suddenly and unaccountably wanted to linger. For the second time he sat down and looked back. Below, the scene had spread out and yet diminished. The horizon had moved farther back; now he was high enough to catch a glimpse of distant emerald-green where a river flowed between enormous banks, of towns so remote that it was impossible to conceive of their having actual being. They were mirages that would vanish with the shimmering heat waves that now hung above the level of the plain. Objects which half an hour ago had seemed close at hand—Joe Palamiro's shack and the Peterson windmill and the upright slab of granite at the mouth of the valley called, for no reason anyone knew of, the Dead Man's Needle—had somehow contracted, and slipped away as if carried on the surface of an outgoing tide. Jed sat for a long time until Paddy, dissatisfied with scanty pickings, came close and nuzzled his shoulder.

"All right, all right," Jed said. "We'll be moving."

He mounted and rode on. The ground was bare and brownish grey. Not even the drenching rain of the day previous could restore life to the few wisps of dry grass that lingered near the top, or the tall reedy stems of upland fox-gloves that rattled mournfully in the wind again blowing across the foothills. His father was right, the boy thought, there was no feed up here for a horse. A horse like the Judson grey, he said to himself, in unthinking qualification.

And when he reached the very top at last and was able to look down the opposite side—down a slope that was strange and steep and menacing although he had seen it once before and it had not seemed menacing then—he remembered what his father had said about the inaccessibility of the Hog's-Back from the Judson side. Dermot was right. No horse could climb that slope. No horse would want to. Jed felt no regret but instead an unexpected lightness of spirit, a strange confusion of happiness and something that made him a little bit afraid. For he *had* seen a horse on the Hog's-Back—a horse more white than grey. He laughed out loud, then looked quickly at the sun. It was swinging low toward the mountains. It would be twilight in an hour and the dark would come soon afterwards.

He rode along the Hog's-Back until checked by the precipitous side of a dry gully, then returned to the highest point of the arching hill-top, and again looked down the great slope that fell away to the west. The world that way looked different, hill rising above hill until at last they broke into the scintillating splendour of white peaks against a pale blue sky. For no reason at all Jed wanted to cry. Instead he shouted loudly at Paddy and drove his heels into the pony's fat sides.

Paddy trotted a few steps and slowed to a walk. It was then that Jed saw the trees. They were directly below him, just over the first big curve of the west slope. At first he could see only their tops, but as he went down they came completely into view—stunted Balm-of-Gileads that looked curiously unreal in their symmetrical grouping on the barren hillside. And low down, between two grey-green trunks, Jed could see a patch of white.

He rode forward at a walk. Paddy snorted once and Jed pulled hard on the reins. He wanted to turn and ride back up the slope and over the summit towards home. But instead he went on slowly, and the dead weight that dragged at his heart made him faint and sick. He reached the circle of trees. Paddy could smell the water now, although the wind was blowing the other way, and snorted again. But Jed said "no" very quietly and with a funny quaver in his voice. He could see the white patch clearly now, above the surface of the water and partly on the ground. And he could hear the heavy buzzing noise made by the swollen blue-bottles as they rose in clouds from the carcass of the grey horse that had died—quickly or slowly, it did not matter now—in the treacherous sucking mud surrounding the hillside spring.

Paddy, scenting death, pawed the ground and whinnied. Jed swung the pony hard and slapped him with the ends of the reins. "Giddap-giddap!" he shouted. He rode over the Hog's-Back at a gallop and on down the other side. Paddy stumbled and almost fell. Jed pulled him in with a savage jerk.

"All right, you old geezer," he said. "Take it easy. No need to break your neck."

It was almost dark when Jed reached home. His father and mother were in the yard waiting for him. "I was on the point of starting after you," Dermot shouted, "when we saw you up there like a god against the setting sun." And he laughed a great booming laugh that echoed across the valley.

FOUR MEN AND A BOX

Leslie Gordon Barnard

They came from the primordial jungle, four gaunt specimens of the human race, walking as men might walk in their sleep, or before a taskmaster whose lash drives them on to the limit of their endurance. Their beards were matted, their skin full of sores, and the leeches had sucked their blood day and night.

They hated each other with the hatred of men bound by a duty, confined by the green walls of a jungle whose paths led through hell and was as eternity. They hated still more, as time went on, the thing they carried; but they bore it as if it were an ark of the covenant and their God was a jealous God.

"We got to get Markgraff's stuff through," they said. "He was a good guy. We promised him."

Of the reward at the journey's end they said nothing; but each man mumbled of it in his own mind, in his own way.

They had gone with Markgraff into his green hell because he paid them well in advance. Now he was dead and they were living. Death had struck him down—some swift tropical disease had ended this geologic madness of his.

They would have understood the whole thing better if his quest had been for gold. But Markgraff had said, smiling: "There are substances which science has found to be more precious than gold." At the end they thought Markgraff had failed, that all he'd found in the jungle was Death. But it seemed otherwise; the box he gave them to take back was heavy. He'd made it himself, roughly hewn, and with the secrecy of the scientist he'd packed and sealed it when he knew that he, himself, was doomed.

"It will take four of you to tote it—two at a time," Markgraff had told them.

"There are four of us," said Barry, the student.

"You'll have to spell each other," Markgraff directed. "I want every man to promise me that he'll stick with it until it's safely delivered. You'll find the address on top. What you have there, if you deliver it to my friend Professor MacDonald at the coast, is more precious than gold. You won't fail? I can assure you that you'll be rewarded."

They promised him because he was a dying man and they respected him. His personality had held them together when, a score of times, with the jungle's vast monotony eating into them, they might have quarreled fatally.

Then Markgraff had smiled at them, and died. He did it quietly, as he did all things—this elderly scientist, this man who'd bound them to him by ties of intangible strength. They buried him in the heart of the jungle, baring their heads, and Barry, the student, spoke brief, remembered words of committal. Even as the clods fell, the jungle loomed larger, more menacing. Each man felt a shrinking of his own stature, a terrible aloneness, a doubt of his fellows, a suspicion that, with Markgraff gone, it would be every man for himself.

They were a curious assortment: Barry, the spectacled student; McCready, the big Irish cook; Johnson, the down-and-out, the bum Markgraff had enticed out of a water-front tavern to follow him; and Jim Sykes, the sailor, who talked a lot about home but never went there.

Sykes had the compass and map, which, when they stopped to rest, he would get out and study. He put a stubby finger on it and said, "There's where we've got to get to." It looked easy—on the map . . .

The jungle deepened about them. They missed Markgraff, who no longer could encourage them with an optimism that was usually justified, who could find in an almost impenetrable tangle some logic for going forward. At first they talked with each other, the sound of their voices important to them. . . . Soon speech became only anathema against the weight they carried, toting Markgraff's box through the forest. . . . Then silence fell on them, and something worse than silence.

Longing for his water-front tavern as a parched soul in Inferno might yearn for water, Johnson began to find that sudden ways opened to him, on the right hand or the left, tempting him. McCready's face grew sullen and dark; he kept repeating, "I'm goin' my own way. I'm not traveling with this outfit any more. I guess I've got the guts to make it." And he would cast a brooding, speculative eye on the map to which Sykes, the sailor, clung.

As for Sykes, he developed a closed-in horror of this jungle, this high-walled man-trap. He wanted the sea. He demanded horizons. He mumbled about it in his sleep, and by day he cursed the death that lay where grotesque insects and deadly reptiles waited for the unwary. He spoke of his home, and how for years he'd meant to get back to the missus and kids—and now never would.

Barry, the student, said little, but there was a girl of whom he was thinking. He'd lie sleepless, tormented by insects, tormented by a face that at times, like the faces of those dear to us, refused at this distance to come clearly. To think of her was to think of a campus, green with spring and russet with autumn; of a sports field, and classrooms, and a library; of dances and moonlit walks, and a sweet, tearing moment of good-by.

Sometimes one or another of them would pray—call out in a way that the insensitive might think was cursing: He had made this fierce jungle, these incredible trees, these flowers, so large that they seemed to reduce man to a pigmy. But the mind cannot quarrel with Nature successfully; so it turns on its own kind. There had been bickerings and quarrels even when Markgraff was with them, but his personality, and his cause, which was their cause, had muted the quarrels.

Now, there was only Markgraff's box, growing heavier as their strength grew less. It was real—when everything else had become a mental haze. It held their bodies when their minds rebelled. It chained them when they would have split apart. Turn and turn about—this routine held them; two men alone would long since have abandoned the precious thing.

They hated it as a prisoner hates his chains, but they carried it as they'd promised Markgraff they would.

They watched each other, covertly, lest any come near the sacred thing except to lift and bear it another torturing mile.

Then came a day when—suddenly—as by a miracle—the walls of the forest opened.

"Glory!" Sykes cried. "We made it." He took out the map, and, putting his cracked lips to it, he kissed it.

"Yes," Johnson breathed, his eyes queer, and no quarrel now on his lips. He even slapped McCready, the cook, on the back and they laughed with strange hysterical laughter. . . .

When they lifted their load again, it seemed lighter, but only for a while. They were weak now, because safety was in sight, and their job all but done. But eventually the four of them bore it up a street, while natives and a few whites stared at them. All four men now were staggering with exhaustion.

All they asked was to deliver it, and have done.

And yet, when they asked for a Professor MacDonald and found him to be a withered man in a greasy white suit, there was a triumph in them for a moment rising above their personal emotions, the glory of a thing shared.

When they'd rested, Professor MacDonald gave them food, and they told him of Markgraff, of his death, and of their promise to him.

It was Johnson who, running his tongue thirstily across his lips, spoke of the reward.

The old man spread his hands in a gesture of inadequacy. "I have nothing," he said, "not a thing to reward you with except my thanks. Markgraff was my friend. He was a clever man. He was more than clever, he was a good man. You have kept faith with what he asked you. I can only thank you."

Derisively Johnson stared at him. "In the box," he said hoarsely. "In the box."

"The box," echoed Sykes eagerly.

"Now—you're talking," McCready said.

"Open it," they demanded. They put their joint strength to it, prying off layer after layer. McCready began to curse. "All that weight, all that damned carrying," he complained, and Johnson said, "Wood, and more damned wood. What kind of a joke is that?"

But Sykes said, "Something is there. I heard it rattle. I heard it when we walked. Look, you're through to it." They all drew close, their minds leaping, remembering the substances which science had unearthed and harnessed, beyond money and beyond price; they stared at the old man when he took the loose bits of rock in his hands, and let them drop. "Worthless," he said, puzzled, trying to feel his way into Markgraff's mind.

"Worthless!" said Sykes dully.

Then McCready, the cook, exploded. "I always thought that guy was nuts. Telling us what was in the box was worth more'n gold."

"No," Barry said quickly. "I remember his exact words. What he told us was 'What you have there, if you deliver it to my friend Professor MacDonald at the coast, is more precious than gold.'"

"So what?" shouted McCready, angry disappointment in his eyes.

"Yeah, so what?" echoed Jim Sykes, the sailor. "I could do with some ruddy gold for the missus and kids, and myself."

Johnson just ran his tongue thirstily along his dry lips.

Barry looked at them all: at McCready, the big Irish cook; at Sykes, the sailor, who might some day go home to his missus and kids; at Johnson, the water-front bum.

Then, he thought of a campus green with spring, and a girl who waited; he thought of the jungle from which they had come—the green hell in which many a man, wandering alone, was now only a heap of whitened bones; and he thought of the dogged resolution which had made four men fight through together to keep a promise, four men held together only by this common cause. This had been Markgraff's gift to them.

"He said we'd be rewarded," Johnson whined. "I heard him say it, myself. Now what do we get out of it?"

Barry turned on him, quickly. "Our lives," he said. "That's what we get—our lives—for what they are worth."

THE WAKE

Patrick Slater

The rough pine coffin lay lidless on a bed in the corner of the ground floor of the cabin. It was a sedate and mournful meeting. With faces long drawn out, and solemn looking as owls, the men stood lining the walls, uttering pious sighs and, betimes, scratching their polls. The women mourners sat on benches, and every few moments one of them would run her fingers through her hair and shriek out: "Oh o o oh oh! . . . Poor Jimmie!" Her body rocked to and fro as the wail gradually died down. At the end of it she would fold her shawl again across her breast. Betimes of the wailings, the men talked of crops and kine; and glancing now and again toward the body, in low guttural tones, made complimentary comments on the life, ancestry and character of the deceased. On entering the room of the dead, the mourner first knelt before the bier to say a prayer for Jimmie's soul; and then a drop of drink was taken. There was tobacco, snuff and whiskey in plenty. Pipes passed from mouth to mouth, and, in the flickering light of the candles, a haze hung in the room like the mist over a plowed field in the plover season.

A queer little old woman came in, all bent double; and after she knelt before the body, she swallowed a tidy drop of poteen, and was given the honor of a chair. Someone thrust a freshly-filled pipe into the ashes and passed it to her.

"God and Mary bless his soul and the souls of all the dead," she sighed; and seated in comfort at her ease, she withdrew like a turtle within the privacy of her shawl.

The woman was short and dusk like a cold winter's day; and she needed a pitch-dark night to make her good-looking. Mary Doyle went about the countryside taking care of sick folk and minding babies. She got a trifle for attending funerals because she was a special hand at keening. Devil a pinch of sorrow had she in her heart for the dead man in his going. The face of her was enough to sour a crock of cream.

The keen, which is a mournful ballad, has four feet to the line as sung in the Irish tongue; and it is only a diversion that makes an end to the number of its verses. Its general purpose is to excite pity, compassion, or hate; and to my mind it is specially effective when used to curse and blast the cruel and treacherous English. In spirit, both the keen and the wake itself, are utterly and entirely pagan. And why Mother Church let such rites get mixed up with the burial of her Christian dead is beyond me. The Irish keen speaks only in terms of unqualified grief; it has a deep and hopeless melancholy at its basis; and finds no place for the joy of the blessed resurrection. In a low tone Mary Doyle began the funeral song:

Cold and silent is his bed!
Och hone!

Damp is the dew of night,
The sun brings warmth
And dries the dew,
But his heart will stay cold,
Machree!

Cold and silent is his repose!
He is gone forever.
He will return no more.
Cold and silent is his grave!
Och hone, Machree!

The keener clapped her hands and rocked her body back and forth as the dirge stretched itself out in weird and melancholy repetition. One after another the other women joined in as a chorus; and their long drawn-out, sobbing wails and piercing shrieks rent the night air. Between whiles, a pipe passed along the benches from woman to woman. The creatures were enjoying themselves immensely.

The keening died down as a fresh group of neighbors arrived and attended to their religious duties. Among them was my boss, Martin Kelly, who had enjoyed a lift getting over with his bad foot. The corpse and Martin were boys from the same parish in the old sod. Yet for years back they had never met but the din of their noise destroyed the place, and, in parting, their sticks usually shook at one another. Only recently there had been a bitter riot between them touching the price of the O'Leary heifer.

Martin rose from his knees with tears of sorrow in his eyes. There was something truly affecting as the man stood, nodding his head solemnly, looking long into the face of his dead neighbor.

"Ah me!" said Martin Kelly, "Jimmie O'Leary was a fine man. Ah! Jimmie makes a pretty corpse!"

Then placing his rough hand on the pallid forehead, Martin sobbed out: "Ah! cold as death is Jimmie's head!"

There are old cart-wheel tracks in every man's brain, and his thoughts slide into familiar ruts without his let or hindrance. As Martin turned sedately from the bier to take his place in the crowd, the old fire sparkled in his eyes, and, with a toss of his head, he exclaimed:

"But colder was the living heart of him!"

Pete O'Leary, the dead man's eldest son, leapt in the air like a goat. In the wink of an eye, Martin and he were hoisting their chins into each other's faces. Pete, who was a chunky young fellow, made a smart pass at Martin's jaw, but failed to make connections. Martin was an older man and a cripple; but he was slim and long bodied. Quick as a flash, he brought his skull down crack, with a vicious butt hitting Pete's face on the line where the eyebrows grow. It was a knockout puck he gave him; and down Pete went to kiss the floor boards.

Trailing his bad foot and coat along the floor, Martin shouted:

"May the devil sweep all the O'Learys together!"

Pete's wife threw her shawl off and rushed screaming to put the prick of youth into the pride of the O'Learys.

"Holy Mary! Pity my heart to be married to a good-for-nothing-at-all!" the woman exclaimed as she set upon the wounded man and belabored him onto his feet again.

The O'Learys did then be letting manners into Martin Kelly with their sticks; and shillelaghs and wallopers came smartly into action. The women bawled themselves hoarse directing the fray, and men were running about with cracked pates, themselves roaring out they were killed entirely. A fat, little fellow on our side was giving blood like a stuck pig; but the O'Leary faction also had plenty of blood to drink. It was a roaring ruction; and everyone felt afterwards it had been highly complimentary to the corpse we were waking.

The arrival of Jimmie's cousins bearing an elegant pig hot-roasted from a spit made a sudden diversion that broke up the brawl. Four men were bearing the savory beast on a litter; and the way of the procession was lit by lanterns made by sticking candles through broken bottoms into the necks of bottles. My heart beat like a watch with the delight of the smell of the roasted pig. I sat down on my heels, and kept a cat's eye on the victuals. Meat and drink were ordained by custom and convenient at a wake. Knives, platters, and the salt stood ready at hand to welcome to the board fatty messes that gladdened the hearts of the mourners into merry talk and stirred up cheerful music as the singers bolted the cracklings and tender meats, and sucked sweet juices out of the bones of the beast. After gorging ourselves, we wiped our hands on an old towel that was passed around; and to comfort themselves, the men had another drink anon. I curled myself up out in the stable and had forty winks.

In the heel of the evening there came from the direction of the whiskey barrel and its dipper the thumbing and squeaking of a fiddle. An old musician scraped away on one or two strings of a fiddle as battered looking as himself. His lean body swayed with his bowing; but the stamp of the man's foot made him the master of the house. Dickens a man or lass in the cabin but began shovelling away with heel and toe! It was Jimmie's daughter Molly that led the spree. What a hub-bub and a clatter! It was enough to hoist the corpse out of the coffin to hear them dancing a four-hand reel.

"Oh o o o oh! Poor Jimmie! Is he so soon forgotten?" wailed Mary Doyle, who was too old and stiff for dancing.

Faith no! Poor Jimmie was not forgotten. The coffin was fetched forward and leaned bolt upright in the chimney corner that the corpse might be observing what was going forward in his honor. The girls bobbed curtsies to the dead man as they tripped by; and some of them asked Jimmie for a dance. Every now and then, he was offered a drop of the hard stuff. During the course of the evening, Martin kneeled down before the fire to redden his baccy pipe by thrusting it into the ashes; and made final peace with his fellow countryman by sticking the stem of it into the dead man's mouth. They made a night till morning of it,—what with drinking, keening, dancing and other tastes of diversion.

By the dawning, the mourners felt cold and stiff, after spending the night seeing Jimmie through the first heel of his long journey; and they were not wishful to burn up much daylight over the dead body of a man who had been called out of the way into glory. As a final mark of respect, bright and early in the morning, the coffin was hoisted on the stout shoulders of the men who, changing off as the miles slowly went by, bore it at long last, and by the longest route, to its grave up the steep boreen at Centreville. Most willingly did the whole countryside augment the toils of their tired bodies by trailing and straggling after the bier, wailing and chanting their griefs.